Math for Liberal Arts Majors

MATH 114

Santa Barbara City College

Mathematics

create.mheducation.com

ISBN-13: 9781308538129

ISBN-10: 130853812X

Contents

i. Letter from the Authors   1
ii. Updated Content   3
iii. Index of Applications   6

Problem Solving   11

1. Introduction   12
2. The Nature of Mathematical Reasoning   14
3. Estimation and Interpreting Graphs   27
4. Problem Solving Strategies   39
5. Summary   49

Sets   55

6. Introduction   56
7. The Nature of Sets   58
8. Subsets and Set Operations   70
9. Using Venn Diagrams to Study Set Operations   81
10. Using Sets to Solve Problems   91
11. Infinite Sets   101
12. Summary   107

Logic   111

13. Introduction   112
14. Statements and Quantifiers   114
15. Truth Tables   124
16. Types of Statements   137
17. Logical Arguments   147
18. Euler Circles   158
19. Summary   166

Topics in Algebra   171

20. Introduction   172
21. The Fundamentals of Algebra   174
22. Solving Linear Equations   186
23. Applications of Linear Equations   200
24. Ratio, Proportion, and Variation   209

25. Solving Linear Inequalities 221
26. Solving Quadratic Equations 232
27. Summary 246

Consumer Math 251

28. Introduction 252
29. Percents 254
30. Simple Interest 265
31. Compound Interest 275
32. Installment Buying 287
33. Student Loans and Home Buying 302
34. Investing in Stocks and Bonds 315
35. Summary 325

Geometry 333

36. Introduction 334
37. Points, Lines, Planes, and Angles 336
38. Triangles 346
39. Polygons and Perimeter 357
40. Areas of Polygons and Circles 364
41. Volume and Surface Area 374
42. Right Triangle Trigonometry 384
43. A Brief Survey of Non-Euclidean and Other Geometries 393
44. Summary 400

Probability and Counting Techniques 409

45. Introduction 410
46. The Fundamental Counting Principle and Permutations 412
47. Combinations 421
48. Basic Concepts of Probability 428
49. Tree Diagrams, Tables, and Sample Spaces 440
50. Probability Using Permutations and Combinations 448
51. Odds and Expectation 454
52. The Addition Rules for Probability 464
53. The Multiplication Rules and Conditional Probability 471
54. The Binomial Distribution 481
55. Summary 488
   A. Appendix: Area Under the Standard Normal Distribution 495
   B. Appendix: Using the TI-84 Plus Graphing Calculator 499
   C. Selected Answers 513
   D. Credits 543
   E. Index 545
   F. Endsheets 559

Credits

i. Letter from the Authors: *Chapter from Math in Our World, Third Edition by Sobecki, Bluman, 2015* 1
ii. Updated Content: *Chapter from Math in Our World, Third Edition by Sobecki, Bluman, 2015* 3
iii. Index of Applications: *Chapter from Math in Our World, Third Edition by Sobecki, Bluman, 2015* 6

Problem Solving 11

1. Introduction: *Chapter from Math in Our World, Third Edition by Sobecki, Bluman, 2015* 12
2. The Nature of Mathematical Reasoning: *Chapter 1-1 from Math in Our World, Third Edition by Sobecki, Bluman, 2015* 14
3. Estimation and Interpreting Graphs: *Chapter 1-2 from Math in Our World, Third Edition by Sobecki, Bluman, 2015* 27
4. Problem Solving Strategies: *Chapter 1-3 from Math in Our World, Third Edition by Sobecki, Bluman, 2015* 39
5. Summary: *Chapter from Math in Our World, Third Edition by Sobecki, Bluman, 2015* 49

Sets 55

6. Introduction: *Chapter from Math in Our World, Third Edition by Sobecki, Bluman, 2015* 56
7. The Nature of Sets: *Chapter 2-1 from Math in Our World, Third Edition by Sobecki, Bluman, 2015* 58
8. Subsets and Set Operations: *Chapter 2-2 from Math in Our World, Third Edition by Sobecki, Bluman, 2015* 70
9. Using Venn Diagrams to Study Set Operations: *Chapter 2-3 from Math in Our World, Third Edition by Sobecki, Bluman, 2015* 81
10. Using Sets to Solve Problems: *Chapter 2-4 from Math in Our World, Third Edition by Sobecki, Bluman, 2015* 91
11. Infinite Sets: *Chapter 2-5 from Math in Our World, Third Edition by Sobecki, Bluman, 2015* 101
12. Summary: *Chapter from Math in Our World, Third Edition by Sobecki, Bluman, 2015* 107

Logic 111

13. Introduction: *Chapter from Math in Our World, Third Edition by Sobecki, Bluman, 2015* 112
14. Statements and Quantifiers: *Chapter 3-1 from Math in Our World, Third Edition by Sobecki, Bluman, 2015* 114
15. Truth Tables: *Chapter 3-2 from Math in Our World, Third Edition by Sobecki, Bluman, 2015* 124
16. Types of Statements: *Chapter 3-3 from Math in Our World, Third Edition by Sobecki, Bluman, 2015* 137
17. Logical Arguments: *Chapter 3-4 from Math in Our World, Third Edition by Sobecki, Bluman, 2015* 147
18. Euler Circles: *Chapter 3-5 from Math in Our World, Third Edition by Sobecki, Bluman, 2015* 158
19. Summary: *Chapter from Math in Our World, Third Edition by Sobecki, Bluman, 2015* 166

Topics in Algebra 171

20. Introduction: *Chapter from Math in Our World, Third Edition by Sobecki, Bluman, 2015* 172
21. The Fundamentals of Algebra: *Chapter 6-1 from Math in Our World, Third Edition by Sobecki, Bluman, 2015* 174
22. Solving Linear Equations: *Chapter 6-2 from Math in Our World, Third Edition by Sobecki, Bluman, 2015* 186
23. Applications of Linear Equations: *Chapter 6-3 from Math in Our World, Third Edition by Sobecki, Bluman, 2015* 200
24. Ratio, Proportion, and Variation: *Chapter 6-4 from Math in Our World, Third Edition by Sobecki, Bluman, 2015* 209
25. Solving Linear Inequalities: *Chapter 6-5 from Math in Our World, Third Edition by Sobecki, Bluman, 2015* 221
26. Solving Quadratic Equations: *Chapter 6-6 from Math in Our World, Third Edition by Sobecki, Bluman, 2015* 232
27. Summary: *Chapter from Math in Our World, Third Edition by Sobecki, Bluman, 2015* 246

Consumer Math 251

28. Introduction: *Chapter from Math in Our World, Third Edition by Sobecki, Bluman, 2015* 252
29. Percents: *Chapter 8-1 from Math in Our World, Third Edition by Sobecki, Bluman, 2015* 254
30. Simple Interest: *Chapter 8-2 from Math in Our World, Third Edition by Sobecki, Bluman, 2015* 265
31. Compound Interest: *Chapter 8-3 from Math in Our World, Third Edition by Sobecki, Bluman, 2015* 275
32. Installment Buying: *Chapter 8-4 from Math in Our World, Third Edition by Sobecki, Bluman, 2015* 287
33. Student Loans and Home Buying: *Chapter 8-5 from Math in Our World, Third Edition by Sobecki, Bluman, 2015* 302
34. Investing in Stocks and Bonds: *Chapter 8-6 from Math in Our World, Third Edition by Sobecki, Bluman, 2015* 315
35. Summary: *Chapter from Math in Our World, Third Edition by Sobecki, Bluman, 2015* 325

Geometry 333

36. Introduction: *Chapter from Math in Our World, Third Edition by Sobecki, Bluman, 2015* 334
37. Points, Lines, Planes, and Angles: *Chapter 10-1 from Math in Our World, Third Edition by Sobecki, Bluman, 2015* 336
38. Triangles: *Chapter 10-2 from Math in Our World, Third Edition by Sobecki, Bluman, 2015* 346
39. Polygons and Perimeter: *Chapter 10-3 from Math in Our World, Third Edition by Sobecki, Bluman, 2015* 357
40. Areas of Polygons and Circles: *Chapter 10-4 from Math in Our World, Third Edition by Sobecki, Bluman, 2015* 364
41. Volume and Surface Area: *Chapter 10-5 from Math in Our World, Third Edition by Sobecki, Bluman, 2015* 374
42. Right Triangle Trigonometry: *Chapter 10-6 from Math in Our World, Third Edition by Sobecki, Bluman, 2015* 384
43. A Brief Survey of Non-Euclidean and Other Geometries: *Chapter 10-7 from Math in Our World, Third Edition by Sobecki, Bluman, 2015* 393
44. Summary: *Chapter from Math in Our World, Third Edition by Sobecki, Bluman, 2015* 400

Probability and Counting Techniques 409

45. Introduction: *Chapter from Math in Our World, Third Edition by Sobecki, Bluman, 2015* 410
46. The Fundamental Counting Principle and Permutations: *Chapter 11-1 from Math in Our World, Third Edition by Sobecki, Bluman, 2015* 412
47. Combinations: *Chapter 11-2 from Math in Our World, Third Edition by Sobecki, Bluman, 2015* 421

48. Basic Concepts of Probability: *Chapter 11-3 from Math in Our World, Third Edition by Sobecki, Bluman, 2015* 428

49. Tree Diagrams, Tables, and Sample Spaces: *Chapter 11-4 from Math in Our World, Third Edition by Sobecki, Bluman, 2015* 440

50. Probability Using Permutations and Combinations: *Chapter 11-5 from Math in Our World, Third Edition by Sobecki, Bluman, 2015* 448

51. Odds and Expectation: *Chapter 11-6 from Math in Our World, Third Edition by Sobecki, Bluman, 2015* 454

52. The Addition Rules for Probability: *Chapter 11-7 from Math in Our World, Third Edition by Sobecki, Bluman, 2015* 464

53. The Multiplication Rules and Conditional Probability: *Chapter 11-8 from Math in Our World, Third Edition by Sobecki, Bluman, 2015* 471

54. The Binomial Distribution: *Chapter 11-9 from Math in Our World, Third Edition by Sobecki, Bluman, 2015* 481

55. Summary: *Chapter from Math in Our World, Third Edition by Sobecki, Bluman, 2015* 488

A. Appendix: Area Under the Standard Normal Distribution: *Chapter A from Math in Our World, Third Edition by Sobecki, Bluman, 2015* 495

B. Appendix: Using the TI-84 Plus Graphing Calculator: *Chapter B from Math in Our World, Third Edition by Sobecki, Bluman, 2015* 499

C. Selected Answers: *Chapter from Math in Our World, Third Edition by Sobecki, Bluman, 2015* 513

D. Credits: *Chapter from Math in Our World, Third Edition by Sobecki, Bluman, 2015* 543

E. Index: *Chapter from Math in Our World, Third Edition by Sobecki, Bluman, 2015* 545

F. Endsheets: *Chapter from Math in Our World, Third Edition by Sobecki, Bluman, 2015* 559

48. Basic Concepts of Probability; Chapter 11-3 from Math in Our World, Third Edition by Sobecki, Bluman, 2015   428

49. Tree Diagrams, Tables and Sample Spaces; Chapter 11-4 from Math in Our World, Third Edition by Sobecki, Bluman, 2015   440

50. Probability Using Permutations and Combinations; Chapter 11-5 from Math in Our World, Third Edition by Sobecki, Bluman, 2015   448

51. Odds and Expectation; Chapter 11-6 from Math in Our World, Third Edition by Sobecki, Bluman, 2015   454

52. The Addition Rules for Probability; Chapter 11-7 from Math in Our World, Third Edition by Sobecki, Bluman, 2015   464

53. The Multiplication Rules and Conditional Probability; Chapter 11-8 from Math in Our World, Third Edition by Sobecki, Bluman, 2015   471

54. The Binomial Distribution; Chapter 11-9 from Math in Our World, Third Edition by Sobecki, Bluman, 2015   481

55. Summary; Chapter from Math in Our World, Third Edition by Sobecki, Bluman, 2015   488

A. Appendix: Area Under the Standard Normal Distribution; Chapter A from Math in Our World, Third Edition by Sobecki, Bluman, 2015   495

B. Appendix: Using the TI-84 Plus Graphing Calculator; Chapter B from Math in Our World, Third Edition by Sobecki, Bluman, 2015   499

C. Selected Answers; Chapter from Math in Our World, Third Edition by Sobecki, Bluman, 2015   513

D. Credits; Chapter from Math in Our World, Third Edition by Sobecki, Bluman, 2015   543

E. Index; Chapter from Math in Our World, Third Edition by Sobecki, Bluman, 2015   545

F. Endsheets; Chapter from Math in Our World, Third Edition by Sobecki, Bluman, 2015   559

Letter from the Authors

Why did we write *Math in Our World*? Liberal Arts Math is different from the other classes we typically teach to underclassmen, and we believe that it requires a different approach. Many of the students have had negative experiences in algebra, and come into any math course thinking it's going to be the same old thing again–finding *x*. Liberal Arts Math provides a great opportunity to show students that math isn't just an abstract subject studied by high-level intellectuals. In this course, we have the opportunity to really teach students about reasoning and thinking, rather than train them to mimic procedures. Who wouldn't look forward to that?

Math in Our World has a different style than you'll find in most college math texts. Both the structure of the chapters and the style of writing are designed to make the students think "Wow, this isn't what I expected… I can actually read and understand this!" We think of it as "teaching backwards": rather than learning the math and then studying how it can be applied, every topic is introduced from a conceptual, applied point of view. The goal is to engage students at the beginning of each topic, helping them to not fall into the old "Why do I have to know this–I'm never going to use it" trap. Both teaching and writing are passions for us. We think that combining Al's twenty-plus years of textbook-writing experience, Dave's background in creative writing, and our years of teaching results in a unique experience for your students.

No one has ever become stronger by watching someone else lift weights, and our students aren't going to be any better at thinking and problem solving unless we encourage them to practice it. *Math in Our World* includes a veritable cornucopia of applications for students to hone their skills. The exercises for this edition were carefully evaluated to ensure that they are engaging for students and apply to fields of study that are common for Liberal Arts Math students. Additionally, we focused on developing significantly more exercises that foster critical thinking. Our goal is to help your students develop into problem solvers and thinkers beyond the halls of academia.

Additionally, while no book can prevent the lack of preparedness of students, we believe Connect Math and LearnSmart will help engage students and encourage them to develop their own questions about the world. Both programs can play an important role in your class by providing opportunities to practice and master the computational as well as conceptual aspects of this course. As authors, we were deeply involved not only in the development of these online tools, but also in the creation of all the supplements for our program to help ensure consistency for students in their digital and text experience.

We're confident this book offers a fantastic vehicle to drive your classes to higher pass rates because of the pedagogical elements, writing style, interesting problem sets, and digital components. We hope you and your students enjoy using *Math in Our World* as much as we enjoyed creating this program together. Good luck, and please don't hesitate to reach out and let us know what you think!

—*Dave and Al*

Visit our website for more information! www.mhhe.com/sobecki

Updated Content

Global Changes

- Every section was evaluated for clarity and writing style, with many rewritten to emphasize the readable, conversational tone.
- All definitions were reevaluated for mathematical precision.
- Dozens of math notes were added to enhance clarity.
- Many section openers were rewritten to enhance readability and student interest.
- Over 2,400 new and revised exercises were added. The two main goals in this large number were to create more realistic, engaging applications, and dramatically increase the number of critical thinking exercises.

CHAPTER 1 Problem Solving

- Many example problems were rewritten to focus on real applications of mathematical thinking and problem solving.
- Three new Sidelights on inductive reasoning, story problems, and vocabulary were added.

CHAPTER 2 Sets

- Features expanded coverage of infinite sets in Section 2-5 to include proofs that certain sets are countable.

CHAPTER 3 Logic

- Over 150 new exercises were added.

CHAPTER 4 Numeration Systems

- Section 4-1 has been rewritten to follow more closely the historical development of numeration systems.
- Mayan mathematics, previously a Sidelight, is now fully covered.

CHAPTER 5 The Real Number System

- Chapter opener was rewritten to reflect newer government spending data.
- Coverage of the golden ratio is included in a Sidelight and exercises.

CHAPTER 6 Topics in Algebra

- Over 180 new exercises were added.

CHAPTER 7 Additional Topics in Algebra

- Updated chapter opener includes recent stock market data.
- Enhanced coverage focuses on slope as rate of change.
- Expanded linear programming includes an example focusing strictly on the math of the procedure before applications.
- Coverage of linear functions now appears in section where functions are introduced.
- Expanded section on covering quadratic and exponential functions to include logarithmic functions.

CHAPTER 8 Consumer Math

- Inserted a new half-section and new chapter opener on student loans.
- New coverage of logarithms in Chapter 7 allows for more realistic interest problems about finding the time needed to reach a financial goal.
- Coverage of annuities was streamlined with just one formula rather than two.
- Inserted a new Sidelight and exercises on leasing new cars vs. buying.
- Added new coverage of the effect of making minimum payments on a credit card.
- Added new coverage of the math of buying and selling bonds.

CHAPTER 9 Measurement

- Over 150 new exercises were added.

CHAPTER 10 Geometry

- Coverage of fractal geometry in Section 10-7 has been greatly expanded.
- Criteria for determining when polygons tessellate were added.

CHAPTER 11 Probability and Counting Techniques

- New Example 4 in Section 11-6 builds the expected value formula through an accessible example.
- Improved our coverage of binomial probability with new examples.

CHAPTER 12 Statistics

- Online supplement on misuses of statistics has been rewritten and moved into the print edition.
- New coverage ties descriptive vs. inferential statistics to our study of deductive vs. deductive reasoning in Chapter 1.
- Examples throughout the chapter have been rewritten to use timely data.
- Inserted new example and problems on deciding if data are approximately normally distributed.
- Inserted new important caution box on the difference between correlation and causation.

CHAPTER 13 Voting Methods

- Over 60 new exercises were added.

CHAPTER 14 Graph Theory

- Includes a new subsection on graph coloring
- New cheapest link algorithm included to contrast with nearest neighbor method

CHAPTER 15 Other Mathematical Systems-Now Online

- Improved coverage of properties of mathematical systems by stating each property in a definition box, along with new explanations.

Index of Applications

Automotive

Alcohol-related fatalities, 380, 708
Average speed, 26
Car accidents, 775
Dealership stock, 407
Distance traveled, 299–300
Driving distance, 15, 245, 418
Driving speed, 15, 36
Driving time, 15, 24, 35, 332–333, 362, 395, 418, 548
Eating while driving, 690
Fuel efficiency, 717, 727
Gas mileage, 31, 35, 329
Gas prices, 538, 706, 734, 770
Imported car sales, 422
Leasing, 335, 475, 485–486
Loans, 474–475, 485–486, 513–514, 516–517
New car depreciation, 283
Purchase price, 517
Rental, 19, 346, 379, 417
Repair and maintenance, 517
Road trips, 26, 362, 417, 835, 872, 875
Seat belt use, 682
Stopping distance, 359
Texting while driving, 14
Thefts, 709–710
Tire life, 757
Used car purchase, 345, 517

Consumer Information

Airline tickets, 394
ATM banking, 690
Bar codes, 153, 186, 190, 202
Battery life, 773
Book prices, 395, 758
Budgeting, 346
Buying power, 380
Cab fare, 376
Cable TV, 22, 24
Carpeting costs, 532, 538, 548, 579, 596
Car purchase, 517
Cell phone costs, 19, 35, 316
Cell phone fees, 346
Chicken prices, 394, 544
Compact fluorescent lightbulb lifetimes, 728
Computer purchase, 344
Concrete needed, 537
Consumer priorities for spending, 734
Copy machine service calls, 728
Cost of milk, 26
Credit card balance, 480–482, 486–487
Credit card finance charge, 480–482, 486–487
Credit card interest, 480, 486–487
Credit card minimum payment, 483
Credit card penalty fees, 26
Credit cards, 446

Credit card usage, 481
Deceptive advertising, 448, 781, 783
Decorating costs, 24
Defective products, 302, 335
Discount prices, 299, 303, 323–324, 417, 445, 449–451
Dorm room furnishing costs, 24
Electric bill, 323
Energy-saving lightbulbs, 24
Estimating total cost, 24
Exchange rate, 528–529
Fast food costs, 24, 343, 394
Fast food preferences, 690, 694
Flower bed construction, 571
Food costs, 343, 418
Furniture costs, 24
Garden mulch, 537
Gas prices, 538, 706
Grocery shopping, 216
Health club membership, 363
Health food prices, 362
Home buying, 346, 491
Home prices, 55, 302, 418–419, 436, 451, 729
Housing industry trends, 451
Ice cream prices, 452
Installment buying, 484, 513–514
Inventory levels, 392
Landscaping costs, 548
Laundry detergent, 728
Lawn fertilizer costs, 547
Leasing a car, 475
Mattress size, 528
Meat prices, 394
Misleading percents, 448, 451–452, 781–782
Monthly payments, 454–457, 475, 490, 492
Movie tickets, 757
Newspaper ad costs, 379
Newspaper advertisements, 66
Paint cost, 24
Paint needed, 334, 363, 537, 586, 596
Party costs, 34
Payment plans, 35
Pizza cost, 376
Pizza toppings, 84, 630
Poster board size, 528, 532
Poster costs, 24
Purchasing party supplies, 399
Remodeling costs, 20
Rental costs for real estate, 24, 31
Sale prices, 303, 362, 448, 450
Sales tax, 298–299, 303, 447, 450, 510
Shopping trip totals, 18, 26, 30
Slipcover fabric needed, 537
Sod costs, 579, 586
Stone wall construction, 571
Storage unit prices, 402
Sugar in soft drink, 419
Television screen size, 530, 570
Term of a loan, 456
Thrift store prices, 394
Ticket prices, 394
Tile prices, 538

Tiling, 537, 578, 611
Unit prices, 336
UPC code, 153, 186, 202
Wii fitness board weight limit, 539

Education

Admissions, 392
Alumni donations, 722
Bachelor's degrees, 450
Class failure, 84
Class grades, 750
Class scheduling, 84, 694
Class size, 33
Costs, 441
Course requirements, 402, 436, 629
Course selection, 66
Debt after graduation, 691
Earning power and, 441
Enrollment in evening classes, 323
Entrance exam scores, 716
Exam-taking strategy, 635
Extra credit, 84
Financial aid, 84, 678
GPAs, 316–317, 700, 716, 774
Grade calculation, 35, 316, 320, 345–346
Grading structure, 408
Graduate programs in mechanical engineering, 717
Graduate school applications, 741
Grouping of students, 218–219
High school dropout rates, 380–381
Law School Admission Test (LSAT), 151
Levels, 245
Levels completed, 380
Majors, 54, 83, 722
Major selection, 716
Missed classes, 735
Nurses with master's degrees, 445
Professor to student ratio, 335
Reasons for failure, 84
SAT scores, 750
Saving for college, 38
Student housing, 41
Student loans, 441, 487–489, 498, 500, 512, 514
Student population, 231
Students' class rankings, 741
Study habits, 419, 702, 705, 734
Study time, 417
Teacher salaries, 757
Test grades, 26, 320, 740, 769
Test scores, 312, 363
Test-taking strategy, 402, 633
Test times, 757
Textbook costs, 38
Textbook purchases, 417
Textbook resales, 38
Textbook sales, 94, 757
True/false questions, 417
Tuition (and fees), 317, 324, 451, 510, 727

Finance

Account balances, 224
Actuarial method, 477–478, 514
Annual percentage rate, 485
Annuities, 467–470, 513
Bank balance, 224, 230
Banker's rule, 457–458
Bankruptcy filings, 714
Bonds, 501, 506–507, 510, 514
Budgeting, 35
Business costs, 431
Business revenues, 431
Capitalized interest, 499
Car loans, 474–475, 477–479
Car rental, 19
Certificate of deposit, 431, 513
Checking account balance, 228, 287
Commissions, 298, 302–303, 417, 447, 450, 509–510, 513
Comparison shopping, 325
Compound interest, 427–428, 431–432, 462–466, 471–473, 510
Computer purchase, 476
Credit card balance, 480–482, 514
Credit card finance charge, 480–482, 514
Credit card interest, 480, 514
Credit card minimum payment, 483, 514
Credit card penalty fees, 26
Credit cards, 446, 513
Credit card usage, 481
Depreciation, 283
Discounted loans, 458–459, 461, 510
Discount prices, 299, 303, 323–324, 417, 445, 510
Dow Jones Industrial Average, 367, 435
Down payment, 499–500
Earning power and education, 441
Earnings calculation, 331
Effective interest rate, 302, 465–466
Estate division, 245, 324, 363
Facebook stock prices, 712, 720
Finance charges, 476–477
Financial aid to students, 84
Foster-care payments, 346
Future value, 302, 453, 455, 467–469, 510
Gift purchases, 343
Home buying, 491, 499–500
Home loan term, 439
Home prices, 419
Hourly earnings, 324
Hourly wage, 24, 34–35
Household income, 770
House sale, 345
Installment purchases, 476
Interest on investment, 302, 323, 391, 394, 427–428, 432, 436
Interest on loans, 284, 432, 453–454, 460–461, 487
Interest on savings, 284, 335

Interest rate, 313, 453–456, 458, 460, 510
Investing, 40, 284, 346, 464, 466, 470, 510, 516, 665, 668
Investment growth, 427–428
Investment property, 547
Leasing a car, 475
Monthly earnings, 324
Monthly payments, 454, 469–470, 475–476, 490, 492, 498, 500, 510
Mortgage interest, 492–495, 499–500
Mortgage payments, 431, 492–496
Mortgages, 492–495, 499–500, 514
Mutual funds, 501, 507, 668
National debt, 207, 286
Nightclub admission prices, 392
Payments to research subjects, 345–346
Payoff amount, 478, 485, 514
P/E ratio, 509
Printer purchase, 477
Profits, 273, 287, 302–303, 359, 380, 405–410, 417, 431, 436, 665, 668
Profit sharing, 229, 273–274
Property tax, 335
Recreational spending, 769
Rent, 35
Rent payments, 324
Rule of 78, 485–486
Running shoe prices, 774
Salaries, 30, 39, 265, 274, 284, 302, 320, 450
Salary increases, 281–282
Sales commissions, 303, 728
Sales tax, 298–299, 303, 447, 450, 510
Sales trends, 418
Sales volume, 402
Saving for a home, 281
Savings account, 394
Shipping costs, 30
Simple interest, 40, 453–456, 458, 460–462, 473, 476, 510
Stock dividends, 501, 508, 741
Stock listing, 501, 508–509, 514
Stock prices, 367, 435, 451, 502, 508–509, 514, 734
Stock proceeds, 505, 508–509, 514
Stock purchase, 505, 509–510, 516
Stock sales, 505–506
Stock sales and Fibonacci numbers, 278
Stock yield, 504, 509, 514, 516
Student loans, 441, 488–489, 512, 514
Take-home pay, 325
Term of a loan, 456–457
Tips, 34, 321–322, 418
Total cost with tax, 298–299, 303, 323, 343, 450
Unearned interest, 478, 485, 514
Unit cost, 418
Wage calculation, 331
Yearly earnings, 24, 324, 773

General Interest

Airplane weight, 540
Air purifier, 596
American Standard Code for Information Interchange (ASCII) code, 200
Animal shelter, 409
Appliance manufacturing, 395–396

Arrestees with priors, 34
Arts community, 85
Athletes' salaries, 265, 274, 320
Banking, 446
Beam strength, 333, 336
Book publishing, 85
Border relationships, 838, 843, 854
Box office revenues, 273
Building heights, 547
Building materials, 402, 595
Building size, 538
Bungee jumping, 284
Cabinetmaking, 395, 402
Calendar design, 633
Capitol rotunda area, 548
Carpentry, 323
Carpet needed, 586
Cell phones, 687, 690
Cell phone tower height, 283
Cement weight, 545
CEO ages, 757
Cigarette consumption, 25
Cigarette taxes, 708, 710
Civilian military contractors, 380
Coins, 34, 446
Coke consumption, 535
College campus design, 869
College campus size, 24
Colors on Web pages, 190
Communications options, 66
Comparison shopping, 325
Computer viruses, 381
Concert tickets, 394
Cookie recipe, 232, 245
Corporate e-mail use, 379
Cost of massage, 741
Crime statistics, 94
Cropping a picture, 330, 335
Currency conversion, 528–529
Cutting a recipe, 245
Deck construction, 34, 321, 363
Diamond size, 528
Dog food consumption, 331
Domain name costs, 379
Driveway coating, 586
Drunk driving, 380, 758
Earnings and happiness, 691
Electrical circuits, 150–151, 256, 316
Elevator weight capacity, 544–545
Encoding account numbers, 169
Encryption, 200
Energy drink, 528
Euler paths and circuits, 851–855
Facebook use, 83
Fear of flying, 691
Felony charges, 66
Fencing, 363, 423–424, 574
Ferry carrying capacity, 544
Ferry service, 836
Fish tank dechlorination, 547
Floor area, 538
Floor plans, 837, 846–847, 854
Food bank supplies, 231
Floor plans, 837, 846–847, 854
Fundraising, 395, 409
Furniture design, 346, 357
Garden planning, 528
Gift purchases, 343
Google use, 83
Government spending, 207, 286, 380
Grocery stockroom, 230
Hair care products, 409
Halloween spending, 323
Healthy body weight, 548
Home improvement, 321, 551, 614

House lot size, 548
House plans, 245
Inaugural address length, 737
Internet cafe set-up, 34
Internet connection, 870
Ladder distance from wall, 360, 570–571, 597, 600
Laptop sales, 717
Law practice, 403
Lighthouses, 218
Loft construction, 571
Lumber, 528
Making combinations, 636–637
Manufacturing costs, 363, 395
Map colors, 843, 846–847
Market caps for largest companies, 741
Market research, 85
Medicare expenditures, 380
Military expenditures, 380
Money, 446
Morse code, 190
Municipal waste, 245
Musical notes, 239, 277
Music preferences, 81
Music sales, 55
National debt, 207, 286
National Park acreage, 708
News sources, 85
Online transactions, 691
Packaging goods for sale, 215, 219, 394, 750, 775
Paper money, 446
Parking fines, 283
Pentagon, 575
Pepsi and Coca-Cola company revenues, 323
Period of pendulum, 256
Peripherals for computer, 66
Permutations, 636–637
Pet food consumption, 331
Picture framing, 34, 528, 576
Picture hanging, 34
Pizza preferences, 84
Plans for worst gift, 38
Plant purchase, 363
Pizza preferences, 84
Postage stamp size, 528
Poster board area, 586
Postnet code, 190
Presidents elected in year with "0" at the end, 803
Productivity in manufacturing, 302–303, 335
Pyramids, 565, 590–591
Quiz show, 284
Radio preferences, 85, 94
Restaurant inventory, 418
Restaurant sales, 717
Roof construction, 565
Rug dimensions, 359
Sea level, 221
Service call schedules, 218
Shareware downloads, 717
Shipping, 35
Skim milk consumption, 334
Snack food selection, 66
Social networking, 757–758, 848
Soda consumption, 287, 537
Soft drink preferences, 79, 667
Spreading rumors, 273
Staircase construction, 570
Steak consumption, 545
Street plans, 838
Swimming pool tiles, 34
Swimming pool vacuum hose, 570
Tattoos and body piercing, 79
Television set life cycles, 757–758

Ticket pricing, 34, 409–410, 418
Ticket purchases, 335
Time needed to complete class project, 336
Titanic's weight, 548
Truck carrying capacity, 538, 544
Uranium production, 545
Vacation planning, 342
Valentine cards, 442
Vanilla ice cream sales, 334
Video frame rates, 219
Video purchases, 395
Web ad costs, 379
Website reach, 25
Weight calculation, 331–332, 336
Weight of water, 533–534, 537
Window caulking, 34
Wiring, 870, 872
Zip codes, 190

General Interest

Building materials, 586, 593

Geometry

Angle measure, 551, 614
Angle of depression, 601
Angle of elevation, 601
Area enclosed by track, 583
Area of a trapezoid, 312
Area of square, 359
Area of triangle, 316, 359
Base and height of triangle, 551, 614
Baseboard size, 576
Carpet area, 532, 579
Cell phone tower height, 283
Cropping a picture, 330, 335
Distance around track, 582
Drink can dimensions, 359
Fence size, 363, 423–424, 574, 576, 587
Fight cage size, 577
Hedge size, 576
Height calculation from shadow, 567
Height of object, 335
Height of object with trigonometry, 601
Lot sizes, 586–587
Object distance with trigonometry, 601–602, 604–605
Object height with trigonometry, 601–602, 604–605
Perimeter of rectangle, 29, 34, 316, 359, 363
Perimeter of triangle, 324
Pizza diameters, 359
Polygons, 577
Pyramids, 595–596
Pythagorean theorem, 261, 359–360, 564, 571, 575, 596, 619
Radius of cylinder, 359
Rectangle area, 551, 587, 614
Rectangle dimensions, 357
Rectangle perimeter, 423–424, 431, 551, 574, 576–577, 586–587, 614
Stage lighting, 576
Tower height, 571
Track distance, 582, 586–587
Tree height, 570

Triangles in construction, 577, 586–587
Volume of cone, 591, 595
Volume of cylinder, 316, 589, 595
Volume of pyramid, 590, 595
Volume of rectangular solid, 316, 359, 588
Volume of room, 538
Volume of sphere, 591
Volume of swimming pool, 535, 538, 589, 595

Health and Nutrition

Aerobics, 66
Age and walking speed, 419
Alcohol consumption, 53, 84
Alcohol-related fatalities, 380
Antidepressants, 85
Birthweight, 539, 544, 548
Blood pressure, 752, 757
Blood types, 623, 642
Body mass index (BMI), 260, 264
Body surface area, 303, 365
Breakfast habits, 335
Calories used in exercise, 31, 362, 417, 757
Cancer in females, 662
Cause of death, 641, 643, 662, 716
Cigarette consumption, 25, 727
Cigarette smoking and health, 84
Diabetes clinical trial, 636
Diet, 346, 402, 687, 695
Diseases, 381
Drug administration, 323, 547
Drug dosages, 291, 303, 361–362, 417
E.R. usage in heat wave, 323
Exercise habits, 362–363, 769
Fat content of cafeteria food, 84
Fever, 548
Fitness classes, 84
Flu outbreaks, 735
Healthy body weight, 544, 548
Hearing loss in elderly, 94
Heart attack risk factors, 82
Ice cream's fat content, 528
Indoor smoking ban, 119
Lead poisoning in children, 782
Organ transplants, 715
Overweight and blood pressure, 682
Pain reliever, 775
People living with HIV, 450
Protein bars, 35
Seat belt use, 682
Students' health complaints, 716
Team selection, 35
Weight gain, 431, 541
Weight loss, 335, 377, 380, 418, 541, 544, 548

Labor

Age and missed days of work, 769
Aptitude testing, 775
Average hours worked, 40
Earnings and happiness, 691
Food service industry, 450
Full-time employment rates, 690
Green jobs, 451
Hiring practices, 385, 400
Hospital size and number of personnel, 760, 766
Hospital staffing, 359
Hourly wages, 757–758, 775

Hours worked by undergraduates, 25
Husband/wife earnings differences, 690
Job satisfaction, 691
Layoffs, 283
Licensed nurse practitioners employed, 717
Manufacturing, 402
Minimum wage, 775
Nurses, 74
Painter's charges, 379
Productivity and time of day, 25
Registered nurses employed, 717
Retirement benefits, 690
Salaries, 30, 39, 265, 274, 284, 302, 320, 450, 690, 757–758, 776
Staffing, 629
Take-home pay calculation, 325, 331, 346, 417–418
Time spent at work, 346
Tips, 34, 321–322, 418
Unemployment, 231, 245, 368, 691, 709, 716, 727, 770, 776
Wages and number hired, 400
Workers' years of service, 716
Workforce trends, 335
Workplace fatalities, 21, 735, 782–783

Numbers

Average of two, 316
Base eight (octal) system, 182–183, 187, 195, 197, 200–201
Base five system, 180–182, 192–193, 198, 201
Base four system, 197, 201
Base number problems, 189
Base sixteen (hexadecimal) system, 182–183, 185, 187, 194, 200–201
Base sixty system, 164
Base ten system, 154, 162–163, 180, 183–184, 190–191
Base three system, 185, 191, 201
Base twelve system, 185
Base two (binary) system, 153, 185, 187–188, 190, 193, 200
Divisibility tests, 209, 219
Exponential decline, 433
Exponential growth, 433, 438
First coordinate of vertex, 433
Geometric sequences, 284
Kruskal's algorithm, 871–872
Linear decline, 433
Linear growth, 433
Patterns, 4, 12
Properties of real number system, 262, 264
Quadratic decline, 433
Quadratic growth, 433
Roman numerals, 169
Value of pi, 248

Probability

Angry Birds championship, 653
Animal adoptions, 673
Band competition, 653
Band scheduling, 629
Betting, 663, 667
Birthday problem, 658
Blackjack, 645
Blood types, 642
Book selection, 655

Candy selection, 642
Card games, 645, 655
Cards dealt, 66, 635, 655, 674, 683
Cause of death, 641, 643
Cell phone contacts, 629
Cell phone type, 644
Code words, 629
Coin toss, 621, 637–638, 647, 652–653, 667–668, 677, 683, 689, 693–696
Combination lock, 656, 659
Commercial scheduling, 629
Committee selection, 632, 635, 658–659
Computer display, 652
Craps, 654
Dating, 644
Dice roll, 621, 637–638, 644, 646, 651–652, 654, 661–663, 666–668, 671–672, 675, 677, 683–684, 690, 693–694
"Diet Fractions" game, 697
Draft lottery, 650
Drawing a card from a deck, 637–638, 650, 653, 656, 661, 666, 669–672, 677–678, 680, 683, 694–695
Extended warranty, 668
Eye color, 646
Finalist selection, 635
Finishing order, 625
Fortune teller, 652
Gambling, 621, 663, 666, 668, 693, 696–697
Gambling and expected value, 664–666
Game selection, 644
Game shows, 644
Gender of children, 644
Gin Rummy, 645
Handedness, 646
Hate crimes, 644, 681
Homicide methods, 683
ID card digits, 629, 659
Juror assignment, 640
Life insurance, 668
Lotteries, 265, 324, 380, 621, 626, 628, 636, 644, 659–660, 663, 668, 675, 693
Lotto games, 684
Magazine selection, 657
Multiple-choice quiz, 687, 691
Names on list, 644
Opinion survey, 644–646, 667, 674, 683, 690–691, 695
Passwords, 626–627, 629
Pie selection, 670
Poker, 635, 645, 655, 659, 662, 675
Popular male names, 645
Promotional campaign, 629, 635
Raffle, 629, 646, 653, 659, 664–665, 668
Roulette, 621, 663, 666–667, 693
Scratch-off tickets, 668
Seat belt use, 682
Selection at random, 644–646, 655, 658–660, 664, 669–675, 678–690, 694, 697
Shared birthday, 683
Shared birth month, 683
Shell game, 668
Slot machines, 665
Songs played, 629
Struck by lightning, 628
Task assignment, 629

Television show scheduling, 629
Three-digit codes, 623
True/false tests, 645, 653, 687, 691
Win/lose/tie outcomes of a game, 639, 653

Science and Nature

Astronomical units, 280
Average high temperature, 722
Average monthly rainfall, 737
Average precipitation, 78
Average snowfall, 230, 757
Average temperature, 226, 231, 545, 717, 757
Birthweight, 539, 544, 548
Body surface area, 303, 365
Carbon dating, 429, 432
Cells in human body, 273
Centripetal force, 316
Comet orbit, 584
Decibels, 432
Distance Earth travels in a year, 271
Distance from Sun, 280
Distance traveled during acceleration, 316
Dolphin swimming, 431
Dropped object speed, 255–256, 357, 359
Dropped object time, 255–256, 357, 359, 363
Earthquakes, 432, 724
Einstein's mass-energy formula $(e = mc^2)$, 302, 316
Electrical resistance of conductor, 316, 363
Electric current, 302, 363
Electricity generated by nuclear energy, 20
Energy production, 683, 738, 782
Experimentation, 218, 629
Fahrenheit and Celsius temperature conversion, 542–545, 548
Fahrenheit temperature, 300, 312, 546
Freshwater weight, 533–534, 538
Gas pressure, 333, 336
Global warming, 695
Grains of sand on Coney Island, 273
Healthy body weight, 544
Heat energy from electricity, 302
Height of launched object, 302
Hemoglobin content, 273
Kinetic energy, 302
Lab rat costs, 24
Largest baby, 539
Light illumination, 316
Light-years, 273
Mouse maze learning, 728
Oven cooling, 418
Periodic cicadas, 219
Period of pendulum, 256
Planetary distances, 273, 280
Pollen weight, 273
Population growth, 230, 426, 431, 439, 448
Power of electric circuit, 316
Pregnancy length, 750
Projectile motion, 302, 422–423, 430–431, 433, 437
Protons in water, 273
Puppy weight, 541

Radioisotope decay, 437
Rat breeding, 230
Reaction times and blood alcohol level, 758
Reaction times of dogs, 717
Richter scale, 432, 724
Search for extraterrestrial life, 179
Seawater weight, 533, 537
Size of atom, 273
Sound intensity, 336, 432
Space station crew, 633
Speed of light, 271, 273, 528
Speed of sound, 287
Support beam, 333, 336
Surface area of Mars, 595
Temperature conversions, 300, 312, 542
Tornados per year, 345
Vertical distance from Mt. McKinley to Death Valley, 40
Vertical distance from Pike's Peak to Death Valley, 230
Volcanoes, 708
Voltage of electric circuit, 256
Volume of liquid, 537–538
Volume of moon, 595
Water from snowmelt, 334
Water in waterfall, 538
Weather forecasting, 639
Weight of liquid, 534, 537
Weight on moon, 523
Wildlife population, 330
Windchill factor, 324
Wind speed and airplane flight time, 324

Sports, Leisure, and Hobbies

Athletes' body mass index (BMI), 264
Athletes' salaries, 265, 274, 320
Athletes' weights, 335–336, 734, 737
Auto race track size and area, 582–583
Auto racing, 245
Baseball batting order, 629
Baseball diamond size, 570, 576
Baseball field size, 528
Baseball franchise values, 775
Baseball games won, 706
Baseball players' heights, 731
Baseball players' heights/weights, 774
Baseball playoffs, 326
Baseball team records, 219, 735, 738
Baseball teams in playoffs, 76
Baseball team's win rate, 447
Basketball court area, 528
Basketball court size, 528
Basketball games lost, 713, 720
Basketball lineup, 629
Basketball players' heights/weights, 667, 731
Basketball score averages, 26
Basketball team rankings, 721, 741
Basketball team record, 718
Basketball teams in Big Ten, 625
Biking, 218
Bowling lane length, 528
Bowling league, 218
Boxing weight classes, 541
Bungee jumping, 284

Calories used in exercise, 31, 362, 417
Cities with major league baseball teams, 85
Cities with NBA basketball teams, 85
College football polls, 793
Distance covered by walker and runner, 385
Earned run average in baseball, 316
ESPN broadcast, 274
Exercise habits, 362–363, 769
Female joggers, 335
Fitness training, 243
Football field size, 531, 547, 577
Football field turf, 586
Football franchise values, 709
Football pass, 528
Football playoffs, 629
Football team rankings, 741
Football team records, 219, 718, 727, 738, 774
Golf, 735, 741
Golf Masters tournament, 724
Golf scores, 154
Heisman trophy balloting, 785, 829
Hockey wins, 769
Homerun records, 708
Karate, 336
Marathon distance, 548
Marathon finisher, 741
Marathon sponsorship cost, 417
Marathon time, 548
Oddsmaking, 660, 667
Participation by sport, 326
Perimeter of track, 303
Playoffs, 287
Rounds of golf played, 437
Running on track, 528
Running time, 36
Slugging percentage in baseball, 316
Soccer field size, 577
Swimming pool costs, 26
Swimming pool size, 528, 535, 538, 589
Tae Kwon Do, 673
Team selection, 35
Triathlon, 243, 323, 548, 570
Volume of a basketball, 592
Walking speed, 577
Weightlifting, 541
Women's teams, 95

Statistics and Demographics

Adolescents in prison, 510
Age distribution, 727, 741, 756, 774
Attorneys employed, 727, 734
Average college student's characteristics, 718
Average waiting time at bank, 757
Calories in cafeteria food, 755
Calories in microwave dinners, 734
Car thefts, 709–710
Cattle on farms, 739
Cell phone subscribers, 450
Children's hospitals' sizes, 773
Chinese children adopted, 381
Corporate net worth, 728

Credit card usage, 481
Crime statistics, 94, 770, 782
Death row inmates freed, 719
eBay bids, 727
Electricity production cost, 741
Ethnicity, 43, 93
Existing home sales, 727, 742, 758
Foreign-born as percentage of population, 422
Garbage generated per person, 752–753
Gas prices, 734
Heights of army recruits, 734
Heights of students, 741
Home sales, 727
Home size, 758
Homicide methods, 683
Homicide rates, 41, 727, 741
Homicides and temperature, 699, 772
Homicide statistics, 773–774
Identity theft, 54, 690, 710
Illegal immigrants, 53
Immigrants' preferences for country, 335
Inmate populations, 317, 362
Internet usage, 741
IQ test scores, 741, 744–745, 758
Junk e-mail, 734
Level of education completed, 380
Male nurses, 445
Most populous states, 245
Native American population, 773–774
Number of Americans over age 65, 380
Number of drive-in theaters, 741
Number of hospitals, 734
Number of immigrants, 53
Nurses with master's degrees, 445
Obesity prevalence, 335
Odometer readings, 734
On-campus burglaries, 727
People living with HIV, 450
Population growth, 230, 426, 431, 439, 448
Population statistics, 438
Poverty, 245
Poverty threshold, 376, 381
President's religion, 335
Racial demographics, 43, 93, 329
Salaries, 776
Self-reporting of race, 43
Single parents, 727
Sports participation, 326
Student loan debt, 488
Surveys, 707–708, 711
Tallest buildings, 734, 760, 766, 769
Taxicab registrations in NYC, 716
Temperatures, 775
Test scores, 740–741, 754, 775
Unemployment, 368, 709, 716, 727, 776
Uninsured, 245, 287
Unmarried mothers, 413, 415
Violent crime, 714, 727
Website loading times, 719
Women in Congress, 324
Workplace fatalities, 21, 735, 782–783

Travel

Air, 334, 641
Air fares between cities, 863
Airline passengers' suitcase weight, 774

Airline passenger totals, 709, 741
Airline routes, 403
Airline tickets, 394
Automobile, 641
Commuting by bike, 324
Distances between cities, 245, 861, 863
Driving speed, 15
Driving time, 15, 24, 332, 858–859, 864
Express bus passengers, 774
Fatal airline accidents, 722
Metric conversions, 519, 546
Road trips, 26, 362, 417, 835, 872, 875
Safety, 641
Shuttle bus, 218
Temperatures in Aruba, 548, 730
Traffic, 528, 547, 864

Voting

Adams' method of apportionment, 816–817, 821–822, 831
Alabama paradox in apportionment, 823, 826–827, 831
Apportionment, 811–814, 820–822, 827, 831, 833
Approval voting, 807, 809–810, 831
Borda count method, 795, 799–801, 809, 829
Federal elections, 381
Hamilton's method of apportionment, 814–815, 820, 826–827, 831, 833
Head-to-head comparison criterion, 789–790, 810, 831
Heisman trophy, 785, 829
Huntington-Hill method of apportionment, 819, 821, 831
Irrelevant alternatives criterion, 809–810, 830
Jefferson's method of apportionment, 815–816, 821–822, 831
Monotonicity criterion, 799
New states paradox in apportionment, 825, 827, 831
Pairwise comparison, 804, 808–809, 830
Plurality method, 788–789, 793, 800–801, 830–831
Plurality-with-elimination method, 797, 800–801, 809, 830–831
Politicians' use of logic, 150
Polls, 94, 789
Population paradox in apportionment, 824, 827
Preference tables, 787–788, 791–793, 801, 830
Presidential elections, 245, 792–793
Presidential primary, 324
Weather effects, 789
Webster's method of apportionment, 817–818, 821, 831

Problem Solving

CHAPTER **1**

Problem Solving

Outline

1-1   The Nature of Mathematical Reasoning

1-2   Estimation and Interpreting Graphs

1-3   Problem-Solving Strategies

Summary

MATH IN ▸ Criminal Investigation

In traditional cops-and-robbers movies, crime fighters use guns and fists to catch criminals, but in real life, often it's brain power that brings the bad guys to justice. That's why the TV show *CSI* marked a revolution of sorts when it debuted in October 2000: it featured scientists fighting crime, not tough guys. Solving a case is intimately tied to the process of problem solving: investigators gather and organize as much relevant information as they can, then use logic and intuition to formulate a plan. Hopefully, this will lead them to a suspect.

This same strategy is the essence of problem solving in many walks of life other than criminal justice. Students in math classes often ask, "When am I going to use what I learn?" The best answer to that question is, "Every day!" Math classes are not only about facts and formulas: they're also about exercising your mind, training your brain to think logically, and learning effective strategies for solving problems. And not just math problems. Every day of our lives, we face a wide variety of problems: they pop up in our jobs, in school, and in our personal lives. Which computer should you buy? What should you do when your car starts making an awful noise? What would be a good topic for a research paper? How can you get all your work done in time to go to that party Friday night?

Chapter 1 of this book is dedicated to the most important topic we'll cover: an introduction to some of the classic techniques of problem solving. These techniques will prove to be useful tools that you can apply in the rest of your education.

But more importantly, they can be applied just as well to situations outside the classroom.

And this brings us back to our friends from *CSI*. The logic and reasoning that they use to identify suspects and prove their guilt are largely based on problem-solving skills we'll study in this chapter. By the time you've finished the chapter, you should be able to evaluate the situations below, all based on episodes of *CSI*. In each case, you should identify the type of reasoning, inductive or deductive, that was used and decide whether the conclusion would stand up as proof in a court of law.

1. After a violent crime, the investigators identify a recently paroled suspect living in the area who had previously committed three very similar crimes.

2. A homeless man is found dead from exposure after being roughed up. His wrists look like he had been handcuffed, and fingerprints on his ID lead them to a local police officer.

3. A murder victim grabbed a pager from the killer while being attacked and threw it under the couch. With the suspect identified, the investigators found that his DNA matched DNA found under the victim's fingernails.

4. A series of five bodies are found posed like mannequins in public places. The lead suspect is an artist that is found to have sketches matching the poses of all five victims.

For answers, see Math in Criminal Investigation Revisited on page 37

Section 1-1   The Nature of Mathematical Reasoning

LEARNING OBJECTIVES

☐ 1. Identify two types of reasoning.

☐ 2. Use inductive reasoning to form conjectures.

☐ 3. Find a counter-example to disprove a conjecture.

☐ 4. Explain the difference between inductive and deductive reasoning.

☐ 5. Use deductive reasoning to prove a conjecture.

A big part of being an adult is making decisions on your own—every day is full of them, from the simple, like what to eat for breakfast, to the critical, like a choice of major. If you make every decision based on a coin flip, you won't get very far in life. Instead, it's important to be able to analyze a situation based on logical thinking. What are the possible outcomes of making that decision? How likely is it that each choice will have positive or negative consequences? We call the process of logical thinking **reasoning**. It doesn't take a lot of imagination to understand how important reasoning is in everyone's life.

You may not realize it, but every day in your life, you use two types of reasoning to make decisions and solve problems: *inductive reasoning* or *induction,* and *deductive reasoning* or *deduction.*

> **Inductive reasoning** is the process of reasoning that arrives at a general conclusion based on the observation of specific examples.

For example, suppose that your instructor gives a surprise quiz every Friday for the first four weeks of your math class. At this point, you might make a **conjecture**, or educated guess, that you'll have a surprise quiz the next Friday as well. As a result, you'd probably study before that class.

☑ 1. Identify two types of reasoning.   This is an example of inductive reasoning. By observing certain events for four *specific* Fridays, you arrive at a general conclusion. Inductive reasoning is useful in everyday life, and it is also useful as a problem-solving tool in math, as shown in Example 1.

EXAMPLE 1   **Using Inductive Reasoning to Find a Pattern**

A game show contestant is given the following string of numbers:

$$1, 2, 4, 5, 7, 8, 10, 11, 13, \underline{\quad}, \underline{\quad}, \underline{\quad}$$

She'll win \$1,500 if she can continue the pattern and fill in the three blanks. Use inductive reasoning to find a correct answer.

SOLUTION

To find patterns in strings of numbers, it's often helpful to think about operations that can turn a number into the next one. In this case, we can use addition to find a regular pattern:

$$1 \underset{+1}{} 2 \underset{+2}{} 4 \underset{+1}{} 5 \underset{+2}{} 7 \underset{+1}{} 8 \underset{+2}{} 10 \underset{+1}{} 11 \underset{+2}{} 13 \underset{+1}{} \underline{\quad} \underset{+2}{} \underline{\quad} \underset{+1}{} \underline{\quad}$$

The pattern seems to be to add 1, then add 2, then add 1, then add 2, etc. So a reasonable conjecture for the next three numbers is 14, 16, and 17.

▼ **Try This One 1**

Use inductive reasoning to find a pattern and make a reasonable conjecture for the next three numbers by using that pattern.

 1, 4, 2, 5, 3, 6, 4, 7, 5, __, __, __

EXAMPLE 2   **Using Inductive Reasoning to Find a Pattern**

Make a reasonable conjecture for the next figure in the sequence.

SOLUTION

In the first four figures, the flat part goes from facing up to right, down, then left. There's also a solid circle • in each figure. The sequence then repeats with an open circle ◦ in each figure, so in the next one, the flat part should face left and have an open circle:

Recognizing, describing, and creating patterns are important in many fields. Many types of patterns are used in music such as following an established pattern, altering an established pattern, and producing variations on a familiar pattern.

▼ **Try This One 2**

Make a reasonable conjecture for the next figure in the sequence.

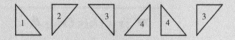

EXAMPLE 3   **Using Inductive Reasoning to Make a Conjecture**

When two odd numbers are added, will the result always be an even number? Use inductive reasoning to determine your answer.

Math Note

In Example 3, it's impossible to try EVERY pair of odd numbers, so we can't be absolutely positive that the sum is always even. Inductive reasoning often leads us to a reasonable conclusion, but very seldom will it lead to certainty about that conclusion.

SOLUTION

First, let's try several specific examples of adding two odd numbers:

$$3 + 7 = 10 \qquad 25 + 5 = 30$$
$$5 + 9 = 14 \qquad 1 + 27 = 28$$
$$19 + 9 = 28 \qquad 21 + 33 = 54$$

Since all the answers are even, it seems reasonable to conclude that the sum of two odd numbers will be an even number.

☑ 2. Use inductive reasoning to form conjectures.

▼ Try This One 3

If two odd numbers are multiplied, is the result always odd, always even, or sometimes odd and sometimes even? Use inductive reasoning to answer.

One number is *divisible* by another number if the remainder is zero after dividing. For example, 16 is divisible by 8 because $16 \div 8$ has remainder zero, but 17 is not divisible by 8 because $17 \div 8$ has remainder 1.

EXAMPLE 4   **Using Inductive Reasoning to Test a Conjecture**

Math Note

Once again, inductive reasoning can't tell us for certain that the conjecture is true. On the other hand, in this case it's at least *possible* to try every four-digit number. But on the fun scale, that would rank somewhere in between a root canal and sitting on a tack.

Use inductive reasoning to decide if the following conjecture is likely to be true: any four-digit number is divisible by 11 if the difference between the sum of the first and third digits and the sum of the second and fourth digits is divisible by 11.

SOLUTION

Let's make up a few examples. For 1,738, the sum of the first and third digits is $1 + 3 = 4$, and the sum of the second and fourth digits is $7 + 8 = 15$. The difference is $15 - 4 = 11$, so if the conjecture is true, 1,738 should be divisible by 11. To check: $1,738 \div 11 = 158$ (with no remainder).

For 9,273, $9 + 7 = 16$, $2 + 3 = 5$, and $16 - 5 = 11$. So if the conjecture is true, 9,273 should be divisible by 11. To check: $9,273 \div 11 = 843$ (with no remainder).

Let's look at one more example. For 7,161, $7 + 6 = 13$, $1 + 1 = 2$, and $13 - 2 = 11$. Also $7,161 \div 11 = 651$ (with no remainder), so the conjecture is true for this example as well. While we can't be positive based on three examples, inductive reasoning indicates that the conjecture is likely to be true.

▼ Try This One 4

Use inductive reasoning to decide if the following conjecture is likely to be true: if the sum of the digits of a number is divisible by 3, then the number itself is divisible by 3.

Inductive reasoning can definitely be a useful tool in decision making, and we use it very often in our lives. But it has one very obvious drawback: because you can very seldom verify conclusions for every possible case, you can't be positive that the conclusions you're drawing are correct. In the example of the class in which a quiz is given on four consecutive Fridays, even if that continues for 10 more weeks, there's still a chance that there won't be a quiz the following Friday. And if there's even one Friday on which a quiz is not given, then the conjecture that there will be a quiz every Friday proves to be false.

This is a useful observation: while it's not often easy to prove that a conjecture is true, it's much simpler to prove that one is false. All you need is to find one specific example that contradicts the conjecture. This is known as a **counterexample**. In the quiz example, just one Friday without a quiz serves as a counterexample: it proves that your conjecture that there would be a quiz every Friday is false. In Example 5, we'll use this idea to prove that a conjecture is false.

EXAMPLE 5	**Finding a Counterexample**

Find a counterexample that proves the conjecture below is false.

Conjecture: A number is divisible by 3 if the last two digits are divisible by 3.

SOLUTION

We'll pick a few numbers at random whose last two digits are divisible by 3, then divide them by 3, and see if there's a remainder.

1,527: Last two digits, 27, divisible by 3; $1{,}527 \div 3 = 509$
11,745: Last two digits, 45, divisible by 3; $11{,}745 \div 3 = 3{,}915$

At this point, you might start to suspect that the conjecture is true, but you shouldn't! We've only checked two cases, and there are infinitely many possibilities.

1,136: Last two digits, 36, divisible by 3; $1{,}136 \div 3 = 378\frac{2}{3}$

This counterexample shows that the conjecture is false.

☑ 3. Find a counterexample to disprove a conjecture.

▼ Try This One 5

Find a counterexample to disprove the conjecture that the name of every month in English contains either the letter y or the letter r.

CAUTION	*Remember:* One counterexample is enough to show that a conjecture is false. But one positive example is *never* enough to show that a conjecture is true.

EXAMPLE 6	**Making and Testing a Conjecture**

Use inductive reasoning to make a conjecture about the number of sections a circle is divided into when a given number of points on the circle are connected by chords. (A chord is a line connecting two points on a circle.) Then test the conjecture with one further example.

SOLUTION

We'll draw several circles, connect the points with chords, and then count the sections.

> *Math Note*
>
> Example 6 illustrates what is, in some sense, the very essence of math and science: we have an idea that something might be true, and we use inductive reasoning to test it. But the result of the example shows why inductive reasoning can't be used to *prove* results: what appears to be true after looking at several examples can still turn out to be false.

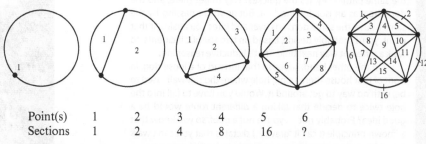

Point(s)	1	2	3	4	5	6
Sections	1	2	4	8	16	?

Looking at the pattern in the number of sections, we see that a logical guess for the next number is 32. In fact, the number appears to be 2 raised to the power of 1 less than the number of points. This will be our conjecture. Let's see how we did by checking with six points:

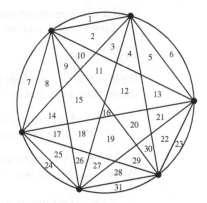

Uh oh . . . there are 31 sections! It looks like our conjecture is not true.

▼ Try This One 6

Given that there are 31 sections with 6 points, guess how many there will be with 7, and then check your answer.

The other method of reasoning that we will study is called *deductive reasoning,* or *deduction.*

Deductive reasoning is the process of reasoning that arrives at a conclusion based on previously accepted general statements. It does not rely on specific examples.

Here's an example of deductive reasoning. At many colleges, a student has to be registered for at least 12 hours to be considered full-time. So we accept the statement

---

Sidelight OF FUZZY DOGS AND INDUCTIVE REASONING

Here's a clever way to understand the difference between inductive and deductive reasoning. Suppose a friend invites you over to his new apartment, and while walking over there, you come across a house with a loose dog in the yard. As you pass, the dog runs over and bites you on the ankle. Ouch! If you're walking back to your friend's place again a week later, you might decide to take the same path—hey, it's the quickest way to get there, and the dog bite was an isolated incident. But as you're passing by the same house, the same dog runs over and bites you again. At that point, you'd probably decide, based on two specific incidents, to walk a different way next time. That's inductive reasoning.

On the other hand, suppose that instead of a loose dog, in front of that house there's a big hole where the sidewalk used to be, with no way to get around it. Would you have to fall into the hole twice to decide that taking a different route would be a good idea? Probably not . . . you're not a goof, so you know that a known principle (I call it "gravity") dictates that you can't walk over a big hole without falling in. That's deductive reasoning.

"A student is full-time if he or she is registered for at least 12 hours" as true. If we're then told that a particular student has full-time status, we can conclude that she or he is registered for at least 12 hours. The key is that we can be *positive* that this is true. This is what separates deductive reasoning from inductive reasoning. Example 7 illustrates the difference between using inductive and deductive reasoning in math.

☑ 4. Explain the difference between inductive and deductive reasoning.

EXAMPLE 7   Using Deductive Reasoning to Prove a Conjecture

Math Note

Here's another way to think about the difference between inductive and deductive reasoning: inductive reasoning begins with *specific* examples, and leads to a more *general* conclusion. Deductive reasoning starts with a *general* principle, and uses it to draw conclusions about *specific* examples. In short:

Inductive: Specific → General
Deductive: General → Specific

Consider the following problem: think of any number. Multiply that number by 2, then add 6, and divide the result by 2. Next subtract the original number. What is the result?

(a) Use inductive reasoning to make a conjecture for the answer.
(b) Use deductive reasoning to prove your conjecture.

SOLUTION

(a) Inductive reasoning will be helpful in forming a conjecture. We'll choose a few specific numbers at random and perform the given operations to see what the result is.

Number:	12	5	43
Multiply by 2:	$2 \times 12 = 24$	$2 \times 5 = 10$	$2 \times 43 = 86$
Add 6:	$24 + 6 = 30$	$10 + 6 = 16$	$86 + 6 = 92$
Divide by 2:	$30 \div 2 = 15$	$16 \div 2 = 8$	$92 \div 2 = 46$
Subtract the original number:	$15 - 12 = 3$	$8 - 5 = 3$	$46 - 43 = 3$
Result:	3	3	3

At this point, you may be tempted to conclude that the result is always 3. But this is just a conjecture: we've tried only three of infinitely many possible numbers! As usual when using inductive reasoning, we can't be completely sure that our conjecture is always true. But at this point, it seems like it would at least be worth the effort to see if we can prove that our conjecture is true.

(b) The problem with the inductive approach is that it requires using specific numbers, and we know that we can't check every possible number. Instead, we'll choose an *arbitrary* number and call it *a*. If we can show that the result is 3 in this case, that will tell us that this is the result for *every* number. Remember, we'll be doing the exact same operations, just on an arbitrary number *a*, for "any old number."

Number:	a
Multiply by 2:	$2a$
Add 6:	$2a + 6$
Divide by 2:	$\dfrac{2a + 6}{2} = \dfrac{2a}{2} + \dfrac{6}{2} = a + 3$
Subtract the original number:	$a + 3 - a = 3$

Now we know for sure that the result will always be 3, and our conjecture is proved.

☑ 5. Use deductive reasoning to prove a conjecture.

▼ Try This One 7

Consider the following problem: think of any number. Multiply that number by 3, then add 30, and divide the result by 3. Next subtract the original number. What is the result?

(a) Use inductive reasoning to make a conjecture for the answer.
(b) Use deductive reasoning to prove your conjecture.

Sidelight **MAKING AN ARBITRARY POINT**

In common usage, the word *arbitrary* is often misinterpreted as a synonym for *random*. When reaching into a bag of potato chips, you make a random selection, and some people would also call this an arbitrary selection. But in math, the word *arbitrary* means something very different. When randomly selecting that chip, you have still chosen a specific chip—it is probably not representative of every chip in the bag. Some chips will be bigger, and others smaller. Maybe you got that one gross little burned chip. Yuck.

When we use *arbitrary* in math, we're referring to a non-specific item that is able to represent *all* such items. In the series of calculations we looked at above, we could never be sure

that the result will always be 3 by choosing specific numbers. Why? Because we'd have to try it for *every* number, which is of course impossible. You have better things to do than spend the rest of your life testing number after number. The value of performing the calculation on an *arbitrary* number *a* is that this one calculation proves what will happen for *every* number you choose. It is absolutely crucial in the study of mathematics to understand that choosing specific numbers can almost never *prove* a result, because you can't try every number. Instead, we'll rely on using arbitrary numbers and deductive reasoning. Now ponder this deep question: is there such a thing as an arbitrary potato chip?

Let's try another example. Try to focus on the difference between inductive and deductive reasoning, and the fact that inductive reasoning is great for giving you an idea about what the truth might be for a given situation, but deductive reasoning is needed for proof.

EXAMPLE 8 | **Using Deductive Reasoning to Prove a Conjecture**

Calculator Guide

If you use a calculator to try the repeated operations in Example 8, you'll need to press ▣ (scientific calculator) or ▣ (graphing calculator) after every operation, or you'll get the wrong result. Suppose you simply enter the whole string:

Standard Scientific Calculator

12 ➕ 50 ✖ 2 ➖ 12 ▣

Standard Graphing Calculator

12 ➕ 50 ✖ 2 ➖ 12 ▣

The result is 100, which is incorrect. In Chapter 5, we'll find out why when we study the order of operations.

Use inductive reasoning to arrive at a general conclusion, and then prove your conclusion is true by using deductive reasoning.

Pick a number:
Add 50:
Multiply by 2:
Subtract the original number:
Result:

SOLUTION

Approach: Induction

Try a couple different numbers and make a conjecture.

Original number:	12	50
Add 50:	12 + 50 = 62	50 + 50 = 100
Multiply by 2:	62 × 2 = 124	100 × 2 = 200
Subtract the original number:	124 − 12 = 112	200 − 50 = 150
Result:	112	150

A reasonable conjecture is that the final answer is 100 more than the original number.

Approach:	Deduction
Pick an arbitrary number:	*a*
Add 50:	*a* + 50
Multiply by 2:	2(*a* + 50) = 2*a* + 100
Subtract the original number:	2*a* + 100 − *a*
Result:	*a* + 100

Our conjecture was right: the final answer is always 100 more than the original number.

▼ Try This One 8

Arrive at a conclusion by using inductive reasoning, and then try to prove your conclusion by using deductive reasoning.

Pick a number:

Add 16:

Multiply by 3:

Add 2:

Subtract twice the original number:

Subtract 50:

Result:

Now that we've seen how inductive and deductive reasoning can be used, let's review by distinguishing between the two types of reasoning in some real situations.

EXAMPLE 9   Comparing Inductive and Deductive Reasoning

The last six times we played our archrival in football, we won, so I know we're going to win on Saturday. Did I use inductive or deductive reasoning?

SOLUTION

This conclusion is based on six specific occurrences, not a general rule that we know to be true. (No team wins *every* game!). I used inductive reasoning.

▼ Try This One 9

There is no mail delivery on holidays. Tomorrow is Labor Day so I know my student loan check won't show up. Did I use inductive or deductive reasoning?

EXAMPLE 10   Comparing Inductive and Deductive Reasoning

The syllabus states that any final average between 80 and 90% will result in a B. If I get 78% on my final, my overall average will be 80.1%, so I'll get a B. Did I use inductive or deductive reasoning?

SOLUTION

Although we're talking about a specific person's grade, the conclusion that I'll get a B is based on a general rule: all scores in the 80s earn a B. So this is deductive reasoning.

▼ Try This One 10

Everyone I know in my sorority got at least a 2.5 GPA last semester, so I'm sure I'll get at least a 2.5 this semester. Did I use inductive or deductive reasoning?

Remember that both inductive reasoning and deductive reasoning are useful tools for problem solving. But the biggest difference between them is that conclusions drawn from inductive reasoning, no matter how reasonable, are still at least somewhat uncertain. In Problems 69–74, we'll distinguish between *weak* and *strong* inductive arguments. But conclusions drawn by using deductive reasoning can be considered definitely true, as long as the general rules used to draw the conclusion are known to be true.

In addition, you should take a minute or two to think about the fact that to disprove a conjecture, you only need to find *one specific example* for which it's not true. But to prove a conjecture, you have to show that it's true in *every* possible case.

Answers to Try This One

1   Pattern: every entry is 1 more than the one that comes two spots before it. The next three numbers are 8, 6, 9.

2

3   Always odd

4   True

5   June has neither a y nor an r.

6   There are 57.

7   10

8   The result is the original number.

9   Deductive

10   Inductive

EXERCISE SET 1-1

Writing Exercises

1. Explain the difference between inductive and deductive reasoning.
2. What is meant by the term *conjecture*?
3. Give an example of a decision you made based on inductive reasoning that turned out well, and one that turned our poorly.
4. What is a counterexample? What are counterexamples used for?
5. Explain why you can never be sure that a conclusion you arrived at using inductive reasoning is true.
6. Explain the difference between an arbitrary number and a number selected at random.

Computational Exercises

For Exercises 7–16, use inductive reasoning to find a pattern, and then make a reasonable conjecture for the next number or item in the sequence.

7. 1   2   4   7   11   16   22   29   __
8. 6   10   22   58   166   490   __
9. 10   20   11   18   12   16   13   14   14   12   15   __
10. 2   3   8   63   3,968   __
11. 100   99   97   94   90   85   79   __
12. 9   12   11   14   13   16   15   18   __

13.  _____

14. 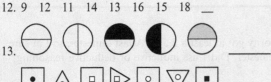 _____

15.  _____

16. _____

For Exercises 17–20, find a counterexample to show that each statement is false.

17. The sum of any three odd numbers is even.
18. When an even number is added to the product of two odd numbers, the result will be even.
19. When an odd number is squared and divided by 2, the result will be a whole number.

20. When any number is multiplied by 6 and the digits of the answer are added, the sum will be divisible by 6.

For Exercises 21–24, use inductive reasoning to make a conjecture about a rule that relates the number you selected to the final answer. Try to prove your conjecture by using deductive reasoning.

21. Pick a number:
Double it:
Subtract 20 from the answer:
Divide by 2:
Subtract the original number:
Result:

22. Pick a number:
Multiply it by 9:
Add 21:
Divide by 3:
Subtract three times the original number:
Result:

23. Pick a number:
Add 6:
Multiply the answer by 9:
Divide the answer by 3:
Subtract 3 times the original number:
Result:

24. Pick an even number:
Multiply it by 4:
Add 8 to the product:
Divide the answer by 2:
Subtract 2 times the original number:
Result:

For Exercises 25–34, use inductive reasoning to find a pattern for the answers. Then use the pattern to guess the result of the final calculation, and perform the operation to see if your answer is correct.

25. $12,345,679 \times 9 = 111,111,111$
$12,345,679 \times 18 = 222,222,222$
$12,345,679 \times 27 = 333,333,333$
$\vdots$
$12,345,679 \times 72 = ?$

26. $0^2 + 1 = 1$
$1^2 + 3 = 2^2$
$2^2 + 5 = 3^2$
$3^2 + 7 = 4^2$
$4^2 + 9 = 5^2$
$5^2 + 11 = ?$

27. $999,999 \times 1 = 0,999,999$
$999,999 \times 2 = 1,999,998$
$999,999 \times 3 = 2,999,997$
$\vdots$
$999,999 \times 9 = ?$

28. $1 = 1^2$
$1 + 2 + 1 = 2^2$
$1 + 2 + 3 + 2 + 1 = 3^2$
$\vdots$
$1 + 2 + 3 + 4 + 5 + 6 + 7 + 6 + 5 + 4 + 3 + 2 + 1 = ?$

29. $9 \times 9 = 81$
$99 \times 99 = 9,801$
$999 \times 999 = 998,001$
$9,999 \times 9,999 = 99,980,001$
$99,999 \times 99,999 = ?$

30. $1 \times 8 + 1 = 9$
$12 \times 8 + 2 = 98$
$123 \times 8 + 3 = 987$
$1,234 \times 8 + 4 = 9,876$
$12,345 \times 8 + 5 = ?$

31. $1 \cdot 1 = 1$
$11 \cdot 11 = 121$
$111 \cdot 111 = 12,321$
$1,111 \cdot 1,111 = 1,234,321$
$11,111 \cdot 11,111 = ?$

32. $9 \cdot 91 = 819$
$8 \cdot 91 = 728$
$7 \cdot 91 = 637$
$6 \cdot 91 = 546$
$5 \cdot 91 = ?$

33. Explain what happens when the number 142,857 is multiplied by the numbers 2 through 8.

34. A Greek mathematician named Pythagoras is said to have discovered the following number pattern. Find the next three sums by using inductive reasoning. Don't just add!
$1 = 1$
$1 + 3 = 4$
$1 + 3 + 5 = 9$
$1 + 3 + 5 + 7 = 16$
$1 + 3 + 5 + 7 + 9 = ?$
$1 + 3 + 5 + 7 + 9 + 11 = ?$
$1 + 3 + 5 + 7 + 9 + 11 + 13 = ?$

35. Use inductive reasoning to make a conjecture about the next three sums, and then perform the calculations to verify that your conjecture is true.
$1 + \dfrac{1}{2} = \dfrac{3}{2}$
$1 + \dfrac{1}{2} + \dfrac{1}{2 \cdot 3} = \dfrac{5}{3}$
$1 + \dfrac{1}{2} + \dfrac{1}{2 \cdot 3} + \dfrac{1}{3 \cdot 4} = \dfrac{7}{4}$
$1 + \dfrac{1}{2} + \dfrac{1}{2 \cdot 3} + \dfrac{1}{3 \cdot 4} + \dfrac{1}{4 \cdot 5} = ?$
$1 + \dfrac{1}{2} + \dfrac{1}{2 \cdot 3} + \dfrac{1}{3 \cdot 4} + \dfrac{1}{4 \cdot 5} + \dfrac{1}{5 \cdot 6} = ?$
$1 + \dfrac{1}{2} + \dfrac{1}{2 \cdot 3} + \dfrac{1}{3 \cdot 4} + \dfrac{1}{4 \cdot 5} + \dfrac{1}{5 \cdot 6} + \dfrac{1}{6 \cdot 7} = ?$

36. Use inductive reasoning to determine the unknown sum, then perform the calculation to verify your answer.
$2 = 1(2)$
$2 + 4 = 2(3)$
$2 + 4 + 6 = 3(4)$
$2 + 4 + 6 + 8 = 4(5)$
$2 + 4 + 6 + 8 + 10 + 12 + 14 = ?$

In Exercises 37–40, use inductive reasoning to find a pattern, then make a reasonable conjecture for the next three items in the pattern.

37. d b e c f d __ __ __
38. a b c e d f i g h o __ __ __

39. J F M A __ __ __
40. D N O S A __ __ __

Applications in Our World

In Exercises 41–58, determine whether the type of reasoning used is inductive or deductive reasoning.

41. The last four congressional representatives from this district were all Republicans. I don't know why the Democratic candidate is even bothering to run this year.

42. I know I will have to work a double shift today because I have a migraine and every time I have a migraine I get stuck pulling a double.

43. If class is canceled, I go to the beach with my friends. I didn't go to the beach with my friends yesterday; so class was not canceled.

44. On Christmas Day, movie theaters and Chinese restaurants are always open, so this Christmas Day we can go to a movie and get some Chinese takeout.

45. For the first three games this year, the parking lot was packed with tailgaters, so we'll have to leave extra early to find a spot this week.

46. Every time Beth sold back her textbooks, she got about 10% of what she paid for them; so this semester she realized it would not be worth the effort to sell back her books at all.

47. Experts say that opening email attachments that come from unknown senders is the easiest way to get a virus on your computer. Shauna constantly opens attachments from people she doesn't know, so she'll probably end up with a virus on her system.

48. Whenever Marcie let friends set her up on a blind date, the guy turned out to be a total loser. This time, when a friend offered to fix her up, she decided the guy would be a loser, so she declined.

49. Dr. Spalsbury's policy is that any student whose cell phone goes off during class will be asked to leave. So when Ericka forgot to turn hers off and it rang during a quiz, out the door she went.

50. While experimenting on learning in mice, a biology student was able to successfully train six different mice to finish a maze, so she was really surprised when the next one was unable to learn the maze.

51. Since Josie ate a diet of mostly foods high in saturated fat, she was not surprised when her doctor said her cholesterol levels were too high.

52. In the past, even when Chris followed a recipe, her meal was either burned or underdone. Now her party guests know to eat before they attend her dinners so they won't starve all evening.

53. Working as a nurse in a hospital requires at least a two-year degree in this state, so when I was in the emergency room last week I asked the nurse where he went to college.

54. Marathon runners should eat extra carbs before a big race, and since Mark did not eat enough carbs before the race, he felt sluggish the entire time.

55. Organizing chapter contents in your own words before the test will decrease the amount of study you have to do before a test. When Scott tried this method, he was pleasantly surprised at how fast he was able to study.

56. The last several network dramas I've followed have been canceled just when I started getting into them. So I'm not going to bother watching the new one they're advertising even though it looks good, because I don't want to be disappointed when it gets canceled.

57. Rollerblading without knee pads and a helmet is said to be dangerous. So when I got my first pair of Rollerblades, I made sure to get a helmet and knee pads.

58. Whenever Sarah drove over the speed bumps near the dorm too fast, her CD player would skip around like crazy. So this time before she entered the dorm parking lot, she paused the CD.

Critical Thinking

59. Do a Google search for the string "studies texting while driving." Suppose that you've driven while texting ten times in the past without any incident. How likely would you be to text while driving if you use (a) inductive reasoning, and (b) deductive reasoning based on your Google search? Describe your reasoning in each case.

60. Just about everyone had a conversation like this with their parents at some point in their childhood: "But all my friends are doing it!" "If your friends jumped off a bridge, would you jump too?" Describe how arguments like this apply to inductive and deductive reasoning. Specifically, what type of reasoning is each person using, and who in your opinion makes a stronger argument?

61. (a) Find a likely candidate for the next two numbers in the following sequence: 2, 4, 8, . . .

(b) Was your answer 16 and 32? How did you get that answer? Can you find a formula with variable n that provides the numbers in your sequence?

(c) My answer is 14 and 22. How did I get that answer? Can you find a formula with variable n that provides the numbers in my sequence? (*Note:* the last question is NOT easy!)

(d) Fill in the following table by substituting the given values of n into the formula. Can you answer the last question in part (c) now? Based on all parts of this problem, what can you conclude about finding a pattern when you have just a bit of information to use?

n	1	2	3	4	5
$n^2 - n + 2$					

62. (a) Find a likely candidate for the next two numbers in the following sequence: 3, 9, 27, . . .

(b) Was your answer 81 and 243? How did you get that answer? Can you find a formula with variable n that provides the numbers in your sequence?

(c) My answer is 57 and 99. How did I get that answer? (*Hint:* Find differences between the first two pairs of terms and look for a pattern.) Can you find a formula with variable n that provides the numbers in my sequence? (*Note:* this is NOT easy!)

(d) Fill in the following table by substituting the given values of n into the formula. Can you answer the last question in part (c) now? Based on all parts of this problem, what can you conclude about finding a pattern when you have just a bit of information to use?

n	1	2	3	4	5
$6n^2 - 12n + 9$					

63. (a) In several of the problems in this section, you looked at a string of numbers then decided what the next number would be. This time, write a string of five numbers with a pattern so that the next number in the string would be 10.

(b) Next, write a string of five numbers with a pattern so that the next two numbers in the string would be 10 and 13.

(c) Finally, write a string of five numbers with a pattern so that the next three numbers in the string would be 10, 13, and 17.

64. Refer to problem 63.

(a) Write a string of three numbers so that the next number in the string would be $\frac{4}{81}$.

(b) Next, write a string of three numbers so that the next two numbers in the string would be $\frac{4}{81}$ and $-\frac{5}{243}$.

(c) Find a formula with variable n that provides the numbers in your sequence.

Problems 65 and 66 use the formula average speed = distance/time.

65. Suppose that you drive a certain distance at 20 miles per hour, then turn around and drive back the same distance at 60 miles per hour.

(a) Choose at least four different distances and find the average speed for the whole trip. Then use inductive reasoning to make a conjecture as to what the average speed is in general.

(b) Use algebra to prove your conjecture from part (a).

66. Suppose that you drive a certain distance at 40 miles per hour, then turn around and drive twice as far at 20 miles per hour.

(a) Choose at least four different distances and find the average speed for the whole trip. Then use inductive reasoning to make a conjecture as to what the average speed is in general.

(b) Use algebra to prove your conjecture from part (a).

67. The following figure is called *Pascal's triangle*. It has many uses in mathematics and other disciplines. Use inductive reasoning to find the numbers in the last row. (*Hint:* The entries that aren't 1 are obtained by using addition.)

68. Here's a variation on Pascal's triangle from problem 67. Fill in the bottom line.

$$
\begin{array}{ccccccccccc}
& & & & & 2 & & & & & \\
& & & & 2 & & 2 & & & & \\
& & & 2 & & 4 & & 2 & & & \\
& & 2 & & 8 & & 8 & & 2 & & \\
& 2 & & 16 & & 64 & & 16 & & 2 & \\
2 & & \_ & & \_ & & \_ & & \_ & & 2 \\
\end{array}
$$

All conclusions drawn from inductive reasoning aren't created equal. We can distinguish between a **weak inductive argument**, *where a conclusion is drawn from just a few specific instances, and a* **strong inductive argument**, *where a conclusion is drawn from a large amount of observations. In problems 69–74, classify each argument as weak or strong induction, and discuss your reasoning.*

69. The Cubs lost the first six games of the season. They have NO chance tonight.

70. There are 52 people on my flight to the Bahamas, and 40 of them brought carry-on bags to avoid paying baggage fees. So I'm thinking that about 80% of air travelers bring carry-ons to avoid fees.

71. Just over one thousand Americans were polled by CNN in October of 2011, and almost 70% felt that Congress had done nothing to address the problems facing America. I conclude that a majority of Americans were unhappy with Congress at that point.

72. I played the first nine holes of a local golf course last night, and the grass was brown on all nine of them. I imagine all nine holes on the back nine are burned out, too.

73. There were 104,000 people at the Ohio State-Michigan State game last year. Almost all of them cheered when Ohio State scored, so the game must have been played in Ohio.

74. All three high school math teachers I had were kind of nerdy. I guess that all math teachers are nerds.

75. The numbers 1, 3, 6, 10, 15, . . . are called *triangular numbers* since they can be displayed as shown.

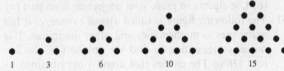

The numbers 1, 4, 9, 16, 25, . . . are called *square numbers* since they can be displayed as shown.

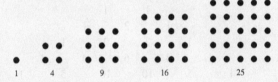

The numbers 1, 5, 12, 22, 35, . . . are called *pentagonal numbers* since they can be displayed as shown.

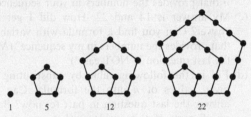

(a) Using inductive reasoning, find the next three triangular numbers.
(b) Using inductive reasoning, find the next three square numbers.
(c) Using inductive reasoning, find the next three pentagonal numbers.
(d) Using inductive reasoning, find the first four hexagonal numbers.

76. Refer to Exercise 75. The formula for finding triangular numbers is $\dfrac{n[1n - (-1)]}{2}$ or $\dfrac{n(n + 1)}{2}$. The formula for finding square numbers is $\dfrac{n(2n - 0)}{2}$ or n^2. The formula for pentagonal numbers is $\dfrac{n(3n - 1)}{2}$. Find the formula for hexagonal numbers, using inductive reasoning.

Section 1-2   Estimation and Interpreting Graphs

LEARNING OBJECTIVES

- [ ] 1. Identify some uses for estimation.
- [ ] 2. Round numbers to a given level of accuracy.
- [ ] 3. Estimate the answers to problems in our world.
- [ ] 4. Use estimation to obtain information from graphs.

Everyone likes buying items on sale, so we should all be familiar with the idea of finding a rough approximation for a sale price. If you're looking at a pair of shoes that normally sells for $70 and the store has a 40% off sale, you might figure that the shoes are a little more than half price, which would be $35, so they're probably around $40. We will call the process of finding an approximate answer to a math problem **estimation**. Chances are that you use estimation a lot more than you realize, unless you carry a calculator with you everywhere you go. (Okay, so your cell phone has a calculator, but how often do you use it?)

Estimation comes in handy in a wide variety of settings. When the auto repair shop technicians look over your car to see what's wrong, they can't know for sure what the exact cost will be until they've made the repairs, so they will give you an estimate. When you go to the grocery store and have only $20 to spend, you'll probably keep a rough estimate of the total as you add items to the cart. (Imagine buying a week's worth of groceries and keeping track of every price to the penny on your cell phone. Who has time for that?) If you plan on buying carpet for a room, you'd most likely measure the square footage and then estimate the total cost as you looked at different styles of carpet. You could find the exact cost if you really needed to, but often an estimate is good enough for you to make a sound buying decision.

Estimation is also a really useful tool in checking answers to math problems, particularly word problems. Let's say you're planning an outing for a student group you

belong to, and lunch is included at $3.95 per person. If 24 people signed up and you were billed $94.80, you could use estimation to quickly figure that this is a reasonable bill. Since 24 is close to 25, and $3.95 is close to $4.00, the bill should be close to 25 × $4.00 = $100.

You also use estimation when rounding numbers for simplicity. If someone asks your height and age, you might say 5′11″ and 20, even if you're actually 5′10½″ (everyone fudges a little) and 20 years, 4 months, and 6 days old.

Since the process of estimating uses rounding, we'll start with a brief review of rounding numbers. This is based on the concept of place value. The **place value** of a digit in a number tells the value of the digit in terms of ones, tens, hundreds, etc. For example, in the number 325, the 3 means 3 hundreds or 300 since its place value is hundreds. The 2 means 2 tens, or 20, and the 5 means 5 ones. A place value chart is shown here, along with instructions for rounding numbers.

☑ 1. Identify some uses for estimation.

Steps for Rounding Numbers

1. Locate the place-value digit of the number that is being rounded. Here is the place-value chart for whole numbers and decimals:

8,	9	8	5,	7	3	0,	2	6	1	•	2	3	5	6	7	8
billions	hundred-millions	ten-millions	millions	hundred-thousands	ten-thousands	thousands	hundreds	tens	ones		tenths	hundredths	thousandths	ten-thousandths	hundred-thousandths	millionths

2a. If the digit to the right of the place-value digit is 0 through 4, don't change the place-value digit.

2b. If the digit to the right of the place-value digit is 5 through 9, add 1 to the place-value digit.

Note: When you round whole numbers, replace all digits to the right of the digit being rounded with zeros. When you round decimal numbers, drop all digits to the right of the digit that is being rounded.

> **Math Note**
>
> We often use the word *nearest* to describe the place value to round to. Instead of saying, "Round to the hundreds place," we might say, "Round to the nearest hundred."

EXAMPLE 1   **Rounding Numbers**

Round each number to the place value given.

(a) 7,328 (hundreds)   (c) 32.4817 (tenths)
(b) 15,683 (thousands)   (d) 0.047812 (ten-thousandths)

SOLUTION

(a) In the number 7,328, 3 is in the hundreds place, so it's the digit being rounded. Since the digit to the right is 2, the digit 3 remains the same, and the 2 and 8 are replaced by zeros. The rounded number is 7,300.

(b) In the number 15,683, the 5 is the digit to be rounded. Since the digit to the right is 6, add 1 to the 5 and replace the digits 6, 8, and 3 with zeros. The rounded number is 16,000.

(c) In the number 32.4817, the 4 is the digit to be rounded. Since the digit to the right of the 4 is 8, add 1 to the 4 to get 5 and drop all digits to the right of the 4. The rounded number is 32.5.

(d) In the number 0.047812, the 8 is the digit to be rounded. Since the digit to the right of 8 is 1, the 8 remains the same. The digits 1 and 2 are dropped, and the rounded number is 0.0478.

▼ **Try This One 1**

2. Round numbers to a given level of accuracy.

Round each number to the place value given.

(a) 372,651 (hundreds)   (c) 0.37056 (thousandths)
(b) 32.971 (ones)   (d) 1,465.983 (hundredths)

Estimation

When we use estimation to simplify numerical calculations, we use two steps:

1. Round the numbers being used to numbers that make the calculation simple.
2. Perform the operation or operations involved.

EXAMPLE 2   **Estimating Total Cost When Shopping**

The owner of an apartment complex needs to buy six refrigerators for a new building. She chooses a model that costs $579.99 per refrigerator. Estimate the total cost of all six.

SOLUTION

Step 1 Round the cost of the refrigerators. In this case, rounding up to $600 will make the calculation easy.

Step 2 Perform the calculation: $600 × 6 = $3,600. Our estimated cost is $3,600. (The actual cost will be a little less than $3,600—since we rounded the price up, our estimate will be high.)

▼ **Try This One 2**

At one ballpark, large frosty beverages cost $7.25 each. Estimate the cost of buying one for each member of a group consisting of four couples. Is the actual cost more or less than your answer?

Students often wonder, "How do I know what digit to round to?" It would be nice if these were an exact answer to that question, but there isn't—it depends on the individual numbers. In Example 2, the cost of the refrigerators could have been rounded from $579.99 to $580. Then the cost estimate would be $580 × 6 = $3,480. This is a much closer estimate because we rounded the cost to the nearest dollar, rather than the nearest $100. But the calculation is harder.

Deciding on how much to round is really a tradeoff: ease of calculation versus accuracy. In most cases you'll get a more accurate result if you round less, but the calculation will be a little harder. Since there's no exact rule, it's important to evaluate the situation and use good old-fashioned common sense. And remember, when you are estimating, there is no one correct answer.

Sidelight JUST HOW BIG ARE BIG NUMBERS?

Back when we were still living in caves, really large numbers probably weren't of much use. Early humans could use their fingers and toes to count their families and possessions, and I imagine that was good enough. How the world has changed! In the 21st century, we're bombarded with large numbers from every direction, and being able to have some perspective on the size of those numbers is a useful skill. The truth is that most people have absolutely no idea how big a number like a million actually is.

Not too long ago, a million was a really big number, but between the contracts of professional athletes and entertainers, world population and government spending, a million almost seems commonplace. So is a million that big?

One million is a one followed by six zeros (1,000,000). If you wanted to count to a million and you counted one number each second with no time off to eat or sleep, it would take you just about $11\frac{1}{2}$ days. Wow. A stack of one million pennies would be almost a mile high; a pile of one million dollar bills would weigh almost a ton. As of this writing, the federal minimum wage is $7.25 per hour. If you worked 40 hours a week at a minimum wage job, it would take you over 66 years to make one million dollars—before taxes!

Add three more zeros to the end of a million and you get one billion (1,000,000,000); that makes a billion equal to 1,000 million. In 2010, the federal government spent about $7\frac{1}{2}$ billion dollars—per DAY. So how big is a billion?

Counting to one billion by ones would take you about 32 years (no rest or sleep, of course). A billion pennies would make a stack almost 1,000 miles high; a pile of one billion dollar bills would be about the size of a medium-sized office building,

and weigh over a thousand tons. And guess what? From some perspectives, a billion isn't even that much.

In 2010, the federal government spent 414 billion dollars just paying *interest* on the national debt. (And guess where that money is coming from?) Here's the actual amount of money spent by our government in 2010: $3,721,000,000,000. I would be willing to bet that 80% of the population can't even read that number out loud, let alone have any perspective on just how big it is. For the record, that's 3 trillion, 721 billion dollars. It would take over 100,000 YEARS to count that high. Everyone knows that a person making a million dollars a year is wealthy, but he or she would have to work for 3.721 million years to make the amount of money the feds spend in one year.

Once you get past a trillion, things get just plain silly. A quadrillion is one followed by 15 zeros. Eighteen zeros gives you a quintillion, and 21 zeros a sextillion. The entire Earth weighs about 6 sextillion, 570 quintillion tons; the weight of all the people on Earth is a mere 525 million tons. The largest number with a name ending in -illion that I know of is the vigintillion, which has 63 zeros.

So is that the biggest number of all? Not even close. A nine-year-old girl came up with the name "googol" in 1938 to describe one followed by 100 zeros. Scientists think this is more than the total number of protons in our universe. But if you want to make a googol look small, go up to a googolplex, which is one followed by a googol of zeros. It's almost impossible to imagine how large a number this is, but writing it out would require a piece of paper far longer than the known universe.

Finally, here's an easy way to show that there IS no biggest number: give me any number, and I can give you a bigger one by adding one to it. Maybe a million isn't so big after all.

EXAMPLE 3   Estimating the Cost of a Cell Phone

You're considering a new cell phone plan where you have to pay $179 up front for the latest phone, but the monthly charge of $39.99 includes unlimited minutes and messaging. Estimate the cost of the phone for 1 year if there are no additional charges.

SOLUTION

Step 1 We can round the cost of the phone to $180 and the monthly charge to $40.

Step 2 The monthly cost estimate for 1 year will be $40 × 12 = $480; add the estimated cost of the phone to get an estimated total cost of $480 + $180 = $660.

▼ Try This One 3

A rental car company charges a rate of $78 per week to rent an economy car. For an up-front fee of $52, you can upgrade to a midsize car. Estimate the cost of renting a midsize car for 3 weeks.

20   **Chapter 1**   Problem Solving

| EXAMPLE 4 | **Estimating Remodeling Costs** |

Math Note

While rounding up or down to intentionally get either an over-or underestimate can be useful, for calculations involving addition and multiplication, rounding one quantity up and the other down can reduce the total error.

The Osbueño family plans on remodeling the living room. They will be replacing 21 square yards of carpet at a cost of $23 per square yard (installed), and they also need to have 26 linear feet of wallpaper installed. They'd like to keep the total cost around $1,000. Estimate the cost per foot of wallpaper that they can afford.

SOLUTION

First, we'll estimate how much is going to be spent on carpet: we can round the 21 square yards down to 20, and the $23 per square yard up to $25, giving us 20 × $25 = $500. So the Osbueños will have about $500 left to spend on wallpaper.

We can round the 26 linear feet down to 25, and use division to estimate the price per foot: $500 ÷ 25 = $20, so they should be looking for wallpaper that costs no more than $20 per linear foot installed.

☑ 3. Estimate the answers to problems in our world.

▼ **Try This One 4**

Next up for the Osbueños: a bedroom remodel. They will have 28 linear feet of wall painted at $12 per foot, and need 19 square yards of carpet. If the budget for the bedroom is $900, estimate the price per square yard of carpet they can afford.

In some situations, it makes the most sense to either overestimate or underestimate an answer. If you were buying groceries and had only $40 on hand, you'd want to overestimate the costs to make sure you had enough money to pay for them. If you needed to earn money to pay tuition for next semester, you'd want to underestimate how much you could earn each week so that the actual amount is definitely more than you need.

In our world, useful or interesting information is often displayed in graphical form. In Examples 5–7, we'll illustrate how estimation applies to interpreting graphical information.

A **bar graph** is used to compare amounts or percentages using either vertical or horizontal bars of various lengths; the lengths correspond to the amounts or percentages, with longer bars representing larger amounts.

| EXAMPLE 5 | **Obtaining Information from a Bar Graph** |

The graph shown represents the percentage of electricity generated by nuclear energy in five countries. Find the approximate percentage of electricity generated by nuclear energy in France, and estimate the difference between the highest and lowest percentages shown.

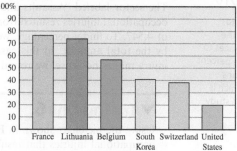

Percentage of Electricity Generated by Nuclear Energy

Source: *The World Almanac and Book of Facts*

SOLUTION

The first vertical bar represents the percentage for France. Reading across from the height of the bar to the vertical axis, we see that the height is a little bit more than halfway between 70 and 80%, so we estimate that the answer is about 76%. This is the highest percentage. The lowest is the United States, which appears to be right at 20%. So the difference between the highest and lowest percentages shown is about 56%.

▼ Try This One 5

Using the graph shown in Example 5, find the approximate percentage of electricity generated by nuclear energy for Switzerland, and estimate how much smaller this percentage is than the one for Belgium.

A **pie chart**, also called a **circle graph**, is constructed by drawing a circle and dividing it into parts called sectors, according to the size of the percentage of each portion in relation to the whole.

EXAMPLE 6   Obtaining Information from a Pie Chart

The pie chart shown represents the number of fatal occupational injuries in the United States for 2010. If the total number of fatal injuries was 4,547 for the year, estimate how many resulted from assaults and violent acts.

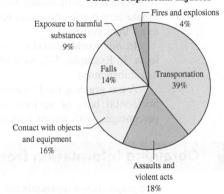

Fatal Occupational Injuries

- Fires and explosions 4%
- Exposure to harmful substances 9%
- Falls 14%
- Transportation 39%
- Contact with objects and equipment 16%
- Assaults and violent acts 18%

Source: U.S. Bureau of Labor Statistics

> **Math Note**
>
> To change a percent to decimal form, move the decimal point two places to the left and drop the percent sign: 18 percent means "18 per hundred," which is 18/100, or 0.18. We'll study percents in detail in Section 8-1.

SOLUTION

The sector labeled "Assaults and violent acts" indicates that 18% of the total fatal occupational injuries resulted from assaults and violent acts. So we need to find 18% of 4,547. To find a percentage, we multiply the decimal equivalent of the percentage by the total amount. In this case, we get $0.18 \times 4,547 = 818.46$. Since 0.46 fatal injury makes no sense, we round to 818.

▼ Try This One 6

Using the pie chart shown in Example 6, find the approximate number of fatal occupational injuries that resulted from transportation incidents.

A **time series graph** or **line graph** shows how the value of some variable quantity changes over a specific time period.

EXAMPLE 7   Obtaining Information from a Line Graph

The graph shown indicates the number of cable TV distribution points in the United States from 1960 to 2010.

(a) Find the approximate number of distribution points in 1970.
(b) Find the average rate at which the number of distribution points changed between 1990 and 2010.
(c) Estimate the year in which the number of distribution points first reached 7,000.

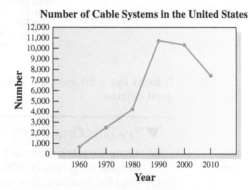

Source: National Cable and Telecommunications Association

SOLUTION

(a) Locate the year 1970 on the horizontal axis and move up to the line on the graph. At this point, move horizontally to the point on the vertical axis as shown.

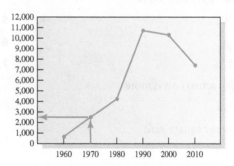

The height is about halfway between 2,000 and 3,000; so there were about 2,500 cable distribution points in the United States in 1970.

(b) The point corresponding to 1990 is just below height 11,000, so we can estimate about 10,800 distribution points in 1990. The height of the point for 2010 is about halfway between 7,000 and 8,000, so an estimate of 7,500 is reasonable. Subtracting, we find that the approximate change in number of distribution points is 7,500 − 10,800, or −3,300 (the negative represents a decrease in amount). This occurred over a span of 20 years, so the rate of change is

$$\frac{-3{,}300 \text{ distribution points}}{20 \text{ years}} = -165 \text{ distribution points per year}$$

In other words, between 1990 and 2010, the number of distribution points on average decreased by 165 points per year.

(c) This question is basically the opposite of part (a): we're given a number of distribution points (a height on the graph), and are asked to find the corresponding year. So we locate 7,000 on the vertical axis and move across to the graph, then move down to find the value on the horizontal axis.

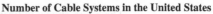

Number of Cable Systems in the United States

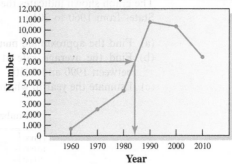

It looks like a bit less than halfway between 1980 and 1990, so 1984 seems like a good estimate.

▼ Try This One 7

4. Use estimation to obtain information from graphs.

(a) Using the graph shown in Example 7, find the approximate number of cable distribution points in 2000.
(b) Find the average rate of change in number of distribution points from the lowest to the highest number.
(c) Estimate the year in which the number fell below 9,000 after it started to decline.

Answers to Try This One

1 (a) 372,700
   (b) 33
   (c) 0.371
   (d) 1,465.98

2 About $56; actual cost is more

3 About $290

4 About $30 per square yard

5 About 39%; about 18%

6 About 1,773

7 (a) About 10,300
   (b) About 333 more distribution points per year
   (c) About 2003

EXERCISE SET 1-2

Writing Exercises

1. Think of three situations in our world where you could use estimation.
2. Explain why an exact answer to a math problem isn't always necessary.
3. How can estimation be used as a quick check to see if the answer to a math problem is reasonable?
4. Describe the rules for rounding numbers to a given place.

5. Explain why there is never a single, correct answer to a question that asks you to estimate some quantity.
6. Explain how to estimate the size of a quantity from a bar graph.
7. How is information described in a pie chart? What sort of information works well with pie charts?
8. How can you tell when a quantity is getting larger over time from looking at a time-series graph?

24   **Chapter 1**   Problem Solving

Computational Exercises

For Exercises 9–28, round the number to the place value given.

9. 2,861 (hundreds)
10. 732.6498 (thousandths)
11. 3,261,437 (ten-thousands)
12. 9,347 (tens)
13. 62.67 (ones)
14. 45,371,999 (millions)
15. 218,763 (hundred-thousands)
16. 923 (hundreds)
17. 3.671 (hundredths)
18. 56.3 (ones)
19. 327.146 (tenths)
20. 83,261,000 (millions)
21. 5,462,371 (ten-thousands)
22. 7.8662 (thousandths)
23. 272,341 (hundred-thousands)
24. 63.715 (tenths)
25. 264.97348 (ten-thousandths)
26. 1,655,432 (thousands)
27. 482.6002 (hundredths)
28. 426.861356 (hundred-thousandths)

For Exercises 29–32, estimate the result of the computation by rounding the numbers involved, then use a calculator to find the exact value and find the percent error. (Note: percent error is equal to error/exact value, written as a percentage.)

29. $-4.21(7.38 + 3.51)$
30. $10.24(-8.93 + 2.77)$
31. $\dfrac{\sqrt{9.36}}{7.423 - 9.1}$
32. $\dfrac{47.256 - 9.90}{\sqrt{24.501}}$

Applications in Our World

33. Estimate the total cost of eight energy-saving light-bulbs on sale for $16.99 each.
34. Estimate the cost of five months of HD cable at $39.95 per month.
35. Estimate the time it would take you to drive 237 miles at 37 miles per hour.
36. Estimate the distance you can travel in 3 hours 25 minutes if you drive on average 42 miles per hour.
37. Estimate the sale price of a futon you saw on eBay that costs $178.99 and is now on sale for 60% off.
38. Estimate the sale price of a Blu-ray player that costs $42.99, on sale for 15% off.
39. Estimate the total cost of the following meal at McDonald's:

Quarter pounder with cheese	$2.89
Supersized fries	$1.89
Small shamrock shake	$1.29

40. Estimate the total cost of the following items for your dorm room:

Loft bed	$159.95
Beanbag chair	$49.95
Storage cubes	$29.95
Lava lamp	$19.95

41. A group of five architecture students enters a design for an eco-friendly building in a contest, and wins third place, with a prize of $950. Estimate how much each student will get.
42. A biology lab houses 47 rats for experiments, and they go through about 105 pounds of food each week. Estimate how much food the average rat eats per week.
43. If Erin earns $48,300.00 per year, estimate how much she earns per hour. Assume that she works 40 hours per week and 50 weeks per year.
44. If Jamaal earns $8.75 per hour, estimate how much he would earn per year. Assume that he works 40 hours per week and 50 weeks per year.

45. Estimate the cost of putting up a decorative border in your dorm room if your room is 24 feet long and 18 feet wide and the border costs $5.95 every 10 feet.
46. Estimate the cost of painting a homecoming float if the area to be painted is 12 feet by 16 feet and a quart of paint that covers 53 square feet costs $11.99.
47. The Tea Party at a large university plans to line both sides of a 30-foot-long hallway with posters endorsing a candidate for state senate. Each of the posters costs them $4.95, they're 2 feet wide, and there will be 5 feet between posters. Estimate how much this will cost.
48. Estimate your cost to live in an apartment for 1 year if the rent is $365.00 per month and utilities are $62.00 per month.

Use the information shown in the graph for Exercises 49–52. The graph gives the areas of various college campuses in acres.

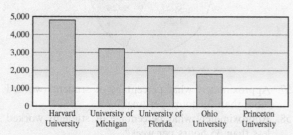

Source: http://colleges.usnews.rankingsandreviews.com

49. Estimate the area of the campus of the University of Michigan.
50. Estimate the area of the campus of Princeton University.
51. Estimate the difference between the largest campus shown and the smallest campus shown.
52. Estimate the area of each of the two universities that are approximately the same size.

Use the information shown in the graph for Exercises 53–56. The graph represents a survey of 1,385 office workers and shows the percent of people who indicated what time of day is most productive for them.

Most Productive Time of Day

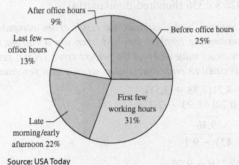

Source: USA Today

53. Estimate the number of people who feel they are most productive outside normal office hours.
54. Estimate the number of people who feel they are most productive before late morning.
55. How many more people feel they're most productive in the first few working hours compared to those that feel they're most productive in the last few office hours?
56. How many times more people are most productive before office hours compared to after?

Use the information shown in the graph for Exercises 57–60. The graph represents a survey of undergraduates enrolled in college in the 2003–2004 school year.

Hours per Week Worked by College Students Ages 22 or Younger

Source: www.acenet.edu

57. Approximately what percentage of students worked more than 21 hours per week?
58. Approximately what percentage of students worked less than 35 hours per week?
59. On one campus, 620 students under the age of 22 work 35 or more hours. If this student body is average in terms of work hours, about how many students of that age would you expect there to be on the entire campus?
60. In a survey at one community college, 310 respondents aged 22 or under said they don't work at all. If this student body is average in terms of work

hours, about how many people would you expect were surveyed?

Use the line graph shown for Exercises 61–66. The graph shows annual cigarette consumption (in billions) for the United States for the years 1900 to 2010.

Cigarette Consumption in the United States

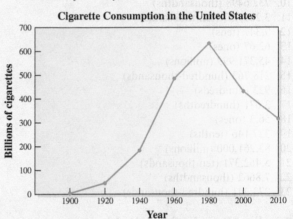

Source: www.infoplease.com

61. Estimate the number of cigarettes smoked in 1950.
62. Estimate the number of cigarettes smoked in 1985.
63. Estimate the year or years in which 200 billion cigarettes were smoked.
64. Estimate the year or years in which 400 billion cigarettes were smoked.
65. Find the average rate of change in cigarette consumption for the years shown when consumption was increasing.
66. Find the average rate of change in cigarette consumption for the years shown when consumption was decreasing.

Use the information in the graph for Exercises 67–70. The graph shows the average daily reach for the five most visited sites on the Internet for the three-month period ending December 2, 2011. (Reach is the percentage of global Internet users who visit a site.)

Average Daily Reach for Top Five Websites in the World

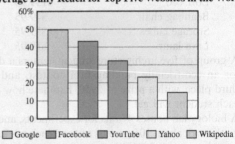

67. Estimate the average daily reach for Yahoo.
68. Estimate the average daily reach for YouTube.
69. Estimate the combined average daily reach for Google and Wikipedia.
70. Estimate the difference in average daily reach between the first and fifth most visited sites.

26   Chapter 1 Problem Solving

Use the information in the graph for Exercises 71–74. The graph shows the average penalty fees for credit cards for 2002 to 2009.

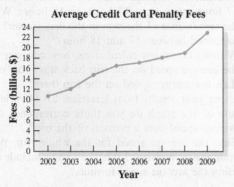

Average Credit Card Penalty Fees

Source: USA Today

71. Estimate the change in credit card penalty fees from 2002 to 2005.
72. Estimate the change in credit card penalty fees from 2004 to 2009.
73. Estimate the average rate of change in penalty fees from 2002 to 2005.
74. Estimate the average rate of change in penalty fees from 2004 to 2009.
75. In Jared's math class, he scored 84, 92, 79, and 86 on the first four tests. He needs at least an 80% overall test average to earn the B he's shooting for. Without doing any computation at all, make a guess as to the score you think he would need on the final (which is worth two test grades) to have an average of at least 80%. Then find what his average would be if he got the score you guessed. How did you do?

76. Entering a postseason basketball tournament, Marta's goal is to average at least 15 points per game for the tournament. (Marta is not the greatest team player in the world.) She scores 16, 12, 9, and 18 in the first four games. How many points do you think she will need to score in the remaining two games to reach her goal? First, make a guess without doing any computation. Then find what her average would be if she scored the number of points you guessed. How did you do?

77. One of the most valuable uses of estimation is to roughly keep track of the total cost of items when shopping. Use rounding to estimate the total cost of the following items at a grocery store: 4 cans of green beans at 79 cents each; 8 cups of yogurt at 49 cents each; a 29-ounce steak at $5.80 per pound; 4 energy drinks at $1.29 each; and 100 ounces of mineral water at $3.08 per gallon. (*Hint:* You may need to look up conversions for units of weight and volume.)

78. Refer to Problem 77. In getting my swimming pool ready for summer, I usually buy the following supplies. Use rounding to estimate the total cost: 8 boxes of baking soda at 89 cents per box; 20 gallons of bleach at $1.29 for 96 ounces; 8 pounds of chlorine stabilizer at $11.99 for a 4-pound bottle; and four 24-can cases of refreshments at 60 cents per can.

Critical Thinking

79. Sometimes graphs are drawn in such a way as to support a conclusion that may or may not be true. Look at the graph and see if you can find anything misleading.

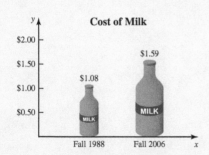

Cost of Milk

80. The choice of labeling on a graph can have a profound effect on how the information is perceived. Compare the graph to the one from Exercises 71–74. It contains the same information as the earlier graph. Why does it appear to show a much sharper increase in credit card penalty fees?

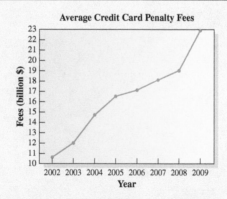

Average Credit Card Penalty Fees

Recall that the average speed of an object over some time period is calculated using the formula: speed = distance/time. The following graph describes an overnight road trip to go to an off-campus party at another college: the horizontal axis is hours driven, and the vertical axis is miles from the home campus. Use the graph to answer questions 81 through 86.

81. Estimate the average speed over the first hour of the trip, then the first two hours, the first three hours,

and the first four hours. Based on your results, write a description of the trip.

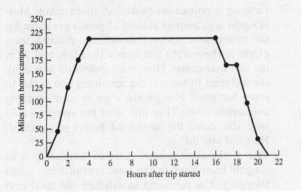

82. How long did the road-trippers stay at the other school? How far away was it from their own campus?

83. Estimate the average speed from time 16 hours to 17 hours, then from 17 hours to 18 hours. What is the significance of the sign in the first answer? What happened between 17 and 18 hours?

84. Without doing any calculations, how can you tell if the average speed on the trip back was more or less than the average speed on the trip there?

85. Using your results from Exercises 81–84, what feature of the graph do you think corresponds to the average speed over a portion of the trip?

86. Find the average speed for the whole trip. Why is your answer nonsense? What can you conclude about using the average speed formula?

Section 1-3   Problem-Solving Strategies

LEARNING OBJECTIVES

☐ 1. State the four steps in the basic problem-solving procedure.

☐ 2. Solve problems using a diagram.

☐ 3. Solve problems using trial and error.

☐ 4. Solve problems involving money.

☐ 5. Solve problems using calculation.

☑ 1. State the four steps in the basic problem-solving procedure.

Here's an idea that can help you understand your math classes better: once in a while, think about what some of the math words you take for granted actually mean in English. For example, have you ever thought about why we call math problems "problems?" In real life, when a problem confronts you, you probably think about different strategies you might use to overcome an obstacle and then decide on the best course of action. So why not use that same strategy in solving math problems? This is probably the single biggest reason why taking math classes is useful to *anyone*: math is all about learning and practicing problem-solving strategies.

A Hungarian mathematician named George Polya did a lot of research on the nature of problem solving in the first half of the 20th century. His biggest contribution to the field was an attempt to identify a series of steps that were fundamental to problem-solving strategies used by great thinkers throughout human history. One of his books, published in 1945 (and still a big seller on Amazon!), set forth these basic steps. *How to Solve It* is so widely read that it has been translated into at least 17 languages.

Polya's strategy isn't necessarily earth-shattering: its brilliance lies in its simplicity. It provides four basic steps that can be used as a framework for problem solving in any area, from math to home improvements.

Polya's Four-Step Problem-Solving Procedure

Step 1   *Understand the problem.* The best way to start any problem is to write down information that's provided as you come to it. Especially with longer word problems, if you read the whole thing all at once and don't DO anything, it's easy to get overwhelmed. If you read the problem slowly and carefully, writing down information as it's provided, you'll always at least have a start on the problem. Another great idea: carefully identify and *write down* what it is they're asking you to find; this almost always helps you to devise a strategy.

Step 2   *Devise a plan to solve the problem.* This is where problem solving is at least as much art as science—there are many, many ways to solve problems. Some common strategies: making a list of possible outcomes;

drawing a diagram; trial and error; finding a similar problem that you already know how to solve; and using arithmetic, algebra, or geometry.

Step 3   *Carry out your plan to solve the problem.* After you've made a plan, try it out. If it doesn't work, try a different strategy! There are many different ways to attack problems. Be persistent!

Step 4   *Check your answer.* It's always a good idea to think about whether or not your answer is reasonable, and in many cases you'll be able to use math to check your answer and see if it's exactly correct. If not, don't forget what we learned about estimation in Section 1-2—that can be a big help in deciding if an answer is reasonable.

In each of the examples in this section, we'll illustrate the use of Polya's four-step procedure.

EXAMPLE 1   Solving a Problem Using a Diagram

Math Note

Sometimes problems will contain extraneous information. In Example 1, the height of the plants is immaterial to the distance between them, so you can (and should) ignore that information. Students sometimes get into trouble by trying to incorporate *all* the information provided without considering relevance.

A gardener is asked to plant eight tomato plants that are 18 inches tall in a straight line with 2 feet between each plant. How much space is needed between the first plant and the last one?

SOLUTION

Be careful—what seems like an obvious solution is not always correct! You might be tempted to just multiply 8 by 2, but instead we'll use Polya's method.

Step 1   *Understand the problem.* In this case, the key information given is that there will be eight plants in a line, with 2 feet between each. We're asked to find the total distance from the first to the last.

Step 2   *Devise a plan to solve the problem.* This sounds a lot like a situation where drawing a diagram would be a big help, so we'll start there.

Step 3   *Carry out the plan to solve the problem.* The diagram would look like this:

Now we can use the picture to add up the distances:

$$2 + 2 + 2 + 2 + 2 + 2 + 2 = 14 \text{ feet}$$

Step 4   *Check the answer.* There are eight plants, but only seven spaces of 2 feet between them. So $7 \times 2 = 14$ feet is right.

▼ Try This One 1

Suppose you want to cut a 4-foot-long party sub into 20 pieces by first cutting it lengthwise down the middle, then making a series of crosscuts. How many cuts in all would you need?

EXAMPLE 2   **Solving a Perimeter Problem**

Scientists and inventors often use sketches to organize their thoughts as Leonardo da Vinci did. He wrote backward in Latin to protect his work.

A campus group is setting up a rectangular area for a tailgate bash. They have 100 feet between two roads to use as width and 440 feet of fence to use. What length will use up the total amount of fence and enclose the biggest space?

SOLUTION

Step 1 *Understand the problem.* We're asked to consider a rectangular area, so there will be four sides. We're told that the width is 100 feet and that the four sides add up to 440 feet. (That is, the perimeter is 440 feet.) We're asked to find the length.

Step 2 *Devise a plan to solve the problem.* This is another classic example of a problem where a diagram will be useful. This should help us to figure out all the dimensions.

Step 3 *Carry out the plan to solve the problem.* Our diagram looks like this:

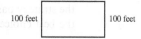

100 feet   100 feet

(Since the area is rectangular, the opposite sides have the same length.) Of the 440 feet of fence, 200 feet is accounted for in our diagram. That leaves $440 - 200 = 240$ feet to be divided among the remaining two sides. Each has length 120 feet.

Step 4 *Check the answer.* If there are two sides with width 100 feet and two others with length 120 feet, the perimeter is $100 + 100 + 120 + 120 = 440$ feet.

☑ 2. Solve problems using a diagram.

▼ **Try This One 2**

A rectangular poster promoting the tailgate bash in Example 2 is restricted to 10 inches in width to fit bulletin board restrictions. The printer suggests a perimeter of 56 inches for maximum savings in terms of setup. How tall will the posters be?

| EXAMPLE 3 | **Solving a Problem Using Trial and Error** |

Math Note

The trial and error method works nicely in Example 3, but for many problems, there are just too many possible answers to try. It's useful for some problems, and can be a *great* way to help understand a problem, but you shouldn't rely on it for every problem.

Marcus decides to go Christmas shopping at a Game Stop store, planning to buy gently used DVDs and video games for eight friends and relatives (one item per person). The DVDs are $8 each, and the video games are $14 each (both including tax). If Marcus has budgeted $95 total, how many of each item can he buy?

SOLUTION

Step 1 *Understand the problem.* The key information: total of eight items purchased; $95 dollars to spend; $8 for each DVD, $14 for each video game. We're asked to find how many DVDs and how many video games will result in a cost of $95.

Step 2 *Devise a plan to solve the problem.* I can easily figure out the total cost if I have a specific number of each item, so let's try a combination at random and see if that helps. If Marcus buys one game and seven DVDs, the cost is $1 \times \$14 + 7 \times \$8 = \$70$. This isn't right, but now we have a strategy.

Games	DVDs	Total
1	7	$70

Step 3 *Carry out the plan.* We'll keep trying combinations until we find the right one.

Games	DVDs	Total	Games	DVDs	Total
1	7	$70	4	4	$88
2	6	$76	5	3	$94
3	5	$82	6	2	$100

At this point, we can stop. The pattern shows that when we add more games, the total cost goes up. There's no combination that adds to exactly $95, but if Marcus buys five games and three DVDs it will cost $94, which is the best choice.

Step 4 *Check your answer.* One of the nice things about using trial and error is that the strategy basically IS checking your answer . . . we already know we found the best choice.

☑ 3. Solve problems using trial and error.

▼ **Try This One 3**

Michelle shipped some packages for her boss and can't find the receipt, but she needs an itemized list to get reimbursed. Here's what she remembers: there were 12 packages total, split between small flat-rate boxes ($5 each) and medium flat-rate boxes ($10.50 each). The total cost was about $110. How many of each type did she ship?

| EXAMPLE 4 | **Solving a Problem Involving Salary** |

So you've graduated from college and you're ready for that first real job. In fact, you have two offers! One pays an hourly wage of $19.20 per hour, with a 40-hour work week. You work for 50 weeks and get 2 weeks' paid vacation. The second offer is a salaried position, offering $41,000 per year. Which job will pay more?

SOLUTION

Step 1 *Understand the problem.* The important information is that the hourly job pays $19.20 per hour for 40 hours each week, and that you will be paid for 52 weeks per year. We are asked to decide if that will work out to be more or less than $41,000 per year.

Step 2 *Devise a plan to solve the problem.* We can use multiplication to figure out how much you would be paid each week and then multiply by 52 to get the yearly amount. Then we can compare to the salaried position.

Step 3 *Carry out the plan to solve the problem.* Multiply the hourly wage by 40 hours; this shows that the weekly earnings will be $19.20 × 40 = $768. Now we multiply by 52 weeks: $768 × 52 = $39,936. The salaried position, at $41,000 per year, pays more.

Step 4 *Check the answer.* We can figure out the hourly wage of the job that pays $41,000 per year. We divide by 52 to get a weekly salary of $788.46. Then we divide by 40 to get an hourly wage of $19.71. Again, this job pays more.

☑ 4. Solve problems involving money.

▼ Try This One 4

A condo on the water in Myrtle Beach can be rented for $280 per day, with a nonrefundable application fee of $50. Another one down the beach can be rented for $2,100 per week. Which condo costs less for a week's stay?

EXAMPLE 5   **Solving a Problem Using Calculation**

Nutritionists often say that you need to burn 3,500 calories while exercising to shed one pound of excess body fat. A general rule of thumb on exercise is that an average-sized person can burn about 100 calories while walking a mile at a fairly brisk pace. How many miles per day would an average person have to walk in order to shed a pound of body fat in a week?

SOLUTION

Step 1 *Understand the problem.* We're told that a person needs to burn 3,500 calories in 7 days to shed a pound of body fat, and that she'll burn 100 calories while walking a mile. We're asked to find the number of miles she needs to walk each day.

Step 2 *Devise a plan.* We'll calculate how many calories need to be burned each day, then divide by 100 to see how many miles need to be walked.

Step 3 *Carry out the plan.* Since 3,500 calories need to be burned in 7 days, divide 3,500 by 7 to get 500 calories per day. Then divide 500 calories by 100 calories per mile to get 5 miles. An average person would need to walk 5 miles per day to lose one pound of body fat in a week.

Step 4 *Check the answer.* First, 5 miles per day times 100 calories is 500 calories per day. Multiply that by 7 days, and we get the 3,500 calories we need.

▼ Try This One 5

Megan's car gets 28 miles per gallon on long trips. She leaves home, bound for a friend's house 370 miles away. If she makes the drive in 6 hours, how many gallons of gas per hour is the car burning?

Sidelight **A LEGENDARY PROBLEM SOLVER**

Archimedes is considered by some to be the greatest mathematician of the ancient world. But he is best known for a famous problem he solved in the bathtub.

King Hieron II of Syracuse ordered a solid gold crown from a goldsmith sometime around 250 BCE. He suspected that the crown was not really solid gold, but he didn't want to have it melted down to check, because of course that would ruin it. He asked his friend Archimedes if he could figure out a way to determine whether the crown really was pure gold without destroying it.

After some serious thought, Archimedes decided to relax by taking a bath. While sitting in the tub, he saw that the water level rose in proportion to his weight. Suddenly, he realized that he had discovered the solution to his problem. By placing the crown in a full tub of water, he could tell how much of it was gold by weighing the amount of water that overflowed. Legend has it that Archimedes was so excited by this burst of inspiration that he forgot to clothe himself and ran naked through the streets of Syracuse, shouting "Eureka" ("I have found it!"), a performance that would most likely get him arrested, or maybe institutionalized, today.

It turns out that the crown was not solid gold, and the goldsmith either was placed in jail or had his head removed

from his shoulders, depending on which account you believe. The moral of this story is that you never know where inspiration in solving a problem might come from. But please put your clothes on before sharing your latest brilliant insight with the world.

The world is an imperfect place, my friends, and not every problem can be solved. A big part of problem solving is being able to recognize when there is no solution.

EXAMPLE 6   **Recognizing a Problem with No Solution**

The grade in Marlene's history class will be determined completely by three tests, each worth 100 points. She scored 78 and 84 on the first two tests, but still hopes to get an A, which would require an average of 92. What's the minimum score she can get on the third test?

SOLUTION

Step 1 *Understand the problem.* We're given two test scores of 78 and 84, and asked about the average for three tests. Specifically, we want it to be at least 92.

Step 2 *Devise a plan.* We'll start by seeing what the average would be if Marlene scores 100 on the last test, then decide how much lower she can go and still have an average of at least 92.

Step 3 *Carry out the plan.* With a third test score of 100, Marlene's average would be

$$\frac{78 + 84 + 100}{3} = \frac{262}{3} = 87.3$$

Uh oh: bad news for Marlene. Even with a perfect score, her average will be only 87.3, so it's not possible for her to get an A.

Step 4 *Check the answer.* In this case, we already checked our answer as part of the plan, so we know there's no solution to the problem.

☑ 5. Solve problems using calculation.

Math Note

One of the hardest things to do as a math instructor is come up with good examples to use as practice for problem solving. We try to write problems that are realistic, but sometimes it's really helpful to practice problem-solving strategies on problems that don't sound worthwhile (Exercises 5–8 are good examples of this).

So try not to get too wrapped up in whether or not a problem sounds like something a real person might need to solve: focus on the four-step strategy and remember that exercise for your mind is just as important as exercise for your body.

▼ Try This One 6

A student teacher wants to divide his sixth grade class into groups to work on a project. He'd like to have somewhere between 3 and 6 students in each group, and wants every group to have the same number of students. Find the group sizes that will accommodate a class of 26 students.

Strategies for Understanding a Problem

One reason that problem solving is challenging is that every problem can be a little different. But here are some suggestions for helping to understand a problem and devise a strategy for solving it.

- If the problem describes something that can be diagrammed, a drawing almost always helps.

- Write down all the numeric information in the problem. This often helps to organize your thoughts.

- Sometimes making a chart to organize information is helpful, especially when you're trying to use trial and error.

- Don't expect that you'll know exactly how to solve a problem after reading it once! Most often you'll need to read through a problem several times, and even then you may need to just try some approaches before finding one that works.

Answers to Try This One

1	Ten	**4**	The condo for $280 per day costs less for a week.
2	18 inches	**5**	About 2.2 gallons per hour
3	Three small and nine medium	**6**	None of those group sizes will work.

EXERCISE SET 1-3

Writing Exercises

1. List and describe the four steps in problem solving.
2. Discuss what you should do first when given a word problem to solve.
3. Discuss different ways you might be able to check your answer to a problem.

4. Why is trial and error not always a good problem-solving strategy?

Computational Exercises

5. One number is 6 more than another number, and their sum is 22. Find the numbers.

6. One number is 7 more than another number. Their sum is 23. Find the numbers.

7. If 24 is added to a number, it will be 3 times as large as it was originally. Find the number.

8. If the smaller of two numbers is one-half of the larger number and the sum of the two numbers is 57, find the numbers.

9. The sum of the digits of a two-digit number is 7. If 9 is subtracted from the number, the answer will be the number with the digits reversed. Find the number.

10. If the sum of the digits of a two-digit number is 7 and the tens digit is one more than the ones digit, find the number.

11. When the mortgage is completely paid off for Mark and Lynne's house, it will be 5 times as old as it is now. If they have 28 years left on the mortgage, how old is the house right now?

12. Hoang has worked as a nurse at Springfield General Hospital for 5 years longer than her friend Bill. Four years ago, she had been at the hospital for twice as long. How long has each been at the hospital?

13. When a retired police officer passes away, he leaves $140,000 to be divided among his two children and three grandchildren. The will specifies that each child is to get twice as much as each grandchild. How much does each get?

14. At the dog park, there are several dogs with their owners. Counting heads, there are 12; counting legs, there are 38. How many dogs and owners are there?

15. Arrange the digits 1, 2, and 3 to form two numbers divisible by 6.

16. Nine athletes from a co-ed track team stop for lunch. The men eat four pieces of pizza each, the women eat two pieces each, and the coach eats three pieces of pizza. If the team bought four pizzas, each cut into eight pieces, and there were five pieces left over (mmm, doggy bag), how many men and women were on the team?

Applications in Our World

17. Barney and Betty break into a parking meter with $5.05 in dimes and quarters in it (legal disclaimer: don't do this), and agree that Barney will get all the dimes, and Betty will get all the quarters. (Barney isn't terribly bright.) Barney ends up with five more coins than Betty. How much money did each get?

18. A tip jar contains twice as many quarters as dollar bills. If it has a total of $12 in it, how many quarters and how many dollar bills does it contain?

19. A fraternity charged $2.00 admission for dudes and $1.00 admission for ladies to their finals week bash. The fraternity made $75 and sold 55 tickets. How many ladies attended the party?

20. While reviewing the previous day's arrest report, a police sergeant notices that nine suspects were arrested, all of whom had either one or two previous arrests. Including yesterday's arrests, there were 19 total arrests among them. How many suspects had less than two prior arrests?

21. Mae receives $87 for working one 8-hour day. One day she had to stop after working 5 hours because of a doctor's appointment. How much did she make that day?

22. The manager of the new campus Internet café wants to put six PCs on each table with 3 feet between the PCs and 2 feet on each end. The PCs measure $1\frac{1}{2}$ feet wide and 21 inches high. What length of tables should the Internet café order?

23. Bob is building a deck that is 32 feet long, and he has posts that are 6 inches square to use to build the railing. If he puts the posts 4 feet apart with one on each end, how many posts will he use?

24. Suzie hangs 10 pictures that each measure $8\frac{1}{2}$ inches wide on a wall. She spaces them 6 inches apart with 2 inches on each end, so that they fit perfectly on the wall. How wide is the wall?

25. You want to cut a width of mat board to frame pictures so you can fit six pictures that have a width of 6 inches each with 2 inches between them and a 1-inch border. How wide should you cut the mat board?

26. A physical therapy facility is building a new pool that is 60 feet long and 5 feet deep. They have ordered enough tile for a 220-foot-long border around the edge. How wide should the pool be to ensure that all tiles are used?

27. A landscape architect is planning a new nature area in the middle of an urban campus. She wants the length to be twice the width, and wants to put a 3-foot-high retaining wall around the perimeter. There will be 300 total feet of wall installed. How wide will this area be?

28. A standard tube of silicone caulk will make a 3/16″ bead of caulk 50 feet long. Manuel plans to seal all the window casings in his house; there are three windows that measure 2 feet by 3 feet, three that measure 4 feet by 5 feet, and two that measure 6 feet by 4 feet. How many tubes of caulk will Manuel need?

29. Felicia is decorating a ballroom for a Spring Fling gala at her college. The decorative lights the committee has chosen come in boxes of 12 lights, with

each string having a length of 20 feet. The room is 70 feet long and twice as wide. How many boxes of lights should Felicia buy so that the strings go all the way around the perimeter of the room once? How many lights will there be?

30. Two students are paid a total of $60 for leading a campus tour at freshman orientation. The tour lasts approximately 2 hours. If Sam works for $1\frac{1}{2}$ hours, Pete works $\frac{1}{2}$ hour, and each makes the same hourly wage, how much does each receive?

31. You have one-half of an energy drink left. If you drink one-half of that, how much of your energy drink do you have left?

32. A small beverage company has 832 bottles of water to ship. If there are 6 bottles per case, how many cases are needed and how many bottles will be left over?

33. Kam's monthly budget includes $256 for food, $125 for gasoline, and $150 for utilities. If he earns $1,624 per month after taxes, how much money is left for other expenses?

34. Cheryl is training for a half-marathon, and is supplementing her diet with protein bars the week before the race. Each bar has 20 grams of protein and 15 grams of carbs. Cheryl's personal trainer would like for her to take in an extra 300 grams of carbs and 350 grams of protein during that week. How many protein bars should Cheryl buy?

35. A physical education teacher plans to divide the seventh graders at Wilson Middle School into teams of equal size for a year-ending mock Olympic event. He wants each team to have between 5 and 9 students, and all teams need to have the same number of students. The seventh grade at Wilson consists of three classes; one with 24 students, one with 26, and one with 21. How many students should be on each team?

36. Bart is taking a pass-fail math class, and needs to average 70% to get a passing grade. The grade is determined by five 50-point tests, and Bart's doing really well: on the first four tests, he scored 48, 45, 45, and 47. The week of the final test, Bart has a really important chemistry test that he wants to focus on, but he doesn't want to risk failing math. Find the range of scores Bart can get on test five that will result in failing the class.

37. If a family borrows $12,381 for an addition to their home, and the loan is to be paid off in monthly payments over a period of 5 years, how much should each payment be? (Interest has been included in the total amount borrowed.)

38. On the way to the airport on December 8, 2011, my wife's car hit a huge hole in a construction area, damaging the front right wheel. The temporary tire forced us to decrease our average speed by 15 miles per hour. If the 39-mile drive usually takes us

45 minutes, how much time should we have budgeted for the drive home from the airport?

39. Four friends decide to rent an apartment. Because each will be using it for different lengths of time, Mary will pay $\frac{1}{2}$ of the monthly rent, Jean will pay $\frac{1}{4}$ of the monthly rent, Claire will pay $\frac{1}{8}$ of the monthly rent, and Margie will pay the rest. If the monthly rent is $2,375, how much will each person pay?

40. Harry fills up his Jeep with gasoline and notes that the odometer reading is 23,568.7 miles. The next time he fills up his Jeep, he pays for 12.6 gallons of gasoline. He notes his odometer reading is 23,706.3 miles. How many miles per gallon did he get?

41. A clerk earns $9.50 per hour and is paid time and a half for any hours worked over 40. Find the clerk's pay if he worked 46 hours during a specific week.

42. A cell phone company charges 35 cents per minute during the daytime and 10 cents per minute during the evening for those who go over their allotted monthly minutes. If Sally went 32 minutes over her monthly minutes, find out how much she'd save if she went 32 minutes over her monthly minutes during the evening compared to during the daytime.

Last week at Chili's, my wife and I played a game on a tabletop video screen. The object is to move your frog so that it hits every lily pad exactly once. The frog cannot move diagonally and cannot go back in the direction it came from. Lily pads disappear after the frog jumps off of them, and the frog can't jump over an existing lily pad. In Exercises 43 and 44, find a path that wins each game.

43.

44.

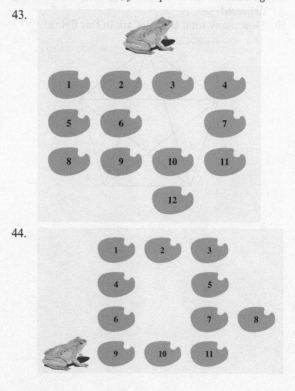

Critical Thinking

45. A king decided to pay a knight one piece of gold for each day's protection on a 6-day trip. The king took a gold bar 6 inches long and paid the knight at the end of each day; however, he made only two cuts. How did he do this?

46. At the finals of the campus-wide Brainbowl League Tournament, your team was asked to measure out exactly 1 gallon of water using only a 5-gallon and a 3-gallon container, without wasting any water. Your team completed the task. How did they do it?

47. What is the smallest number of cars that can tailgate in a straight line at a football game so that one car is in front of two cars, one car is behind two cars, and one car is between two cars?

48. To purchase a computer for the Student Activities office, the freshman class decides to raise $\frac{1}{3}$ of the money, and the sophomore class decides to raise $\frac{1}{2}$ of the money. The Student Government Association agrees to contribute the rest, which amounted to $400. What was the cost of the computer?

49. An important message about troop movements has to be delivered in person across a stretch of desert. The Jeeps available to make the trip can carry enough fuel to get them halfway across the desert, and there are no fueling stations along the way. There are a number of identical Jeeps, all of which can transfer their fuel to any other, but there are no fuel containers available or ropes to tow extra Jeeps. Be a hero and devise a strategy to get the message delivered.

50. How many total triangles are in this figure?

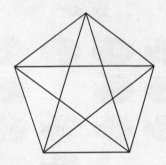

51. A professional driver completes one lap around the track at Daytona International Speedway at 80 miles per hour. How fast would he have to drive a second lap to make his overall average 160 miles per hour?

52. If you run around a quarter-mile track at some average speed *s*, at what average speed would you need to run a second lap to make your overall average twice as much as it was for the first lap?

Almost everyone thinks at first that the next two problems can't be solved, but I promise you they can be!

53. A math professor writes down two consecutive whole numbers from the range from 1 through 10. She tells one of the numbers to Maurice, and the other to Hani. Maurice says to Hani, "I don't know your number." Hani replies, "And I don't know your number." Maurice then says, "Now I know what your number is." What are the two numbers? (There are four different solutions to this problem!)

54. Two women playing golf have the following conversation.

Jasmine: How old are your kids?

Judi: I have three kids, and the product of their ages is 36.

Jasmine: That's not enough information to figure out their ages.

Judi: The sum of their ages is exactly the number of holes we have played so far today.

Jasmine: Still not enough information.

Judi: My oldest child almost always wears a red hat.

Jasmine: Okay, now I know how old they are.

How old are the three kids?

CHAPTER **1**   # Summary

Section	Important Terms	Important Ideas
1-1	Inductive reasoning Deductive reasoning Conjecture Counterexample	**In math** (and in life!), we can use two types of reasoning: inductive and deductive. Inductive reasoning is the process of arriving at a general conclusion based on observing specific examples. Deductive reasoning is the process of arriving at a conclusion based on known rules and principles. Remember: inductive goes from specific to general, and deductive goes from general to specific.
1-2	Estimation Place Value Bar graph Pie chart Time series graph	**In many** cases, it isn't necessary to find the exact answer to a problem. When only an approximate answer is needed, you can use estimation. This is often accomplished by rounding the numbers used in the problem and then performing the necessary operation or operations.
1-3	Polya's four-step problem-solving procedure	**A mathematician** named George Polya devised a procedure to solve mathematical problems. The steps of his procedure are (1) understand the problem, (2) devise a plan to solve the problem, (3) carry out the plan to solve the problem, and (4) check the answer.

MATH IN ▶ Criminal Investigation REVISITED

1. The suspect was identified by specific incidents in the past, which makes this inductive reasoning that would not hold up in court without further evidence.

2. Fingerprints positively identify the officer as having had contact with the victim. This is deductive reasoning and would be useful in court.

3. Like fingerprints, DNA can positively show that the suspect had physical contact with the victim. This evidence, based on deductive reasoning, would hurt the suspect badly in court.

4. While this is compelling evidence, it's based on assuming that those five drawings indicate the artist is the killer. While unlikely, it could be a coincidence based on five drawings, so this is inductive reasoning. It might impress a jury to some extent, but wouldn't be sufficient for a conviction.

Review Exercises

Section 1-1

For Exercises 1–4, make reasonable conjectures for the next three numbers or letters in the sequence.

1. 3 4 6 7 9 10 12 13 15 16 __ __ __
2. 2 7 4 9 6 11 8 13 __ __ __
3. 4 z 16 w 64 t 256 __ __ __
4. 20 A 18 C 15 F 11 J __ __ __

For Exercises 5 and 6, make a reasonable conjecture and draw the next figure.

5.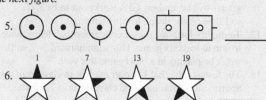

6.

38 **Chapter 1** Problem Solving

For Exercises 7 and 8, find a counterexample to show that each statement is false.

7. The product of three odd numbers will always be even.
8. The sum of three multiples of 5 will always end in a 5.

For Exercises 9 and 10, use inductive reasoning to find a rule that relates the number selected to the final answer, and then try to prove your conjecture, using deductive reasoning.

9. Pick an even number.

Add 6:
Divide the answer by 2:
Add 10:
Result:

10. Pick a number.

Multiply it by 9:
Add 18 to the number:
Divide by 3:
Subtract 6:
Result:

In Exercises 11 and 12, use inductive reasoning to find the next two equations in the pattern:

11. $337 \times 3 = 1,011$
    $337 \times 6 = 2,022$
    $337 \times 9 = 3,033$

12. $33 \times 33 = 1,089$
    $333 \times 333 = 110,889$
    $3333 \times 3333 = 11,108,889$

13. Use inductive reasoning to solve the last equation.

$$\sqrt{1} = 1$$
$$\sqrt{1 + 3} = 2$$
$$\sqrt{1 + 3 + 5} = 3$$
$$\sqrt{1 + 3 + 5 + 7} = 4$$
$$\sqrt{1 + 3 + 5 + 7 + 9 + 11 + 13 + 15 + 17} = ?$$

14. One of the statements is true, and one is not. Use inductive reasoning to decide which is which.

    (a) If a number is divisible by 3, then its square is divisible by 9.
    (b) The square of a two-digit number has three digits.

In Exercises 15–18, decide whether inductive or deductive reasoning was used.

15. My professor has given extra credit to his students for contributing canned goods to a food pantry during finals week for the last 5 years, so I know I'll get a chance for some easy extra credit on my final.

16. A GPA of 3.5 is required to make the dean's list. I checked with all my teachers to see what my final grades will be, and my GPA works out to be 3.72, so I'll be on the dean's list this semester.

17. To qualify for bowl games, college football teams have to win at least six games. Our team finished 5–7, so they won't be playing in a bowl game this year.

18. The fastest time that I've ever made it to class from my apartment is 8 minutes, and class starts in 7 minutes, so I'll be late today.

Section 1-2

For Exercises 19–23, round each number to the place value given.

19. 132,356 (thousands)
20. 186.75 (ones)
21. 14.63157 (ten-thousandths)
22. 0.6314 (tenths)
23. 3,725.63 (tens)
24. Estimate the cost of four lawn mowers if each one costs $329.95.
25. Estimate the cost of five textbooks if they cost $115.60, $89.95, $29.95, $62.50, and $43.10.
26. According to the trip computer on my car, I averaged 19.7 miles per gallon on my last tank of gas and drove 364 miles. Estimate the size of the gas tank.
27. A family of six consists of four people older than 12 and two people 12 or under. Tickets into an amusement park are $57.95 for those over 12 and $53.95 for those 12 and under. Estimate how much it would cost the family to go to the amusement park.
28. At M.T. Wallatts University, it costs a student $689 per credit-hour to attend.

    (a) Estimate the cost for a student to attend one semester if he registers for 9 credit-hours.
    (b) If a student makes $11 an hour at her part-time job (after taxes) and works 30 hours a week, approximately how many weeks will she have to work to afford one semester with 9 credit-hours?

29. Isn't it nice that Christmastime and fall semester book buyback come at the same time? Looks like everyone on your list is getting college logo merchandise this year! Suppose you get $130 for selling back your books (yeah, right). If college logo T-shirts are $19.75 each and sweatpants are $17.15 each, estimate how many of each you could buy with your book money. (*Hint:* There are many different combinations!)

*The following pie chart was published in USA **Today** on December 22, 2011. It shows what one thousand respondents to a survey plan to do with the worst holiday gift they receive. Use the chart to answer Exercises 30–33.*

Plans for the Worst Gift You Get This Year

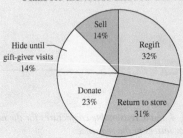

30. How many people plan to either regift or sell their worst gift?
31. How many more people plan to return the gift to a store than donate the gift?
32. How many people will not end up keeping the gift?

33. What can you conclude from adding up all of the percentages in the chart?

Use the information shown in the graph for Exercises 34–38. The graph shows the average weekly salary (in dollars) for U.S. production workers from 1970 to 2010.

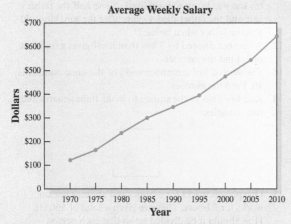

Average Weekly Salary

Source: *World Almanac and Book of Facts*

34. Estimate the weekly salary in 1988.
35. Estimate the year in which weekly salary went over $400.
36. Find the average rate of change in salary between 1970 and 2010.
37. Just looking at the graph, would you guess that the average rate of change was greater from 1985 to 1995 or from 2000 to 2010? Explain how you made your choice, then find each rate of change to see if you guessed correctly.
38. Use the graph to make an estimate for average weekly salary in 2012, then use the Internet to find how accurate your guess was. The U.S. Bureau of Labor website is a good place to start.

Section 1-3

39. Cindy has 32 flyers about a campus symposium on environmental issues that she is organizing. She gave away all but 9. How many did she have left?
40. A tennis team played 40 matches. The team won 20 more matches than they lost. How many matches did the team lose?
41. If Iesha weighs 110 pounds when standing on one foot on a scale, how much will she weigh when she stands on a scale with both feet?
42. A small mocha latte and biscotti together cost $3.40. If the mocha latte cost $0.40 more than the biscotti, how much did each cost?
43. I put a new floor on my deck a couple of years ago. The deck is rectangular, and measures 10 feet by 40 feet. The deck boards come in 12-foot lengths, and are $5\frac{1}{2}$ inches wide. I planned to leave a half-inch gap between boards that are laying next to each other side-to-side; boards that meet end-to-end were to be placed with no gap in between. Find the smallest number of boards I could have used for the job.

44. Mary got $80 in tips last night for her waitressing job at the campus café. She spent $8.00 downloading songs online to her MP3 player and then spent $\frac{1}{3}$ of the remainder on tickets for the spring dance on Saturday. How much did she have left?
45. Your science textbook and its accompanying lab packet cost $120. If the textbook costs twice as much as the lab packet, how much did the lab packet cost?
46. Fill in the squares with digits to complete the problem. There are several correct answers.

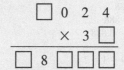

47. In 10 years, my house will be 5 times as old as it was 10 years ago. How old is it now?
48. At times during the summer in Alaska, the day is 18 hours longer than the night. How long is each?
49. Using +, −, and ×, make a true equation. Do not change the order of the digits.

$$2 \quad 9 \quad 6 \quad 7 \quad = \quad 17$$

50. Tina and Joe are doing homework problems together for their math class. Joe says to Tina, "If I do one more problem, then we'll have both done the same number of problems." Tina says to Joe, "If I do one more problem, than I will have done twice the number you have!" How many problems has each one done so far?
51. Can you divide a pie into 11 pieces with four straight cuts? The cuts must go from rim to rim but not necessarily through the center. The pieces need not be identical.
52. How many triangles are in the figure shown here?

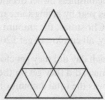

53. This one's a classic: two trains are 200 miles apart, traveling toward each other, each going 20 miles per hour. A really speedy fly takes off from one train and flies directly toward the other at 60 miles per hour. When it reaches the train, it bounces off and flies back to the first train. The fly repeats the trip until the trains collide and the poor little guy gets squashed. How far did the fly fly?
54. The sum of two numbers is 120 and the difference is 15. Find the numbers.
55. A health food store charges $2.00 per pound for high-protein nature mix and $2.75 for low-carb soy medley. If 10 pounds of the two items mixed together costs $24.50, find the amount of each type in the mixture.
56. Taylor had $1,000 to invest. He invested part of it at 8% and part of it at 6%. If his total simple interest was $76.00, find how much he invested for 1 year at each rate. (Simple interest is the amount invested times the interest rate.)

Chapter 1 Practice Test

1. Make a reasonable conjecture for the next three numbers on the list:

   2 5 4 8 6 11 8 ___ ___ ___

2. What state logically goes next on this list?

   Kansas, Louisiana, Maine, Nebraska, Ohio

3. Use inductive reasoning to find the solution to the problem; then check it by performing the calculation.

   $0 \cdot 9 + 8 = 8$
   $9 \cdot 9 + 7 = 88$
   $98 \cdot 9 + 6 = 888$
   $987 \cdot 9 + 5 = 8{,}888$
   $\vdots$
   $9{,}876{,}543 \cdot 9 + 1 = ?$

4. Use inductive reasoning to find the solution to the problem; then check it by performing the calculation.

   $6 \times 7 = 42$
   $66 \times 67 = 4{,}422$
   $666 \times 667 = 444{,}222$
   $6{,}666 \times 6{,}667 = ?$

5. Use inductive reasoning to find a rule that relates the number you selected to the final answer, and try to prove your conjecture.

   Pick a number:
   Add 10 to the number:
   Multiply the answer by 5:
   Add 15 to the answer:
   Divide the answer by 5:
   Result:

6. There were 12 students in line to register for the Underwater Basketweaving 101 course. All but 2 changed their minds. How many remained in line?

7. An eccentric business owner decides to give holiday bonuses this year by giving some money for each of the 12 days of Christmas; the amount doubles each day. On the 12th day, all employees get $204.80.

   (a) On which day did they get close to $25?
   (b) How much did they get on the first day?
   (c) What was the total amount of the bonuses?

8. What are the next two letters in the sequence, T, T, F, F, S, S, . . . ? (*Hint:* It has something to do with numbers.)

9. By moving just one coin, make two lines, each three coins long. There are two solutions!

10. A ship is docked in harbor with a rope ladder hanging over the edge, and 9 feet of the ladder is above the waterline. The tide is rising at 8 inches per hour. After 6 hours, how much of the ladder remains above the waterline?

11. This problem was written by the famous mathematician Diophantus. Can you find the solution?

    The boyhood of a man lasted $\frac{1}{6}$ of his life; his beard grew after $\frac{1}{12}$ more; after $\frac{1}{7}$ more he married; 5 years later his son was born; the son lived to one-half the father's age; and the father died 4 years after the son. How old was the father when he died?

12. A number divided by 3 less than itself gives a quotient of $\frac{8}{5}$. Find the number.

13. The sum of $\frac{1}{2}$ of a number and $\frac{1}{3}$ of the same number is 10. Find the number.

14. Add five lines to the square to make three squares and two triangles.

15. One person works for 3 hours and another person works for 2 hours. They are given a total of $60.00. How should it be divided up so that each person receives a fair share?

16. The sum of the reciprocals of two numbers is $\frac{5}{6}$ and the difference is $\frac{1}{6}$. Find the numbers. (*Hint:* The reciprocal of a number n is $\frac{1}{n}$.)

17. Sam scored 72 and 78 on her first two hundred-point tests.

    (a) What score does she need on the third test to bring her average up to 80%?
    (b) If she gets that score, what's the lowest score she can get on the last exam to get an A−, which is assigned to average scores between 90% and 92%?

18. Mt. McKinley is about 20,300 feet above sea level, and Death Valley is 280 feet below sea level. Find the vertical distance from the top of Mt. McKinley to the bottom of Death Valley, and the average rate of change in height if an adventurer travels from the summit of Mt. McKinley to the deepest part of Death Valley in 3 days.

19. Mark's mother is 32 years older than Mark. The sum of their ages is 66 years. How old is each?

20. Round 1,674,253 to the nearest hundred-thousand.

21. Round 1.3752 to the nearest hundredth.

22. Estimate the cost of Stuart's new wardrobe for his campus interview if a blazer costs $69.95, a new tie costs $32.54, and new pants cost $42.99.

23.

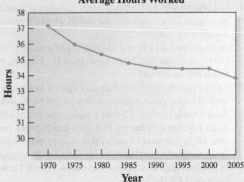

Source: *World Almanac and Book of Facts*

(a) Using the graph, estimate the average number of hours per week U.S. production workers worked in 1980 and 2005.

(b) Estimate when average hours worked dropped below 35.

(c) Find the average rate of change in hours worked from 1975 to 2000.

24. Using the pie chart, of the 3,646 students surveyed at seven residential universities, estimate the number of students surveyed who do not live in a residence hall, and how many more live with parents than in a frat or sorority house.

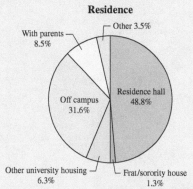

Residence

Other 3.5%
With parents 8.5%
Off campus 31.6%
Residence hall 48.8%
Other university housing 6.3%
Frat/sorority house 1.3%

Source: http://www.acha-ncha.org/data/DEMOGF06.html

The bar graph shows the number of homicides in 2010 per 100,000 residents for the five U.S. cities with the highest murder rates; the table shows the population of each city in that year. Use this information in Exercises 25–27.

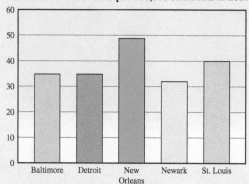

Number of Homicides per 100,000 Residents in 2010

Baltimore, Detroit, New Orleans, Newark, St. Louis

Source: FBI Uniform Crime Reports

City	Population in 2010
Baltimore	639,929
Detroit	899,447
New Orleans	356,317
Newark	280,379
St. Louis	355,151

25. The rates for Baltimore, Detroit, and Newark are all similar. Which city do you think had the most homicides of the three?

26. Which city on the list had the most total homicides? The least?

27. Chicago had 435 homicides in 2012 and a population of 2,833,649. Make a copy of the bar graph and draw in a sixth bar corresponding to Chicago's homicide rate.

Projects

1. One of my students asked me an intriguing question this past semester: he was really bothered by the fact that his chemistry professor claimed that "science can never really prove anything," and wanted me to try and explain what he meant. In fact, this issue is ALL about inductive and deductive reasoning. Do an Internet search for the string "can science prove anything," and research the argument. Then discuss it with group members or friends, and write a paper that provides your opinion on whether science can or cannot prove anything. One of the main focuses of your paper should be what you've learned about inductive and deductive reasoning.

2. Many of the problems in this book are based on real data, and the fact is that I know all of that stuff off the top of my head. Just kidding—I get most of it from the Internet. One GREAT source of data is the U.S. Statistical Abstract, which can be found at *www.census. gov/compendia/statab.* Your mission is to write your own problems based on estimation from graphs. Look through the statistical abstract, and find some data on a topic you find interesting. Draw a bar graph corresponding to the data, then write at least six questions for students in another group based on the graph. Do the same for a pie chart, and a time-series

graph (use different topics for each type of chart). When all groups have completed their questions, you can exchange information and answer the questions. Try to shoot for a range of difficulties: some simple problems and some challenging ones. Looking at the problems in Section 1-2 would probably help—they're brilliant.

3. One reason that Polya's method has stood the test of time is that it is used not just in math, but also for any problem needing to be solved. For each of the problems listed, write a paragraph explaining how each of the steps in Polya's method could be applied.

(a) A homeowner has a small set of stairs leading from his back door down to a featureless backyard. He would like to have a place for outdoor parties during the summer.

(b) Your car has been making a really funny noise whenever you go over 50 miles per hour.

(c) You've balanced your checkbook and found out that you won't have enough money to pay for tuition and books next semester.

(d) One of your friends heard something you said about him behind his back, and now he is very upset with you.

Sets

CHAPTER 2

Sets

Outline

2-1   The Nature of Sets

2-2   Subsets and Set Operations

2-3   Using Venn Diagrams to Study Set Operations

2-4   Using Sets to Solve Problems

2-5   Infinite Sets

      Summary

MATH IN > **Demographics**

It seems hard to believe now, but it wasn't until Jackie Robinson debuted for the Brooklyn Dodgers in 1947 that non-whites were allowed to compete in major professional sports. There was a handful of isolated pioneers before Jackie, but most historians will tell you that Branch Rickey, the owner of the Dodgers at the time, ushered in a new era of diversity in American society with his bold move. It didn't hurt that Robinson was both a great player and an exemplary figure off the field.

Fast-forward to November 2009, when perhaps the most famous and richest athlete on the planet was Tiger Woods, a golfer who is part white, part African-American, and part Asian. It says something about our society that someone who was already wildly famous for doing good things on the golf course became even MORE famous for doing bad things off the course. But the positive we can take from Tiger's tale, at least from a societal standpoint, is that like him or not, for the most part, he is judged on the merits of his actions, not his racial makeup.

The fact is that American society is becoming more diverse every year, to the point where even defining what we mean by *race* isn't so easy anymore. The most common racial groups referred to in population statistics are white, black, Asian, and Hispanic, but many people fall into more than one category (including the 44th President of the United States!). But it's even more confusing than that: *Hispanic* isn't really a race, but rather an ethnic group, and many Hispanics also report themselves as either white or black.

Sorting it all out to get any sort of meaningful picture of what we as Americans look like isn't easy, and the techniques of set theory are very useful tools in trying to do so. In this chapter, we'll define what we mean by sets, and we'll study sets and how they can be used to organize information in an increasingly complex world. The concept of sets has been used extensively since people began studying mathematics, but it wasn't until the late 1800s that the theory of sets was studied as a specific branch of math. One of the major tools that we will use to study sets—the Venn diagram—was introduced in an 1880 paper by a man named John Venn. These diagrams allow us to picture complicated relationships between sets of objects, like people of certain races.

Because race and ethnicity are self-reported in a variety of different ways, it's very difficult to find detailed data on the breakdown of races, but there are some reasonable estimates out there. The following estimates were cobbled together from a number of different sources (and if you think THAT was easy, think again). In a group of 1,000 randomly selected Americans, 777 would self-report as white, 139 as black, and 149 as Hispanic. In addition, 19 would self-report as black and white, 18 as black and Hispanic, and 85 as white and Hispanic. Finally, 7 would self-report as all three. Based on these estimates, after completing this chapter, you should be able to answer the following questions:

1. How many of the original 1,000 report as white only, black only, and Hispanic only?
2. How many report as Hispanic and black, but not white?
3. How many report as either Hispanic or black?
4. How many report as none of white, black, or Hispanic?

For answers, see Math in Demographics Revisited on page 93

44   **Chapter 2**   Sets

Section 2-1   The Nature of Sets

Have you ever thought about the role that grouping things plays in everyday life? You have a group of friends, a group of family members, a group of classmates, and a group of coworkers. You have a group of keys, groups of clothes, electronics, foods, TV shows, and many others. Our entire world is divided into groups of things, or what we call *sets*. So studying sets from a mathematical standpoint is a good opportunity to study how math is used in our world.

LEARNING OBJECTIVES

☐ 1. Define set.

☐ 2. Write sets three different ways.

☐ 3. Define the empty set.

☐ 4. Find the cardinality of a set.

☐ 5. Classify sets as finite or infinite.

☐ 6. Decide if two sets are equal or equivalent.

☑ 1. Define set.

Basic Concepts

We will begin with a basic definition of sets.

> A **set** is a collection of objects.

In our study of sets, we'll want to restrict our attention to sets that are well-defined. A set is **well-defined** if for any given object, we can objectively decide whether it is or is not in the set. For example, the set "letters of the English alphabet" is well-defined since it consists of the 26 symbols we use to make up our alphabet, and no other objects. The set "tall people in your class" is not well-defined because who exactly belongs to that set is open to interpretation. In short, to be well-defined, the definition of what is or is not in a set has to be based on facts, not opinions.

Each object in a set is called an **element** or a **member** of the set. One method of designating a set is called the **roster method**, in which elements are listed between braces, with commas between the elements. The order in which we list elements isn't important: {2, 5, 7} and {5, 2, 7} are the same set. Often, we will name sets by using a capital letter.

Laws that specify who can vote in a specific election determine a well-defined set of people. There are many other laws that might affect certain sets, like the set of businesses in a certain industry. These laws need to clearly define the set the law applies to—if that set were not well-defined, it would be almost impossible to enforce the law.

EXAMPLE 1   **Listing the Elements in a Set**

Write the set of months of the year that begin with the letter M.

Math Note

The commas make it clear that it is the words, not the letters, that are the elements of the set.

SOLUTION

The months that begin with M are March and May. So, the answer can be written in set notation as

$$M = \{\text{March, May}\}$$

Each element in the set is separated by a comma.

▼ **Try This One 1**

Write the set of months that end with the letter *y*.

In math, the set of *counting numbers* or **natural numbers** is defined as $N = \{1, 2, 3, 4, \ldots\}$. (When we are designating sets, the three dots, or *ellipsis,* mean that the list of elements continues indefinitely in the same pattern.) The set $E = \{2, 4, 6, 8, \ldots\}$ is the set of **even natural numbers** and the set $O = \{1, 3, 5, 7, \ldots\}$ is the set of **odd natural numbers**.

EXAMPLE 2   Writing Sets Using the Roster Method

> **Math Note**
>
> You can list an element of a set more than once if it means a lot to you, but it's common to choose not to list repeats. For example, the set of letters in the word letters is written as {l, e, t, r, s}.

Use the roster method to do the following:

(a) Write the set of natural numbers less than 6.
(b) Write the set of odd natural numbers greater than 4.

SOLUTION

(a) $\{1, 2, 3, 4, 5\}$
(b) $\{5, 7, 9, 11, \ldots\}$

> ▼ **Try This One 2**
>
> Write each set, using the roster method.
>
> (a) The set of even natural numbers from 80 to 90.
> (b) The set of odd natural numbers greater than 10.

CAUTION

Students often wonder how many elements of a set to write before ending with an ellipsis. The correct answer is "seven." Just kidding—there is no set rule. Just make sure to include enough initial numbers that the pattern is clear. For Example 2(b), just writing {5, 7,...} would leave any number of possible interpretations: {5, 7, 8, 10, 11, 13, 14, 16,...}, {5, 7, 10, 14,...} are two that come to mind.

The symbol $\in$ is used to show that an object is a member or element of a set. For example, if A is the set of days of the week, we could write Monday $\in A$, and read this as "Monday is an element of set A." Likewise, we could write Friday $\in A$.

When an object is not a member of a set, we use the symbol $\notin$. Since "Icecreamday" is not a day of the week (although it probably should be), we can write Icecreamday $\notin A$, and read this as "Icecreamday is not an element of A."

EXAMPLE 3   Understanding Set Notation

> **Math Note**
>
> Be sure to use correct symbols when you show membership in a set. For example, the notation $\{6\} \in \{2, 4, 6\}$ is incorrect since the set {6} is not a member of this set: only the number 6 is.

Decide whether each statement is true or false.

(a) Oregon $\in A$, where A is the set of states west of the Mississippi River.
(b) $27 \in \{1, 5, 9, 13, 17, \ldots\}$
(c) z $\notin$ {v, w, x, y, z}

SOLUTION

(a) Oregon is west of the Mississippi, so Oregon is an element of A. The statement is false.
(b) The pattern shows that each element is 4 more than the previous element. So the next three elements are 21, 25, and 29; this shows that 27 is not in the set. The statement is false.
(c) The letter z is an element of the set, so the statement is false.

▼ Try This One 3

Decide whether each statement is true or false.

(a) July $\in A$, where A is the set of months between Memorial Day and Labor Day.
(b) $21 \in \{2, 5, 8, 11, \ldots\}$
(c) map $\notin$ {m, a, p}

There are three common ways to designate sets:

1. The *list* or *roster* method.
2. The *descriptive* method.
3. *Set-builder* notation.

We already know a lot about using the list or roster method; the elements of the set are listed in braces and are separated by commas, as in Examples 1 through 3. The **descriptive method** uses a short statement to describe the set.

EXAMPLE 4   Describing a Set Using the Descriptive Method

Use the descriptive method to describe the set B containing 2, 4, 6, 8, 10, and 12.

SOLUTION

All of the elements in the set are even natural numbers, and all are less than 14, so B is the set of even natural numbers less than 14.

▼ Try This One 4

Use the descriptive method to describe the set A containing $-3, -2, -1, 0, 1, 2, 3$.

Math Note

When you hear *variable*, you might automatically think *letter*, like *x* or *y*. But you should think about what the word *variable* really means: something that can change, or vary. A variable is just a symbol that represents some number or object that can change.

The third method of designating a set is **set-builder notation**, and this method uses *variables*.

A **variable** is a symbol (usually a letter) that can represent different elements of a set.

Set-builder notation uses a variable, braces, and a vertical bar | that is read as "such that." For example, the set {1, 2, 3, 4, 5, 6} can be written in set-builder notation as

$$\{x \mid x \in N \ \text{ and } \ x < 7\}$$

It is read as "the set of elements x such that x is a natural number and x is less than 7." We can use any letter or symbol for the variable, but it's common to use x. (If you need a review of inequality symbols, see Table 6-4 on page 338.)

EXAMPLE 5   Writing a Set Using Set-Builder Notation

Use set-builder notation to designate each set, then write how your answer would be read aloud.

(a) The set R contains the elements 2, 4, and 6.
(b) The set W contains the elements red, yellow, and blue.

SOLUTION

(a) $R = \{x \mid x \in E \text{ and } x < 7\}$, the set of all x such that x is an even natural number and x is less than 7.

(b) $W = \{x \mid x \text{ is a primary color}\}$, the set of all x such that x is a primary color.

> ### ▼ Try This One 5
>
> Use set-builder notation to designate each set, then write how your answer would be read aloud.
>
> (a) The set K contains the elements $10, 12, 14, 16, 18$.
> (b) The set W contains the elements Democrat and Republican.

Math Note

We use the symbol E to represent the set of even natural numbers. Also, note that there could be more than one way to write a set in set-builder notation. In Example 5, we could have written $W = \{x \mid x \text{ is a color in the flag of Colombia}\}$.

EXAMPLE 6   Using Different Set Notations

Designate the set S with elements $32, 33, 34, 35, \ldots$ using

(a) The roster method.   (b) The descriptive method.   (c) Set-builder notation.

SOLUTION

(a) $\{32, 33, 34, 35, \ldots\}$
(b) The set S is the set of natural numbers greater than 31.
(c) $\{x \mid x \in N \text{ and } x > 31\}$

> ### ▼ Try This One 6
>
> Designate the set with elements $11, 13, 15, 17, \ldots$ using
>
> (a) The roster method.   (b) The descriptive method.   (c) Set-builder notation.

If a set contains many elements, we can again use an ellipsis to represent the missing elements as long as we illustrate a clear pattern. For example, the set $\{1, 2, 3, \ldots, 99, 100\}$ includes all the natural numbers from 1 to 100. Likewise, the set $\{a, b, c, \ldots, x, y, z\}$ includes all the letters of the alphabet.

EXAMPLE 7   Writing a Set Using an Ellipsis

Using the roster method, write the set containing all even natural numbers between 99 and 201.

SOLUTION

$\{100, 102, 104, \ldots, 198, 200\}$

> ### ▼ Try This One 7
>
> Using the roster method, write the set of odd natural numbers between 50 and 500.

☑ 2. Write sets three different ways.

There are some situations in which it's necessary to define a set with no elements. For example, the set of female Presidents of the United States would contain no people, so it has no elements (at least as of this writing).

A set with no elements is called an **empty set** or **null set**. The symbols used to represent the empty set are { } or $\varnothing$.

| **EXAMPLE 8** | **Identifying Empty Sets** |

> **Math Note**
>
> In December 2011, a group of scientists from Japan and Russia announced that it hoped to clone a woolly mammoth from long-frozen DNA found in Siberia within 5 years. I think we can all agree that would be super-cool. So I reserve the right to change my answer to Example 8(b).

Which of the following sets are empty?

(a) The set of woolly mammoth fossils in museums
(b) $\{x \mid x$ is a living woolly mammoth$\}$
(c) $\{\varnothing\}$
(d) $\{x \mid x$ is a natural number between 1 and 2$\}$

SOLUTION

(a) There is certainly at least one woolly mammoth fossil in a museum somewhere, so the set is not empty.
(b) Woolly mammoths have been extinct for almost 8,000 years, so this set is most definitely empty.
(c) Be careful! Each instance of { } and $\varnothing$ represents the empty set, but $\{\varnothing\}$ is a set with one element: $\varnothing$.
(d) This set is empty because there are no natural numbers between 1 and 2.

▼ **Try This One 8**

Which of the following sets are empty?

(a) $\{x \mid x$ is a natural number divisible by 7$\}$
(b) $\{x \mid x$ is a human being living on Mars$\}$
(c) $\{\{ \ \}\}$
(d) The set Z consists of the living people on earth who are over 200 years old.

CAUTION

Make sure you don't write the empty set as $\{\varnothing\}$: the brackets indicate a set containing what's inside, so that symbol represents a set containing one element: the empty set.

☑ 3. Define the empty set.

Cardinal Number of a Set

The number of elements in a set is called the *cardinal number* of a set. For example, the set $R = \{2, 4, 6, 8, 10\}$ has a cardinal number of 5 since it has 5 elements. This could also be stated by saying the **cardinality** of set R is 5. Formally defined,

The **cardinal number** of a set is the number of elements in the set. For a set A the symbol for the cardinality is $n(A)$, which is read as "n of A."

| **EXAMPLE 9** | **Finding the Cardinality of a Set** |

Find the cardinal number of each set.

(a) $A = \{5, 10, 15, 20, 25, 30\}$ (c) $C = \{16\}$
(b) $B = \{x \mid x \in N \text{ and } x < 16\}$ (d) $\varnothing$

SOLUTION

(a) $n(A) = 6$ since set A has 6 elements
(b) B is the set $\{1, 2, 3, 4, \ldots, 14, 15\}$, which has 15 elements. So $n(B) = 15$.
(c) $n(C) = 1$ since set C has 1 element
(d) $n(\varnothing) = 0$ since there are no elements in an empty set

---

☑ 4. Find the cardinality of a set.

▼ Try This One 9

Find the cardinal number of each set.

(a) $A = \{z, y, x, w, v\}$ (c) $C = \{$Chevrolet$\}$
(b) $B = \{x \in E$ and x is between 15 and 31$\}$

Finite and Infinite Sets

Sets can be classified as *finite* or *infinite*.

> A set is called **finite** if it has no elements, or has cardinality that is a natural number. A set that is not finite is called an **infinite set**.

The set $\{p, q, r, s\}$ is a finite set since it has four members: p, q, r, and s. The set $\{10, 20, 30, \ldots\}$ is an infinite set since it has an unlimited number of elements: the natural numbers that are multiples of 10.

EXAMPLE 10   Classifying Sets as Finite or Infinite

Math Note

If you're wondering how to describe the cardinality of an infinite set, you're going to love Section 2-5.

Classify each set as finite or infinite.

(a) $\{x \mid x \in N$ and $x < 100\}$
(b) Set R is the set of letters used to make Roman numerals.
(c) $\{100, 102, 104, 106, \ldots\}$
(d) Set M is the set of people in your immediate family.
(e) Set S is the set of songs that can be written.

SOLUTION

(a) The set is finite since there are 99 natural numbers that are less than 100.
(b) The set is finite since the letters used are C, D, I, L, M, V, and X.
(c) The set is infinite since it consists of an unlimited number of elements.
(d) The set is finite since there is a specific number of people in your immediate family.
(e) The set is infinite because an unlimited number of songs can be written.

☑ 5. Classify sets as finite or infinite.

▼ Try This One 10

Classify each set as finite or infinite.

(a) Set P is the set of numbers that are multiples of 6.
(b) $\{x \mid x$ is a member of the U.S. Senate$\}$
(c) $\{3, 6, 9, \ldots, 24\}$
(d) The set of all possible computer passwords

Math Note

All equal sets are equivalent since both sets will have the same number of members, but not all equivalent sets are equal.

Equal and Equivalent Sets

In set theory, it is important to understand the concepts of *equal* sets and *equivalent* sets.

Two sets A and B are **equal** (written $A = B$) if they have exactly the same members or elements. Two finite sets A and B are said to be **equivalent** (written $A \cong B$) if they have the same number of elements: that is, $n(A) = n(B)$.

For example, the two sets {a, b, c} and {c, b, a} are equal since they have exactly the same members, a, b, and c. Also the set {4, 5, 6} is equal to the set {4, 4, 5, 6} since 4 need not be written twice in the second set. The set of all names of students in your class and the set of their student ID numbers are equivalent sets because they have the same number of elements, but they have different elements so the sets are not equal.

EXAMPLE 11   Deciding If Sets Are Equal or Equivalent

State whether each pair of sets is equal, equivalent, or neither.

(a) {p, q, r, s}; {a, b, c, d}
(b) {8, 10, 12}; {12, 8, 10}
(c) {213}; {2, 1, 3}
(d) {1, 2, 10, 20}; {2, 1, 20, 11}
(e) {even natural numbers less than 10}; {2, 4, 6, 8}

SOLUTION

(a) Equivalent
(b) Equal and equivalent
(c) Neither
(d) Equivalent
(e) Equal and equivalent

▼ Try This One 11

State whether each pair of sets is equal, equivalent, or neither.

(a) {d, o, g}; {c, a, t}
(b) {run}; {r, u, n}
(c) {t, o, p}; {p, o, t}
(d) {10, 20, 30}; {1, 3, 5}

The elements of two equivalent sets can be paired in such a way that they are said to have a *one-to-one correspondence* between them.

Two sets have a **one-to-one correspondence** of elements if each element in the first set can be paired with exactly one element of the second set and each element of the second set can be paired with exactly one element of the first set.

EXAMPLE 12   Putting Sets in One-to-One Correspondence

Show that (a) the sets {8, 16, 24, 32} and {s, t, u, v} have a one-to-one correspondence and (b) the sets {x, y, z} and {5, 10} do not have a one-to-one correspondence.

Two sets of basketball teams on the court have a one-to-one correspondence. (Assuming each has five healthy players!)

SOLUTION

(a) We need to demonstrate that each element of one set can be paired with one and only one element of the second set. One possible way to show a one-to-one correspondence is this:

$$\{8, \quad 16, \quad 24, \quad 32\}$$
$$\updownarrow \quad \updownarrow \quad \updownarrow \quad \updownarrow$$
$$\{s, \quad t, \quad u, \quad v\}$$

(b) The elements of the sets $\{x, y, z\}$ and $\{5, 10\}$ can't be put in one-to-one correspondence. No matter how we try, there will be an element in the first set that doesn't correspond to any element in the second set.

▼ Try This One 12

Show that the sets {North, South, East, West} and {sun, rain, snow, sleet} have a one-to-one correspondence.

Using one-to-one correspondence, we can decide if two sets are equivalent without actually counting the elements: if two sets are equivalent, they have the same cardinality. This can come in handy for large sets, and *really* handy for infinite sets!

☑ 6. Decide if two sets are equal or equivalent.

Correspondence and Equivalent Sets

Two sets are

- Equivalent if you can put their elements in one-to-one correspondence.

- Not equivalent if you cannot put their elements in one-to-one correspondence.

Answers to Try This One

1   {January, February, May, July}

2   (a) {80, 82, 84, 86, 88, 90}
    (b) {11, 13, 15, 17, . . .}

3   (a) True   (b) False   (c) True

4   The set of integers from -3 to 3

5   (a) $K = \{x \mid x \in E, x > 9, \text{ and } x < 19\}$, the set of all x such that x is an even natural number, x is greater than 9, and x is less than 19.
    (b) $W = \{x \mid x \text{ is a major American political party}\}$, the set of all x such that x is a major American political party.

6   (a) {11, 13, 15, 17, . . .}

    (b) The set of odd natural numbers greater than 10
    (c) $\{x \mid x \in N, x \text{ is odd, and } x > 10\}$

7   {51, 53, 55, . . . , 497, 499}

8   (b) and (d)

9   (a) 5   (b) 8   (c) 1

10   (a) Infinite   (b) Finite   (c) Finite   (d) Infinite

11   (a) Equivalent   (c) Equal and equivalent
    (b) Neither   (d) Equivalent

12
North	South	East	West
$\updownarrow$	$\updownarrow$	$\updownarrow$	$\updownarrow$
Sun	Rain	Snow	Sleet

EXERCISE SET 2-1

Writing Exercises

1. Explain what a set is.
2. What does it mean for a set to be well-defined?
3. Write an example of a set that is well-defined, and one that is not. (No stealing examples from the book!)
4. List and describe three ways to write sets.
5. What is the difference between equal and equivalent sets?
6. Explain the difference between a finite and an infinite set.
7. What is meant by "one-to-one correspondence between two sets"?
8. Define the empty set and give two examples of an empty set.

Computational Exercises

For Exercises 9–22, write each set using the roster method. Do not include repeats. You may have to do a bit of Internet research for some problems.

9. *T* is the set of letters in the word *thinking*.
10. *A* is the set of letters in the word *Alabama*.
11. *P* is the set of natural numbers between 50 and 60.
12. *R* is the set of even natural numbers between 10 and 40.
13. $C = \{x | x \in N \text{ and } x < 9\}$
14. $F = \{x | x \in N \text{ and } x > 100\}$
15. $G = \{x | x \in N \text{ and } x > 10\}$
16. *B* is the set of natural numbers greater than 100.
17. *Y* is the set of natural numbers between 2,000 and 3,000.
18. $Z = \{x | x \in N \text{ and } 500 < x < 6,000\}$
19. *C* is the set of colors in the flags of the states that begin with *O*.
20. *S* is the set of current U.S. senators from states that begin with *A*.
21. *L* is the set of ligaments in the human knee.
22. *A* is the set of capitals of the seven mainland countries in Central America.

For Exercises 23–28, decide if the statement is true or false.

23. $5 \in \{1, 3, 5, 7\}$
24. $8 \notin \{2, 4, 6, \ldots\}$
25. $\frac{1}{2} \notin N$
26. $0.6 \in N$
27. $\{x | x \text{ is a living stegosaurus}\}$ is an empty set.
28. Cleveland $\in \{x | x \text{ is one of the United States}\}$

For Exercises 29–36, write each set, using the descriptive method.

29. $\{5, 10, 15, 20, \ldots\}$
30. $\{4, 8, 12, 16\}$
31. $\{13, 26, 39, 52\}$
32. $\{7, 14, 21, 28, \ldots\}$
33. $\{s, t, e, v, n\}$
34. $\{a, u, g, s, t\}$
35. $\{100, 101, 102, \ldots, 199\}$
36. $\{21, 22, 23, \ldots, 29, 30\}$

For Exercises 37–42, write each set, using set-builder notation.

37. $\{10, 20, 30, 40, \ldots\}$
38. $\{3, 6, 9, 12, \ldots\}$
39. *X* is the set of odd natural numbers less than 16.
40. *Z* is the set of natural numbers between 70 and 76.
41. $\{red, white, blue\}$
42. $\{black, white, grey\}$

For Exercises 43–48, list the elements in each set.

43. *H* is the set of natural numbers less than 0.
44. $\{x | x \in N \text{ and } 70 < x < 80\}$
45. $\{x | x \text{ is a season of the year}\}$
46. *R* is the set of letters that can be both a vowel and a consonant.
47. $\{x | x \text{ is an even natural number between 100 and 120}\}$
48. $\{x | x \text{ is an odd natural number between 90 and 100}\}$

For Exercises 49–54, state whether each collection is well-defined or not well-defined.

49. *L* is the set of contestants booted off the island in the first 8 weeks of *Survivor* in 2012.
50. $\{I | I \text{ is a death row inmate in Texas}\}$
51. $\{NBA \text{ players that had awesome dunks last week}\}$
52. *N* is the set of patients that deserve a heart transplant.
53. $B = \{x | x \text{ is a large number}\}$
54. $C = \{x | x \text{ is a number greater than the number of people in the United States}\}$

For Exercises 55–60, decide if the statement is true or false.

Let *A* = the set of U.S. state capitals
$B = \{10, 20, 30, 40, \ldots\}$
C = the set of presidents of the United States

55. $35 \in B$
56. Benjamin Franklin $\in C$
57. Philadelphia $\notin A$
58. $350 \in B$
59. Cheyenne $\in A$
60. James Madison $\in C$

For Exercises 61–68, state whether each set is infinite or finite.

61. $\{x | x \in N \text{ and } x \text{ is even}\}$
62. $\{1, 2, 3, \ldots, 999, 1,000\}$

63. K is the set of letters of the English alphabet.
64. $\{x \mid x \in$ years in which the past Presidents of the United States were born$\}$
65. $\{x \mid x \in N$ and x is a number whose last digit is zero$\}$
66. $\varnothing$
67. $\{x \mid x$ is a current television program$\}$
68. $\{x \mid x$ is a fraction$\}$

For Exercises 69–74, state whether each pair of sets is equal, equivalent, or neither.

69. $\{s, t, u, v, w\}$ and $\{t, v, w, s, u\}$
70. $\{1, 2, 3, 4, 5\}$ and $\{10, 20, 30, 40, 50\}$
71. $\{2, 4, 6, 8\}$ and $\{2, 4, 6, 8, \ldots\}$
72. $\{three\}$ and $\{t, h, r, e, e\}$
73. $\{3\}$ and $\{\varnothing\}$
74. $\{x \mid x \in$ months with exactly 30 days$\}$ and $\{April, June, September, November\}$

For Exercises 75–78, show that each pair of sets is equivalent by using a one-to-one correspondence.

75. $\{10, 20, 30, 40\}$ and $\{40, 10, 20, 30\}$
76. $\{w, x, y, z\}$ and $\{1, 2, 3, 4\}$

77. $\{x \mid x \in N\}$ and $\{x \mid x$ is a multiple of 4$\}$
78. $\{x \mid x$ is an odd natural number less than 11$\}$ and $\{x \mid x$ is an even natural number less than 12$\}$

For Exercises 79–86, find the cardinal number for each set.

79. $A = \{63, 72, 51, 44\}$
80. $B = \{10, 11, 12, \ldots, 20\}$
81. $C = \{x \mid x$ is a day of the week$\}$
82. $D = \{x \mid x$ is a month of the year$\}$
83. $E = \{three\}$
84. $F = \{t, h, r, e, e\}$
85. $G = \{x \mid x \in N$ and x is negative$\}$
86. $H = \varnothing$

For Exercises 87–92, determine whether each statement is true or false.

87. All equal sets are equivalent.
88. No equivalent sets are equal.
89. $n(\{\varnothing\}) = 0$
90. $E = \{2, 4, 6, 8, \ldots\}$ is a finite set
91. $\{1, 2, 3, 4, \ldots\}$ is equivalent to $\{10, 20, 30, 40, \ldots\}$
92. $n(\{\ \}) = 0$

Applications in Our World

93. The table shows the top 10 states in number of immigrants granted permanent resident status in 2010.

State	Number of Immigrants	% of Total Immigrants to United States
California	208,446	20.0
New York	147,999	14.2
Florida	107,276	10.3
Texas	87,750	8.4
New Jersey	56,920	5.5
Illinois	37,909	3.6
Massachusetts	31,069	3.0
Virginia	28,607	2.7
Maryland	26,450	2.5
Georgia	24,833	2.4

Source: *The World Almanac and Book of Facts*, 2012.

(a) List the set of states with more than 100,000 immigrants.
(b) List the set of states in the top 10 with fewer than 50,000 immigrants.
(c) List $\{x \mid x$ is a state with at least 5% of the immigrant total$\}$.
(d) List $\{x \mid x$ is a state with between 3% and 9% of the immigrant total$\}$.

94. This table shows the top 10 states in terms of illegal immigrant population (estimated) in 2010. This problem uses this table and the one from Exercise 93.

State	Number of Immigrants	% of Total Illegal Immigrant Population
California	2,570,000	23.8
Texas	1,770,000	16.4
Florida	760,000	7.0
Illinois	490,000	4.5
Arizona	470,000	4.4
Georgia	460,000	4.3
New York	460,000	4.3
North Carolina	390,000	3.6
New Jersey	370,000	3.4
Nevada	260,000	2.4

Source: *The World Almanac and Book of Facts*, 2012.

(a) List the set of states that rank in the top five in both legal and illegal immigration.
(b) List the set of states in both of the top tens that have a higher percentage of legal immigrants than illegal.
(c) Write a description of a set of states that is empty based on the data in the two tables.
(d) Using the information in the two tables, write a verbal description of the set {California, New York, Texas, Florida}.

95. Excessive alcohol consumption by those aged 18–24 affects nearly all U.S. college students, whether they choose to drink or not. Some consequences of excessive drinking are listed in the next table.

54   **Chapter 2** Sets

Consequence	Average Number of College Students Aged 18–24 Affected per Year
Death	1,825
Injury	599,000
Assault	696,000
Sexual abuse	97,000
Unsafe sex	400,000
Health problems	150,000
Drunk driving	3,360,000

Source: http://www.collegedrinkingprevention.gov/StatsSummaries/snapshot.aspx

(a) List the set of the three consequences with the most students affected by excessive alcohol consumption.

(b) List the set of consequences that affect between 100,000 and 600,000 college students each year.

(c) Find the set $\{x \mid x$ is a consequence of which over a half million students are affected$\}$.

(d) Find the set $\{x \mid x$ is the average number of college students affected by sexual abuse, death, or health problems$\}$.

(e) If A is the set of students affected by health problems, injury, or drunk driving, can you find $n(A)$? Why or why not?

96. The number of bachelor's degrees awarded in the United States in the top 10 majors for 2009 is listed in the table, with data for 1999 and 2004 as well.

Major	1999	2004	2009
Business	240,947	307,149	347,985
Social sciences and history	124,658	150,357	168,500
Health professions	85,214	73,934	120,488
Education	107,086	106,278	101,708
Psychology	73,636	82,098	94,271
Visual and performing arts	54,404	77,181	89,140
Biological and biomedical sciences	64,608	61,509	80,756
Communication	51,384	70,968	78,009
Engineering	58,260	63,558	69,133
English	49,800	53,984	55,462

Source: http://nces.ed.gov/programs/digest/d10/tables/dt10_282.asp

(a) List the set of majors that increased in popularity every year listed.

(b) List the set of majors that did not increase in popularity from 2004 to 2009.

(c) List the set of majors that had between 50,000 and 110,000 degrees awarded in 2009.

(d) Find the set $\{x \mid x$ increased in popularity between 1999 and 2004$\}$.

(e) To find the percent increase P between an original amount O and a new amount N, use the following formula: $P = (N - O)/O$. Calculate the percent increase for any major that saw an increase in degrees awarded between 2004 and 2009. List the set of majors that increased at least 30%.

97. Identity theft is now one of the most costly crimes in the United States, and younger adults are the most affected. Of 251,000 identity theft complaints made to the FTC in 2010, over 30% of the victims were under the age of 30. The following charts show types of identity theft fraud reported in 2010 and the percentage of victims by age.

Types of Identity Theft Fraud Reported in 2010

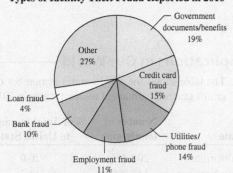

Source: ftc.gov

Percentage of Victims by Age

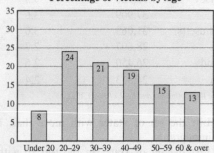

(a) List the set of the two types of identity fraud with the lowest percentage of reported crimes.

(b) List the set of age groups that are above 18%.

(c) List the set of identity fraud types that make up more than 17% of reported crimes.

(d) Find the set $\{x \mid x$ is a percentage of those 40 and over who are victims of identity fraud$\}$.

(e) Find the set $\{x \mid x$ is a type of fraud that has between 10% and 20% of reported crimes$\}$.

98. The rise of digital distribution for music has coincided with the downfall of the compact disc, at least in terms of sales. The chart shows the number of compact discs and downloaded albums sold (in millions) for some recent years, along with the value of those sales (in 10 millions).

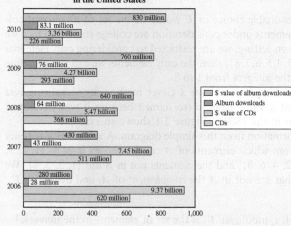

CD vs. Downloaded Album Sales in the United States

(a) List the set of years in which the value of CD sales exceeded the value of album downloads.

(b) List the set of years in which the value of album downloads was lower than the year before.

(c) List the set $\{x \mid x$ is a year in which the number of CDs sold decreased by more than 100 million units$\}$.

(d) List the set $\{x \mid x$ is a dollar value for album downloads that represented more than a $100 million increase from the previous year$\}$.

99. Housing prices have been in the news a lot in recent years, as the boom that began in 2004 gave way to the bust just a few years later. The graph below displays the median housing prices for all houses sold in the United States between 2003 and 2010.

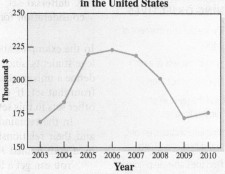

Median Home Prices of Existing Homes in the United States

Source: National Association of Realtors

(a) List the set of years in which the median price was above $200,000.

(b) List the set of years in which the median price was between $170,000 and $200,000.

(c) Find $\{x \mid x$ is a year in which the median price increased from the year before$\}$.

(d) Find $\{x \mid x$ is a year in which the median price decreased from the year before$\}$.

Critical Thinking

100. If $A \cong B$ and $A \cong C$, is $B \cong C$? Explain your answer.

101. Is $\{0\}$ equivalent to $\varnothing$? Explain your answer.

102. Write two sets that are equivalent but not equal. Why is it not possible to write two sets that are equal but not equivalent?

103. We know that two sets are equivalent if we can match up their elements in a one-to-one correspondence.

(a) Which set has more elements: $A = \{1, 2, 3, 4, 5, 6, \ldots\}$ or $B = \{2, 4, 6, 8, 10, \ldots\}$?

(b) Write out a correspondence between A and B where every element in A gets matched with its double in B. Does this change your mind about your answer to part (a)? (If you find this problem interesting, you'll like Section 2-5 very much.)

104. Explain why each of the following sets is not well-defined.

(a) The set of all Americans

(b) The set of luxury cars in the 2011 model year

(c) The set of all colleges with a legitimate chance to win the NCAA basketball tournament (There are at least two reasons!)

(d) The set of all jobs that pay over $50,000 per year

(e) The set of mothers

105. (a) List all of the different sets you can form using only the elements in the set $\{2, 4, 6\}$.

(b) There are eight sets that can be formed in part (a). Did you find seven of them? If so, can you figure out why you missed one?

Section 2-2   Subsets and Set Operations

When we classify things in our world, sets often have relationships with one another. For example, you are a member of both the set of college students and the set of students taking a college math course. You could be in the set of sophomores or the set of juniors, but not in both. You might be in the set of students living off campus and the set of students who walk to class. In this section, we'll be studying relationships between sets.

To begin, we need to consider a new concept called a *universal set.*

> A **universal set**, symbolized by U, is the set of all potential elements under consideration for a specific situation.

LEARNING OBJECTIVES

☐ 1. Define the complement of a set.

☐ 2. Find all subsets of a set.

☐ 3. Use subset notation.

☐ 4. Find the number of subsets for a set.

☐ 5. Find intersections, unions, and differences of sets.

☐ 6. Find the Cartesian product of two sets.

In the examples above, a reasonable choice of U would be the set of all current college students, since all the elements under consideration are college students. Once we define a universal set in a given setting, we are restricted to considering only elements from that set. If $U = \{1, 2, 3, 4, 5, 6, 7, 8\}$, then the only elements we can use to define other sets in this setting are the integers from 1 to 8.

In the remainder of this chapter, we'll use a clever method for visualizing sets and their relationships called a *Venn diagram* (so named because it was developed by a man named John Venn in the 1800s). Figure 2-1 shows an example.

You can get a lot of information from this simple diagram. A set called A is being defined. The universal set from which elements of A can be chosen is $U = \{1, 2, 3, 4, 5, 6, 7, 8\}$. The set A is $\{2, 4, 6, 8\}$, and the elements not in A are $\{1, 3, 5, 7\}$. We will call the elements in U that are not in A the *complement* of A, and denote it A'.

> The **complement** of a set A, symbolized A', is the set of elements in the universal set that are *not* in A. Using set-builder notation, the complement of A is $A' = \{x \mid x \in U \text{ and } x \notin A\}$.

Math Note

The complement of the universal set is the empty set: $U' = \varnothing$. The complement of the empty set is the universal set: $\varnothing' = U$.

In a Venn diagram, the complement of a set A is all the things inside the rectangle that are not inside the circle representing set A. This is shown in Figure 2-2.

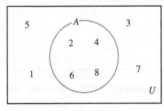

Figure 2-1

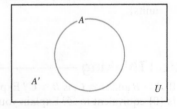

Figure 2-2

EXAMPLE 1   Finding the Complement of a Set

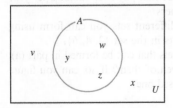

Figure 2-3

Let $U = \{v, w, x, y, z\}$ and $A = \{w, y, z\}$. Find A' and draw a Venn diagram that illustrates these sets.

SOLUTION

Using the list of elements in U, we just have to cross out the ones that are also in A. The elements left over are in A'.

$$U = \{v, \cancel{w}, x, \cancel{y}, \cancel{z}\} \qquad A' = \{v, x\}$$

The Venn diagram is shown in Figure 2-3.

☑ 1. Define the complement of a set.

▼ **Try This One 1**

Let $U = \{10, 20, 30, 40, 50, 60, 70, 80, 90\}$ and $A = \{10, 30, 50\}$. Find A' and draw a Venn diagram that illustrates these sets.

Subsets

At the beginning of the section, we pointed out that you're in both the set of college students and the set of students taking a college math course. Notice that everyone in the second set is automatically in the first one. We could say that the set of students taking a college math course is contained in the set of all college students. When one set is contained in a second set, we call the smaller set a *subset* of the larger one.

If every element of a set A is also an element of a set B, then A is called a **subset** of B. The symbol $\subseteq$ is used to designate a subset; in this case, we write $A \subseteq B$.

An alternate definition is that A is a subset of B if there are no elements in A that are not also in B.

Here are a couple of observations about subsets.

- Every set is a subset of itself. Every element of a set A is of course an element of set A, so $A \subseteq A$.

- The empty set is a subset of every set. The empty set has no elements, so for any set A, you can't find an element of $\varnothing$ that is not also in A.

If we start with the set $\{x, y, z\}$, let's look at how many subsets we can form:

Number of Elements in Subset	Subsets with That Number of Elements	
3	$\{x, y, z\}$	(One subset)
2	$\{x, y\}, \{x, z\}, \{y, z\}$	(Three subsets)
1	$\{x\}, \{y\}, \{z\}$	(Three subsets)
0	$\varnothing$	(One subset)

So for a set with three elements, we can form eight subsets.

There are many subsets of this set of spring breakers: the subset of female students, the subset of guys hitting on those female students, the subset of students who had their fake I.D. confiscated by the police, and so on.

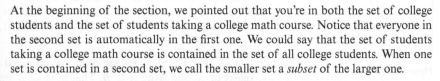

EXAMPLE 2   Finding All Subsets of a Set

Find all subsets of $A = \{\textit{American Idol, Survivor}\}$.

SOLUTION

The subsets are

$\{\textit{American Idol, Survivor}\}$
$\{\textit{American Idol}\}$
$\{\textit{Survivor}\}$
$\varnothing$

Note that a set with 2 elements has 4 subsets.

▼ **Try This One 2**

Find all subsets of $B = \{$Verizon, T-Mobile, AT&T$\}$.

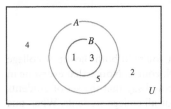

Figure 2-4 $B \subset A$

To indicate that a set is not a subset of another set, the symbol $\not\subseteq$ is used. For example, $\{1, 3\} \not\subseteq \{0, 3, 5, 7\}$ since $1 \notin \{0, 3, 5, 7\}$.

Of the four subsets in Example 2, only one is equal to the original set. We will call the remaining three *proper subsets* of A. The Venn diagram for a proper subset is shown in Figure 2-4. In this case, $U = \{1, 2, 3, 4, 5\}$, $A = \{1, 3, 5\}$, and $B = \{1, 3\}$.

> If a set A is a subset of a set B and is not equal to B, then we call A a **proper subset** of B, and write $A \subset B$. That is, $A \subseteq B$ and $A \neq B$.

EXAMPLE 3   **Finding Proper Subsets of a Set**

Find all proper subsets of $\{x, y, z\}$.

SOLUTION

$\{x, y\}$ $\{x, z\}$ $\{y, z\}$
$\{x\}$ $\{y\}$ $\{z\}$
$\varnothing$

▼ **Try This One 3**

Find all proper subsets of $\{\blacklozenge, \blacktriangledown, \spadesuit, \clubsuit\}$.

☑ 2. Find all subsets of a set.

The symbol $\not\subset$ is used to indicate that the set is not a proper subset. For example, $\{1, 3\} \subset \{1, 3, 5\}$, but $\{1, 3, 5\} \not\subset \{1, 3, 5\}$.

EXAMPLE 4   **Understanding Subset Notation**

Decide if each statement is true or false.

Math Note

It's important not to confuse the concept of subsets with the concept of elements. For example, the statement $6 \in \{2, 4, 6\}$ is true since 6 is an element of the set $\{2, 4, 6\}$, but the statement $\{6\} \in \{2, 4, 6\}$ is false since it states that the set containing the element 6 is an element of the set containing 2, 4, and 6. However, it *is* correct to say that $\{6\} \subseteq \{2, 4, 6\}$, or that $\{6\} \subset \{2, 4, 6\}$.

(a) $\{1, 3, 5\} \subseteq \{1, 3, 5, 7\}$
(b) $\{a, b\} \subset \{a, b\}$
(c) $\{x \mid x \in E \text{ and } x > 10\} \subset N$
(d) $\{r, s, t\} \not\subset \{t, s, r\}$
(e) $\{$Lake Erie, Lake Huron$\} \not\subseteq$ The set of Great Lakes

(f) $\varnothing \subset \{5, 10, 15\}$
(g) $\{u, v, w, x\} \subseteq \{x, w, u\}$
(h) $\{0\} \subseteq \varnothing$

SOLUTION

(a) All of 1, 3, and 5 are in the second set, so $\{1, 3, 5\}$ is a subset of $\{1, 3, 5, 7\}$. The statement is true.

(b) Even though $\{a, b\}$ is a subset of $\{a, b\}$, it is not a proper subset, so the statement is false.

(c) Every element in the first set is a natural number, but not all natural numbers are in the set, so that set is a proper subset of the natural numbers. The statement is true.

(d) The two sets are identical, so $\{r, s, t\}$ is not a proper subset of $\{t, s, r\}$. The statement is true.

(e) Lake Erie and Lake Huron are both Great Lakes, so the set {Lake Erie, Lake Huron} is a subset of the set of Great Lakes. The statement is false.

(f) True: the empty set is a proper subset of every set except itself.

(g) False: v is an element of {u, v, w, x} but not {x, w, u}.

(h) The set on the left has one element, 0. The empty set has no elements, so the statement is false.

▼ Try This One 4

Decide if each statement is true or false.

(a) $\{8\} \subseteq \{x \mid x$ is an even natural number$\}$

(b) $\{6\} \subseteq \{1, 3, 5, 7, \ldots\}$

(c) $\{2, 3\} \subseteq \{x \mid x \in N\}$

(d) $\{a, b, c\} \subset \{$letters of the alphabet$\}$

(e) $\varnothing \in \{x, y, z\}$

(f) $\varnothing \subseteq \{$red, yellow, blue$\}$

(g) $\{100, 200, 300, 400\} \subset \{200, 300, 400\}$

(h) $\{\varnothing\} \subseteq \varnothing$

☑ 3. Use subset notation.

A set with one element has two subsets—itself and the empty set. We have seen that if a set has two elements, there are four subsets, and if a set has three elements, there are eight subsets. This is an excellent opportunity to use the inductive reasoning that we practiced in Chapter 1!

Number of elements	0	1	2	3
Number of subsets	1	2	4	8

Math Note

In Problem 111, we'll look at an alternate approach to developing the formula for the number of subsets. It uses deductive reasoning rather than inductive reasoning.

Based on this pattern, it's reasonable to conjecture that a set with 4 elements will have 16 subsets, a set with 5 elements will have 32 subsets, and so forth. (Notice that the number of subsets in each case is 2 raised to the number of elements.) It turns out that this is always the case. We also know that the number of proper subsets of a set is always 1 less than the total number of subsets, since only the set itself is excluded when forming proper subsets. We conclude:

The Number of Subsets for a Finite Set

If a finite set has n elements, then the set has 2^n subsets and $2^n - 1$ proper subsets.

EXAMPLE 5   Finding the Number of Subsets of a Set

Find the number of subsets and proper subsets of the set $\{1, 3, 5, 7, 9, 11\}$.

SOLUTION

The set has $n = 6$ elements, so there are 2^n, or $2^6 = 64$, subsets. Of these, $2^n - 1$, or 63, are proper. (Recall that 2^6 means $2 \cdot 2 \cdot 2 \cdot 2 \cdot 2 \cdot 2$, which is 64.)

▼ Try This One 5

☑ 4. Find the number of subsets for a set.

Find the number of subsets and proper subsets of the set {OSU, USC, KSU, MSU, UND, PSU, UT, FSU}.

Intersection and Union of Sets

At the beginning of the section, we pointed out that you might be in both the set of students living off campus and the set of students who walk to class. We will identify objects that are common to two or more sets by using the term *intersection*.

> The **intersection** of two sets A and B, symbolized by $A \cap B$, is the set of all elements that are in both sets. In set-builder notation, $A \cap B = \{x \mid x \in A \text{ and } x \in B\}$.

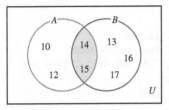

Figure 2-5 $A \cap B = \{14, 15\}$

For example, if $A = \{10, 12, 14, 15\}$ and $B = \{13, 14, 15, 16, 17\}$, then the intersection $A \cap B = \{14, 15\}$, since 14 and 15 are the only elements that are common to both sets. The Venn diagram for $A \cap B$ is shown in Figure 2-5. Notice that the elements of A are placed inside the circle for set A, and the elements of B are inside the circle for set B. The elements in the intersection are placed into the portion where the circles overlap: $A \cap B$ is the shaded portion.

Intersection is an example of a **set operation**—a rule for combining two or more sets to form a new set. The intersection of three or more sets consists of the set of elements that are in every single set. Note that the word *and* is sometimes used to indicate intersection; $A \cap B$ is the set of elements in A and B.

EXAMPLE 6   **Finding Intersections**

If $A = \{5, 10, 15, 20, 25\}$, $B = \{0, 10, 20, 30, 40\}$, and $C = \{30, 50, 70, 90\}$, find

(a) $A \cap B$ (b) $B \cap C$ (c) $A \cap B \cap C$

SOLUTION

(a) The elements 10 and 20 are in both sets A and B, so $A \cap B = \{10, 20\}$.
(b) The only member of both sets B and C is 30, so $B \cap C = \{30\}$.
(c) This example illustrates that it makes perfect sense to find the intersection of more than two sets: we just need to find numbers that are in all three sets. But in this case, there aren't any. This tells us that the intersection is empty: $A \cap B \cap C = \varnothing$.

▼ Try This One 6

If $A = \{$Cleveland, Indianapolis, Chicago, Des Moines, Detroit$\}$, $B = \{$New York, Los Angeles, Chicago, Detroit$\}$, and $C = \{$Seattle, Los Angeles, San Diego$\}$, find $A \cap B$, $B \cap C$, and $A \cap B \cap C$.

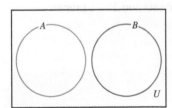

Figure 2-6 $A \cap B = \varnothing$

When the intersection of two sets is the empty set, the sets are said to be *disjoint*. For example, the set of students who stop attending class midway through a term and the set of students earning A's are disjoint, because you can't be a member of both sets. The Venn diagram for a pair of disjoint sets A and B is shown in Figure 2-6. If the sets have no elements in common, the circles representing them don't overlap at all.

Another way of combining sets to form a new set is called *union*.

> The **union** of two sets A and B, symbolized by $A \cup B$, is the set of all elements that are in either set A or set B (or both). In set-builder notation,
>
> $$A \cup B = \{x \mid x \in A \text{ or } x \in B\}$$

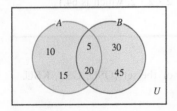

Figure 2-7 $A \cup B$

For example, if $A = \{5, 10, 15, 20\}$ and $B = \{5, 20, 30, 45\}$, then the union $A \cup B = \{5, 10, 15, 20, 30, 45\}$. Even though 5 and 20 are in both sets, we list them only once in the union. The Venn diagram for $A \cup B$ is shown in Figure 2-7. The set $A \cup B$ is the shaded area consisting of all elements in either set.

EXAMPLE 7	**Finding Unions**

If $A = \{0, 1, 2, 3, 4, 5\}$, $B = \{2, 4, 6, 8, 10\}$, and $C = \{1, 3, 5, 7\}$, find each.

(a) $A \cup B$　　　　(b) $A \cup C$　　　　(c) $A \cup B \cup C$

SOLUTION

To find a union, just make a list of all the elements from each set without writing repeats.

(a) $A \cup B = \{0, 1, 2, 3, 4, 5, 6, 8, 10\}$
(b) $A \cup C = \{0, 1, 2, 3, 4, 5, 7\}$
(c) $A \cup B \cup C = \{0, 1, 2, 3, 4, 5, 6, 7, 8, 10\}$

▼ **Try This One 7**

If $A = \{a, b, c, d, e\}$, $B = \{a, c, e, g, i\}$, and $C = \{b, d, f, h, j\}$, find $A \cup B$, $A \cup C$, and $A \cup B \cup C$.

What about operations involving more than two sets and more than one operation? Just like with operations involving numbers, we use parentheses to indicate an order of operations. This is illustrated in Example 8.

EXAMPLE 8	**Performing Set Operations**

Let $A = \{l, m, n, o, p\}$, $B = \{o, p, q, r\}$, and $C = \{r, s, t, u\}$. Find each set.

(a) $(A \cup B) \cap C$　　　　(b) $A \cap (B \cup C)$　　　　(c) $(A \cap B) \cup C$

SOLUTION

The key is to perform the operation in parentheses first.

(a) First find $A \cup B$: $A \cup B = \{l, m, n, o, p, q, r\}$. Then intersect this set with set C; the only common element is r, so $(A \cup B) \cap C = \{r\}$.
(b) First find $B \cup C$: $B \cup C = \{o, p, q, r, s, t, u\}$. Then intersect this set with set A to get $\{o, p\}$.
(c) First find $A \cap B$: $A \cap B = \{o, p\}$. Then find the union of this set with set C to get $\{o, p, r, s, t, u\}$.

▼ **Try This One 8**

If $A = \{2, 3, 4, 5, 6, 7\}$, $B = \{7, 8, 9, 10\}$, and $C = \{0, 5, 10, 15, 20\}$, find $A \cup (B \cap C)$, $(A \cap B) \cup C$, and $A \cap (B \cup C)$.

CAUTION

When combining union and intersection with complements as we will in Example 9, we'll have to be extra careful. Pay particular attention to the parentheses and to whether the complement symbol is inside or outside the parentheses.

EXAMPLE 9   **Performing Set Operations**

> **Math Note**
>
> Don't forget the importance of the universal set when finding complements: the complement of a set A is all of the elements in *the universal set* that are not in A, not all of the objects in the universe that are not in A.

If $U = \{10, 20, 30, 40, 50, 60, 70, 80\}$, $A = \{10, 30, 50, 70\}$, $B = \{40, 50, 60, 70\}$, and $C = \{20, 40, 60\}$, find each set.

(a) $A' \cap C'$ (b) $(A \cap B)' \cap C$ (c) $B' \cup (A \cap C')$

SOLUTION

(a) First, write A' and C': $A' = \{20, 40, 60, 80\}$ and $C' = \{10, 30, 50, 70, 80\}$. Now note that 80 is the only element common to both: $A' \cap C' = \{80\}$.
(b) The parentheses tell us that we should find $A \cap B$ first: $A \cap B = \{50, 70\}$. Next we find the complement: $(A \cap B)' = \{10, 20, 30, 40, 60, 80\}$. Finally, we find the intersection of this set and C: $(A \cap B)' \cap C = \{20, 40, 60\}$.
(c) First, find $A \cap C'$: $C' = \{10, 30, 50, 70, 80\}$, and all but 80 are also in A, so $A \cap C' = \{10, 30, 50, 70\}$. Next note that $B' = \{10, 20, 30, 80\}$. Now form the union: $B' \cup (A \cap C') = \{10, 20, 30, 50, 70, 80\}$.

▼ Try This One 9

Let $U = \{1, 2, 3, 4, 5, 6, 7, 8\}$, $A = \{1, 3, 5, 7\}$, $B = \{2, 4, 6, 8\}$, and $C = \{2, 3, 5, 7\}$. Find each set.

(a) C' (b) $(A \cup B)'$ (c) $A' \cap C'$ (d) $(A \cup B) \cap C'$

The union and intersection of sets are commonly used in real life—it's just that you might not have thought of it in those terms. For example, the intersection of the set of U.S. citizens older than 17 and the set of U.S. citizens who are not convicted felons makes up the set of those eligible to vote. The union of the set of your mom's parents and your dad's parents forms the set of your grandparents.

Set Subtraction

The third set operation we'll study is called the *difference* of sets. We also call it *set subtraction* and use a minus sign to represent it.

> The **difference** of set A and set B is the set of elements in set A that are *not* in set B. In set-builder notation, $A - B = \{x \mid x \in A \text{ and } x \notin B\}$.

EXAMPLE 10   **Finding the Difference of Two Sets**

> **Math Note**
>
> Sometimes operations can be written in terms of other operations. For example, $3 - 5$ is also $3 + (-5)$. Can you think of a way to write $A - B$ using intersection and complement? Drawing a Venn diagram might help.

Let $A = \{4, 6, 8, 10\}$, $B = \{2, 6, 12\}$, and $C = \{8, 10\}$.

Find each set.

(a) $A - B$ (b) $B - C$ (c) $(A - B) - C$

SOLUTION

(a) Start with the elements in set A and take out the elements in set B that are also in set A. In this case, only 6 is removed, and $A - B = \{4, 8, 10\}$.
(b) Start with the elements in set B and take out the elements in set C that are also in set B. In this case, none of the elements in B are also in C. So $B - C = \{2, 6, 12\}$.

(c) We already know that $A - B = \{4, 8, 10\}$; now we need to find any elements that are also in C and throw them out. Both 8 and 10 are in C, so $(A - B) - C = \{4\}$.

☑ 5. Find intersections, unions, and differences of sets.

▼ **Try This One 10**

Let $L = \{a, c, e, f, g, i\}$, $M = \{b, d, k, l, m, n\}$, and $N = \{a, b, d, k, l, m\}$. Find each set.

(a) $L - M$ (b) $N - M$ (c) $(N - M) - L$

Cartesian Products

The fourth set operation we'll study is called the *Cartesian product* or *cross product*. To define it, we need to first define an *ordered pair*. An ordered pair is a pair of numbers or objects that are associated by writing them together in a set of parentheses, like (3, 5). In this ordered pair, 3 is called the *first component* and 5 is called the *second component*. As indicated by the term *ordered pair*, the order in which numbers are written is important: (3, 5) is not the same ordered pair as (5, 3).

The **Cartesian product** (denoted $A \times B$) of two sets A and B is formed by writing all possible ordered pairs in which the first component is an element of A and the second component is an element of B. Using set-builder notation, $A \times B = \{(x, y) \mid x \in A \text{ and } y \in B\}$. The Cartesian product $A \times B$ is usually read aloud as "A cross B."

If you're familiar with a deck of playing cards, it provides a simple way to understand the point of the Cartesian product. If A is the set of the four suits (clubs, diamonds, hearts, spades) and B is the set of the 13 denominations (ace through 10, jack, queen, king), then the Cartesian product $A \times B$ is the set of cards. Every element in $A \times B$ describes both a suit and a denomination, which is exactly how you describe each card.

EXAMPLE 11   **Finding Cartesian Products**

Math Note

It's important to note that the Cartesian product of two sets is also a set, so it should be enclosed within braces.

If $A = \{$freshman, sophomore, junior$\}$ and $B = \{$quarterback, running back$\}$, find $A \times B$ and describe its significance.

SOLUTION

To start, we'll write ordered pairs with first component freshman: (freshman, quarterback), (freshman, running back). In the same way, we'll write ordered pairs with first component sophomore, then junior to get $A \times B$.

$A \times B = \{$(freshman, quarterback), (freshman, running back), (sophomore, quarterback), (sophomore, running back), (junior, quarterback), (junior, running back). This set describes the class and position for a subset of players on a college football team.

☑ 6. Find the Cartesian product of two sets.

▼ **Try This One 11**

If $C = \{$20 mg, 40 mg$\}$ and $D = \{$Vicodin, Xanax, Lipitor$\}$, find $C \times D$ and describe its significance.

CAUTION

Even though we use a multiplication sign for Cartesian product, it has nothing to do with multiplying elements!

64   **Chapter 2** Sets

So far, we've used Venn diagrams as a way to picture certain sets. In the next two sections we'll study how these diagrams can be used to study set operations in greater depth and in a variety of applied settings.

Answers to Try This One

1 $A' = \{20, 40, 60, 70, 80, 90\}$

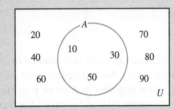

2 {Verizon, T-Mobile, AT&T}, {Verizon, T-Mobile}, {Verizon, AT&T}, {T-Mobile, AT&T}, {Verizon}, {T-Mobile}, {AT&T}, $\varnothing$

3 {♦, ♥, ♠}, {♦, ♥, ♣}, {♦, ♠, ♣}, {♥, ♠, ♣}, {♦, ♥}, {♦, ♠}, {♦, ♣}, {♥, ♠}, {♥, ♣}, {♠, ♣}, {♦}, {♥}, {♠}, {♣}, $\varnothing$

4 (a) True   (c) True   (e) False   (g) False
     (b) False (d) True   (f) True   (h) False

5 Subsets: $2^8 = 256$; proper subsets: 255

6 $A \cap B = \{$Chicago, Detroit$\}$;
     $B \cap C = \{$Los Angeles$\}$; $A \cap B \cap C = \varnothing$

7 $A \cup B = \{$a, b, c, d, e, g, i$\}$;
     $A \cup C = \{$a, b, c, d, e, f, h, j$\}$;
     $A \cup B \cup C = \{$a, b, c, d, e, f, g, h, i, j$\}$

8 $A \cup (B \cap C) = \{2, 3, 4, 5, 6, 7, 10\}$
     $(A \cap B) \cup C = \{0, 5, 7, 10, 15, 20\}$
     $A \cap (B \cup C) = \{5, 7\}$

9 (a) {1, 4, 6, 8}   (c) {4, 6, 8}
     (b) $\varnothing$ (d) {1, 4, 6, 8}

10 (a) $L - M = \{$a, c, e, f, g, i$\}$
      (b) $N - M = \{$a$\}$
      (c) $(N - M) - L = \varnothing$

11 (a) $C \times D = \{$(20 mg, Vicodin), (20 mg, Xanax), (20 mg, Lipitor), (40 mg, Vicodin), (40 mg, Xanax), (40 mg, Lipitor)$\}$. This describes different dosages for three prescription drugs.

EXERCISE SET 2-2

Writing Exercises

1. What is a subset?
2. Explain the difference between a subset and a proper subset.
3. Explain the difference between a subset and an element of a set.
4. Explain why the empty set is a subset, but not a proper subset, of itself.
5. Explain the difference between the union and intersection of two sets.

6. When are two sets said to be disjoint?
7. What is a universal set?
8. What is the complement of a set?
9. Write an example from real life that represents the union of sets and explain why it represents union. Then do the same for intersection.
10. Write an example from real life that represents the difference of sets and explain why it represents difference.

Computational Exercises

For Exercises 11–14, let $U = \{2, 3, 5, 7, 11, 13, 17, 19\}$, $A = \{5, 7, 11, 13\}$, $B = \{2\}$, $C = \{13, 17, 19\}$, *and* $D = \{2, 3, 5\}$. *Find each set.*

11. A' 13. C'
12. B' 14. D'

15. If $U =$ the set of natural numbers and $A = \{4, 6, 8, 10, 12, \ldots\}$, find A'.
16. If $U =$ the set of odd natural numbers and $B = \{13, 15, 17, 19, 21, 23, \ldots\}$, find B'.

For Exercises 17–24, find all subsets and all proper subsets of each set.

17. {r, s, t}
18. {2, 5, 7}
19. {1, 5}
20. {c, d}
21. ∅
22. { }
23. {w, x, y, z}
24. {1, 2, 3, 4}

For Exercises 25–34, state whether each is true or false.

25. {3} ⊆ {1, 3, 5}
26. {a, b, c} ⊂ {c, b, a}
27. {1, 2, 3} ⊆ {123}
28. ∅ ⊂ ∅
29. ∅ ∈ { }
30. $\{x \mid x \in E$ and $x > 100\} \subset \{x \mid x \in N$ and $x > 52\}$
31. {3} ∈ {1, 3, 5, 7, ... }
32. $\{x \mid x \in N$ and $x > 10\} \subseteq \{x \mid x \in N$ and $x \geq 10\}$
33. ∅ ⊂ {a, b, c}
34. {7, 11, 13, 17} ⊆ {17, 13, 11}

For Exercises 35–40, find the number of subsets and proper subsets each set has. Do not list the subsets.

35. {25, 50, 75}
36. {a, b, c, d, ... , z}
37. ∅
38. {0}
39. {x, y}
40. {2, 4, 6, 8, 10, ... , 30}

For Exercises 41–50, use the Venn diagram to find the elements in each set.

41. U
42. A
43. B
44. A ∩ B
45. A ∪ B
46. A'
47. B'
48. (A ∪ B)'
49. (A ∩ B)'
50. A ∩ B'

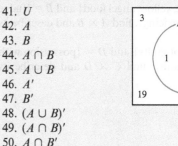

For Exercises 51–60, let

U = {11, 12, 13, 14, 15, 16, 17, 18, 19, 20}
A = {14, 15, 16, 17}
B = {11, 13, 15, 17, 19}
C = {12, 14, 15, 19, 20}

Find each set.

51. A ∪ C
52. A ∩ B
53. A'
54. (A ∩ B) ∪ C
55. A' ∩ (B ∪ C)
56. (A ∩ B) ∩ C
57. (A ∪ B)' ∩ C
58. A ∩ B'
59. (B ∪ C) ∩ A'
60. (A' ∪ B)' ∪ C'

For Exercises 61–70, let

$U = \{x \mid x \in N$ and $x < 25\}$
$W = \{x \mid x \in N$ and $5 < x < 15\}$

$X = \{x \mid x \in$ even natural numbers less than 10$\}$
$Y = \{x \mid x \in N$ and $20 < x < 25\}$
$Z = \{x \mid x \in$ odd natural numbers less than 13$\}$

Find each set.

61. W ∩ Y
62. X ∪ Z
63. W ∪ X
64. (X ∩ Y) ∩ Z
65. W ∩ X
66. (Y ∪ Z)'
67. (X ∪ Y) ∩ Z
68. (Z ∩ Y) ∪ W
69. W' ∩ X'
70. (Z ∪ X)' ∩ Y

For Exercises 71–74, let

U = {1, 2, 3, ...}
A = {3, 6, 9, 12, ...}
B = {9, 18, 27, 36, ...}
C = {2, 4, 6, 8, ...}

Find each set.

71. A ∩ B
72. A' ∩ C
73. A ∩ (B ∪ C')
74. A ∪ B

For Exercises 75–80, let

U = {p, q, r, s, t, u, v, w}
A = {p, q, r, s, t}
B = {r, s, t, u, v}
C = {p, r, t, v}

Find each set.

75. C − B
76. A − C
77. B − C
78. B − A
79. B ∩ C'
80. C ∩ A'

For Exercises 81–84, let

D = {11, 12, 13, 14, 15, ...}
$M = \{x \mid x \in E$ and $x > 10\}$
$T = \{x \mid x \in N$ and $x < 100\} \cup \{x \mid x \in O$ and $x > 100\}$

Find each set.

81. D − M
82. T − D
83. (D − M) − T
84. (T − D) − M

For Exercises 85–88, let

A = {9, 12, 18}
B = {1, 2, 3}

Find each set.

85. A × B
86. B × A
87. A × A
88. B × B

For Exercises 89–92, use the Venn diagram to write each set in terms of A, B, and/or U.

89. {1, 2, 3, 4}
90. {2, 3, 5, 6, 7, 8, 9}
91. {2, 3, 6, 7, 8}
92. {1, 4}

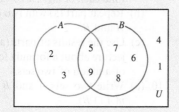

Applications in Our World

93. A student can have a cell phone, a laptop, and an iPod while hanging out on campus between classes. List all the sets of different communication options a student can select, considering all, some, or none of these technologies.

94. If a person is dealt five cards and has a chance of discarding any number including 0, how many choices will the person have?

95. A college freshman can choose one, some, or all of the following classes for her first semester: an English class, a math class, a foreign language class, a science class, a philosophy class, a physical education class, and a history class. How many different possibilities does she have for her new schedule?

96. Since the student union is being remodeled, there is a limited choice of foods and drinks a student can buy for a snack between classes. Students can choose none, some, or all of these items: pizza, fries, big soft pretzels, Coke, Diet Coke, and Hawaiian Punch. How many different selections can be made?

97. Suzie is buying a new laptop for school and can select none, some, or all of the following choices of peripherals: a laser mouse, a DVD burner, a Web cam, or a jump drive. How many different selections of peripherals are possible for her laptop?

98. To integrate aerobics into her exercise program, Claire can select one, some, or all of these machines: treadmill, cycle, and stair stepper. List all possibilities for her aerobics selection.

99. This want ad is looking for a person who's in the intersection of three sets. What are those three sets?

100. This personal was posted on Craigslist: "Wife wanted, must be able to dig and clean worms or be able to clean fish. Must have own boat with motor. Please send photograph of motor boat." Write a statement involving three sets, intersection, and union that describes this fine gentleman's requirements for a life partner.

Exercises 101–104 use the following sets:

U = the set of all people who have been charged with a felony

A = the set of people who are on trial or awaiting trial on felony charges

B = the set of people who have been convicted of a felony

C = the set of people who have been convicted of a felony and have been released from prison

D = the set of people who were charged with a felony and found not guilty

E = the set of people who were charged with a felony and had charges dropped before standing trial

Write a verbal description of each set.

101. (a) $B \cup C$ (b) $C \cup D$ (c) $D \cup E$

102. (a) A' (b) C' (c) E'

103. (a) $B \cap C$ (b) $A \cap B$ (c) $C \cap B'$

104. (a) $(A \cup B)'$ (b) $(B \cup D)'$ (c) $A - (B \cap C)$

105. If A = {chocolate, yellow, angel food} and B = {fudge icing, cream cheese icing}, find $A \times B$ and describe its significance.

106. If C = {guilty, not guilty} and D = {possession with intent, DUI, assault}, find $C \times D$ and describe its significance.

Critical Thinking

107. Can you find two sets whose union and intersection are the same set?

108. Pick three medications and find a resource on the Internet that lists the possible side effects of each. Find the intersection of the sets.

109. (a) Make up two sets A and B with somewhere between 4 and 8 elements in each so that $A \cap B$ is nonempty. Find each of $n(A)$, $n(B)$, $n(A \cup B)$, and $n(A \cap B)$.

    (b) Repeat part (a) with two completely different sets A and B.

    (c) Use the results of parts (a) and (b) to make a conjecture about a formula for finding the cardinality of a union of two sets.

110. (a) Write two sets A and B for which $n(A \cup B) > n(A \cap B)$.

    (b) Write two sets A and B for which $n(A \cup B) = n(A \cap B)$.

    (c) Can you write two sets A and B for which $n(A \cup B) < n(A \cap B)$? Use a Venn diagram to illustrate why you can or cannot.

111. Here's an alternate approach to developing the formula for the number of subsets for a set with n elements. If a set has two elements, when forming a subset, there are two choices for each element: it's either in the subset or it's not. If we multiply two choices for the first element by two choices for the second element, we get four choices of subset. (This illustrates an important idea we'll encounter in Chapter 11 called the fundamental counting principle.) Generalize this idea to derive the formula for the number of subsets.

Section 2-3   Using Venn Diagrams to Study Set Operations

LEARNING OBJECTIVES

☐ 1. Illustrate set statements involving two sets with Venn diagrams.

☐ 2. Illustrate set statements involving three sets with Venn diagrams.

☐ 3. Use De Morgan's laws.

☐ 4. Use Venn diagrams to decide if two sets are equal.

☐ 5. Use the formula to find the cardinality of a union of two sets.

The world we live in is a pretty complicated place. Everywhere you look, there are interactions between sets of people, businesses, products, objects—we could go on, but you probably get the picture. The more complicated these interactions are, the more challenging it can be to sort them out. One good way to get a handle on a complicated situation is to diagram it. When we're dealing with sets, Venn diagrams will be our tool of choice.

In this section, we'll develop a method for drawing Venn diagrams that will help us to illustrate set operations. We'll start with diagrams involving interactions between two sets, as in Figure 2-8. Notice that there are four distinct regions in a Venn diagram illustrating two sets A and B. We'll want to number the regions for reference; we use Roman numerals so that we don't confuse the number of the region with elements in the set or the cardinality of the set.

The procedure that we will use to illustrate set statements, found in the box below, is demonstrated in Examples 1 and 2.

Illustrating a Set Statement with a Venn Diagram

Step 1   Draw a diagram for the sets, with Roman numerals in each region.

Step 2   Using those Roman numerals, list the regions described by each set.

Step 3   Find the set of numerals that correspond to the set given in the set statement.

Step 4   Shade the area corresponding to the set of numerals found in step 3.

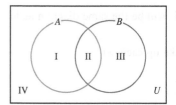

Figure 2-8

Region I   represents the elements in set A that are not in set B.
Region II   represents the elements in both sets A and B.
Region III   represents the elements in set B that are not in set A.
Region IV   represents the elements in the universal set that are in neither set A nor set B.

EXAMPLE 1   **Drawing a Venn Diagram**

Draw a Venn diagram to illustrate the set $(A \cup B)'$.

SOLUTION

Step 1   Draw the diagram and label each area with a Roman numeral.

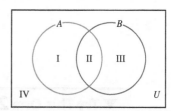

Step 2   From the diagram, list the regions that make up each set.

$U = \{I, II, III, IV\}$
$A = \{I, II\}$
$B = \{II, III\}$

Step 3 Using the sets in step 2, find $(A \cup B)'$.
First, all of I, II, and III are in either A or B, so $A \cup B = \{$I, II, III$\}$. The only region not in $A \cup B$ is IV, so the complement is $(A \cup B)' = \{$IV$\}$.

Step 4 Shade region IV to illustrate $(A \cup B)'$.

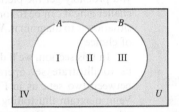

▼ Try This One 1

Draw a Venn diagram to illustrate the set $A' \cap B$.

EXAMPLE 2   **Drawing a Venn Diagram**

Draw a Venn diagram to illustrate the set $A \cap B'$.

> ## Math Note
>
> In any problem where we're asked to illustrate a set statement involving two sets, Steps 1 and 2 will be exactly the same.

SOLUTION

Step 1 Draw the diagram and label each area. This will be the same diagram as in Step 1 of Example 1.

Step 2 From the diagram, list the regions that make up each set.

$U = \{$I, II, III, IV$\}$
$A = \{$I, II$\}$
$B = \{$II, III$\}$

Step 3 Using the sets in step 2, find $A \cap B'$.
First, regions I and IV are outside of set B. Of these two regions, I is also in set A, so $A \cap B' = \{$I$\}$.

Step 4 Shade region I to illustrate $A \cap B'$.

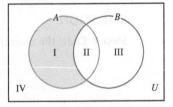

✓ 1. Illustrate set statements involving two sets with Venn diagrams.

▼ Try This One 2

Draw a Venn diagram to illustrate the set $A' \cup B$.

In the opener for this chapter, we asked you to solve a more complicated problem involving three sets of people: those self-reporting as white, black, or Hispanic. Venn diagrams

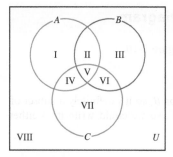

Figure 2-9

are great for sorting out information of this nature, and we'll want some experience with Venn diagrams involving three sets before we move on to solving those problems.

Fortunately, the procedure we used for two sets can be used for three sets as well: you just get a more complicated diagram (see Figure 2-9).

Region I represents the elements in set *A* but not in set *B* or set *C*.
Region II represents the elements in set *A* and set *B* but not in set *C*.
Region III represents the elements in set *B* but not in set *A* or set *C*.
Region IV represents the elements in sets *A* and *C* but not in set *B*.
Region V represents the elements in sets *A*, *B*, and *C*.
Region VI represents the elements in sets *B* and *C* but not in set *A*.
Region VII represents the elements in set *C* but not in set *A* or set *B*.
Region VIII represents the elements in the universal set *U*, but not in set *A*, *B*, or *C*.

EXAMPLE 3   **Drawing a Venn Diagram with Three Sets**

Draw a Venn diagram to illustrate the set $A \cap (B \cap C)'$.

SOLUTION

Step 1 Draw and label the diagram as in Figure 2-9.

Step 2 From the diagram, list the regions that make up each set.

$U = \{I, II, III, IV, V, VI, VII, VIII\}$
$A = \{I, II, IV, V\}$
$B = \{II, III, V, VI\}$
$C = \{IV, V, VI, VII\}$

Step 3 Using the sets in step 2, find $A \cap (B \cap C)'$.
First, find $B \cap C$: $B \cap C = \{V, VI\}$. The complement is $(B \cap C)' = \{I, II, III, IV, VII, VIII\}$. Regions I, II, and IV are also part of *A*, so $A \cap (B \cap C)' = \{I, II, IV\}$.

Step 4 Shade regions I, II, and IV to illustrate $A \cap (B \cap C)'$.

> *Math Note*
>
> When illustrating complicated sets like $A \cap (B \cap C)'$, don't forget to find the set in parentheses first. That's why the parentheses are there!

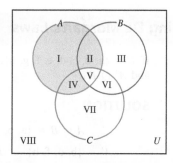

▼ Try This One 3

Draw a Venn diagram to illustrate the set $(A \cap B') \cup C$.

To get even better at working with Venn diagrams, it's helpful to turn the process around, starting with a shaded diagram and figuring out what set it represents, as in Example 4.

70   **Chapter 2**   Sets

EXAMPLE 4   **Finding a Set Corresponding to a Venn Diagram**

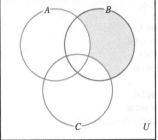

Figure 2-10

Write the set illustrated by the Venn diagram in Figure 2-10.

SOLUTION

The shaded portion is completely inside the circle for B, so it's definitely a subset of B. But it doesn't include anything in either A or C, so we could write it as either $B - (A \cup C)$, or $B \cap (A \cup C)'$.

▼ **Try This One 4**

Write the set illustrated by the Venn diagram in Figure 2-11.

De Morgan's Laws

There are two very well-known formulas that are useful in simplifying some set operations. They're named in honor of a 19th-century mathematician named Augustus De Morgan.

First, we'll write the formulas and illustrate each with an example. Then we'll see how Venn diagrams can be used to prove the formulas.

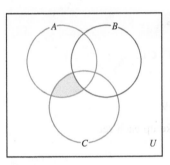

Figure 2-11

 2. Illustrate set statements involving three sets with Venn diagrams.

De Morgan's Laws
For any two sets A and B,
$(A \cup B)' = A' \cap B'$
$(A \cap B)' = A' \cup B'$

The first law states that the complement of the union of two sets will always be equal to the intersection of the complements of each set.

EXAMPLE 5   **Using De Morgan's Laws**

If $U = \{a, b, c, d, e, f, g, h\}$, $A = \{a, c, e, g\}$, and $B = \{b, c, d, e\}$, find $(A \cup B)'$ and $A' \cap B'$.

SOLUTION

$$A \cup B = \{a, b, c, d, e, g\} \quad \text{and} \quad (A \cup B)' = \{f, h\}$$
$$A' = \{b, d, f, h\} \quad B' = \{a, f, g, h\} \quad \text{and} \quad A' \cap B' = \{f, h\}$$

Notice that $(A \cup B)'$ and $A' \cap B'$ are equal, illustrating the first of De Morgan's laws.

▼ **Try This One 5**

If $U = \{15, 30, 45, 60, 75, 90, 105\}$, $A = \{30, 60, 90\}$, and $B = \{15, 45, 75, 90\}$, find $(A \cup B)'$ and $A' \cap B'$.

Sidelight **NOW AND VENN**

Venn diagrams are generally credited to the British mathematician John Venn, who introduced them in an 1880 paper as they are used today. That makes it sound like a pretty old concept, but the general idea can be traced back much further. The great mathematician Leonhard Euler used similar diagrams in the 1700s, and other figures like them can be traced as far back as the 1200s!

While it's absolutely true that John Venn was a classic academic—at one time writing or lecturing in each of morality, mathematics, logic, probability theory, philosophy, metaphysics, and history—he had a somewhat surprising hobby: building machines. In particular, he was best known for building a machine for bowling cricket balls (which is roughly analogous to pitching in baseball). His machine was so good that in 1909 it "clean bowled" one of the top cricket players of the time on four occasions, which is kind of like a turn-of-the-century pitching machine striking out Babe Ruth.

The second of De Morgan's laws states that the complement of the intersection of two sets will equal the union of the complements of the sets.

| EXAMPLE 6 | **Using De Morgan's Laws** |

Math Note

In Examples 6 and 7, we're looking at specific examples, so we're using inductive reasoning to conclude that De Morgan's laws are likely to be true. In Example 8, we'll use deductive reasoning to *prove* them.

☑ 3. Use De Morgan's laws.

If $U = \{10, 11, 12, 13, 14, 15, 16\}$, $A = \{10, 11, 12, 13\}$, and $B = \{12, 13, 14, 15\}$, find $(A \cap B)'$ and $A' \cup B'$.

SOLUTION

$$A \cap B = \{12, 13\} \quad \text{and} \quad (A \cap B)' = \{10, 11, 14, 15, 16\}$$
$$A' = \{14, 15, 16\} \quad B' = \{10, 11, 16\}; \quad A' \cup B' = \{10, 11, 14, 15, 16\}$$

Notice that $(A \cap B)'$ and $A' \cup B'$ are equal, illustrating the second of De Morgan's laws.

▼ **Try This One 6**

If $U = \{ABC, NBC, CBS, Fox, USA, TBS, TNT, MTV\}$, $A = \{NBC, Fox, USA, TBS\}$, and $B = \{ABC, NBC, CBS, Fox\}$, find $(A \cap B)'$ and $A' \cup B'$.

Now that we know how to illustrate sets with Venn diagrams, we can use them to show that two sets that look different are actually the same. In Example 7, we'll illustrate the procedure by proving the first of De Morgan's laws. We'll leave the second one for you to try.

| EXAMPLE 7 | **Using Venn Diagrams to Show Equality of Sets** |

Use Venn diagrams to show that $(A \cup B)' = A' \cap B'$, proving the first of De Morgan's laws.

SOLUTION

Start by drawing the Venn diagram for $(A \cup B)'$.

Step 1 Draw the figure (as shown in Step 4).

Step 2 Set U contains regions I, II, III, and IV. Set A contains regions I and II, and B contains regions II and III.

Step 3 $A \cup B = \{I, II, II\}$, so $(A \cup B)' = \{IV\}$.

Step 4 Shade region IV to illustrate $(A \cup B)'$.

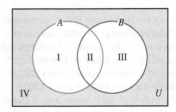

Next draw the Venn diagram for $A' \cap B'$. Steps 1 and 2 are the same as above.

Step 3 $A' = \{III, IV\}$ and $B' = \{I, IV\}$, so $A' \cap B' = \{IV\}$.

Step 4 Shade region IV to illustrate $A' \cap B'$.

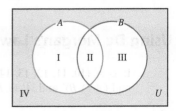

Since the diagrams for each side of the equation are identical, we use deductive reasoning to conclude that $(A \cup B)' = A' \cap B'$.

▼ Try This One 7

Use Venn diagrams to show that $(A \cap B)' = A' \cup B'$.

Here's an example using three sets.

EXAMPLE 8   Using Venn Diagrams to Decide If Two Sets Are Equal

Decide if the two sets are equal using Venn diagrams: $(A \cup B) \cap C$ and $(A \cap C) \cup (B \cap C)$.

SOLUTION

The set $A \cup B$ consists of regions I through VI. Of these, IV, V, and VI are also in C, so $(A \cup B) \cap C$ consists of regions IV, V, and VI.

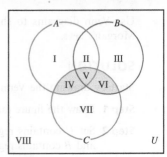

Math Note

As you get more comfortable working with Venn diagrams, you'll probably be able to shade the regions illustrated by a set without formally going through our four-step process, like we are doing in Example 8.

The set $A \cap C$ consists of regions IV and V, and the set $B \cap C$ consists of regions V and VI. Their union is regions IV, V, and VI.

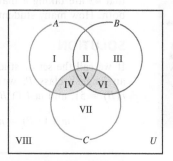

Since the shaded areas are the same, the two sets are equal.

☑ 4. Use Venn diagrams to decide
    if two sets are equal.

▼ Try This One 8

Decide if the two sets are equal using Venn diagrams: $B \cup (A \cap C)$ and $(A \cup B) \cap (B \cup C)$.

The Cardinal Number of a Union

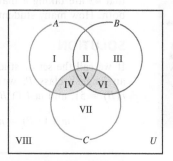

Figure 2-12

If 10 of your friends belong to the set of students taking a math class, and 14 belong to the set of students taking an English class, how many are in the union of those two sets? If your first instinct is 24, you're not alone—that's sort of the standard guess. And it might actually be right, but only if none of your friends are taking both a math and English class. If any of them are in both classes, you'd be counting them twice by just adding the number of friends in each set. Venn diagrams can be used to analyze this situation.

As you can see in Figure 2-12, if we start with the number of elements in A, we're counting all the members in regions I and II. When we add the number of elements in B, we're counting all the members in regions II and III. Do you see the issue? The elements in region II get counted twice. We can fix that by subtracting the number of elements in region II. Since region II represents $A \cap B$, we get the following useful formula:

Math Note

In words, the formula to the right says that to find the number of elements in the union of A and B, you add the number of elements in A and B and then subtract the number of elements in the intersection of A and B.

The Cardinality of a Union

If $n(A)$ represents the cardinal number of set A, then for any two finite sets A and B, $n(A \cup B) = n(A) + n(B) - n(A \cap B)$.

Next, we'll see how this formula can be used in an applied situation.

EXAMPLE 9   Using the Formula for Cardinality of a Union

In a survey of 100 randomly selected freshmen walking across campus, it turns out that 42 are taking a math class, 51 are taking an English class, and 12 are taking both. How many students are taking either a math class or an English class?

SOLUTION

If we call the set of students taking a math class A and the set of students taking an English class B, we're asked to find $n(A \cup B)$. We're told that $n(A) = 42$, $n(B) = 51$, and $n(A \cap B) = 12$. So,

$$n(A \cup B) = n(A) + n(B) - n(A \cap B) = 42 + 51 - 12 = 81$$

▼ **Try This One 9**

☑ 5. Use the formula to find the cardinality of a union of two sets.

A poll of 200 doctors across the nation found that 112 were assisted in their office by registered nurses, 83 were assisted by licensed practical nurses, and 21 were assisted by both. How many were assisted by at least one type of nurse?

In this section, we saw how Venn diagrams can be used to illustrate sets, prove equality of two sets, and solve problems. We'll explore the problem-solving aspect of Venn diagrams further in Section 2-4, and learn how to solve problems like the one in the chapter opener.

Answers to Try This One

1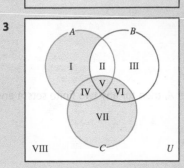

2

3

4 $(A \cap C) - B$ or $(A \cap C) \cap B'$

5   Both are {105}.

6   Both are {ABC, CBS, USA, TBS, TNT, MTV}.

7   Both diagrams are

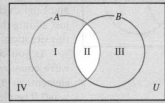

8   Both diagrams are

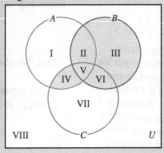

9   174

EXERCISE SET 2-3

Writing Exercises

1. One of your buddies is paging through your textbook and sees some Venn diagrams. He asks "What's the point of these pictures?" How would you answer?
2. Explain in your own words how to draw a Venn diagram representing the set $A \cup B$.
3. Explain in your own words how to draw a Venn diagram representing the set $A \cap B$.
4. How can we use Venn diagrams to decide if two sets that look different are actually equal?
5. Describe in your own words what De Morgan's laws say.
6. Describe in your own words how to find the cardinal number of the union of two sets.

Computational Exercises

For Exercises 7–30, draw a Venn diagram and shade the sections representing each set.

7. $A \cup B'$
8. $(A \cup B)'$
9. $A' \cup B'$
10. $A' \cup B$
11. $A' \cap B'$
12. $A \cap B'$
13. $A \cup (B \cap C)$
14. $A \cap (B \cup C)$
15. $(A \cup B) \cup (A \cap C)$
16. $(A \cup B) \cap C$
17. $(A \cup B) \cap (A \cup C)$
18. $(A \cap B) \cup C$
19. $(A \cap B)' \cup C$
20. $(A \cup B) \cup C'$
21. $A \cap (B \cup C)'$
22. $A' \cap (B' \cup C')$
23. $(A' \cup B') \cap C$
24. $A \cap (B \cap C)'$
25. $(A \cup B)' \cap (A \cup C)$
26. $(B \cup C) \cup C'$
27. $A' \cap (B' \cap C')$
28. $(A \cup B)' \cap C'$
29. $A' \cap (B \cup C)'$
30. $(A \cup B) \cap (A \cap C)$

For Exercises 31–38, determine whether the two sets are equal using Venn diagrams.

31. $(A \cap B)'$ and $A' \cup B'$
32. $(A \cup B)'$ and $A' \cup B'$
33. $(A \cup B) \cup C$ and $A \cup (B \cup C)$
34. $A \cap (B \cup C)$ and $(A \cap B) \cup (A \cap C)$
35. $A' \cup (B \cap C')$ and $(A' \cup B) \cap C'$
36. $(A \cap B) \cup C'$ and $(A \cap B) \cup (B \cap C')$
37. $(A \cap B)' \cup C$ and $(A' \cup B') \cap C$
38. $(A' \cup B') \cup C$ and $(A \cap B)' \cap C'$

For Exercises 39–50, use the following Venn diagram to find the cardinality of each set.

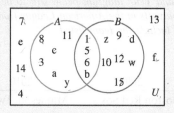

39. $n(A)$
40. $n(B)$
41. $n(A \cap B)$
42. $n(A \cup B)$
43. $n(A')$
44. $n(B')$
45. $n(A' \cap B')$
46. $n(A' \cup B')$
47. $n(A - B)$
48. $n(B - A)$
49. $n(A \cap (B - A))$
50. $n(B' \cup (B - A))$

For Exercises 51–60, use the following information:

$U = \{x \mid x \text{ is a natural number less than } 20\}$
$A = \{x \mid x \text{ is an odd natural number less than } 16\}$
$B = \{x \mid x \text{ is a prime number greater than } 5\}$

{Note: The prime numbers less than 20 are 2, 3, 5, 7, 11, 13, 17, and 19}. Find the cardinality of each set.

51. $n(A)$
52. $n(B)$
53. $n(A \cap B)$
54. $n(A \cup B)$
55. $n(A \cap B')$
56. $n(A' \cup B)$
57. $n(A')$
58. $n(B')$
59. $n(A - B)$
60. $n(B' - A)$

76   **Chapter 2** Sets

Applications in Our World

In Exercises 61–64, A = {people who drive an SUV} and B = {people who drive a hybrid vehicle}. Draw a Venn diagram of the following, and write a sentence describing what the set represents.

61. $A \cup B$ 63. A'
62. $A \cap B$ 64. $(A \cap B)'$

In Exercises 65–68, O = {students in online courses}, B = {students in blended courses}, and T = {students in traditional courses}. Draw a Venn diagram of the following, and write a sentence describing what the set represents.

65. $O \cap (T \cup B)$
66. $B \cup (O \cap T)$
67. $B \cap O \cap T$
68. $(B \cup O) \cap (T \cup O)$

In Exercises 69–72, D = {students voting Democrat}, R = {students voting Republican}, and I = {students voting Independent}. Draw a Venn diagram of the following, and write a sentence describing what the set represents.

69. $D' \cup R$ 71. $(D \cup R) \cap I'$
70. $D' \cap I'$ 72. $I - (D \cup R)$

In Exercises 73–76, G = {people who regularly use Google}, Y = {people who regularly use Yahoo!}, and B = {people who regularly use Bing}. Draw a Venn diagram of the following, and write a sentence describing what the set represents.

73. $G - Y$
74. $G - (Y \cap B)$
75. $G' \cap Y' \cap B'$
76. $(Y \cap B) \cup (Y \cap G)$

The table and Venn diagram below are to be used for Exercises 77–82. The table shows the four baseball teams that made the playoffs in the American League from 2009 to 2011. For each exercise, write the region(s) of the Venn diagram that would include the team listed.

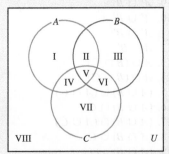

Year	2009	2010	2011
Teams	Boston Red Sox	Minnesota Twins	Detroit Tigers
	Los Angeles Angels	New York Yankees	New York Yankees
	Minnesota Twins	Tampa Bay Rays	Tampa Bay Rays
	New York Yankees	Texas Rangers	Texas Rangers

Note: set A represents 2009 playoff teams, set B represents 2010 playoff teams, and set C represents 2011 playoff teams.

77. Boston Red Sox   80. Minnesota Twins
78. Detroit Tigers   81. New York Yankees
79. Texas Rangers   82. Seattle Mariners

Critical Thinking

83. For two finite sets A and B, is $n(A - B)$ equal to $n(A) - n(B)$? If not, can you find a formula for $n(A - B)$?
84. Can you find a formula for $n(A \cap B)$ in terms of only $n(A)$ and $n(B)$? Why or why not? See if you can find a formula for $n(A \cap B)$ using any sets you like.
85. Make a conjecture about another form for the set $(A \cup B \cup C)'$ based on the first of De Morgan's laws. Check out your conjecture by using a Venn diagram.
86. Make a conjecture about another form for the set $(A \cap B \cap C)'$ based on the second of De Morgan's laws. Check out your conjecture by using a Venn diagram.

In Exercises 87–92, (a) use a Venn diagram to show that the two sets are not equal in general; (b) try to find specific sets A, B (and C if necessary) for which the two sets are equal; and (c) try to find a general condition under which the two sets are always equal. Recall that U represents the universal set.

87. $A \cap B$ and B
88. $A - B$ and A
89. $(A \cap B)'$ and U
90. $(A \cap B)'$ and A'
91. $(A - C) \cap B$ and $B \cap A$
92. $(A - C) \cup (B - A)$ and $B - C$

Section 2-4   Using Sets to Solve Problems

LEARNING OBJECTIVES

☐ 1. Solve problems using Venn diagrams.

We live in the information age—every time you turn around, somebody somewhere is trying to gather information about you, your opinions, and (most commonly) your spending habits. Surveys are conducted by the thousands every day, and every person, pet, pastime, and product are classified. The things we've learned about sets can be very helpful in interpreting information from surveys and classifications, and that will be the focus of this section.

When things are classified into two distinct sets, we can use a two-set Venn diagram to interpret the information. This is illustrated in Example 1.

EXAMPLE 1   **Solving a Problem Using a Venn Diagram**

In 2011, there were 39 states that had some form of casino gambling in the state, 43 states that sold lottery tickets of some kind, and 34 states that had both casinos and lotteries. Draw a Venn diagram to represent the survey results, and find how many states have only casino gambling, how many states have only lotteries, and how many states have neither.

SOLUTION

Step 1 Draw a Venn diagram with circles for casino gambling (C) and lotteries (L), labeling the regions with Roman numerals as usual.

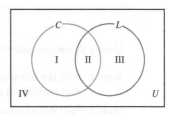

Step 2 Thirty-four states have both, so put 34 in the intersection of C and L, which is region II.

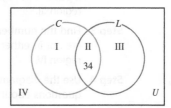

Step 3 Since 39 states have casino gambling and 34 have both, there must be 5 that have only casino gambling. Put 5 in region I. Since 43 states have lotteries and 34 have both, there are 9 that have only lotteries. Put 9 in region III.

Math Note

The first piece of information we're given is that 39 states have casino gambling, so it's tempting to begin by putting 39 in region I.

But this isn't right—region I represents states that have casino gambling but NOT lotteries, and we don't know that number yet. If we know the number in the intersection, that's where we'll always start.

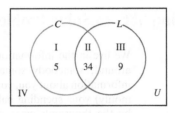

Step 4 Now 48 states are accounted for, so there must be 2 left to put in region IV.

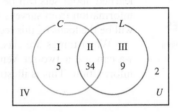

Now we can answer the questions easily. There are 5 states that have casino gambling but not lotteries (region I), 9 that have lotteries but not casinos (region III), and just 2 that have neither (region IV). In case you're wondering, those two states are Hawaii and Utah.

▼ Try This One 1

In an average year, Columbus, Ohio, has 163 days with some rain, 63 days with some snow, and 24 days with both. Draw a Venn diagram to represent these averages, and find how many days have only rain, only snow, and neither.

We can use the results of Example 1 to write a general procedure for using a Venn diagram to interpret information that can be divided into two sets.

Using Venn Diagrams with Two Sets

Step 1 Find the number of elements that are common to both sets and write that number in region II.

Step 2 Find the number of elements that are in set *A* and not set *B* by subtracting the number in region II from the total number of elements in *A*. Then write that number in region I. Repeat for the elements in *B* but not in region II, and write in region III.

Step 3 Find the number of elements in *U* that are not in either *A* or *B*, and write it in region IV.

Step 4 Use the diagram to answer specific questions about the situation.

Quick Vote

Are you worse off financially than you were in recent years?

○ Yes
○ No
○ About the same

VOTE or see results

Many news websites include daily surveys, like this one from cnn.com.

One of the most useful applications of Venn diagrams is for studying the results of surveys. Whether they are for business-related research or just to satisfy curiosity, surveys seem to be everywhere these days, especially online. Example 2 analyzes the results of a survey on tattoos and body piercings.

EXAMPLE 2   **Solving a Survey Problem Using a Venn Diagram**

In a survey published in the *Journal of the American Academy of Dermatologists*, 500 people were asked by random telephone dialing whether they have a tattoo and/or a body piercing. Of these, 79 reported having a tattoo only, 31 reported having a piercing only, and 151 reported having at least one of the two. Draw a Venn diagram to represent these results and use your diagram to find the percentage of respondents that have a tattoo, that have a piercing, that have both, and that have neither.

SOLUTION

In this example, we'll have to adapt the procedure from Example 1 because we don't know the number that have both. The key is to begin by putting in information we're given that corresponds exactly to one of the regions in our Venn diagram.

Step 1 We're told that 79 people have only a tattoo, which means we can put 79 in region I. We're also told that 31 have only a piercing, so that goes in region III.

Step 2 There are 151 with a tattoo, a piercing, or both. This is the union of sets T and P, which makes up regions I, II, and III. We already know there are 110 people in regions I and III combined (79 + 31), so there must be 151 − 110 = 41 people in region II.

Step 3 There are 151 of the 500 accounted for so far, so region IV must contain 500 − 151 = 349 people.

Step 4 There is a total of 120 people in the regions that make up set T, so 120 people have tattoos; 120/500 = 0.24, so 24% have tattoos. Seventy-two have piercings (14.4%), 41 have both (8.2%), and 349 have neither (69.8%).

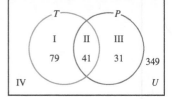

▼ Try This One 2

According to an online survey on Howstuffworks.com, 12,595 people gave their thoughts on Coke vs. Pepsi. Of these, 5,786 drink only Coke, 3,763 drink only Pepsi, and 11,405 drink at least one. Draw a Venn diagram to represent these results and use your diagram to find the percentage of respondents that drink Coke, that drink Pepsi, that drink both, and that drink neither.

When a classification problem or a survey consists of three sets, a similar procedure is followed, using a Venn diagram with three sets. We just have more work to do since there are now eight regions instead of four.

Sidelight **HOW MUCH IS YOUR OPINION WORTH?**

Communication in our society is becoming cheaper, easier, and more effective all the time. In the age of cell phones and Internet communication, businesses are finding it simpler than ever to contact people for their opinions, and more and more people are finding out that companies are willing to pay to hear what they have to say. There are literally hundreds of companies in the United States today whose main function is to gather opinions on everything from political candidates to potato chips. In fact, over $6 *billion* is spent on market research in the United States each year. Maybe you'll think twice the next time somebody asks you for your opinion for free.

EXAMPLE 3	Solving a Problem Using a Three-Set Venn Diagram

A criminal justice major is studying the frequency of certain types of crimes in a nearby county. He studies the arrest records of 300 inmates at the county jail, specifically asking about drug-related offenses, domestic violence, and theft of some sort. He finds that 194 had been arrested for theft, 210 for drug offenses, and 170 for domestic violence. In addition, 142 had arrests for both theft and drugs, 111 for both drugs and domestic violence, 91 for both theft and domestic violence, and 45 had been arrested for all three. Draw a Venn diagram to represent these results, and find the number of inmates that had been arrested for

(a) Only drug-related offenses.
(b) Theft and domestic violence but not drugs.
(c) Theft or drugs.
(d) None of these offenses.

SOLUTION

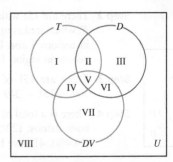

Step 1 The only region we know for sure from the given information is region V—the number of inmates arrested for all three offenses. So we begin by putting 45 in region V.

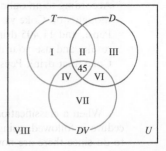

Step 2 There are 142 inmates with arrests for both theft and drugs, but we have to subtract the number arrested for all three offenses to find the number in region II: 142 − 45 = 97. In the same way, we get 91 − 45 = 46 in region IV (both theft and domestic violence) and 111 − 45 = 66 in region VI (both drugs and domestic violence).

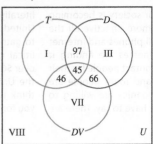

Step 3 Now we can find the number of elements in regions I, III, and VII. There were 194 inmates arrested for theft, but $97 + 45 + 46 = 188$ are already accounted for in the diagram, so that leaves 6 in region I. Of the 210 inmates with drug arrests, $97 + 45 + 66 = 208$ are already accounted for, leaving just 2 in region III. There were 170 inmates arrested for domestic violence, with $46 + 45 + 66 = 157$ already accounted for. This leaves 13 in region VII.

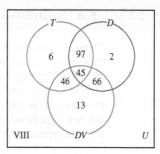

Step 4 Adding up all the numbers in the diagram so far, we get 275. That leaves 25 in region VIII.

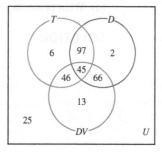

Step 5 Now that we have the diagram completed, we turn our attention to the questions.

  (a) Inmates arrested only for drug-related offenses are in region III: there were just 2.

  (b) Theft and domestic violence with no drug arrests is region IV, so there were 46 inmates.

  (c) Those arrested for either theft or drugs are in all regions except VII and VIII. So there are only $13 + 25 = 38$ that weren't arrested for at least one of those, and $300 - 38 = 262$ that were.

  (d) Only 25 inmates (outside of all circles) haven't been arrested for any of those offenses.

> ## Math Note
>
> Notice that in filling in the Venn diagram in Example 3, we started with the number of elements in the innermost region and worked our way outward.

☑ 1. Solve problems using Venn diagrams.

▼ Try This One 3

An online music service surveyed 500 customers and found that 270 listen to hip-hop music, 320 listen to rock, and 160 listen to country. In addition, 140 listen to both rock and hip-hop, 120 listen to rock and country, and 80 listen to hip-hop and country. Finally, 50 listen to all three. Draw a Venn diagram to represent the results of the survey and find the number of customers who

(a) Listen to only hip-hop.
(b) Listen to rock and country but not hip-hop.
(c) Don't listen to any of these three types of music.
(d) Don't listen to country music.

Rather than write a general procedure for three-set Venn diagram problems, we'll solve one more example with different information provided, showing that again the key is to write in the given information that applies exactly to certain regions, then use subtraction to find other regions one-by-one.

EXAMPLE 4   **Solving a Problem Using a Three-Set Venn Diagram**

Three of the most dangerous risk factors for heart attack are high blood pressure, high cholesterol, and smoking. In a survey of 690 heart attack survivors, 62 had only high cholesterol among those three risk factors; 36 had only smoking, and 93 had only high blood pressure. There were 370 total with high cholesterol, 159 with high blood pressure and cholesterol that didn't smoke, and 23 that smoked and had high cholesterol but not high blood pressure. Finally, 585 had at least one risk factor. Draw a Venn diagram representing this information and use it to answer the following questions.

(a) How many survivors had all three risk factors?
(b) How many had exactly two of the three risk factors?
(c) How many had none?
(d) What percentage were smokers?

SOLUTION

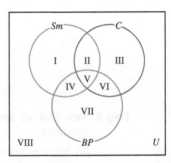

Step 1   Fill in the regions we know exact values for. In this case, there are five: 62 only high cholesterol (region III), 36 only smoking (region I), 93 only high blood pressure (region VII), 159 with high blood pressure and cholesterol but no smoking (region VI), and 23 with high cholesterol but not high blood pressure (region II).

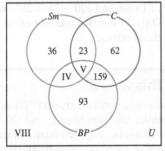 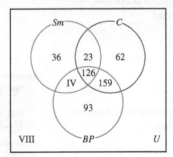

Step 2   There were 370 total with high cholesterol, and we have 23 + 62 + 159 = 244 accounted for so far, so region V must contain 370 − 244 = 126 survivors.

Step 3   The last piece of information we have is that 585 had at least one risk factor. This will allow us to find the remaining two regions. All of the numbers currently in the diagram add up to 499, so region IV must contain 585 − 499 = 86 survivors. Also, if 585 patients had at least one risk factor, that leaves 690 − 585 = 105 in region VIII.

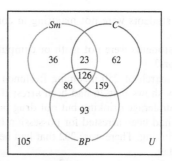

Step 4 Now we can answer a whole bunch of questions about the study.

   (a) The intersection of all three risk factors contains 126 survivors.
   (b) Regions II, IV, and VI are patients that had exactly two of the risk factors: This is 86 + 23 + 159 = 268 survivors.
   (c) From region VIII we see that 105 patients had none of the risk factors.
   (d) The total number inside the smoker circle is 36 + 23 + 126 + 86 = 271; this represents 271/690, or 39.3% of the survivors.

▼ Try This One 4

Three other risk factors are obesity, family history of heart disease, and stress. Of the group of heart attack patients in Example 4, 213 had a family history of heart disease, 47 of those also suffered from stress but not obesity, 60 were obese but had no stress issues, and 12 were neither stressed nor obese. Stress was a factor for 170 total, 8 of whom had no family history and weren't obese. There were 396 patients with none of these three risk factors.

(a) How many of the patients were obese?
(b) What percentage had all three of these risk factors?
(c) How many were not obese and did not have a family history of heart disease?

We've come a pretty long way from simply defining what sets and elements are! In this section, we've seen that Venn diagrams can be effectively used to sort out some pretty complicated situations in our world. And the better you are at interpreting information, the better equipped you'll be to survive and thrive in the information age.

Answers to Try This One

1 Only rain: 139; only snow: 39;
   neither: 163 (assuming it's not leap year!)

2 Coke: 60.7%; Pepsi: 44.6%
   both: 14.7%, neither: 9.4%

3 (a) 100   (c) 40
   (b) 70   (d) 340

4 (a) 227   (b) 13.6%   (c) 404

EXERCISE SET   2-4

Applications in Our World

1. In a survey of 85 college students, 72 use Facebook, 31 use Google+, and 21 use both.
   (a) How many use Google+ only?
   (b) How many use Facebook only?
   (c) How many use neither?

2. In a class of 25 students, 18 were math majors, 12 were computer science majors, and 7 were dual majors in math and computer science.
   (a) How many students were majoring in math only?

(b) How many students were not majoring in computer science?

(c) How many students were not math or computer science majors?

3. A court record search of 250 incoming freshmen at a state university shows that 26 had been arrested at some point for underage drinking but not drug possession, and 12 had been arrested for possession but not underage drinking. There were 202 that had been arrested for neither.

(a) How many of the students had been arrested for drug possession?

(b) How many had been arrested for underage drinking?

4. Twenty-five mice were involved in a biology experiment involving exposure to chemicals found in cigarette smoke. Fifteen developed at least one tumor, nine suffered from respiratory failure, and four developed tumors and had respiratory failure.

(a) How many only got tumors?

(b) How many didn't get a tumor?

(c) How many suffered from at least one of these effects?

5. Out of 20 students taking a midterm psychology exam, 15 answered the first of two bonus questions, 13 answered the second bonus question, and 2 didn't bother with either one.

(a) What percentage of students tried both questions?

(b) What percentage tried at least one question?

6. In a study of 400 entrées served at 75 campus cafeterias, 70 had less than 10 grams of fat but not less than 350 calories; 48 had less than 350 calories but not less than 10 grams of fat; 140 had over 350 calories and over 10 grams of fat.

(a) What percentage of entrées had less than 10 grams of fat?

(b) What percentage of entrées had less than 350 calories?

7. The financial aid department at a college surveyed 70 students, asking if they receive any type of financial aid. The results of the survey are summarized in the table below.

Financial Aid	Number of Students
Scholarships	16
Student loans	24
Private grants	20
Scholarships and loans	9
Loans and grants	11
Scholarships and grants	7
Scholarships, loans, and grants	2

(a) How many students got only scholarships?

(b) How many got loans and private grants but not scholarships?

(c) How many didn't get any of these types of financial aid?

8. The manager of a campus gym is planning the schedule of fitness classes for a new school year, and will decide how often to hold certain classes based on the interests of students. She polls 47 students at various times of day, asking what type of classes they'd be interested in attending. The results are summarized in the table below.

Type of Class	Students Interested
Yoga	17
Pilates	13
Spinning	12
Yoga and pilates	9
Pilates and spinning	3
Yoga and spinning	5
All three	2

(a) How many students are interested in yoga or spinning, but not pilates?

(b) How many are interested in exactly two of the three classes?

(c) How many are interested in yoga but not pilates?

9. One semester in a chemistry class, 14 students failed due to poor attendance, 23 failed due to not studying, 15 failed because they did not turn in assignments, 9 failed because of poor attendance and not studying, 8 failed because of not studying and not turning in assignments, 5 failed because of poor attendance and not turning in assignments, and 2 failed because of all three of these reasons.

(a) How many failed for exactly two of the three reasons?

(b) How many failed because of poor attendance and not studying but not because of not turning in assignments?

(c) How many failed because of exactly one of the three reasons?

(d) How many failed because of poor attendance and not turning in assignments but not because of not studying?

10. According to a survey conducted by the National Pizza Foundation that I just now made up, out of 109 customers surveyed, 32 prefer pizzas with just pepperoni, 40 with just sausage, and 18 with only onions. Thirteen big-time carnivores like pepperoni and sausage, 10 customers prefer sausage and onions, 9 customers like pepperoni and onions; in each case, the third item could be included as well. Seven go all out, ordering all three.

(a) How many customers prefer pepperoni, or sausage, or pepperoni and sausage with no onions?

(b) What about sausage, or onions, or sausage and onions with no pepperoni?

(c) How many go the boring route—none of those toppings?

11. Two hundred patients suffering from depression enrolled in a clinical trial to test the effects of various antidepressants. Zoloft was given to 27% of patients, Lexapro was given to 30%, and Prozac was given to 27%. Thirteen percent were treated with at least Zoloft and Lexapro, 11.5% were given at least Lexapro and Prozac, 7% were given at least Zoloft and Prozac, and 4% were treated with all three drugs.

(a) How many patients in the trial were given at most two of the three drugs?

(b) How many patients were treated with Zoloft and Prozac but not Lexapro?

(c) How many patients were given a placebo containing none of the three drugs?

12. A survey of 96 students on campus showed that 29 read the *Campus Observer* student newspaper that morning, 24 read the news via the Internet that morning, and 20 read the local city paper that morning. Eight read the *Campus Observer* and the Internet news that morning, while four read the Internet news and the local paper, seven read the *Campus Observer* and the local city paper, and one person read the *Campus Observer*, the Internet news, and the local paper.

(a) How many read the Internet news or local paper but not both?

(b) How many read the Internet news and the local paper but not the *Campus Observer?*

(c) How many read the Internet news or the *Campus Observer* or both?

13. Of the 50 largest cities in the United States, 11 have a team in the National Basketball Association but not a major league baseball team; 9 have a major league baseball team but not a team in the NBA; 12 have neither.

(a) How many cities have both a major league baseball team and a team in the NBA?

(b) Chicago, New York, and Los Angeles have two baseball teams, but Los Angeles is the only city with two basketball teams. Each of those cities has teams in both leagues. How many teams are there in each league?

14. One hundred new books are released nationally over a busy 3-day stretch in December. Eight had an e-book version available only on Amazon, 5 were available only on Google books, and 18 were available only on iTunes. There were 26 total available on Google, 7 that could be found on both Amazon and Google but not iTunes, and 4 that could be found on both iTunes and Google but not Amazon. Draw a Venn diagram representing this information and use it to answer the following questions.

(a) How many books were available on all three services?

(b) Explain why you can't find the number of books that were not available on any of the three services.

(c) If every book released was available as an e-book on at least one of Amazon, Google, or iTunes, how many were available on Amazon and iTunes but not Google?

(d) In that case, how many were available on exactly two of those three services?

15. A marketing firm is hired to conduct research into the listening habits of drivers in a large urban area. On the first day, 121 drivers were surveyed: 26 listen to FM radio while driving, 4 of whom listen to only FM. Eight more listen to FM and AM only, while 4 listen to FM and satellite only. There were 6 that listen to only AM, 22 that listen to only satellite, and 69 that listen to at least one of the three.

(a) Are there more people who listen to satellite radio, or more who listen to none of the three types in the survey?

(b) How many more listen to AM radio than FM?

(c) How many listen to some form of radio, but not AM?

16. The arts communities in 230 cities across the country were rated according to whether or not they have an art museum, a symphony orchestra, and a ballet company. There are 119 cities with an art museum; 20 of those also have ballet but no orchestra, and 41 have an orchestra but no ballet; 30 have neither. Of the 75 cities with a ballet company, 10 have an orchestra as well, but lack an art museum. Twenty-two cities have only an orchestra.

(a) What percentage of the cities has an orchestra?

(b) How many more cities are there with none of these three than with all of them?

(c) If you pick a city at random from this list to travel to and really want to go either to an art museum or an orchestral concert, what is the percent chance that you'll end up disappointed?

Critical Thinking

17. A researcher was hired to examine the drinking habits of energy drink consumers. Explain why he was fired when he published the results below, from a survey of 40 such consumers:

23 said they drink Red Bull.
18 said they drink Monster.
19 said they drink G2.
12 said they drink Red Bull and Monster.

6 said they drink Monster and G2.

7 said they drink Red Bull and G2.

2 said they drink all three (not at the same time, hopefully).

2 said they don't drink any of the three brands.

18. The marketing research firm of OUWant12 designed and sent three spam advertisements to 40 e-mail accounts. The first one was an ad for hair removal cream, the second was an ad for Botox treatments, and the third was an ad for a new all lima bean diet. Explain why, when the following results occurred, the sponsors discontinued their services.

23 recipients deleted the ad for hair removal cream without looking at it.

18 recipients deleted the ad for Botox treatments.

19 recipients deleted the ad for the all lima bean diet.

12 recipients deleted the ads for hair removal cream and Botox treatments.

6 recipients deleted the ads for Botox treatments and the all lima bean diet.

7 recipients deleted the ads for the hair removal cream and the all lima bean diet.

2 recipients deleted all three ads.

19. A TV network considering new contracts to televise pro sports hires a marketing consultant to conduct a survey of randomly selected TV viewers asking them which of football, baseball, and basketball they go out of their way to watch on TV. Of those surveyed, 35 watch baseball, 235 watch basketball, 295 watch football, 90 watch basketball and football, and 560 watch none of the three.

(a) Explain why this is not enough information to find the total number of people surveyed.

(b) Upon looking at the results more carefully, a member of the consultant team discovers that every single person who watches baseball also watches basketball, and none of those people watch football. Now can you find the number of people surveyed?

(c) How many people watch only football? How many watch only basketball?

Section 2-5   Infinite Sets

Infinity is a concept that's tremendously difficult for us human beings to wrap our minds around. Because our thoughts are shaped by experiences in a physical world with finite dimensions, things that are infinitely large always seem just out of our grasp. Whether you're a believer in the Big Bang theory or creationism, you probably think that one or the other must be true because the alternative is too far beyond our experience: that time didn't have a beginning at all, but extends infinitely far in each direction. Some philosophers feel that human beings are fundamentally incapable of grasping the concept of something infinitely large at all!

The study of infinity and infinite sets from a mathematical standpoint is a relatively young one compared to the history of math in general. For at least a couple of thousand years, the nature of infinity so confounded the greatest human minds that they chose to not deal with it at all. And yet in working with a set as simple as the natural numbers, we deal with infinite sets in math all the time. It's an interesting paradox.

LEARNING OBJECTIVES

☐ 1. Formally define infinite sets.

☐ 2. Show that a set is infinite.

☐ 3. Find a general term for an infinite set.

☐ 4. Define countable and uncountable sets.

A Definition of Infinite Sets

Recall from Section 2-1 that a set is considered to be finite if the number of elements is either zero or a natural number. Otherwise, it is considered to be an infinite set. For example, the set $\{10, 20, 30, 40\}$ is finite because the number of elements (four) is a natural number. But the set $\{10, 20, 30, 40, \dots\}$ is infinite because the number of elements is unlimited, and therefore not a natural number.

The night sky may look infinite, but have you ever thought about what that really means?

☑ 1. Formally define infinite sets.

You might recognize an infinite set when you see one, but it's not necessarily easy to make a precise definition of what it means for a set to be infinite (other than the obvious definition, "not finite"). The German mathematician Georg Cantor, widely regarded as the father of set theory, is famous for his 19th-century study of infinite sets. Cantor's simple and elegant definition of an infinite set is as follows:

A set is **infinite** if it can be placed into a one-to-one correspondence with a proper subset of itself.

First, notice that a finite set definitely does not meet the condition in this definition: if a set has some finite number of elements, let's say 10, then any proper subset has at most 9 elements, and an attempt at one-to-one correspondence will always leave out at least one member.

The trickier thing is to understand how an infinite set can meet this definition. We'll illustrate with an infinite set we know well, the set of natural numbers $\{1, 2, 3, 4, \ldots\}$. The set of even natural numbers $\{2, 4, 6, 8, \ldots\}$ is of course a proper subset: every even number is also a natural number, but there are natural numbers that are not even numbers. Now we demonstrate a clever way to put these two sets into a one-to-one correspondence: match each natural number with its double.

$$1 \leftrightarrow 2, \quad 2 \leftrightarrow 4, \quad 3 \leftrightarrow 6, \quad 4 \leftrightarrow 8, \ldots$$

In general, we can define our correspondence as matching any n from the set of natural numbers with a corresponding even number $2n$. This is a one-to-one correspondence because every natural number has a match (its double), and every even number has a match (its half). So we've put the natural numbers into one-to-one correspondence with a proper subset, proving that they are an infinite set.

Let's try another example.

EXAMPLE 1   **Showing That a Set Is Infinite**

Show that the set $\{5, 10, 15, 20, 25, \ldots\}$ is an infinite set.

SOLUTION

A simple way to put this set in correspondence with a proper subset of itself is to match every element n with its double $2n$:

$$\{5, \ 10, \ 15, \ 20, \ 25, \ldots\}$$
$$\updownarrow \ \ \updownarrow \ \ \updownarrow \ \ \updownarrow \ \ \updownarrow$$
$$\{10, \ 20, \ 30, \ 40, \ 50, \ldots\}$$

The second set, $\{10, 20, 30, 40, 50, \ldots\}$ is a proper subset of the first, and the two are in one-to-one correspondence, so $\{5, 10, 15, 20, 25, \ldots\}$ is an infinite set.

☑ 2. Show that a set is infinite.

▼ **Try This One 1**

Show that the set $\{-1, -2, -3, -4, -5, \ldots\}$ is an infinite set.

88   **Chapter 2**   Sets

Sidelight **THE INFINITE HOTEL**

Suppose a hotel in some far-off galaxy was so immense that it actually had infinitely many rooms, numbered 1, 2, 3, 4,.... There's a big convention of creepy alien creatures in town, so every room is filled. A weary traveler drags into the lobby and asks for a room, and when he's informed that the hotel is full, he protests that the hotel can most definitely accommodate him. Do you agree? Can they find a room for him without kicking someone out?

People tend to be split on this question about half and half: half think they can't accommodate him because all the rooms are full, and half think they can because there are infinitely many rooms. In fact, the traveler is correct—it just takes inconveniencing every other guest! If the manager asks every guest to move into the room whose number is 1 higher than his or her current room, everyone that was originally in a room still has one, and our traveler can rest his weary body in room 1.

This clever little mind exercise is a consequence of the fact that the natural numbers form an infinite set—they can be put in one-to-one correspondence with a proper subset of themselves by corresponding any n with $n + 1$.

A General Term for an Infinite Set

One consequence of the way we showed that the set of natural numbers is infinite is that we can find a generic formula for the set of even numbers: $2n$, where n is the set $\{1, 2, 3, 4, \ldots\}$. We will call $2n$ in this case a **general term** of the set of even numbers. Notice that we said "a general term," not "the general term." There are other general terms we could write for this set: $2n - 6$, where n is the set $\{4, 5, 6, 7, \ldots\}$, is another possibility. But in most cases the simplest general term is the one where the first listed number is obtained from substituting in 1 for n, and that's the one we'll typically find.

EXAMPLE 2   **Finding a General Term for an Infinite Set**

Find a general term for the set $\{4, 7, 10, 13, 16, \ldots\}$.

Math Note

Finding a general term for a set is not always easy. In some cases, it can be very difficult or even impossible. You may need to do some trial and error before finding a formula that works.

☑ 3. Find a general term for an infinite set.

SOLUTION

We should always begin by trying to recognize a pattern in the numbers of the set. In this case, the pattern is that the numbers increase by 3. When this is the case, $3n$ is a good choice, because as n increases by 1, $3n$ increases by 3. But simply using $3n$ will give us the set $\{3, 6, 9, 12, \ldots\}$, which is not quite what we want. We remedy that by adding 1 to our general term, to get $3n + 1$. (We encourage you to check that answer by substituting in $1, 2, 3, \ldots$ for n to see that it generates the set $\{4, 7, 10, 13, 16, \ldots\}$.)

▼ **Try This One 2**

Find a general term for the set $\{2, 8, 14, 20, 26, \ldots\}$.

Different Kinds of Infinity?

Quick, which set is bigger, the set of natural numbers or the set of real numbers? You probably answered the set of real numbers. But both sets are infinitely large, so aren't they the same size? Cantor attacked this problem in the late 1800s. He defined a set to be **countable** if it is finite or can be placed into one-to-one correspondence with the natural numbers and an infinite set to be **uncountable** if it cannot. He used the symbol $\aleph_0$, pronounced aleph-null or aleph-naught (aleph is the first letter of the Hebrew alphabet), to represent the cardinality of a countable set.

EXAMPLE 3	Showing That a Set Is Countable

Show that the set of integers is countable.

SOLUTION

If a set is finite, it's automatically countable, so that's at least worth considering. But obviously the integers are not a finite set, so we need to find a way to put them in one-to-one correspondence with the natural numbers. We could match up 0 with 1, 1 with 2, 2 with 3, and so on, but that would leave out the negatives. So let's get fancier:

Natural numbers	1	2	3	4	5	6	7	8	9	...
Integers	0	1	−1	2	−2	3	−3	4	−4	...

This works because we can see that every integer will eventually get matched with a natural number, so this defines a one-to-one correspondence. The proof would be stronger, though, if we can define a formula for the correspondence. For every natural number n,

$$ n \rightarrow \begin{cases} \dfrac{n}{2} & \text{if } n \text{ is even} \\[2ex] -\dfrac{n-1}{2} & \text{if } n \text{ is odd} \end{cases} $$

defines a one-to-one correspondence.

4. Define countable and uncountable sets.

▼ Try This One 3

Show that the set of positive rational numbers with denominators 2 or 3 is a countable set. (Rational numbers are fractions with integers in the numerator and denominator.)

Now the obvious question is this: What kinds of sets are uncountable? And how do you prove this? That, friends, is not an easy question at all. In fact, one of Cantor's greatest achievements was showing that the set of real numbers is not countable.

Sidelight THE SAD CASE OF THE MAN WHO WAS TOO INSIGHTFUL

Whoever coined the phrase "true genius is never recognized in its own time" would have LOVED Georg Cantor. Simply being known as the founder of what is now a major branch of mathematics (set theory) is a tremendous accomplishment, but it was Cantor's unique ability to formalize a study of the infinite that was both his greatest achievement, and ultimately his greatest curse.

For centuries, the study of math essentially ignored the fact that its most basic building blocks—the natural and real numbers—were infinite sets; infinity simply wasn't studied. For the most part, this was attributed to religious beliefs—infinity was thought to be the realm of God alone, and attempts to study it scientifically were considered inappropriate by some, and outright heresy by others. To say the very least, Cantor's work was not celebrated at the time it was produced. Two of Cantor's greatest critics were also among the most celebrated mathematicians of the late 1800s, Henri Poincaré and Leopold Kronecker.

Poincaré referred to Cantor's work as "a grave disease infecting mathematics." Kronecker evidently preferred personal attacks, labeling Cantor a "scientific charlatan," a "renegade," and a "corrupter of youth." And this was from mathematicians—the religious philosophers felt that he should be imprisoned, or worse.

This criticism weighed heavily on poor Georg, who was first hospitalized for severe depression in 1884 after 10 years of founding work on set theory. Although he remained active as a mathematician until 1913, he was in and out of institutions, and spent the last 5 years of his life in a sanatorium, dying in 1918.

But believe it or not, it could have been worse. Some of the ideas that we now accept about infinity can be traced back to the Italian philosopher, mathematician, and astronomer Giordano Bruno, who was rewarded for his groundbreaking understanding of the infinite nature of the universe by being burned at the stake on February 17, 1600.

So if you guessed that there are more real numbers than natural numbers, you were right. But the study of infinite sets is a strange and interesting one, with unexpected results at nearly every turn. For example, it can be shown that the cardinality of the set of numbers just between 0 and 1 is exactly the same as the cardinality of the entire set of real numbers! If you find these ideas interesting, you'll get a big kick out of Projects 3 and 4 at the end of this chapter.

Answers to Try This One

1 Can be done in many ways: one choice is to correspond -1 with -2, -2 with -4, and in general $-n$ with $-2n$.

2 $6n - 4$

3 One possibility:

$$
\begin{array}{cccccc}
1 & 2 & 3 & 4 & 5 & 6\ldots \\
\updownarrow & \updownarrow & \updownarrow & \updownarrow & \updownarrow & \updownarrow \\
\frac{1}{2} & \frac{1}{3} & \frac{2}{2} & \frac{2}{3} & \frac{3}{2} & \frac{3}{3}\ldots
\end{array}
$$

$$
n \rightarrow \begin{cases} \dfrac{(n+1)/2}{2} & \text{if } n \text{ is odd} \\ \dfrac{n/2}{3} & \text{if } n \text{ is even} \end{cases} \quad \text{or} \quad n \rightarrow \begin{cases} \dfrac{(n+1)}{4} & \text{if } n \text{ is odd} \\ \dfrac{n}{6} & \text{if } n \text{ is even} \end{cases}
$$

EXERCISE SET 2-5

Writing Exercises

1. Define an infinite set, both in your own words and by using Cantor's definition.
2. What is meant by a general term for an infinite set?
3. What does it mean for a set to be countable?

4. Explain how you can tell that the set of natural numbers and the set of even numbers have the same cardinality.

Computational Exercises

For Exercises 5–20, find a general term for the set.

5. $\{7, 14, 21, 28, 35,\ldots\}$
6. $\{1, 8, 27, 64, 125,\ldots\}$
7. $\{4, 16, 64, 256, 1{,}024,\ldots\}$
8. $\{1, 4, 9, 16, 25,\ldots\}$
9. $\{-3, -6, -9, -12, -15,\ldots\}$
10. $\{22, 44, 66, 88, 110,\ldots\}$
11. $\left\{\frac{1}{4}, \frac{1}{2}, \frac{3}{4}, 1, \frac{5}{4}, \frac{3}{2}, \frac{7}{4},\ldots\right\}$
12. $\left\{\frac{1}{6}, \frac{1}{3}, \frac{1}{2}, \frac{2}{3}, \frac{5}{6}, 1,\ldots\right\}$
13. $\{2, 6, 10, 14, 18,\ldots\}$
14. $\{1, 4, 7, 10, 13,\ldots\}$
15. $\left\{\frac{2}{3}, \frac{3}{4}, \frac{4}{5}, \frac{5}{6}, \frac{6}{7},\ldots\right\}$
16. $\left\{1, \frac{1}{8}, \frac{1}{27}, \frac{1}{64}, \frac{1}{125},\ldots\right\}$
17. $\{100, 200, 300, 400, 500,\ldots\}$
18. $\{50, 100, 150, 200, 250,\ldots\}$
19. $\{-4, -7, -10, -13, -16,\ldots\}$
20. $\{-3, -5, -7, -9, -11,\ldots\}$

For Exercises 21–30, show each set is an infinite set.

21. $\{3, 6, 9, 12, 15,\ldots\}$
22. $\{10, 15, 20, 25, 30,\ldots\}$
23. $\{9, 18, 27, 36, 45,\ldots\}$
24. $\{4, 10, 16, 22, 28,\ldots\}$
25. $\{2, 5, 8, 11, 14,\ldots\}$
26. $\{20, 24, 28, 32, 36,\ldots\}$
27. $\{10, 100, 1{,}000, 10{,}000,\ldots\}$
28. $\{100, 200, 300, 400, 500,\ldots\}$
29. $\left\{\frac{5}{1}, \frac{5}{2}, \frac{5}{3}, \frac{5}{4}, \frac{5}{5},\ldots\right\}$
30. $\left\{\frac{1}{2}, \frac{1}{4}, \frac{1}{8}, \frac{1}{16},\ldots\right\}$

For Exercises 31–34, show that the given set is countable. (See Example 3 for guidance.)

31. $\{5, 10, 15, 20, 25,\ldots\}$
32. $\{-3, -6, -9, -12, -15, -18,\ldots\}$
33. The set of numbers whose square root is a whole number
34. The set of negative rational numbers with denominators 5 and 7

Critical Thinking

35. The set of rational numbers is the set of all possible fractions that have integer numerators and denominators. Intuitively, do you think there are more rational numbers than natural numbers? Why? Do you think that the set of rational numbers is countable?

36. Can you think of any set of tangible objects that is infinite? Why or why not?

37. Study Example 3 carefully, then compare it to Example 2. What did we actually prove in Example 2 without even realizing it?

38. True or false: a subset of an infinite set is infinite.

Exercises 39 and 40 use the fact that the cardinality of the set of natural numbers $\{1, 2, 3, 4, \ldots\}$ is $\aleph_0$.

39. (a) Define a one-to-one correspondence between the set of natural numbers and the set $\{0, 1, 2, 3, 4, \ldots\}$.

(b) Write an arithmetic problem involving $\aleph_0$ that is illustrated by part (a). (*Hint:* How many more elements than the natural numbers does the set $\{0, 1, 2, 3, 4, \ldots\}$ have?

40. (a) Define a one-to-one correspondence between the set of natural numbers and the set of all integers excluding zero.

(b) Write an arithmetic problem involving $\aleph_0$ that is illustrated by part (a).

In Exercises 41–46, find the cardinality of the given set. You may find the ideas in Exercises 39 and 40 helpful.

41. $\{10, 11, 12, 13, 14, \ldots\}$
42. $\{-1, -2, -3, -4, -5, \ldots\}$
43. $\{1, 3, 5, 7, 9, \ldots, 29\}$
44. $\{2, 4, 6, 8, 10, \ldots, 24\}$
45. The set of odd natural numbers.
46. The set of even negative integers.

CHAPTER **2** # Summary

Section	Important Terms	Important Ideas

2-1	Set
	Roster method
	Element
	Well-defined
	Natural numbers
	Descriptive method
	Set-builder notation
	Variable
	Finite set
	Infinite set
	Cardinal number
	Empty set
	Equal sets
	Equivalent sets
	One-to-one
	   correspondence
		A set is a collection of objects; a set is well-defined if any object can be objectively determined to be either in the set or not in the set. Each object is called an element or member of the set. We use three ways to identify sets: the roster method, the descriptive method, and set-builder notation. A finite set contains a specific number of elements, while an infinite set contains an unlimited number of elements. If a set has no elements, it is called an empty set or a null set.
		
		    Two sets are equal if they have the same elements, and two finite sets are equivalent if they have the same number of elements. Two sets are said to be in one-to-one correspondence if it's possible to pair the elements so that each element in the first set has exactly one match in the second set, and vice versa.

2-2	Universal set
	Complement
	Subset
	Proper subset
	Intersection
	Union
	Subtraction
	Cartesian
	   product
		The universal set is the set of all elements used for a specific problem or situation. The complement of a specific set is a set that consists of all elements in the universal set that are not in the specific set.
		
		    A set A is called a subset of another set B if every element in A is also in B. We call A a proper subset of B if there's at least one element in B that's not in A. The union of two sets is the set of all elements that are in at least one of the sets. The intersection is the set of all elements in both sets.
		
		    The difference of set A and set B, denoted $A - B$, is the set of elements in set A but not in set B. The Cartesian product of two sets A and B is $A \times B = \{(x, y) \mid x \in A \text{ and } y \in B\}$.

2-3	Venn diagram	**A mathematician** named John Venn devised a way to represent sets pictorially. His method uses overlapping circles to represent the sets. Items in the intersection of the sets are placed where the circles overlap. De Morgan's laws for two sets A and B are $(A \cup B)' = A' \cap B'$ and $(A \cap B)' = A' \cup B'$. For any two finite sets A and B, $n(A \cup B) = n(A) + n(B) - n(A \cap B)$.
2-4		**Venn diagrams** can be used to solve problems in our world involving surveys and classifications.
2-5	Infinite set General term Countable set Uncountable set	**An infinite** set can be placed in a one-to-one correspondence with a proper subset of itself. A set is called countable if it is finite or if there is a one-to-one correspondence between the set and the set of natural numbers. A set is called uncountable if it is not countable. The natural numbers are an example of an infinite set that is countable, and the real numbers are an uncountable set.

MATH IN ▷ Demographics REVISITED

The Venn diagram shown to the right
is based on the given demographic
estimates:

1. White only: 680; black only: 109;
   Hispanic only: 53

2. Hispanic and black, but not
   white: 11

3. Hispanic or black: 270

4. None of white, black, or
   Hispanic: 50

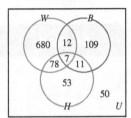

Review Exercises

Section 2-1

For Exercises 1–8, write each set in roster notation.

1. The set D is the set of even numbers between 50 and 60.
2. The set F is the set of odd numbers between 3 and 40.
3. The set L is the set of letters in the word *letter*.
4. The set A is the set of letters in the word *Arkansas*.
5. The set B is $\{x \mid x \in N \text{ and } x > 500\}$.
6. The set C is the set of natural numbers between 5 and 12.
7. M is the set of men that have walked on the moon.
8. W is the set of women that have walked on the moon.

For Exercises 9–12, write each set using set-builder notation.

9. $\{18, 20, 22, 24\}$
10. $\{5, 10, 15, 20\}$
11. $\{101, 103, 105, 107, \ldots\}$
12. $\{8, 16, 24, \ldots 72\}$

For Exercises 13–20, state whether the set is finite or infinite.

13. $\{x \mid x \in N \text{ and } x \geq 9\}$
14. $\{4, 8, 12, 16, \ldots\}$
15. $\{$annoying commercials$\}$
16. $\{3, 7, 9, 12\}$
17. $\varnothing$
18. $\{$people who have red hair$\}$
19. $\{$10 digit numbers$\}$
20. Which of the sets in Exercises 13–19 are not well-defined?

Section 2-2

For Exercises 21–24, decide if the statement is true or false.

21. $\{80, 100, 120, \ldots\} \subseteq \{40, 80, 120, \ldots\}$
22. $\{6\} \subset \{6, 12, 18\}$
23. $\{5, 6, 7\} \subseteq \{5, 7\}$
24. $\{a, b, c\} \subset \{a, b, c\}$
25. Find all subsets of $\{r, s, t\}$.
26. How many subsets and proper subsets does the set $\{a, e, i, o, u, y\}$ have?

*For Exercises 27–38, let $U = \{p, q, r, s, t, u, v, w, x, y, z\}$,
$A = \{p, r, t, u, v\}$, $B = \{t, u, v, x, y\}$, and $C = \{s, w, z\}$.
Find each.*

27. $A \cap B$
28. $B \cup C$
29. $(A \cap B) \cap C$
30. B'
31. $A - B$
32. $B - A$
33. $(A \cup B)' \cap C$
34. $B' \cap C'$
35. $(B \cup C) \cap A'$
36. $(A \cup B) \cap C'$
37. $(B' \cap C') \cup A'$
38. $(A' \cap B) \cup C$

39. If $K = \{x \mid x \in N, x > 25\}$ and $L = \{x \mid x \in E, x > 10\}$, find $K \cap L$, $K \cup L$, and $L - K$.

40. (a) If $A = \{$play video games, watch TV, go for a run$\}$ and $B = \{$go to class, go to work$\}$, find $A \times B$ and describe its significance.
    (b) For the sets in part (a), find $B \times A$. What is the difference in what this set signifies compared to $A \times B$?

Section 2-3

For Exercises 41–46, use the Venn diagram below. Describe the region or regions provided in each problem, using set operations on A and B. There may be more than one right answer.

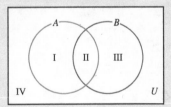

41. Region I
42. Region II
43. Region III
44. Region IV
45. Regions I and III
46. Regions I and IV

For Exercises 47–50, draw a Venn diagram and shade the appropriate area for each.

47. $A' \cap B$
48. $(A \cup B)'$
49. $(A' \cap B') \cup C$
50. $A \cap (B \cup C)'$

94   **Chapter 2**   Sets

51. If $n(A) = 15$, $n(B) = 9$, and $n(A \cap B) = 4$, find $n(A \cup B)$.
52. If $n(A) = 24$, $n(B) = 20$, and $n(A \cap B) = 14$, find $n(A \cup B)$.

The table and Venn diagram below are to be used for Exercises 53–56. The table shows the top five states in terms of number of violent crimes per 100,000 citizens in each year from 2008 to 2010. For each exercise, write the region of the Venn diagram that would include the state listed.

Year	2008	2009	2010
	1. Nevada	1. Nevada	1. Vermont
	2. South Carolina	2. South Carolina	2. Nevada
	3. Tennessee	3. Tennessee	3. Alaska
	4. Delaware	4. New Mexico	4. Delaware
	5. Florida	5. Delaware	5. Tennessee

Source: infoplease.com

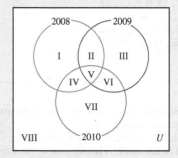

53. Florida
54. Delaware
55. South Carolina
56. Arkansas

Section 2-4

57. On the eve of the 2012 Iowa Republican caucuses, 250 likely voters were polled: 90 were supporters of Mitt Romney, 48 supported Ron Paul, and 20 were supporters of both candidates.
    (a) How many of those polled supported neither of those candidates?
    (b) How many supported only Ron Paul?

58. A hearing specialist conducts a study on hearing loss at certain frequencies among a group of patients in a retirement community. Of 94 residents tested, 10 had significant hearing loss at low frequencies but not high, 40 had significant loss at high frequencies but not low, and 26 showed no significant hearing loss at all.
    (a) How many residents had hearing loss at both low and high frequencies?
    (b) What percentage suffer from hearing loss at high frequencies?

59. Fifty-three callers to a campus radio station were asked what they usually listened to while driving to school. Of those asked, 22 listened to a local radio station, 18 listened to satellite radio, 33 listened to MP3 players, 8 listened to a local radio station and satellite radio, 13 listened to satellite radio and MP3 players, 11 listened to a local radio station and an MP3 player, and 6 listened to all three.
    (a) How many listened to only satellite radio?
    (b) How many listened to local radio stations and MP3 players but not satellite radio?
    (c) How many listened to none of these?

60. The manager of a campus bookstore finds that in the last hour before closing, 41 students bought two or more textbooks. Of these, 4 used cash only, 5 used a financial aid voucher only, and 5 used a debit card only. Seven used a debit card and financial aid voucher and no cash; three used cash and a debit card with no financial aid assistance. Sixteen students total used a debit card for at least part of their purchase, while 9 used none of those forms of payment.
    (a) How many students used all of cash, debit card, and financial aid voucher?
    (b) Did more students use cash or financial aid vouchers?
    (c) What percentage of students did not use a financial aid voucher?

Section 2-5

61. Find a general term for the set $\{-5, -7, -9, -11, -13, \ldots\}$
62. Show that the set $\{12, 24, 36, 48, 60, \ldots\}$ is an infinite set.
63. Show that the set in Exercise 62 is countable.

Chapter Test

For Exercises 1–4, write each set in roster notation.

1. The set P is the set of even natural numbers between 90 and 100.
2. The set K is the set of letters in the word *envelope*.
3. $X = \{x \mid x \in N \text{ and } x < 80\}$
4. The set J is the set of months of the year that begin with the letter J.

For Exercises 5 and 6, write each set using set-builder notation.

5. $\{12, 14, 16, 18\}$ 6. $\{4, 8, 16, \ldots 128\}$

For Exercises 7–11, state whether the set is finite or infinite.

7. $\{x \mid x \in N \text{ and } x \text{ is a multiple of } 6\}$
8. $\{a, b, c, \ldots, s, t\}$
9. The set V is the set of people with awesome hair.
10. Explain why the set in Exercise 9 is not well-defined. Your answer should be written so that someone who has no idea what "well-defined" means would understand.
11. Find all subsets and all proper subsets of the set of states that border California. How do you know how many subsets you're looking for?

For Exercises 12–16, let U = {a, b, c, d, e, f, g, h, i, j, k},
A = {a, b, d, e, f}, B = {a, g, i, j, k}, and C = {e, h, j}. Find each.

12. $(A \cap B) \cup C$
13. $(A \cup B)'$
14. $A - B$
15. $(A - B) - C$
16. Draw and shade a separate Venn diagram for each set:
    $B - A, B' \cup A, A \cup B \cup C$
17. Find both Cartesian products that can be formed using the set in Exercise 11 and set C in Exercises 12-16.

For Exercises 18–20, draw a Venn diagram for each set.

18. $A' \cap B$
19. $(A \cap B)'$
20. $(A' \cup B') \cap C'$
21. If $n(A) = 1,500$, $n(B) = 1,150$, and $n(A \cap B) = 350$, find $n(A \cup B)$.
22. A student studying for a master's degree in sports management is working on a thesis about the prevalence of women's college sports since Title IX mandated equal access to women. He compiles data on 119 schools with football teams that compete in the NCAA FBS (which most fans still call Division 1-A), and finds that 69 have a women's golf team, 63 have a field hockey team, and 83 have a women's swimming team. There are 28 schools that field teams in all three sports. Forty-six have golf and women's swimming teams, 40 have women's swimming and field hockey teams, and 47 have women's golf and field hockey teams.
    (a) How many schools have a women's golf team, but no women's swimming or field hockey?
    (b) What percentage of teams have at least two of the three sports?
    (c) If you pick one of the schools in the study at random, what's the percent chance that it has none of those three sports?
23. Find a general term for the set {15, 30, 45, 60, 75,...}.
24. Show that the set {1, 2, 3, 4,...} ∪ {−1, −2, −3, −4,...} is countably infinite. (*Hint:* There are actually two separate questions to answer!)

For Exercises 25–30, state whether each is true or false.

25. {s, e, s, a, m, e} is equivalent to {s, a, m, e}
26. {4, 8, 12, 16,...} $\subseteq$ {2, 4, 6, 8,...}
27. {15} $\subset$ {3, 6, 9, 12,...}
28. 9 $\notin$ {2, 4, 5, 6, 10}
29. {a, e, i, o, u, y} $\subseteq$ {a, e, i, o, u}
30. {12} $\in$ {12, 24, 36,...}

Projects

1. Have the students in your class fill out this questionnaire:

    A. Gender: Male _____   Female _____
    B. Age: Under 21 _____   21 or older _____
    C. Work: Yes _____   No _____

    Draw a Venn diagram, and from the information answer these questions:
    (a) How many students are female?
    (b) How many students are under 21?
    (c) How many students work?
    (d) How many students are under 21 and work?
    (e) How many students are males and do not work?
    (f) How many students are 21 or older and work?
    (g) How many students are female, work, and are under 21?

2. If you've had a pulse for this entire chapter, you know that surveys play a big role in the way that Venn diagrams are used to organize information. Now it's time for you to design a survey of your very own. You should make the topic of the survey something you find interesting, and design the survey so that the results can be summarized and studied using a Venn diagram with three sets. You can accomplish this by asking three separate questions, or by designing a single-question poll where responders can choose any, all, or none of the responses.
    Once you've designed, written, and conducted your survey, organize the results with a Venn diagram, then write a report on your findings. Don't just include the raw numbers—the most important part of a survey is often summarizing and interpreting the meaning of survey results. You may want to keep this requirement in mind when designing your survey—it's pretty hard to write an intelligent interpretation if the questions are totally unconnected.

3. You may have wondered why we stated in Section 2-5 that the set of real numbers is uncountable, but didn't back that up. The short answer is that it's a pretty involved process to prove that result. It's not all that hard, but it's VERY clever and kind of subtle. The good news is you can find the proof on about ten thousand different Web pages by searching for "Cantor diagonal." Find a page that describes Cantor's diagonal argument in a way that you can understand, then put together a demonstration for classmates to help them understand why the real numbers are uncountable. *Extra credit*: Include a discussion of the fact that the set of real numbers has the same cardinality of just the real numbers between zero and one.

4. If you're really interested by the ideas of counting infinite sets, you'll find this project extra interesting. One of the strangest, most fascinating sets ever introduced is known as the Cantor set. It starts with the set of all real numbers between zero and one, and throws away a sequence of portions. Do an online or library search (they still have actual libraries, right?) for the Cantor set, and answer the following questions about it:
    (a) How can you be sure that there's at least SOMETHING in the Cantor set? (You'll find that at first glance, it looks like the set might be empty.)
    (b) How do you know that the Cantor set is not only nonempty, but infinite?
    (c) Is the Cantor set countable or uncountable? How do you know that?
    (d) What's the total length of all intervals that are discarded when defining the Cantor set? Why is that such a shocking result?

Logic

3-1   Statements and Quantifiers   3-4   Logical Arguments

3-2   Truth Tables   3-5   Euler Circles

3-3   Types of Statements   Summary

CHAPTER **3**

Logic

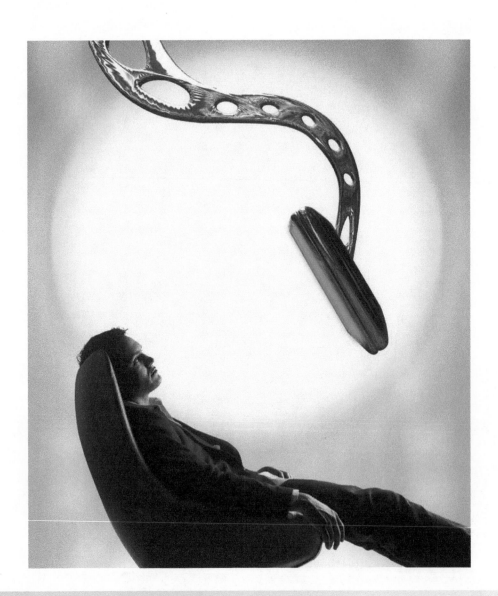

Outline

3-1   Statements and Quantifiers   **3-4**   Logical Arguments

3-2   Truth Tables   **3-5**   Euler Circles

3-3   Types of Statements   Summary

MATH IN ▶ **Mind Control**

The term *mind control* is an absolute favorite of conspiracy theorists and science fiction writers, but is it real? That largely depends on what you mean by the term, but I can guarantee you one thing: there are a LOT of people and organizations out there that are trying to control the way you think each and every day. Everywhere you turn in modern society, someone is trying to convince you of something. "Buy my product!" "Vote for the guy I like!" "You can't afford NOT to lease a car from our dealership!" "Bailing out banks is a horrible idea!" "You should go out with me, and soon!" "Pledge our fraternity—all the other ones stink!" Should I go on?

Logic is sometimes defined as correct thinking or correct reasoning, but many folks refer to logic by a more casual name: *common sense*. Regardless of what you call it, the ability to think logically is crucial for all of us because our lives are inundated daily with advertisements, contracts, product and service warranties, political debates, and news commentaries, to name just a few. People often have problems processing these things because of misinterpretation, misunderstanding, and faulty logic.

You can look up the truth or falseness of a fact on the Internet, but that won't help you in analyzing whether a certain claim is logically valid. The term *common sense* is really misleading, because evaluating logical arguments involves skills that are anything but common—but we're here to help! Forget what you've seen about mind control in the movies: the best way to control someone's mind is to bias their thinking by using their emotions and opinions against them. And that's where this chapter comes in. To decide whether or not an argument makes sense, our goal will be to study the structure of the argument without thinking about the particular topic: to make that possible, we'll use variables to stand in for sentences so that

we won't *know* what the exact topic is. This allows us to focus simply on whether you can logically draw a conclusion based on certain types of statements.

To that end, we've written some claims below. To be honest, some of them are a little controversial, touching on hot-button issues like religion, politics, and the most contentious of all, college football. We sincerely apologize if any of these statements offends you, but our aim is to illustrate how difficult it can be to decide if an argument is logically sound when you're distracted by emotion and strongly held beliefs. Your job is to evaluate each claim as a logical argument, and decide if the argument is valid: that is, if the conclusion can be logically drawn from a set of statements. The skills you learn in this chapter wll help you to do so, but making your best guess now might prove to be very enlightening later on.

- Where there's smoke, there's fire.
- People with lots of money are always happy. My neighbour is so happy you just want to smack him sometimes, so I guess he has a lot of money.
- Every team in the SEC is good enough to play in a bowl game. Florida State isn't in the SEC, so it doesn't belong in a bowl game.
- Scripture is the word of God. I know this because it says so in the Bible.
- If Iraq has weapons of mass destruction, we should go to war to make sure they never use them. It turned out they didn't have WMDs, so we shouldn't have started the war.
- There'll be a toga party on the moon before a school like Butler makes the Final Four. Butler went to the Final Four in both 2010 and 2011, so there must have been a big ol' party on the moon.

For answers, see Math in Mind Control Revisited on Page 148

Section 3-1   Statements and Quantifiers

LEARNING OBJECTIVES

☐ 1. Define and identify statements.

☐ 2. Define the logical connectives.

☐ 3. Write the negation of a statement.

☐ 4. Write statements symbolically.

For dozens of years, surveys done by marketing companies have shown that the primary concern for a majority of American women is taking care of their families. So it's no coincidence that a lot of the household products that are traditionally bought by women are advertised in a way that plays on that concern. The implication, sometimes overt and sometimes subconscious, is that if you're a good mom that cares about your family, you'll buy this particular product. It's easy to say that people can't possibly fall for stunts that blatant, but here's all the evidence you need that it works: advertisers keep doing it.

This is exactly the sort of mind control we talked about in the chapter opener: the advertiser doesn't want you to think about the fact that their actual argument is silly, so they try to tug at your heart strings. But today, you begin to fight back by beginning your study of **symbolic logic**, which uses letters to represent statements and special symbols to represent words like *and*, *or*, and *not*. This will allow us to remove our emotional bias from an argument so that we can analytically evaluate the logic behind it.

Statements

In the English language there are many types of sentences, including factual statements, commands, opinions, questions, and exclamations. In the objective study of logic, we will use only factual statements.

> A **statement** is a declarative sentence that is either true or false, but not both.

For example, sentences like

> Moose are the largest members of the horse family.
> Radioactive spiders can make you a superhero.
> $2 + 10 = 12$
> $10 - 6 = 143$

are statements because they're either true or false; there are no opinions involved. Whether a sentence is true or false doesn't matter in deciding if it's a statement: the second and fourth statements above are both false, but they're still statements.

On the other hand, these sentences are not statements:

> Give me a bottle of anything and a glazed donut—to go.
> Where in the world did you find gold suede sneakers?
> Dude, that is awesome!
> The guy sitting next to me is kind of goofy.

The first is not a statement because it's a command; the second because it's a question. The third is an exclamation, not a statement, and the fourth is not a statement because the word "goofy" is subjective; someone that seems goofy to you might be cool as the other side of the pillow in my book.

Sidelight WHEN BLACK AND WHITE ISN'T BLACK AND WHITE

Did it strike you as odd that the definition of statement requires a sentence to be "true or false, but not both"? Isn't something either true or false? How can it be both? Glad you asked.

Consider this fun example: "This sentence isn't true." If the sentence is in fact true, it means that it isn't true. But if it's false, it means that it is in fact true. Isn't that bizarre? This is a classic example of what's known as a **paradox**: something that appears to be a statement, but contradicts itself. It's literally impossible to decide if a paradox is true or false, because it's either both or neither depending on whether you're a "glass half full" type of person. An Internet search for the string "paradox example" is hours of fun (but not while you're supposed to be doing your

homework). Here are some examples I liked. See if you can figure out why they're paradoxical.

- There's an exception to every rule.
- I know nothing at all.
- Moderation in all things, including moderation.
- What would happen if Pinocchio said "my nose is about to grow"?
- Does the set of all sets that do not contain themselves contain itself?

EXAMPLE 1   **Recognizing Statements**

Decide which of the following are statements and which are not.

(a) Most scientists agree that global warming is a threat to the environment.
(b) Is that your laptop?
(c) Man, that hurts!
(d) $432 + 8 \div 1.3 = \sqrt{115,000}$
(e) This book is about database management.
(f) Watching reality shows turns your brain to mush.

SOLUTION

Parts (a), (d), and (e) are statements because they can be judged as true or false in a nonsubjective manner.
Part (b) is not a statement because it is a question.
Part (c) is not a statement because it is an exclamation.
Part (f) is not a statement because it requires an opinion (unless there's a scientific study I'm unaware of).

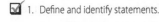 1. Define and identify statements.

▼ Try This One 1

Decide which of the following are statements and which are not.

(a) Those pants rock!
(b) $12 - 8 = 5$
(c) Larry the Cable Guy is the host of *American Idol.*
(d) Cat can send picture messages with her cell phone.
(e) When does the party start?
(f) History is interesting.

Simple and Compound Statements

Statements can be classified as *simple* or *compound*. A **simple statement** contains only one idea. Each of these statements is an example of a simple statement.

My jeans are torn.

My dorm room has a pile of dirty socks in it.

Daytona Beach is in Florida.

A statement like "I'm taking chemistry this semester and I'm going to get an A" is called a *compound statement* since it's formed from more than one simple statement.

> A **compound statement** is a statement formed by joining two or more simple statements with a **connective**. There are four basic connectives used in logic: and (the **conjunction**), or (**disjunction**), if . . . then (**conditional**), and if and only if (**biconditional**).

Here are some examples of compound statements using connectives.

John studied for 5 hours, and he got an A.   (conjunction)

Luisa will run in a mini triathlon or she will play in the campus tennis tournament.   (disjunction)

If I get 80% of the questions on the LSAT right, then I will get into law school. (conditional)

We will win the game if and only if we score more points than the other team. (biconditional)

> **Math Note**
>
> In standard usage, the word *then* is often omitted from a conditional statement; instead of "If it snows, then I will go skiing," you'd probably just say, "If it snows, I'll go skiing."

| EXAMPLE 2 | **Classifying Statements as Simple or Compound** |

Classify each statement as simple or compound. If it is compound, state the name of the connective used.

(a) Our school mascot is a moose.
(b) If you register for WiFi service, you will get 3 days of free access.
(c) Tomorrow is the last day to register for classes.
(d) In the interest of saving the planet, I plan to buy either a hybrid or a motorcycle.

SOLUTION

(a) There are no connectives involved, so this is a simple statement.
(b) This if . . . then statement is compound and uses a conditional connective.
(c) This is a simple statement.
(d) Ultimately, this statement could be restated as "I will buy a hybrid, or I will buy a motorcycle," which makes it a compound statement: specifically, a disjunction.

> **Math Note**
>
> Technically, we've given the names *conjunction, disjunction, conditional,* and *biconditional* to the connectives, but from now on, we'll refer to whole statements using these connectives by those names. For example, we would call the compound statement in Example 2d a disjunction.

☑ 2. Define the logical connectives.

> **▼ Try This One 2**
>
> Classify each statement as simple or compound. If it is compound, state the name of the connective used.
>
> (a) My jacket is both warm and light.
> (b) This is an informative website on STDs.
> (c) If it doesn't rain tomorrow, I'm going windsurfing.
> (d) I'm going to eat at Taco Bell or Wendy's today.
> (e) Yesterday was the deadline to withdraw from a class.

> **Math Note**
>
> We'll worry later about determining whether statements involving quantifiers and connectives are true or false. For now, focus on learning and understanding the terms.

Quantified Statements

Quantified statements involve terms such as *all, each, every, no, none, some, there exists,* and *at least one.* The first five (*all, each, every, no, none*) are called *universal quantifiers* because they either include or exclude every element of the universal set. The latter three (*some, there exists, at least one*) are called *existential quantifiers*

Sidelight A BRIEF HISTORY OF LOGIC

The basic concepts of logic can be attributed to Aristotle, who lived in the fourth century BCE. He used words, sentences, and deduction to prove arguments using techniques we will study in this chapter. About a hundred years later, Euclid formalized geometry using deductive proofs. Both subjects were considered to be the "inevitable truths" of the universe revealed to rational people.

In the 19th century, people began to reject the idea of inevitable truths and realized that a deductive system like Euclidean geometry is only true based on the original assumptions. When the original assumptions are changed, a new deductive system can be created. This is why there are different types of geometry. (Bet you didn't know that! See Section 10-7 on non-Euclidean geometry.)

Eventually, several people developed the use of symbols rather than words and sentences in logic. One such person was George Boole (1815–1864). Boole created the symbols used in this chapter and developed the theory of symbolic logic. He also used symbolic logic in mathematics. His manuscript, entitled "An Investigation into the Laws of Thought, on Which Are Founded the Mathematical Theories of Logic and Probabilities," was published in 1854.

Boole was a friend of Augustus De Morgan, who formulated the laws bearing his name that we studied in Chapter 2.

As we'll see later in this chapter, there are logic versions as well. Much earlier, Leonhard Euler (1707–1783) used circles to represent logical statements and proofs: we'll study these in Section 3-5. The idea was refined by John Venn (1834–1923) into the Venn diagrams that proved so useful in our study of sets. In fact, the term *Venn diagram* wasn't used by Venn (which is good, because that would have been a tad pompous, don't you think?). What did he call his diagrams? Eulerian circles.

because they show the existence of something, but do not include the entire universal set. Here are some examples of quantified statements:

Every student taking Math for Liberal Arts this semester will pass.

No nursing student is also majoring in criminal justice.

Some people who are Miami Hurricane fans are also Miami Dolphin fans.

There is at least one professor in this school who does not have brown eyes.

The first two statements use universal quantifiers, while the third and fourth use existential quantifiers. Note that the statements using existential quantifiers are not "all inclusive" (or all exclusive) as the other two are.

Negation

The *negation* of a statement is a corresponding statement with the opposite truth value. This means that if a statement is true its negation is false, and if a statement is false its negation is true. For example, for the statement "My dorm room is blue," the negation is "My dorm room is not blue." It's important to note that the truth values of these two are completely opposite: one is true, and the other is false—period. You can't negate "My dorm room is blue" by saying "My dorm room is yellow," because it's completely possible that *both* statements are false. To make sure that you have a correct negation, check that if one of the statements is true, the other must be false, and vice versa. The typical way to negate a simple statement is by adding the word *not*, as in these examples:

Statement	Negation
Auburn will win Saturday.	Auburn will not win Saturday.
I took a shower today.	I did not take a shower today.
My car is clean.	My car is not clean.

Math Note

The words *each, every,* and *all* mean the same thing, so what we say about *all* in this section applies to the others as well. Likewise, *some, there exists,* and *at least one* are considered to be the same and are treated that way as well.

TABLE 3-1	Negations of Quantified Statements

Statement contains . . .	Example	Negation	Example
All do	All of my meals are low in fat.	Some do not, or not all do	Some of my meals are not low in fat.
Some do	Some majors require 5 years of study.	None do, or all do not.	There are no majors that require 5 years of study.
Some do not	Some people don't go to football games.	All do	Everyone goes to football games.
None do	No airlines include checked bags for free.	Some do	At least one airline allows a checked bag for free.

You have to be especially careful when negating quantified statements. Consider the example statement "All dogs are fuzzy." It's not quite right to say that the negation is "All dogs are not fuzzy," because if some dogs are fuzzy and others aren't, then both statements are false. All we need for the statement "All dogs are fuzzy" to be false is to find at least one dog that is not fuzzy, so the negation of the statement "All dogs are fuzzy" is "Some dogs are not fuzzy." (In this setting, we define the word *some* to mean *at least one*.)

The negation of quantified statements is summarized in Table 3-1.

EXAMPLE 3	Writing Negations

Write the negation of each of the following quantified statements.

(a) Every student taking Math for Liberal Arts this semester will pass.
(b) Some people who are Miami Hurricane fans are also Miami Dolphin fans.
(c) There is at least one professor in this school who does not have brown eyes.
(d) No nursing student is also majoring in criminal justice.

SOLUTION

(a) Some student taking Math for Liberal Arts this semester will not pass (or, not every student taking Math for Liberal Arts this semester will pass).
(b) No people who are Miami Hurricane fans are also Miami Dolphin fans.
(c) All professors in this school have brown eyes.
(d) At least one nursing student is also majoring in criminal justice.

CAUTION	Be especially careful when negating statements. It's tempting to say that the negation of a statement like "Every student will pass" is "Every student will fail," but it isn't. Not only is it *possible* that both statements are false, in most classes it's *likely* that both are false.

 3. Write the negation of a statement.

▼ Try This One 3

Write the negation of each of the following quantified statements.

(a) All cell phones have cameras.
(b) No woman can win the lottery.
(c) Some professors have Ph.Ds.
(d) Someone in this class will get a B.

TABLE 3-2	**Symbols for the Connectives**	
Connective	**Symbol**	**Name**
and	∧	Conjunction
or	∨	Disjunction
if . . . then	→	Conditional
if and only if	↔	Biconditional

Symbolic Notation

Recall that one of our goals in this section is to write statements in symbolic form to help us evaluate logical arguments objectively. Now we'll introduce the symbols and methods that will be used. The symbols for the connectives *and, or, if . . . then,* and *if and only if* are shown in Table 3-2.

Simple statements in logic are usually denoted with lowercase letters like p, q, and r. For example, we could use p to represent the statement "I get paid Friday" and q to represent the statement "I will go out this weekend." Then the conditional statement "If I get paid Friday, then I will go out this weekend" can be written in symbols as $p \rightarrow q$.

The symbol ∼ (tilde) represents a negation. If p still represents "I get paid Friday," then $\sim p$ represents "I do not get paid Friday."

We often use parentheses in logical statements when more than one connective is involved in order to specify an order. (We'll deal with this in greater detail in the next section.) For example, there is a difference between the compound statements $\sim p \wedge q$ and $\sim(p \wedge q)$. The statement $\sim p \wedge q$ means to negate the statement p first, then use the negation of p in conjunction with the statement q. For example, if p is the statement "Large Coney is a dog" and q is the statement "Guinness is a cat," then $\sim p \wedge q$ reads, "Large Coney is not a dog and Guinness is a cat." The statement $\sim p \wedge q$ could also be written as $(\sim p) \wedge q$. The statement $\sim(p \wedge q)$ means to negate the conjunction of the statement p and the statement q. Using the same statements for p and q as before, the statement $\sim(p \wedge q)$ is written, "It is not the case that Large Coney is a dog and Guinness is a cat."

The same reasoning applies when the negation is used with other connectives. For example, $\sim p \rightarrow q$ means $(\sim p) \rightarrow q$.

Example 4 illustrates in greater detail how to write statements symbolically.

> ### Math Note
>
> For three of the four connectives in Table 3-2, the order of the simple statements doesn't matter: for example, $p \wedge q$ and $q \wedge p$ represent the same compound statement.
>
> The same is true for the connectives ∨ (disjunction) and ↔ (biconditional). The one exception is the conditional (→), where order is crucial.

EXAMPLE 4	**Writing Statements Symbolically**

Let p represent the statement "It is cloudy" and q represent the statement "I will go to the beach." Write each statement in symbols.

(a) I will not go to the beach.
(b) It is cloudy, and I will go to the beach.
(c) If it is cloudy, then I will not go to the beach.
(d) I will go to the beach if and only if it is not cloudy.

SOLUTION

(a) This is the negation of statement q, which we write as $\sim q$.
(b) This is the conjunction of p and q, written as $p \wedge q$.
(c) This is the conditional of p and the negation of q: $p \rightarrow \sim q$.
(d) This is the biconditional of p and not q: $p \leftrightarrow \sim q$.

104   **Chapter 3** Logic

> ▼ **Try This One 4**
>
> Let p represent the statement "I will buy a Coke" and q represent the statement "I will buy some popcorn." Write each statement in symbols.
>
> (a) I will buy a Coke, and I will buy some popcorn.
> (b) I will not buy a Coke.
> (c) If I buy some popcorn, then I will buy a Coke.
> (d) I will not buy a Coke, and I will buy some popcorn.

You probably noticed that some of the compound statements we've written sound a little awkward. It isn't always necessary to repeat the subject and verb in a compound statement using *and* or *or*. For example, the statement "It is cold, and it is snowing" can be written "It is cold and snowing." The statement "I will go to a movie, or I will go to a play" can be written "I will go to a movie or a play." Also the words *but* and *although* can be used in place of *and*. For example, the statement "I will not buy a television set, and I will buy a CD player" can also be written as "I will not buy a television set, but I will buy a CD player."

Statements written in symbols can also be written in words, as shown in Example 5.

| **EXAMPLE 5** | **Translating Statements from Symbols to Words** |

Write each statement in words. Let p = "My dog is a golden retriever" and q = "My dog is fuzzy."

(a) $\sim p$ (b) $p \lor q$ (c) $\sim p \rightarrow q$ (d) $q \leftrightarrow p$ (e) $q \land p$

SOLUTION

(a) My dog is not a golden retriever.
(b) My dog is a golden retriever or my dog is fuzzy.
(c) If my dog is not a golden retriever, then my dog is fuzzy.
(d) My dog is fuzzy if and only if my dog is a golden retriever.
(e) My dog is fuzzy, and my dog is a golden retriever.

If this is your dog (which it's not, because it's mine), statement (e) describes it pretty well.

> ▼ **Try This One 5**
>
> Write each statement in words. Let p = "My friend is a football player" and q = "My friend is smart."
>
> (a) $\sim p$ (b) $p \lor q$ (c) $\sim p \rightarrow q$ (d) $p \leftrightarrow q$ (e) $p \land q$

 4. Write statements symbolically.

In this section, we defined the basic terms of symbolic logic and practiced writing statements using symbols. These skills will be crucial in our objective study of logical arguments, so we're off to a good start.

Answers to Try This One

1 (b), (c), and (d) are statements.

2 (a) (conjunction), (c) (conditional), and (d) (disjunction) are compound; (b) and (e) are simple.

3 (a) Some cell phones don't have cameras.
(b) Some women can win the lottery.
(c) No professors have Ph.Ds.
(d) No one in this class will get a B.

4 (a) $p \wedge q$ (b) $\sim p$ (c) $q \rightarrow p$ (d) $\sim p \wedge q$

5 (a) My friend is not a football player.
(b) My friend is a football player or my friend is smart.
(c) If my friend is not a football player, then my friend is smart.
(d) My friend is smart if and only if my friend is a football player.
(e) My friend is a football player and my friend is smart.

EXERCISE SET 3-1

Writing Exercises

1. Define the term *statement* in your own words.
2. Is the sentence "This sentence is a statement" a statement? Explain.
3. Explain the difference between a simple and a compound statement.
4. Describe the terms and symbols used for the four connectives.

5. Write an example of each type of compound statement we studied: conjunction, disjunction, conditional, and biconditional. The topics should be things you find interesting.
6. Explain why the negation of "All spring breaks are fun" is not "All spring breaks are not fun."

Applications in Our World

For Exercises 7–16, state whether the sentence is a statement or not.

7. Please do not use your cell phone in class.
8. $5 + 9 = 14$
9. $9 - 3 = 2$
10. Nicki is a student in vet school.
11. Who will win the student government presidency?
12. Neither Sam nor Mary arrives to the exam on time.
13. You should carry a cell phone with you.
14. Bill Gates is the founder of Microsoft.
15. Go with the flow.
16. Math is not hard.

For Exercises 17–26, decide if each statement is simple or compound.

17. He goes to parties and hangs out at the coffee shop.
18. Sara got her hair highlighted.
19. Raj will buy an iMac or a Dell computer.
20. Euchre is fun if and only if you win.
21. February is when Valentine's Day occurs.
22. Diane is a chemistry major.

23. If you win the Megabucks multistate lottery, you'll be rich.
24. He listened to his iPod and he typed a paper.
25. $\sqrt{9} = 3$ or -3
26. Malcolm and Alisha will both miss the spring break trip.

For Exercises 27–34, identify each statement as a conjunction, disjunction, conditional, or biconditional.

27. Bob and Tom like stand-up comedians.
28. Either he passes the test, or he fails the course.
29. A number is even if and only if it is divisible by 2.
30. Her nails are long, and they have rhinestones on them.
31. I haven't decided yet if I'm going to the game or to the library to study.
32. If you keep hitting on my girlfriend, I'm gonna bust you up.
33. I'm going to pass bio lab if and only if my experiment works out the way I hope it will.
34. When your battery dies, you need to charge your phone overnight.

For Exercises 35–40, write the negation of the statement.

35. The shirt I'm wearing to my interview is white.
36. Don't worry, your computer doesn't have a virus.
37. The hospital isn't full.
38. My name is not Richard Smoker.
39. Come on, you're not going to flunk this class.
40. Wow, that dude has some big biceps.

For Exercises 41–52, identify the quantifier in the statement as either universal or existential.

41. All fish swim in water.
42. Everyone that buys this hat gets a free bowl of soup.
43. Some people who live in glass houses throw stones.
44. There is at least one person in this class who won't pass.
45. Every happy dog wags its tail.
46. No men can join a sorority.
47. I've seen a four-leaf clover.
48. Each student that participates in this study gets a hundred bucks.
49. As far as I know, nobody's ever survived a fall from Mt. Catherine.
50. Everyone in the class was bored by the professor's lecture.
51. At least one of my friends has an iPhone.
52. No one here gets out alive.

For Exercises 53–64, write the negation of the statements in Exercises 41–52.

For Exercises 65–74, write each statement in symbols. Let p = "Sara is a political science major" and let q = "Jane is a quantum physics major."

65. Sara is a political science major, and Jane is a quantum physics major.
66. Sara is not a political science major.
67. If Jane is not a quantum physics major, then Sara is a political science major.
68. It is not true that Jane is a quantum physics major or Sara is a political science major.
69. It is false that Jane is a quantum physics major.
70. It is not true that Sara is a political science major.

71. Jane is a quantum physics major, or Sara is not a political science major.
72. Jane is not a quantum physics major, or Sara is a political science major.
73. Jane is a quantum physics major if and only if Sara is a political science major.
74. If Sara is a political science major, then Jane is a quantum physics major.

For Exercises 75–84, write each statement in symbols. Let p = "Sophie has been arrested" and q = "Bubba's never been arrested."

75. Bubba has been arrested at least once.
76. Sophie and Bubba have both been arrested.
77. If Bubba's been arrested, then Sophie has been arrested too.
78. You're saying that Sophie's been arrested? That is totally not true.
79. Either Sophie or Bubba has been arrested.
80. When the newspaper reported that Sophie and Bubba had both been arrested, that was inaccurate.
81. Sophie has been arrested if and only if Bubba has not.
82. Neither Bubba nor Sophie has ever been arrested.
83. If Sophie has not been arrested, then Bubba has not.
84. Bubba has never been arrested if and only if Sophie hasn't been arrested either.

For Exercises 85–94, write each statement in words. Let p = "The plane is on time." Let q = "The sky is clear."

85. $p \wedge q$
86. $\sim p \vee q$
87. $q \rightarrow p$
88. $q \rightarrow \sim p$
89. $\sim p \wedge \sim q$
90. $q \leftrightarrow p$
91. $p \vee \sim q$
92. $\sim p \leftrightarrow \sim q$
93. $q \rightarrow (p \vee \sim p)$
94. $(p \rightarrow q) \vee \sim p$

For Exercises 95–104, write each statement in words. Let p = "Mark lives on campus." Let q = "Trudy lives off campus."

95. $\sim q$
96. $p \rightarrow q$
97. $p \vee \sim q$
98. $q \leftrightarrow p$
99. $\sim p \rightarrow \sim q$
100. $\sim p$
101. $p \vee q$
102. $(\sim p \vee q) \vee \sim q$
103. $q \vee p$
104. $(p \vee q) \rightarrow \sim(\sim q)$

Critical Thinking

105. Explain why the sentence "This statement is false" is not a statement.
106. Explain why each of the alleged statements listed at the end of the Sidelight on page 99 is actually a paradox.
107. (a) Write a verbal translation of the statement $a < 20$.

(b) Write the negation of the statement you wrote in (a).
(c) Write your statement from (b) in inequality form.
108. (a) Write a verbal translation of the statement $b > 10$.
(b) Write the negation of the statement you wrote in (a).
(c) Write your statement from (b) in inequality form.

Statements involving negations and quantifiers can be confusing—sometimes intentionally. Evaluate each statement in Exercises 109–112 and try to write exactly what it actually says in simpler language.

109. All of our fans will not be attending all of our games.
110. You can't fool some of the people all of the time.
111. I wouldn't say that everybody doesn't like my history professor.
112. Everyone in this class doesn't have time to do their homework.

Section 3-2   Truth Tables

LEARNING OBJECTIVES

☐ 1. Construct truth tables for the negation, disjunction, and conjunction.

☐ 2. Construct truth tables for the conditional and biconditional.

☐ 3. Construct truth tables for compound statements.

☐ 4. Use the hierarchy of logical connectives.

"You can't believe everything you hear." Chances are you were taught this when you were younger, and it's pretty good advice. In an ideal world, everyone would tell the truth all the time, but in the real world, it is extremely important to be able to separate fact from fiction. When someone is trying to convince you of some point of view, the ability to logically evaluate the validity of an argument can be the difference between being informed and being deceived—and maybe between keeping and being separated from your hard-earned money!

This section is all about deciding when a compound statement is or is not true, based not on the situation itself, but simply on the structure of the statement and the truth of the underlying components. We learned about logical connectives in Section 3-1. In this section, we'll analyze these connectives using *truth tables*. A **truth table** is a diagram in table form that is used to show when a compound statement is true or false based on the truth values of the simple statements that make up that compound statement. This will allow us to analyze arguments objectively.

Negation

According to our definition of *statement,* a statement is either true or false, but never both. Consider the simple statement p = "Today is Tuesday." If it is in fact Tuesday, then p is true, and its negation ($\sim p$) "Today is not Tuesday" is false. If it's not Tuesday, then p is false and $\sim p$ is true. The truth table for the negation of p looks like this.

p	$\sim p$
T	F
F	T

There are two possible conditions for the statement p—true or false—and the table tells us that in each case, the negation $\sim p$ has the opposite truth value.

Conjunction

If we have a compound statement with two component statements p and q, there are four possible combinations of truth values for these two statements:

Possibilities	**Symbolic value of each**	
	p	q
1. p and q are both true.	T	T
2. p is true and q is false.	T	F
3. p is false and q is true.	F	T
4. p and q are both false.	F	F

So when setting up a truth table for a compound statement with two component statements, we'll need a row for each of the four possibilities.

Now we're ready to analyze conjunctions. Recall that a conjunction is a compound statement involving the word *and*. Suppose a friend who's prone to exaggeration tells you, "I bought a new laptop and a new iPad." This compound statement can be symbolically represented by $p \wedge q$, where $p =$ "I bought a new laptop" and $q =$ "I bought a new iPad." When would this conjunctive statement be true? If your friend actually had made both purchases, then of course the statement "I bought a new laptop and a new iPad" would be true. In terms of a truth table, that tells us that if p and q are both true, then the conjunction $p \wedge q$ is true as well, as shown below.

p	q	$p \wedge q$
T	T	T

On the other hand, suppose your friend bought only a new laptop or only a new iPad, or maybe neither of those things. Then the statement "I bought a new laptop and a new iPad" would be false. In other words, if either or both of p and q are false, then the compound statement $p \wedge q$ is false as well. With this information, we complete the truth table for a basic conjunction:

	p	q	$p \wedge q$
Bought laptop and iPad	T	T	T
Bought laptop, not iPad	T	F	F
Bought iPad, not laptop	F	T	F
Bought neither	F	F	F

Truth Values for a Conjunction

The conjunction $p \wedge q$ is true only when both p and q are true.

Disjunction

Next, we'll look at truth tables for *or* statements. Suppose your friend from the previous example made the statement, "I bought a new laptop *or* a new iPad" (as opposed to *and*). If your friend actually did buy one or the other, then this statement would be true. And if he or she bought neither, then the statement would be false. So a partial truth table looks like this:

	p	q	$p \vee q$
Bought laptop and iPad	T	T	
Bought laptop, not iPad	T	F	T
Bought iPad, not laptop	F	T	T
Bought neither	F	F	F

But what if the person actually bought both items? You might lean toward the statement "I bought a new laptop or a new iPad" being false. Believe it or not, it depends on what we mean by the word *or*. There are two interpretations of that word, known as the *inclusive or* and the *exclusive or*. The inclusive or has the possibility of both statements being true; but the exclusive or does not allow for this, that is, exactly one of the two simple statements must be true.

Sidelight LOGICAL GATES AND COMPUTER DESIGN

Logic is used in electrical engineering in designing circuits, which are the heart of computers. The truth tables for *and*, *or*, and *not* are used for computer gates. These gates determine whether electricity flows through a circuit. When a switch is closed, the current has an uninterrupted path and will flow through the circuit. This is designated by a 1. When a switch is open, the path at the current is broken, and it will not flow. This is designated by a 0. The logical gates are illustrated here—notice that they correspond exactly with our truth tables.

This simple little structure is responsible for the operation of almost every computer in the world—at least until quantum computers become a reality. If you're interested, do a Google search for *quantum computer* to read about the future of computing.

AND Gate   OR Gate   NOT Gate

Let's look at an example of each. If I said "Tomorrow, I'm going to class or I'm going to the beach," you would interpret that to mean one or the other but not both will occur: that's the exclusive or. But if an admissions counselor says "You'll get a scholarship if you scored over 30 on the ACT or were in the top 5% of your class," it would be silly to interpret that as one or the other but not both: no school would say "Well, we were going to give you a scholarship if you scored over 30 or were at the top of your class, but since you did both, you'll get nothing and like it." That's the inclusive or. In the study of logic, we'll use the inclusive or, so a disjunctive statement like "I bought a new laptop or an iPad" is considered true if both things occur. This completes our truth table for a disjunction:

	p	q	$p \vee q$
Bought laptop and iPad	T	T	T
Bought laptop, not iPad	T	F	T
Bought iPad, not laptop	F	T	T
Bought neither	F	F	F

Truth Values for a Disjunction

> 1. Construct truth tables for the negation, disjunction, and conjunction.

The disjunction $p \vee q$ is true when either p or q or both are true. It is false only when both p and q are false.

Conditional Statement

A conditional statement, which is sometimes called an *implication*, consists of two simple statements using the connective if . . . then. For example, the statement "If I bought a ticket, then I can go to the concert" is a conditional statement. The first component, in this case "I bought a ticket," is called the *antecedent*. The second component, in this case "I can go to the concert," is called the *consequent*.

Conditional statements are used all the time in math, not just in logic. "If an element is in both set A and set B, then it's in the intersection of A and B" is an example from earlier in the book.

To illustrate the truth table for the conditional statement, we'll think about the following example:

If the Cubs win tomorrow, they make the playoffs.

We'll use p = "the Cubs win tomorrow" and q = "they make the playoffs." This makes our conditional statement $p \rightarrow q$. We'll fill out the truth table by considering four cases.

Case 1: The Cubs win tomorrow, and they make the playoffs (both p and q are true). The statement was that if the Cubs won, they would make the playoffs, so if they win and make the playoffs, the statement was definitely true. So the first line of the truth table is

p	q	$p \rightarrow q$
T	T	T

Cubs win, make playoffs

Case 2: The Cubs win tomorrow, but don't make the playoffs (p is true, but q is false). I told you that if the Cubs won, they'd make the playoffs; if they won and didn't make the playoffs, I'm a liar liar pants on fire, and the conditional statement is false. The second line of the truth table is

p	q	$p \rightarrow q$
T	T	T
T	F	F

Cubs win, don't make playoffs

Case 3: The Cubs lose tomorrow and still make the playoffs (p is false and q is true). This requires some serious thought. My claim was that if the Cubs won, they'd make the playoffs. In order for that claim to be false, the Cubs would have to win and not make the playoffs. That's not the case if they didn't win, so the statement is not false. And we know that if a statement isn't false, it's true! That makes the next line of the truth table

p	q	$p \rightarrow q$
T	T	T
T	F	F
F	T	T

Cubs lose, make playoffs

Case 4: The Cubs lose tomorrow and don't make the playoffs (p and q are both false). This is pretty much the same as Case 3: the statement is only false if the Cubs win and don't make the playoffs, so again if the Cubs lose, the statement isn't false, making it true. This completes the truth table for a conditional.

p	q	$p \rightarrow q$
T	T	T
T	F	F
F	T	T
F	F	T

Cubs lose, don't make playoffs

For Cases 3 and 4, it might help to think of it this way: we'll be optimists and consider a statement to be true unless we have absolute proof that it's false.

Math Note

If you're totally unconvinced by the discussions in Cases 3 and 4, you should take a look at Exercises 63 and 64. In those problems, we'll develop a way to rewrite a conditional statement as a disjunction, in which case we can use what we already know about disjunctions to study truth values.

Truth Values for a Conditional Statement

The conditional statement $p \rightarrow q$ is false only when the antecedent p is true and the consequent q is false.

Biconditional Statement

A biconditional statement is really two statements; it's the conjunction of two conditional statements. For example, the statement "I will stay in and study Friday if and only if I don't have any money" is the same as "If I don't have any money, then I will stay in and study Friday *and* if I stay in and study Friday, then I don't have any money." In symbols, we can write either $p \leftrightarrow q$ or $(p \rightarrow q) \wedge (q \rightarrow p)$. Since the biconditional is a conjunction, for it to be true, both of the statements $p \rightarrow q$ and $q \rightarrow p$ must be true. We will once again look at cases to build the truth table.

Case 1: Both p and q are true. Then both $p \rightarrow q$ and $q \rightarrow p$ are true, and the conjunction $(p \rightarrow q) \wedge (q \rightarrow p)$, which is also $p \leftrightarrow q$, is true as well.

p	q	$p \leftrightarrow q$
T	T	T

Case 2: p is true and q is false. In this case, the implication $p \rightarrow q$ is false, so it doesn't even matter whether $q \rightarrow p$ is true or false—the conjunction has to be false.

p	q	$p \leftrightarrow q$
T	T	T
T	F	F

Case 3: p is false and q is true. This is case 2 in reverse. The implication $q \rightarrow p$ is false, so the conjunction must be as well.

p	q	$p \leftrightarrow q$
T	T	T
T	F	F
F	T	F

Case 4: p is false and q is false. According to the truth table for a conditional statement, both $p \rightarrow q$ and $q \rightarrow p$ are true in this case, so the conjunction is as well. This completes the truth table.

p	q	$p \leftrightarrow q$
T	T	T
T	F	F
F	T	F
F	F	T

A technician who designs an automated irrigation system needs to decide whether the system should turn on *if* the water in the soil falls below a certain level or *if and only if* the water in the soil falls below a certain level. In the first instance, other inputs could also turn on the system.

☑ 2. Construct truth tables for the conditional and biconditional.

Truth Values for a Biconditional Statement

The biconditional statement $p \leftrightarrow q$ is true when p and q have the same truth value and false when they have opposite truth values.

Table 3-3 provides a summary of the truth tables for the basic compound statements and the negation. The last thing you should do is to try and memorize these tables! If you understand how we built them, you can rebuild them on your own when you need them.

TABLE 3-3	**Truth Tables for the Connectives and Negation**

Conjunction (and)

p	q	$p \wedge q$
T	T	T
T	F	F
F	T	F
F	F	F

Disjunction (or)

p	q	$p \vee q$
T	T	T
T	F	T
F	T	T
F	F	F

Conditional (if . . . then)

p	q	$p \rightarrow q$
T	T	T
T	F	F
F	T	T
F	F	T

Biconditional (if and only if)

p	q	$p \leftrightarrow q$
T	T	T
T	F	F
F	T	F
F	F	T

Negation (not)

p	$\sim p$
T	F
F	T

Truth Tables for Compound Statements

Once we know truth values for the basic connectives, we can use truth tables to find the truth values for any logical statement. The key to the procedure is to take it step by step, so that in every case, you're deciding on truth values based on one of the truth tables in Table 3-3. The procedure is illustrated in Example 1.

EXAMPLE 1	**Constructing a Truth Table**

"My leg isn't better, or I'm taking a break" is an example of a statement that can be written as $\sim p \vee q$.

Construct a truth table for the statement $\sim p \vee q$.

SOLUTION

Step 1 Set up a table as shown.

p	q
T	T
T	F
F	T
F	F

The order in which you list the Ts and Fs doesn't matter as long as you cover all the possible combinations. For consistency in this book, we'll always use the order TTFF for p and TFTF for q when these are the only two letters in the logical statement.

Step 2 Find the truth values for $\sim p$ by negating the values for p, and put them into a new column marked $\sim p$.

p	q	$\sim p$
T	T	F
T	F	F
F	T	T
F	F	T

Truth values for $\sim p$ are opposite those for p.

Step 3 Find the truth values for the disjunction $\sim p \vee q$. Use the T and F values for $\sim p$ and q in the second and third columns, and use the disjunction truth table from earlier in the section.

p	q	$\sim p$	$\sim p \vee q$
T	T	F	T
T	F	F	F
F	T	T	T
F	F	T	T

The disjunction is true unless $\sim p$ and q are both false.

The truth values for the statement $\sim p \vee q$ are found in the last column. The statement is true unless p is true and q is false.

▼ Try This One 1

Construct a truth table for the statement $p \vee \sim q$.

When a compound statement has multiple connectives, it will sometimes have parentheses to indicate the order in which we should work with those connectives. We'll find the truth value of statements in parentheses first, as shown in Example 2. (If this doesn't remind you of the order of operations for arithmetic and algebra, you're just not paying attention.)

EXAMPLE 2   Constructing a Truth Table

Construct a truth table for the statement $\sim(p \rightarrow \sim q)$.

SOLUTION

Step 1 Set up the table as in Example 1.

p	q
T	T
T	F
F	T
F	F

"It is not true that if it rains, then we can't go out" is an example of a statement that can be written as $\sim(p \rightarrow \sim q)$.

Step 2 Find the truth values for $\sim q$ by negating the values for q, and put them into a new column.

p	q	$\sim q$
T	T	F
T	F	T
F	T	F
F	F	T

Truth values for $\sim q$ are opposite those for q.

Step 3 Find the truth values for the implication $p \rightarrow \sim q$, using the values in the first and third columns and the implication truth table from earlier in the section.

p	q	$\sim q$	$p \rightarrow \sim q$
T	T	F	F
T	F	T	T
F	T	F	T
F	F	T	T

The conditional is true unless p is true and $\sim q$ is false.

Step 4 Find the truth values for the negation $\sim(p \rightarrow \sim q)$ by negating the values we just found for $p \rightarrow \sim q$.

p	q	$\sim q$	$p \rightarrow \sim q$	$\sim(p \rightarrow \sim q)$
T	T	F	F	T
T	F	T	T	F
F	T	F	T	F
F	F	T	T	F

The negation has opposite values from the $p \rightarrow \sim q$ column.

The truth values for $\sim(p \rightarrow \sim q)$ are in the last column. The statement is true only when p and q are both true.

▼ Try This One 2

Construct a truth table for the statement $p \leftrightarrow (\sim p \land q)$.

We can also construct truth tables for compound statements that involve three or more components. For a compound statement with three simple statements p, q, and r, there are eight possible combinations of Ts and Fs to consider. The truth table is set up as shown in Step 1 of Example 3.

EXAMPLE 3   Constructing a Truth Table with Three Components

Construct a truth table for the statement $p \lor (q \rightarrow r)$.

SOLUTION

Step 1 Set up the table as shown.

p	q	r
T	T	T
T	T	F
T	F	T
T	F	F
F	T	T
F	T	F
F	F	T
F	F	F

"I'll do my math assignment, or if I think of a good topic, then I'll start my English essay" is an example of a statement that can be written as $p \lor (q \rightarrow r)$.

Again, the order of the Ts and Fs doesn't matter as long as all the possible combinations are listed. Whenever there are three letters in the statement, we'll use the order shown in Step 1 for consistency.

Step 2 Find the truth value for the statement in parentheses, $q \rightarrow r$. Use the values in the q and r columns and the conditional truth table from earlier in the section. Put those values in a new column labeled $q \rightarrow r$.

p	q	r	$q \rightarrow r$
T	T	T	T
T	T	F	F
T	F	T	T
T	F	F	T
F	T	T	T
F	T	F	F
F	F	T	T
F	F	F	T

The conditional is true unless q is true and r is false.

Step 3 Find the truth values for the disjunction $p \vee (q \rightarrow r)$, using the values for p from the first column and those we just put in the $q \rightarrow r$ column. Use the truth table for disjunction from earlier in the section, and put the results in a new column.

p	q	r	$q \rightarrow r$	$p \vee (q \rightarrow r)$
T	T	T	T	T
T	T	F	F	T
T	F	T	T	T
T	F	F	T	T
F	T	T	T	T
F	T	F	F	F
F	F	T	T	T
F	F	F	T	T

The disjunction is true unless both p and q → r are false.

The truth values for the statement $p \vee (q \rightarrow r)$ are found in the last column. The statement is true unless p and r are false while q is true.

☑ 3. Construct truth tables for compound statements.

▼ Try This One 3

Construct a truth table for the statement $(p \wedge q) \vee \sim r$.

Here's a summary of the method we've developed for building a truth table to analyze a compound statement: we set up a table with all possible combinations of truth values for the simple statements that make up the compound statement. Then we build new columns, one at a time, by finding truth values for parts of the compound statement using the basic truth tables we developed earlier in this section. If there are parentheses in the compound statement, we find the truth value of the statement or statements in the parentheses first. So one way to ensure that the order in which we evaluate compound statements isn't ambiguous is to always use parentheses.

Once again, this sounds an awful lot like the order of operations for arithmetic: in order to avoid *always* having to use parentheses, we agree on a standard order for multiple operations, using parentheses only when the intent is to violate that order. To accomplish the same thing in dealing with statements in logic, a **hierarchy of connectives** has been agreed upon somewhere along the line. This hierarchy tells us which connectives should be done first when there are no parentheses to guide us:

1. Negation ($\sim$)
2. Conjunction ($\wedge$) or disjunction ($\vee$)
3. Conditional ($\rightarrow$)
4. Biconditional ($\leftrightarrow$)

The connectives higher on the list are done first. The connective that's lowest on the list is done last, so it describes the type of statement overall. For example, $p \vee q \rightarrow r$ is a conditional statement; the hierarchy tells us to first find the disjunction, which means we could write the compound statement as $(p \vee q) \rightarrow r$. That shows that the statement is a conditional: if p or q, then r.

When a compound statement has both a conjunction and a disjunction, we'll need to use parentheses to indicate which should be considered first. A statement like $p \wedge q \vee r$ is ambiguous without parentheses: $(p \wedge q) \vee r$ is a conjunction, and $p \wedge (q \vee r)$ is a disjunction. (In Exercise 59, you'll prove that these two statements are in fact different.)

> ## Math Note
>
> When parentheses are used to emphasize order, the statement $p \vee q \rightarrow r$ is written as $(p \vee q) \rightarrow r$. The statement $p \leftrightarrow q \wedge r$ is written as $p \leftrightarrow (q \wedge r)$.

EXAMPLE 4   **Using the Hierarchy of Connectives**

For each, identify the type of statement using the hierarchy of connectives, and rewrite using parentheses to indicate order.

(a) $\sim p \vee \sim q$ (b) $p \rightarrow \sim q \wedge r$ (c) $p \vee q \leftrightarrow q \vee r$ (d) $p \rightarrow q \leftrightarrow r$

SOLUTION

(a) The negations are higher on the list than the disjunction, so if we add parentheses, we get $(\sim p) \vee (\sim q)$. The statement is a disjunction.
(b) The lowest connective in this statement is conditional, so this is a conditional statement. With parentheses, it looks like $p \rightarrow (\sim q \wedge r)$.
(c) The biconditional is lowest on the list, so the overall statement is a biconditional: $(p \vee q) \leftrightarrow (q \vee r)$.
(d) Again, the biconditional comes last, so the statement is a biconditional: $(p \rightarrow q) \leftrightarrow r$.

▼ Try This One 4

For each, identify the type of statement using the hierarchy of connectives, and rewrite using parentheses to indicate order.

(a) $\sim p \vee q$ (c) $p \vee q \leftrightarrow \sim p \vee \sim q$ (e) $p \leftrightarrow q \rightarrow r$
(b) $p \vee \sim q \rightarrow r$ (d) $p \wedge \sim q$

4. Use the hierarchy of logical connectives.

EXAMPLE 5   An Application of Truth Tables

Use the truth value of each simple statement to determine the truth value of the compound statement.

p: Kate Middleton married Prince William in 2011.
q: Prince William's mother was the Queen of England.
r: barring death or divorce, Kate Middleton will become queen one day.

Statement: $p \lor q \to r$

SOLUTION

The royal wedding of William and Kate was one of the biggest news stories of 2011, so *p* is definitely true. But *q* is not. William's mother was Princess Diana: his grandmother was the queen. William is the eldest son of Prince Charles, who will be king when his mother dies, so if Kate and William stay together and stay alive long enough, they will be king and queen one day, so *r* is true as well.

Now we'll analyze the compound statement. First, according to the hierarchy of connectives, the disjunction should be evaluated: $p \lor q$ is true when either *p* or *q* is true, so in this case, $p \lor q$ is true. Next, the implication $(p \lor q) \to r$ is true if both *r* and $p \lor q$ is true, which is the case here. So the compound statement $p \lor q \to r$ is true.

▼ Try This One 5

Using the simple statements in Example 5, find the truth value of the compound statement $(\sim p \land \sim q) \to r$.

We have seen that truth tables are an effective way to organize truth values for statements, allowing us to determine the truth values of some very complicated statements in a systematic way. In the next section, we'll see why we want to be able to do this when we use truth tables to decide when an argument is logically valid.

Answers to Try This One

1

p	*q*	~*q*	$p \lor \sim q$
T	T	F	T
T	F	T	T
F	T	F	F
F	F	T	T

2

p	*q*	~*p*	$\sim p \land q$	$p \leftrightarrow (\sim p \land q)$
T	T	F	F	F
T	F	F	F	F
F	T	T	T	F
F	F	T	F	T

3

p	*q*	*r*	$p \land q$	~*r*	$(p \land q) \lor \sim r$
T	T	T	T	F	T
T	T	F	T	T	T
T	F	T	F	F	F
T	F	F	F	T	T
F	T	T	F	F	F
F	T	F	F	T	T
F	F	T	F	F	F
F	F	F	F	T	T

4 (a) Disjunction; $(\sim p) \lor q$
(b) Conditional; $(p \lor \sim q) \to r$
(c) Biconditional; $(p \lor q) \leftrightarrow (\sim p \lor \sim q)$
(d) Conjunction; $p \land (\sim q)$
(e) Biconditional; $p \leftrightarrow (q \to r)$

5   True

EXERCISE SET 3-2

Writing Exercises

1. Your boyfriend/girlfriend randomly opens your math book and ends up seeing a truth table in Section 3-2. How would you explain to him or her what the point of a truth table is?

2. Explain the difference between the inclusive and exclusive disjunctions. Write an example of each in plain English, and explain why each is the type of disjunction described.

3. I claim that a biconditional statement is really a conjunction of two conditional statements. Explain why that makes sense.

4. Describe the hierarchy of connectives. What's the point of having one? How do you use it?

Computational Exercises

For Exercises 5–34, construct a truth table for each.

5. $\sim(p \lor q)$
6. $q \to p$
7. $\sim p \land q$
8. $\sim q \to \sim p$
9. $\sim p \leftrightarrow q$
10. $(p \lor q) \to \sim p$
11. $\sim(p \land q) \to p$
12. $(p \lor q) \land (q \lor p)$
13. $(\sim q \land p) \to \sim p$
14. $q \land \sim p$
15. $(p \land q) \leftrightarrow (q \lor \sim p)$
16. $p \to (q \lor \sim p)$
17. $(p \land q) \lor p$
18. $(q \to p) \lor \sim r$
19. $(r \land q) \lor (p \land q)$
20. $(r \to q) \lor (p \to r)$
21. $\sim(p \lor q) \to \sim(p \land r)$
22. $(\sim p \lor \sim q) \to \sim r$
23. $(\sim p \lor q) \land r$
24. $p \land (q \lor \sim r)$
25. $(p \land q) \leftrightarrow (\sim r \lor q)$
26. $\sim(p \land r) \to (q \land r)$
27. $r \to \sim(p \lor q)$
28. $(p \lor q) \lor (\sim p \lor \sim r)$
29. $p \to (\sim q \land \sim r)$
30. $(q \lor \sim r) \leftrightarrow (p \land \sim q)$
31. $\sim(q \to p) \land r$
32. $q \to (p \land r)$
33. $(r \lor q) \land (r \land p)$
34. $(p \land q) \leftrightarrow \sim r$

If p and r are false statements, and q is a true statement, find the truth value of each compound statement in Exercises 35–40.

35. $q \lor (p \land \sim r)$
36. $(p \land q) \lor (q \land r)$
37. $r \to \sim(p \lor q)$
38. $\sim(p \land q) \lor \sim r$
39. $\sim p \land \sim(r \lor \sim q)$
40. $(p \to r) \to (\sim q \land p)$

Applications in Our World

For Exercises 41–46, use the truth value of each simple statement to determine the truth value of the compound statement. Use the Internet if you need help determining the truth value of a simple statement.

41. *p*: Japan bombs Pearl Harbor.
    q: the United States stays out of World War II.
    Statement: $p \to q$

42. *p*: Barack Obama wins the Democratic nomination in 2008.
    q: Mitt Romney wins the Republican nomination in 2008.
    Statement: $p \land q$

43. *p*: NASA sends a manned spacecraft to the Moon.
    q: NASA sends a manned spacecraft to Mars.
    Statement: $p \lor q$

44. *p*: an oppressive regime is overthrown in Egypt in 2011.
    q: free and open elections are held in Egypt in 2011.
    Statement: $p \to q$

45. *p*: Apple releases the iPad.
    q: Apple stops making desktop computers.
    r: Samsung and Amazon release tablet computers.
    Statement: $(p \lor q) \land r$

46. *p*: a large earthquake and tsunami devastate Japan.
    q: some nuclear reactors in Japan are damaged.
    r: Japan stops using nuclear power plants.
    Statement: $p \land q \to \sim r$

Exercises 47–52 are based on the compound statement below.

A new weight loss supplement claims that if you take the product daily and cut your calorie intake by 10%, you will lose at least 10 pounds in the next 4 months.

47. This compound statement is made up of three simple statements. Identify them and assign a letter to each.

48. Write the compound statement in symbolic form, using conjunctions and the conditional.

49. Construct a truth table for the compound statement you wrote in Exercise 48.

50. If you take this product daily and don't cut your calorie intake by 10%, and then don't lose 10 pounds, is the claim made by the advertiser true or false?

51. If you take the product daily, don't cut your calorie intake by 10%, and do lose 10 pounds, is the claim true or false?

52. If you don't take the product daily, cut your calorie intake by 10%, and do lose 10 pounds, is the claim true or false?

Exercises 53–58 are based on the compound statement below.

The owner of a professional baseball team publishes an open letter to fans after another losing season. He claims that if attendance for the following season is over 2 million, then he will add $20 million to the payroll and the team will make the playoffs the following year.

53. This compound statement is made up of three simple statements. Identify them and assign a letter to each.

54. Write the compound statement in symbolic form, using conjunction and the conditional.

55. Construct a truth table for the compound statement you wrote in Exercise 54.

Critical Thinking

59. Construct two truth tables to show that the statement $p \wedge q \vee r$ is ambiguous. (*Hint*: Look back at our discussion of the hierarchy of connectives.)

60. Let's look a little deeper at the statement $p \wedge q \vee r$. Write three simple statements for p, q, and r so that $(p \wedge q) \vee r$ and $p \wedge (q \vee r)$ have different meanings. (*Hint*: The truth tables from Exercise 59 will probably help.)

61. Using the hierarchy for connectives, write the statement $p \rightarrow q \vee r$ by using parentheses to indicate the proper order. Then construct truth tables for $(p \rightarrow q) \vee r$ and $p \rightarrow (q \vee r)$. Are the resulting truth values the same? Are you surprised? Why or why not?

62. In 2003, New York City Council was considering banning indoor smoking in bars and restaurants. Opponents of the ban claimed that it would have a negligible effect on indoor pollution, but a huge negative effect on the economic success of these businesses. Eventually,

56. If attendance goes over 2 million the next year and the owner raises payroll by $20 million, but the team fails to make the playoffs, is the owner's claim true or false?

57. If attendance is less than 2 million but the owner still raises the payroll by $20 million and the team makes the playoffs, is the owner's claim true or false?

58. If attendance is over 2 million, the owner doesn't raise the payroll, but the team still makes the playoffs, is the owner's claim true or false?

the ban was enacted, and a 2004 study by the city department of health found that there was a sixfold decrease in indoor air pollution in bars and restaurants, but jobs, liquor licenses, and tax revenues all increased. Assign truth values to all the premises of the opponents' claim; then write the claim as a compound statement and determine its validity.

63. Consider the following two statements:

"If we scored more points, we won!"
"We didn't score more points, or we won."

Explain why these statements say exactly the same thing from an English standpoint. (We'll deal with them logically in the next question.)

64. Write the two statements in Exercise 63 as compound statements using letters p and q, then construct a truth table for each compound statement. How can you use this to help convince you that the truth table we built for the conditional is correct?

Section 3-3 Types of Statements

LEARNING OBJECTIVES

☐ 1. Classify a statement as a tautology, a self-contradiction, or neither.

☐ 2. Identify logically equivalent statements.

☐ 3. Write negations of compound statements.

☐ 4. Write the converse, inverse, and contrapositive of a statement.

It's no secret that weight loss has become big business in the United States. It seems like almost every week, a new company pops into existence with the latest miracle pill to turn you into a supermodel.

A typical advertisement will say something like "Use of our product may result in significant weight loss." That sounds great, but think about what that statement really means. If use of the product "may" result in signifi-

cant weight loss, it also may not result in any weight loss at all, it may result in weight gain, or it may result in turning you into a pumpkin. In fact, the statement could be translated into "You will lose weight or you will not lose weight." Of course, this statement is always true. In this section, we'll study statements of this type (and others).

Tautologies and Self-Contradictions

In our study of truth tables in Section 3-2, we saw that most compound statements are true in some cases and false in others. What we haven't done is think about whether that's true for *every* compound statement. Some simple examples should be enough to convince you that this is most definitely not the case.

Consider the simple statement "I'm going to Cancun for spring break this year." Its negation is "I'm not going to Cancun for spring break this year." Now think about these two compound statements:

"I'm going to Cancun for spring break this year, or I'm not going to Cancun for spring break this year."

"I'm going to Cancun for spring break this year, and I'm not going to Cancun for spring break this year."

Hopefully, it's pretty clear to you that the first statement is always true, while the second statement is always false (whether you go to Cancun or not). The first is an example of a *tautology,* while the second is an example of a *self-contradiction.*

> A **tautology** is a compound statement that's always true, regardless of the truth values of the simple statements that make it up. A **self-contradiction** is a compound statement that is always false.

CAUTION Don't make the mistake of thinking that every statement is either a tautology or a self-contradiction. We've seen many examples of statements that are sometimes true and other times false.

The sample statements above are simple enough that it's easy to tell that they are always true or always false based on common sense. But for more complicated statements, we'll need to construct a truth table to decide if a statement is a tautology, a self-contradiction, or neither.

EXAMPLE 1   Using a Truth Table to Classify a Statement

Decide if each statement is a tautology, a self-contradiction, or neither.

(a) $(p \wedge q) \rightarrow p$ (b) $(p \wedge q) \wedge (\sim p \wedge \sim q)$ (c) $(p \vee q) \rightarrow q$

SOLUTION

(a) The truth table for statement (a) is

p	q	$p \wedge q$	$(p \wedge q) \rightarrow p$
T	T	T	T
T	F	F	T
F	T	F	T
F	F	F	T

Since the truth table value consists of all Ts, the statement is always true, making it a tautology.

(b) The truth table for statement (b) is

p	q	$\sim p$	$\sim q$	$p \wedge q$	$\sim p \wedge \sim q$	$(p \wedge q) \wedge (\sim p \wedge \sim q)$
T	T	F	F	T	F	F
T	F	F	T	F	F	F
F	T	T	F	F	F	F
F	F	T	T	F	T	F

Since the truth value consists of all Fs, the statement is always false, so it is a self-contradiction.

(c) The truth table for statement (c) is

p	q	$p \vee q$	$(p \vee q) \rightarrow q$
T	T	T	T
T	F	T	F
F	T	T	T
F	F	F	T

Since the statement can be true in some cases and false in others, it is neither a tautology nor a self-contradiction.

Let p = "I am going to a concert" and q = "I will wear black." Translate each statement in Example 1 into a word statement using this choice of p and q. Can you predict which statements are tautologies, self-contradictions, or neither?

☑ 1. Classify a statement as a tautology, a self-contradiction, or neither.

▼ Try This One 1

Decide if each statement is a tautology, a self-contradiction, or neither.

(a) $(p \vee q) \wedge (\sim p \rightarrow q)$ (b) $(p \wedge \sim q) \wedge \sim p$ (c) $(p \rightarrow q) \vee \sim q$

Logically Equivalent Statements

In Exercises 63 and 64 of Section 3-2, we studied the two logical statements $p \rightarrow q$ and $\sim p \vee q$. The truth tables for the two statements are combined into one here:

p	q	$\sim p$	$p \rightarrow q$	$\sim p \vee q$
T	T	F	T	T
T	F	F	F	F
F	T	T	T	T
F	F	T	T	T

Notice that the truth values for both statements are *identical*: TFTT. When this occurs, the statements are said to be *logically equivalent;* that is, both compositions of the same simple statements have the same meaning. For example, the statement "If it snows, I will go skiing" is logically equivalent to saying "It won't snow or I will go skiing." Formally defined,

Math Note

The symbol ⇔ is often used interchangeably with ≡.

Two compound statements are **logically equivalent** if and only if they have the same truth values for all possible combinations of truth values for the simple statements that compose them. The symbol for logically equivalent statements is ≡.

| EXAMPLE 2 | **Identifying Logically Equivalent Statements** |

Decide if the two statements $p \rightarrow q$ and $\sim q \rightarrow \sim p$ are logically equivalent. Then write examples of simple statements p and q and write each compound statement verbally.

SOLUTION

The truth table for the statements is

p	q	$\sim p$	$\sim q$	$p \rightarrow q$	$\sim q \rightarrow \sim p$
T	T	F	F	T	T
T	F	F	T	F	F
F	T	T	F	T	T
F	F	T	T	T	T

Since both statements have the same truth values, they are logically equivalent. Suppose we let $p =$ John's salary level is below the poverty line and $q =$ John qualifies for food stamps. Then $p \rightarrow q$ reads as "If John's salary is below the poverty line, then he qualifies for food stamps," and $\sim q \rightarrow \sim p$ reads as "If John does not qualify for food stamps, then his salary is not below the poverty line."

✓ 2. Identify logically equivalent statements.

▼ **Try This One 2**

Decide which two statements are logically equivalent. Then write examples of simple statements p and q and write each compound statement verbally.

(a) $\sim(p \wedge \sim q)$ (b) $\sim p \wedge q$ (c) $\sim p \vee q$

De Morgan's laws for logic give us some examples of equivalent statements.

De Morgan's Laws for Logic

For any statements p and q,

$$\sim(p \vee q) \equiv \sim p \wedge \sim q \quad \text{and} \quad \sim(p \wedge q) \equiv \sim p \vee \sim q$$

Do you see the similarities between De Morgan's laws for logic and the ones for sets? We're exchanging sets like A and B for statements p and q, and exchanging intersection and union for "and" and "or." We can prove De Morgan's laws using truth tables, but it's more fun to make you do it in the exercises, so that's what we did.

De Morgan's laws are most often used to write the negation of conjunctions and disjunctions. For example, the negation of the statement "I will go to work or I will go to the beach" is "I will not go to work and I will not go to the beach." Notice that when you negate a conjunction, it becomes a disjunction; and when you negate a disjunction, it becomes a conjunction—that is, the *and* becomes an *or,* and the *or* becomes an *and.*

| EXAMPLE 3 | **Using De Morgan's Laws to Write Negations** |

Write the negations of the following statements, using De Morgan's laws.

(a) Studying is necessary and I am a hard worker.
(b) Shoplifting is a felony or a misdemeanor.
(c) I will pass this test or I will drop this class.
(d) The patient needs an RN or an LPN, and she's very sick.

SOLUTION

(a) Studying is not necessary or I am not a hard worker.
(b) Shoplifting is not a felony and is not a misdemeanor.
(c) I will not pass this test and I will not drop this class.
(d) The patient doesn't need an RN and doesn't need an LPN, or she's not very sick.

Math Note

Notice that De Morgan's laws were used twice in part (d). Clever!

> ▼ **Try This One 3**
>
> Write the negations of the following statements, using De Morgan's laws.
>
> (a) I will study for this class or I will fail.
> (b) I will go to the dance club and the restaurant.
> (c) It is not silly or I have no sense of humor.
> (d) The movie is a comedy or a thriller, and it is awesome.

Earlier in this section, we saw that the two statements $p \rightarrow q$ and $\sim p \vee q$ are logically equivalent. Now that we know De Morgan's laws, we can use this fact to find the negation of the conditional statement $p \rightarrow q$.

$$\begin{aligned} \sim(p \rightarrow q) &\equiv \sim(\sim p \vee q) \\ &\equiv \sim(\sim p) \wedge \sim q \qquad \text{Note: } \sim(\sim p) \equiv p \\ &\equiv p \wedge \sim q \end{aligned}$$

This can be checked by using a truth table as shown.

p	q	$\sim q$	$p \rightarrow q$	$\sim(p \rightarrow q)$	$p \wedge \sim q$
T	T	F	T	F	F
T	F	T	F	T	T
F	T	F	T	F	F
F	F	T	T	F	F

$p \rightarrow q$ has truth values that are opposite $p \wedge \sim q$.

So the negation of $p \rightarrow q$ is $p \wedge \sim q$.

For example, if you say "It is not the case that if I get a biology degree then I'll be guaranteed a good job," that's the same thing as saying "I got a biology degree and wasn't guaranteed a good job."

| EXAMPLE 4 | **Writing the Negation of a Conditional Statement** |

Write the negation of the statement "If you agree to go out with me, I'll buy you a late-model vehicle."

SOLUTION

We can write the statement as $p \rightarrow q$, where p = "You agree to go out with me" and q = "I buy you a late-model vehicle." We just found that the negation of $p \rightarrow q$ is

$p \wedge \sim q$. This translates to "You agree to go out with me and I do not buy you a late-model vehicle."

☑ 3. Write negations of compound statements.

▼ Try This One 4

Write the negation of the statement "If the video is popular, then it can be found on YouTube."

Table 3-4 summarizes the negations of the basic compound statements.

TABLE 3-4   Negation of Compound Statements

Statement	Negation	Equivalent Negation
$p \wedge q$	$\sim(p \wedge q)$	$\sim p \vee \sim q$
$p \vee q$	$\sim(p \vee q)$	$\sim p \wedge \sim q$
$p \rightarrow q$	$\sim(p \rightarrow q)$	$p \wedge \sim q$

Variations of the Conditional Statement

Conditional statements play a very big role in logic (as well as in math in general), and one of the ways we can learn more about them is to study three related statements, the *converse*, the *inverse*, and the *contrapositive*. These are defined in Table 3-5.

TABLE 3-5   Variations of a Conditional Statement

Name	In Symbols	In Words
Conditional	$p \rightarrow q$	"If p, then q."
Converse	$q \rightarrow p$	"If q, then p."
Inverse	$\sim p \rightarrow \sim q$	"If not p, then not q."
Contrapositive	$\sim q \rightarrow \sim p$	"If not q, then not p."

In case you're wondering, this puppy dog is mine, too.

We'll use the example "If Tessa is a chocolate Lab, then Tessa is brown" to illustrate the variations of a conditional, and to decide if each is logically equivalent to the original conditional statement. Note that the original conditional statement is true—the thing that makes a Labrador retriever a chocolate Lab is brown fur.

Converse: if Tessa is brown, then Tessa is a chocolate Lab.

Unlike the original statement, this is not true: there are plenty of brown dogs that are not chocolate Labs.

Inverse: if Tessa is not a chocolate Lab, then Tessa is not brown.

Again, not true: Tessa could be a breed other than chocolate Lab and still be brown. (For the record, she isn't, which I can tell because she's sitting on my feet at the moment. But she *could* be.)

Contrapositive: if Tessa is not brown, then Tessa is not a chocolate Lab.

Now this one is true: all chocolate Labs are brown, so if Tessa weren't brown, she couldn't possibly be a chocolate Lab. What these examples show is that we know for sure that the converse and inverse are not logically equivalent to an original conditional statement. This is because we've found a specific example where the converse and inverse have different truth values than the original.

On the other hand, we don't yet know for sure that the original statement and the contrapositive are equivalent: we just showed that in one case they happen to have the same truth value. To see if they're actually equivalent, we can use truth tables.

p	q	$p \to q$	$\sim p$	$\sim q$	$\sim q \to \sim p$
T	T	T	F	F	T
T	F	F	F	T	F
F	T	T	T	F	T
F	F	T	T	T	T

This shows that a conditional and its contrapositive are in fact logically equivalent.

EXAMPLE 5   **Writing the Converse, Inverse, and Contrapositive**

Write the converse, the inverse, and the contrapositive for the statement "If you earned a bachelor's degree, then you got a high-paying job."

SOLUTION

It's helpful to write the original implication in symbols: $p \to q$, where p = "You earned a bachelor's degree" and q = "You got a high-paying job."

Converse: $q \to p$. "If you got a high-paying job, then you earned a bachelor's degree."

Inverse: $\sim p \to \sim q$. "If you did not earn a bachelor's degree, then you did not get a high-paying job."

Contrapositive: $\sim q \to \sim p$. "If you did not get a high-paying job, then you did not earn a bachelor's degree."

> **▼ Try This One 5**
>
> Write the converse, the inverse, and the contrapositive for the statement "If you do well in math classes, then you are intelligent." Then explain why the contrapositive says the same thing as the original statement.

Since we run into conditional statements so often, it's useful to be able to recognize them when words other than "if . . . then" are used. Remember that a conditional statement $p \to q$ is sometimes called an *implication*, and consists of two simple statements: the first (p) is called the **antecedent**, and the second (q) is called the **consequent**. For example, the statement "If you jump into the Arctic Ocean you will freeze your patootie off" consists of the antecedent "You jump into the Arctic Ocean" and the consequent "You will freeze your patootie off" connected by the "if . . . then" connective.

Here are some other ways a conditional can be stated:

p implies q

q if p

p only if q

p is sufficient for q

q is necessary for p

All p are q

Math Note

One of the most common logical flaws that people make in real life is assuming that if a statement is true, its converse is as well. For example, I think we can all agree that the statement "If Sofia makes more than $400,000 per year, then she can buy a Mercedes" is true.

The converse is "If Sofia can buy a Mercedes, then she makes more than $400,000 per year." This isn't true at all! Maybe Sofia makes a much smaller salary, but decides to live in a tent so that most of her money goes to pay for her car.

Or maybe she makes the paltry sum of $300,000 and still buys a Mercedes. In general, if a statement is true, the converse may or may not be true.

In four of these six forms, the antecedent comes first, but for "*q* if *p*" and "*q* is necessary for *p*," the consequent comes first. So identifying the antecedent and consequent is important.

For example, think about the statement "If you drink and drive, you get arrested." Writing it in the different possible forms, we get:

Drinking and driving implies you get arrested.

You get arrested if you drink and drive.

You drink and drive only if you get arrested.

Drinking and driving is sufficient for getting arrested.

Getting arrested is necessary for drinking and driving.

All those who drink and drive get arrested.

Of course, these all say the same thing. To illustrate the importance of getting the antecedent and consequent in the correct order, consider the "*q* if *p*" form, in this case "You get arrested if you drink and drive." If we don't start with the consequent, we get "You drink and drive if you get arrested." This is completely false—there are any number of things you could get arrested for other than drinking and driving.

EXAMPLE 6   Writing Variations of a Conditional Statement

Write each statement in symbols. Let *p* = "A building uses solar heat" and *q* = "The owner will pay less for electricity."

(a) If a building uses solar heat, the owner will pay less for electricity.
(b) Using less electricity is necessary for a building using solar heat.
(c) A building uses solar heat only if the owner pays less for electricity.
(d) Using solar heat is sufficient for paying less on your electric bill.
(e) The owner pays less for electricity if a building uses solar heat.

SOLUTION

(a) If *p*, then *q*; $p \rightarrow q$
(b) *q* is necessary for *p*; $p \rightarrow q$
(c) *p* only if *q*; $p \rightarrow q$
(d) *p* is sufficient for *q*; $p \rightarrow q$
(e) *q* if *p*; $p \rightarrow q$

Actually, these statements all say exactly the same thing!

▼ Try This One 6

Write each statement in symbols. Let *p* = "A student comes to class every day" and *q* = "A student gets a good grade."

(a) A student gets a good grade if a student comes to class every day.
(b) Coming to class every day is necessary for getting a good grade.
(c) A student gets a good grade only if a student comes to class every day.
(d) Coming to class every day is sufficient for getting a good grade.

☑ 4. Write the converse, inverse, and contrapositive of a statement.

In this section, we saw that some statements are always true (tautologies) and others are always false (self-contradictions). We also defined what it means for two statements to be logically equivalent—they have the same truth values. Now we're ready to tie it all together to accomplish our original goal: analyzing logical arguments to decide if they make sense or not.

Answers to Try This One

1 (a) Neither   (b) Self-contradiction
(c) Tautology

2 (a) and (c); Answers will vary.

3 (a) I will not study for this class and I will not fail.
(b) I will not go to the dance club or the restaurant.
(c) It is silly and I have a sense of humor.
(d) The movie is not a comedy and it is not a thriller, or it is not awesome.

4 The video is popular and it cannot be found on YouTube.

5 *Converse*: if you are smart, then you do well in math classes.
Inverse: if you do not do well in math classes, then you are not smart.
Contrapositive: if you are not smart, then you do not do well in math classes.

The original statement claimed that if you do well in math classes, you must be smart. If you weren't smart and still did well in math classes, that would contradict the original statement.

6 (a) $p \rightarrow q$ (b) $q \rightarrow p$ (c) $q \rightarrow p$ (d) $p \rightarrow q$

EXERCISE SET 3-3

Writing Exercises

1. Explain the difference between a tautology and a self-contradiction.
2. Is every statement either a tautology or a self-contradiction? Why or why not?
3. Describe how to find the converse, inverse, and contrapositive of a conditional statement.
4. How can you decide if two statements are logically equivalent?
5. How can you decide if one statement is the negation of another?
6. Is a statement always logically equivalent to its converse? Explain.

Computational Exercises

For Exercises 7–16, determine which statements are tautologies, self-contradictions, or neither.

7. $(p \vee q) \vee (\sim p \wedge \sim q)$
8. $(p \rightarrow q) \wedge (p \vee q)$
9. $(p \wedge q) \wedge (\sim p \vee \sim q)$
10. $(p \vee q) \wedge (\sim p \wedge \sim q)$
11. $(p \leftrightarrow q) \vee \sim (q \leftrightarrow p)$
12. $(p \wedge q) \leftrightarrow (p \rightarrow \sim q)$
13. $(\sim p \rightarrow q) \leftrightarrow (p \vee q)$
14. $(p \rightarrow q) \wedge (q \rightarrow p)$
15. $(p \leftrightarrow q) \wedge (\sim p \leftrightarrow \sim q)$
16. $(p \rightarrow q) \wedge (\sim p \vee q)$

For Exercises 17–26, determine if the two statements are logically equivalent statements, negations, or neither.

17. $\sim q \rightarrow p; \sim p \rightarrow q$
18. $p \wedge q; \sim q \vee \sim p$
19. $\sim (p \vee q); p \rightarrow \sim q$
20. $\sim (p \rightarrow q); \sim p \wedge q$
21. $q \rightarrow p; \sim (p \rightarrow q)$
22. $p \vee (\sim q \wedge r); (p \wedge \sim q) \vee (p \wedge r)$
23. $\sim (p \vee q); \sim (\sim p \wedge \sim q)$
24. $(p \vee q) \rightarrow r; \sim r \rightarrow \sim (p \vee q)$
25. $(p \wedge q) \vee r; p \wedge (q \vee r)$
26. $p \leftrightarrow \sim q; (p \wedge \sim q) \vee (\sim p \wedge q)$

For Exercises 27–32, write the converse, inverse, and contrapositive of each.

27. $p \rightarrow q$
28. $\sim p \rightarrow \sim q$
29. $\sim p \rightarrow \sim (q \wedge p)$
30. $(q \vee \sim r) \rightarrow (p \vee r)$
31. $p \rightarrow (q \vee r)$
32. $(p \vee \sim q) \rightarrow r$

Applications in Our World

In Exercises 33–42, use De Morgan's laws to write the negation of the statement.

33. The patient is septic or she is in shock.
34. The experimental seedlings are growing quickly or they are not diseased.
35. It is not cold and I am soaked.
36. I will walk in the Race for the Cure walkathon and I will be tired.
37. I will go to the beach and I will not get sunburned.
38. The coffee is a latte or an espresso.
39. The suspect is a white male or the witness is not correct.
40. I will go to college and I will get a degree.

41. It is right or it is wrong.
42. The hotel custodial staff is not on strike or it is not at a union meeting.

In Exercises 43–48, use De Morgan's laws to write an equivalent statement.

43. It is not the case that my grade is an A or a B.
44. It's totally false to say that the student has special needs and doesn't belong in this classroom.
45. The prosecuting attorney for this case is not experienced and is not prepared.
46. This firm's managing partner isn't Caucasian or isn't male.
47. It's not true that my friends are not serious about school or are not prepared to work hard.
48. No way is that patient unresponsive and not able to breathe on his own.

For Exercises 49–55, let p = "I need to talk to my friend" and q = "I will send her a text message." Write each of the following in symbols (see Example 6).

49. If I need to talk to my friend, I will send her a text message.
50. If I will not send her a text message, I do not need to talk to my friend.
51. Sending a text message is necessary for needing to talk to my friend.
52. I will send her a text message if I need to talk to my friend.
53. Needing to talk to my friend is sufficient for sending her a text message.
54. I need to talk to my friend only if I will send her a text message.

55. I do not need to talk to my friend only if I will not send her a text message.
56. Are any of the statements in Exercises 49–55 logically equivalent?

For Exercises 57–62, write the converse, inverse, and contrapositive of the conditional statement. Then explain why the contrapositive says the same thing as the original statement.

57. If he graduated with a Bachelor's degree in Management Information Systems, then he will get a good job.
58. If she does not earn $5,000 this summer as a barista at the coffeehouse, then she cannot buy the green Ford Focus.
59. If the *American Idol* finale is today, then I will host a party in my dorm room.
60. If my cell phone will not charge, then I will replace the battery.
61. I will go to Nassau for spring break if I lose 10 pounds by March 1.
62. The politician will go to jail if he gets caught taking kickbacks.

For Exercises 63–68, write the negation of each statement in Exercises 57–62.

63. Negation of Exercise 57.
64. Negation of Exercise 58.
65. Negation of Exercise 59.
66. Negation of Exercise 60.
67. Negation of Exercise 61.
68. Negation of Exercise 62.

Critical Thinking

In Exercises 69–74, decide if the given compound statement is true or false. Be careful, and explain your reasoning.

69. The moon is made of green cheese if and only if Justin Bieber is the king of Siam.
70. The average student takes less than 6 years to complete an undergraduate degree if the University of Southern California is in Tahiti.
71. Drinking and driving increases the risk of an accident if and only if driving on the left side of the road is standard in the United States.
72. If my parents were born in outer space, then Venus orbits around the Earth every 28 days.
73. The current year is before 1970 if there are more than a million people in the United States.
74. Less than 20 people watched the finale of *American Idol* last year if and only if the winner was 14 inches tall.

75. In this section, we wrote the negation of $p \rightarrow q$ by using a disjunction. See if you can write the negation of $p \rightarrow q$ by using a conjunction.
76. Try to write the negation of the biconditional $p \leftrightarrow q$ by using only conjunctions, disjunctions, and negations.
77. Can you think of a true conditional statement about someone you know so that the converse is true as well? How about so that the converse is false?
78. Can you think of a true conditional statement about someone you know so that the inverse is true as well? How about so that the inverse is false?
79. Use truth tables to prove both of De Morgan's laws for logic (see page 122).
80. We defined converse, inverse, and contrapositive for conditional statements. Using these as models, define the converse, inverse, and contrapositive for a biconditional statement $p \leftrightarrow q$. Which, if any, are logically equivalent to the original biconditional?

Section 3-4   Logical Arguments

LEARNING OBJECTIVES

☐ 1. Define *valid argument* and *fallacy*.

☐ 2. Use truth tables to decide if an argument is valid.

☐ 3. Identify common argument forms.

☐ 4. Use common argument forms to decide if arguments are valid.

Common sense is a funny thing in our society: we all think we have it, and we also think that most other people don't. This thing that we call common sense is really the ability to think logically, to evaluate an argument or situation and decide what is and is not reasonable. It doesn't take a lot of imagination to picture how valuable it is to be able to think logically. We're pretty well protected by parents for our first few years of life, but after that the main tool we have to guide us through the perils of life is our brain. The more effectively that brain can analyze and evaluate information, the more successful we're likely to be. The work we've done in building the basics of symbolic logic in the first three sections of this chapter has prepared us for the real point: analyzing logical arguments objectively. That's the topic of this important section.

Valid Arguments and Fallacies

A logical argument consists of two parts: a set of premises and a conclusion based on those premises. Premises are statements that are offered as supporting evidence for the conclusion. Our goal is to decide whether an argument is *valid* or *invalid*.

> An argument is **valid** if the conclusion necessarily follows from the premises, and **invalid** if it's not valid.

Notice that our definition of valid doesn't use the word *true*, because logic is not about deciding if a claim is true: it's about deciding if the claim can be deduced from the premises.

Let's look at an example.

Premise 1:   All students in this class will pass.

Premise 2:   Rachel is a student in this class.

Conclusion: Rachel will pass this class.

Since we are told that ALL students in the class will pass, we can be sure that if Rachel is a student in the class, she will pass. This is an example of a valid argument because the conclusion logically follows from the premises.

It's very important at this point to understand the difference between a true statement and a conclusion to a valid argument. A statement that is known to be false can still be a valid conclusion if it follows logically from the given premises. For example, consider this argument:

Los Angeles is in California or Mexico.

Los Angeles is not in California.

Therefore, Los Angeles is in Mexico.

✓ 1. Define *valid argument* and *fallacy*.

This is a valid argument: if we accept the two premises, then Los Angeles would in fact be in Mexico. We know, however, that Los Angeles is NOT in Mexico, and there's the tricky part. *To be valid, the conclusion of an argument has to follow from the premises whether they're true or not.* In this case, we're accepting the premise "Los Angeles is not in California" even though we know that it's actually false. We can then conclude that the conclusion (Los Angeles is in Mexico) follows logically from that premise. Again, this emphasizes that the validity of an argument is not about whether or not the conclusion is a true statement.

130   **Chapter 3**   Logic

Sidelight   LOGIC AND THE ART OF FORENSICS

Many students find it troubling that an argument can be considered valid even if the conclusion is clearly false. But arguing in favor of something that you don't necessarily believe to be true isn't a new idea by any means—lawyers do it all the time, and it's commonly practiced in the area of formal debate, a style of intellectual competition that has its roots in ancient times.

In formal debate (also known as forensics), speakers are given a topic and asked to argue one side of a related issue. Judges determine which speakers make the most effective arguments and declare the winners accordingly. One of the most interesting aspects is that in many cases, the contestants don't know which side of the issue they will be arguing until right before the competition begins. While that aspect is intended to test the debater's flexibility and preparation, a major consequence is that opinion, and sometimes truth, is taken out of the mix, and contestants and judges must focus on the validity of arguments.

A variety of organizations sponsor national competitions in formal debate for colleges. The largest is an annual championship organized by the National Forensics Association. Students from

well over 100 schools participate in a wide variety of categories. The 2011 team champion was Western Kentucky University, and individual champions came from both WKU and Northwestern University.

Truth Table Method

One method for determining the validity of an argument is by using truth tables. We will use the following procedure.

Procedure for Determining the Validity of Arguments

Step 1   Write the argument in symbols.

Step 2   Write the argument as a conditional statement; use a conjunction between all premises and the implication ($\Rightarrow$) for the conclusion. (*Note:* the $\Rightarrow$ is the same as $\rightarrow$ but will be used to designate an argument.)

Step 3   Set up and construct a truth table as follows:

Symbols | Premise $\wedge$ Premise $\Rightarrow$ Conclusion

Step 4   If all truth values under $\Rightarrow$ are Ts (that is, the statement in the last column is a tautology), then the argument is valid; otherwise, it is invalid.

> **Math Note**
>
> There can be more than two premises in an argument; in that case, put the conjunction sign $\wedge$ between all premises.

EXAMPLE 1   **Deciding If an Argument Is Valid**

Decide if the following argument is valid.

> If a figure has three sides, then it is a triangle.
> This figure is not a triangle.
> ———————————————————
> Therefore, this figure does not have three sides.

SOLUTION

Step 1 *Write the argument in symbols.* Let p = "The figure has three sides," and let q = "The figure is a triangle."
Translated into symbols:

$p \rightarrow q$ (Premise)
$\underline{\sim q}$ (Premise)
$\therefore \sim p$ (Conclusion)

A line is used to separate the premises from the conclusion and the three triangular dots $\therefore$ mean "therefore."

Step 2 *Write the argument as an implication* by connecting the premises with a conjunction and implying the conclusion as shown.

Premise 1		Premise 2		Conclusion
$(p \rightarrow q)$	$\wedge$	$\sim q$	$\Rightarrow$	$\sim p$

Step 3 *Construct a truth table* as shown.

p	q	$\sim p$	$\sim q$	$p \rightarrow q$	$(p \rightarrow q) \wedge \sim q$	$[(p \rightarrow q) \wedge \sim q] \Rightarrow \sim p$
T	T	F	F	T	F	T
T	F	F	T	F	F	T
F	T	T	F	T	F	T
F	F	T	T	T	T	T

Step 4 *Determine the validity of the argument.* Since all the values under the $\Rightarrow$ are true, the argument is valid.

▼ **Try This One 1**

Decide if the argument is valid or invalid.

I will run for student government or I will join the athletic boosters.
I did not join the athletic boosters.
Therefore, I will run for student government.

EXAMPLE 2   **Deciding If an Argument Is Valid**

Decide if this argument is valid: emerging research shows that if cancer patients undergo aromatherapy, depression is lessened. One of my cancer patients is reporting a decrease in depression, so she must have undergone aromatherapy.

SOLUTION

Step 1 *Write the argument in symbols.* Let p = "A cancer patient undergoes aromatherapy" and let q = "The patient suffers less from depression." The argument can then be written as

$p \rightarrow q$ *If aromatherapy, then less depression*
$\underline{q}$ *Less depression*
$\therefore p$ *Therefore, aromatherapy*

Step 2 *Write the argument as an implication.*

$$(p \rightarrow q) \wedge q \Rightarrow p$$

Step 3 *Construct a truth table for the argument.*

p	q	$p \rightarrow q$	$(p \rightarrow q) \wedge q$	$[(p \rightarrow q) \wedge q] \Rightarrow p$
T	T	T	T	T
T	F	F	F	T
F	T	T	T	F
F	F	T	F	T

Step 4 *Determine the validity of the argument.* This argument is invalid since it is not a tautology. (Remember, when the values are not all Ts, the argument is invalid.) In this case, we can't conclude that the patient underwent aromatherapy.

▼ Try This One 2

Decide if this argument is valid: John's boss warned him that if he blew off work to go to the playoff game, he'd get fired. I heard John got fired, so I guess he must have gone to that playoff game. Cool!

CAUTION

Remember that in symbolic logic, whether or not the conclusion is true is not important. The main concern is whether the conclusion follows from the premises.

Consider the following two arguments.

1. Either $2 + 2 \neq 4$ or $2 + 2 = 5$

   $\underline{2 + 2 = 4}$

   So $2 + 2 = 5$.

2. If $2 + 2 \neq 5$ then my feet hurt

   $\underline{\text{My feet don't hurt.}}$

   So $2 + 2 \neq 5$.

In Exercises 63 and 64, you'll construct truth tables for these arguments, and find that the one with the false conclusion is valid, while the one with the true conclusion is not. Did we mention that the validity of an argument is not about whether or not the conclusion is true?

The validity of arguments that have three premises can also be tested using truth tables, as shown in Example 3. In this case, the last column will contain a conjunction of three premises.

EXAMPLE 3   **Deciding If an Argument Is Valid**

Decide if the argument is valid.

$$p \rightarrow r$$
$$q \wedge r$$
$$\underline{p}$$
$$\therefore \sim q \rightarrow p$$

SOLUTION

Step 1 *Write the argument in symbols.* This has been done already.

Step 2 *Write the argument as an implication.* Make a conjunction of all three premises and imply the conclusion:

$$(p \to r) \wedge (q \wedge r) \wedge p \Rightarrow (\sim q \to p)$$

Step 3 *Construct a truth table.* When there are three premises, we will begin by finding the truth values for each premise and then work the conjunction from left to right as shown.

p	q	r	$\sim q$	$p \to r$	$q \wedge r$	$\sim q \to p$	$(p \to r) \wedge (q \wedge r) \wedge p$	$[(p \to r) \wedge (q \wedge r) \wedge p] \Rightarrow (\sim q \to p)$
T	T	T	F	T	T	T	T	T
T	T	F	F	F	F	T	F	T
T	F	T	T	T	F	T	F	T
T	F	F	T	F	F	T	F	T
F	T	T	F	T	T	T	F	T
F	T	F	F	T	F	T	F	T
F	F	T	T	T	F	F	F	T
F	F	F	T	T	F	F	F	T

Since the truth value for $\Rightarrow$ is all Ts, the argument is valid.

☑ 2. Use truth tables to decide if an argument is valid.

> ▼ **Try This One 3**
>
> Decide if the argument is valid.
>
> $p \vee q$
>
> $\underline{q \vee \sim r}$
>
> $\therefore q$

Common Valid Argument Forms

We have seen that truth tables can be used to test an argument for validity. But some argument forms are common enough that they are recognized by special names. When an argument fits one of these forms, we can decide if it is valid or not just by knowing the general form, rather than constructing a truth table.

We'll start with a description of some commonly used valid arguments.

1. **Law of detachment**

   $p \to q$

   $\underline{p}$

   $\therefore q$

   Example:

   If our team wins Saturday, then they go to a bowl game.

   Our team won Saturday.

   ───────────────────────

   Therefore, our team goes to a bowl game.

2. **Law of contraposition**

   $p \to q$

   $\underline{\sim q}$

   $\therefore \sim p$

> **Math Note**
>
> The law of contraposition isn't too hard to remember if you think of why it's named that way: in essence, it says that the contrapositive of a conditional statement says the same thing as the original statement. If p implies q, then not q implies not p.

Example:

If I try hard, I'll get an A.

I didn't get an A.

Therefore, I didn't try hard.

3. **Law of syllogism**, also known as **law of transitivity**:

$$p \rightarrow q$$
$$q \rightarrow r$$
$$\therefore p \rightarrow r$$

Example:

If I make an illegal U-turn, I'll get a ticket.

If I get a ticket, I'll get points on my driving record.

Therefore, if I make an illegal U-turn, I'll get points on my driving record.

4. **Law of disjunctive syllogism**:

$$p \vee q$$
$$\sim p$$
$$\therefore q$$

Example:

My top client demands the penthouse or an executive suite.

He couldn't stay in the penthouse.

Therefore, he stayed in an executive suite.

Common Fallacies

Next, we'll list some commonly used arguments that are invalid.

1. **Fallacy of the converse**:

$$p \rightarrow q$$
$$q$$
$$\therefore p$$

Example:

If it's Friday, then I will go to happy hour.

I am at happy hour.

Therefore, it is Friday.

This is not valid! You can go to happy hour other days, too.

2. **Fallacy of the inverse**:

$$p \rightarrow q$$
$$\sim p$$
$$\therefore \sim q$$

Example:

If I exercise every day, then I will lose weight.

I don't exercise every day.

Therefore, I won't lose weight.

This is also not valid. You could still lose weight without exercising *every* day.

> ### Math Note
>
> If you look closely at the fallacy of the converse and the fallacy of the inverse, they should look familiar. Calling each argument invalid is basically the same as saying the converse and the inverse, respectively, are not logically equivalent to an original conditional statement.

Sidelight **CIRCULAR REASONING**

Circular reasoning (sometimes called "begging the question") is a sneaky type of fallacy in which the premises of an argument contain a claim that the conclusion is true, so naturally if the premises are true, so is the conclusion. But this doesn't constitute evidence that a conclusion is true. Consider the following example: a suspect in a criminal investigation tells the police detective that his statements can be trusted because his friend Sue can vouch for him. The detective asks the suspect how he knows that Sue can be

trusted, and he says, "I can assure you of her honesty." Ultimately, the suspect becomes even more suspect because of circular reasoning: his argument boils down to "I am honest because I am honest."

While this example might seem blatantly silly, you'd be surprised how often people try to get away with this fallacy. A Google search for the string *circular reasoning* brings up hundreds of arguments that are thought to be circular.

3. **Fallacy of the inclusive or**:

$p \vee q$

p

$\therefore \sim q$

Example:

I'm going to take chemistry or physics.

I'm taking chemistry.

Therefore, I'm not taking physics.

Remember, we've agreed that by *or* we mean *one or the other, or both*. So you could be taking both classes.

You will be asked to prove that some of these are invalid by using truth tables in the exercises.

EXAMPLE 4   **Recognizing Common Argument Forms**

Decide if the following arguments are valid, using the given forms of valid arguments and fallacies.

(a) $p \rightarrow q$ (b) $\sim p \rightarrow q$ (c) $\sim p \rightarrow \sim q$ (d) $\sim r \rightarrow s$

   p $\sim q$ $\sim q$ $s \rightarrow t$

   $\therefore q$ $\therefore p$ $\therefore \sim p$ $\therefore \sim r \rightarrow t$

SOLUTION

(a) This is the law of detachment, therefore a *valid* argument.
(b) This fits the law of contraposition with the statement $\sim p$ substituted in place of p, so it is valid.
(c) This fits the fallacy of the converse, using statement $\sim p$ and $\sim q$ rather than p and q, so it is an invalid argument.
(d) This is the law of syllogism, with statements $\sim r$, s, and t, so the argument is valid.

▼ **Try This One 4**

3. Identify common argument forms.

Decide if the arguments are valid, using the commonly used valid arguments and fallacies.

(a) $\sim p \vee q$ (b) $r \vee s$ (c) $\sim p \rightarrow q$ (d) $(p \wedge q) \rightarrow \sim r$

   p s q r

   $\therefore q$ $\therefore \sim r$ $\therefore \sim p$ $\therefore \sim(p \wedge q)$

EXAMPLE 5	**Using Common Argument Forms to Decide If an Argument Is Valid**

Use the given forms of valid arguments and fallacies to decide if each argument is valid.

(a) If you eat a healthy diet, you'll live past 70.

You've really made an effort to eat healthy foods.

Therefore, you'll live past 70.

(b) You can access the Web at this hotel if you pay for Wi-Fi.

You're too broke to pay for Wi-Fi.

So you won't be able to access the Web.

(c) If you watch *Big Brother,* you watch reality shows.

If you watch reality shows, you have time to kill.

Therefore, if you have time to kill, you watch *Big Brother*.

(d) You planned to major in criminal justice or pre-law. Since you're majoring in criminal justice, I guess that means you're not majoring in prelaw.

(e) Botany grads work either in parks or at research labs. Linh got her degree in botany last year and doesn't work at a park, so she must work at a research lab.

SOLUTION

(a) In symbolic form this argument is $(p \rightarrow q) \wedge p \Rightarrow q$. We can see that this is the law of detachment, so the argument is *valid.*

(b) In symbolic form this argument is $(p \rightarrow q) \wedge \sim p \Rightarrow \sim q$. This is the fallacy of the inverse, so the argument is *invalid.*

(c) In symbolic form this argument is $(p \rightarrow q) \wedge (q \rightarrow r) \Rightarrow (r \rightarrow p)$. We know by the law of transitivity that if $(p \rightarrow q) \wedge (q \rightarrow r)$, then $p \rightarrow r$. The given conclusion, $r \rightarrow p$, is the converse of $p \rightarrow r$, so is not equivalent to $p \rightarrow r$ (the valid conclusion). So the argument is *invalid.*

(d) In symbolic form the argument is $(p \vee q) \wedge p \Rightarrow \sim q$. This is the fallacy of the inclusive or, so the argument is *invalid.*

(e) In symbolic form the argument is $(p \vee q) \wedge \sim p \Rightarrow q$. This is the law of disjunctive syllogism, so the argument is *valid.*

Math Note

The first premise of part (b) is a little tricky because the consequent is written first. It could be restated as "If you pay for Wi-Fi, you can access the Web."

☑ 4. Use common argument forms to decide if arguments are valid.

▼ Try This One 5

Determine whether the following arguments are valid using the given forms of valid arguments and fallacies.

(a) If you do well in hospitality management, you'll get a job at a great resort.

You graduated with a 3.8 GPA in hospitality management.

Therefore, you should get a job at a great resort.

(b) If you work hard, you will be a success.

You are not a success.

Therefore, you do not work hard.

(c) Jon is either really cheap, or flat broke. I got a look at his checking account statement and he's not broke, so he must just be cheap.

(d) If my lab rats don't die, I'll get a passing lab grade. Since I passed bio lab, that means the rats didn't die.

Many books define a valid argument this way: an argument is valid if the conclusion must be true when all the premises are true. We chose not to use that terminology because it makes it seem like there's no point in setting up an entire truth table to test an argument—just the row where all premises are true. But that's not accurate. The last column of the truth tables we've used does NOT show truth or falsehood of the *conclusion*: it shows truth or falseness of the *implication* premises → conclusion. Only when this implication is always true can we conclude that an argument is valid.

Answers to Try This One

1   Valid

2   Invalid

3   Invalid

4   (a) Valid   (b) Invalid   (c) Invalid   (d) Valid

5   (a) Valid   (b) Valid   (c) Valid   (d) Invalid

EXERCISE SET 3-4

Writing Exercises

1. Describe the structure of an argument.
2. Describe in your own words what it means for an argument to be valid.
3. When setting up a truth table to test the validity of an argument, why don't we only look at the case where all premises are true?
4. Is it possible for an argument to be valid, yet have a false conclusion? Explain your answer.
5. Is it possible for an argument to be invalid, yet have a true conclusion? Explain your answer.

6. When you are setting up a truth table to determine the validity of an argument, what connective is used between the premises of an argument? What connective is used between the premises and the conclusion? Why do these make sense?
7. Describe what the law of syllogism says, in your own words.
8. Describe why the fallacy of the inclusive or is a fallacy.

Computational Exercises

For Exercises 9–18, using truth tables, decide if each argument is valid.

9. $p \rightarrow q$
    $p \wedge q$
    $\therefore p$

10. $p \vee \sim q$
    q
    $\therefore p \wedge q$

11. $\sim p \vee q$
    p
    $\therefore p \wedge \sim q$

12. $p \leftrightarrow \sim q$
    $p \wedge \sim q$
    $\therefore p \vee q$

13. $\sim p \vee q$
    $q \rightarrow \sim p$
    $\therefore p$

14. $\sim p \leftrightarrow q$
    $\sim p \wedge q$
    $\therefore \sim p \vee q$

15. $p \leftrightarrow q$
    $\sim q$
    $\therefore \sim p$

16. $p \vee \sim q$
    $\sim q \rightarrow p$
    $\therefore p$

17. $p \wedge \sim q$
    $\sim r \rightarrow q$
    $\therefore q$

18. $p \leftrightarrow q$
    $q \leftrightarrow r$
    $\therefore p \wedge q$

In Exercises 19–24, write the given common argument form in symbols, then use a truth table to prove that it either is or is not a valid argument.

19. Law of detachment
20. Law of contraposition
21. Law of syllogism
22. Law of disjunctive syllogism
23. Fallacy of the converse
24. Fallacy of the inclusive or

For Exercises 25–34, decide if the following arguments are valid, using the given forms of valid arguments and fallacies.

25. $p \rightarrow q$
    $\sim q$
    $\therefore \sim p$

26. $p \vee q$
    q
    $\therefore \sim p$

27. $\sim p \to q$
    $\sim q$
    $\therefore \sim p$

28. $p \vee \sim q$
    q
    $\therefore p$

29. $p \to q$
    $r \to \sim q$
    $\therefore p \to \sim r$

30. $p \to q$
    $\sim q$
    $\therefore p$

31. $\sim p \vee q$
    $\sim q$
    $\therefore \sim p$

32. $\sim p \to q$
    $\sim q$
    $\therefore p$

33. $p \vee \sim q$
    q
    $\therefore \sim p$

34. $p \to \sim q$
    $\sim r \to q$
    $\therefore p \to r$

Applications in Our World

For Exercises 35–48, identify p, q, and r if necessary. Then translate each argument to symbols and use a truth table to decide if the argument is valid or invalid.

35. If I don't have to go to summer school, I'll get an internship.
    I have to go to summer school.
    ∴ I won't get an internship.

36. I need to take a grad class in evidence gathering or civil rights.
    I couldn't get into the class on civil rights.
    ∴ I'm taking a class in evidence gathering.

37. If Julia uses monster.com to send out her resume, she will get an interview.
    Julia got an interview.
    ∴ Julia used monster.com to send out her resume.

38. If it snows, I can go snowboarding.
    It did not snow.
    ∴ I cannot go snowboarding.

39. I will go to the party if and only if my ex-boyfriend is not going.
    My ex-boyfriend is not going to the party.
    ∴ I will go to the party.

40. If the gallery opening is Friday, you should finish the piece you're working on.
    If you finish the piece you're working on, then the gallery opening is Friday.
    Therefore, the gallery opening is Friday and you'll finish the piece you're working on.

41. Either I did not study or I passed the exam.
    I did not study.
    ∴ I failed the exam.

42. I will run the marathon if and only if I can run 30 miles by Christmas.
    I can run 30 miles by Christmas or I will not run the marathon.
    ∴ If I ran the marathon, then I was able to run 30 miles by Christmas.

43. If that post-op patient has a high fever, she must have an infection of some sort. If she does have an infection, we'll have to keep her overnight for observation. So if she has a high fever, we'll have to keep her overnight for observation.

44. If you back up your hard drive, then you're protected from data loss. Either you're protected from data loss, or you're some sort of daredevil. That means that if you are a daredevil, you won't back up your hard drive.

45. John Moneybags will get elected if and only if he spends the most money on his campaign. An inside source told me last week that either John will spend the most money or his opponent will hire thugs to intimidate potential voters. Just today I found out that John's opponent decided not to hire thugs for intimidation purposes, so I conclude that John won't win the election.

46. If Allie is a fine arts major, then she lives on campus. Allie's Facebook page says that she lives on campus and her best friend's name is Moose. So if Allie's best friend's name isn't Moose, she's majoring in something other than fine arts.

47. My company will get a huge contract if and only if I convince the client that our company will best represent their interests. If I manage to convince the client of this, I'll get a big bonus this year. So if I don't get a big bonus this year, you'll know that my company didn't get the huge contract.

48. Defendants that are convicted of manslaughter always serve time in prison. The defendant in the case Elena tried was represented by a public defender and was convicted of manslaughter. So if the defendant was represented by a public defender, he will not serve time in prison.

For Exercises 49–56, write the argument in symbols; then decide whether the argument is valid by using the common forms of valid arguments and fallacies.

49. I studied or I failed the class.
    I did not fail the class.
    ∴ I studied.

50. If I go to the student symposium on environmental issues, I will fall asleep.
    If the speaker is interesting, I will not fall asleep.
    ∴ If I go to the student symposium on environmental issues, the speaker will not be interesting.

51. If it is sunny, I will wear SPF 50 sun block.
    It is not sunny.
    ∴ I will not wear SPF 50 sun block.

52. I will backpack through Europe if I get at least a 3.5 grade point average.

I do not get at least a 3.5 grade point average.

∴ I will not backpack through Europe.

53. If we don't lobby the senator's office relentlessly, bills we oppose will pass. Since the Senate just passed a bill we opposed, we must not have lobbied the senator's office relentlessly.

54. Jason told me that if he got an A in anthropology, he'd run across the main campus quad wearing nothing but a sombrero. Since he did that yesterday (yuck), he must have gotten an A in anthropology.

55. I will absolutely not wear a Speedo at the beach or I'll be embarrassed. I'm not embarrassed at the beach today, so you can be sure I didn't wear a Speedo.

56. If an internship requires collecting specimens at sea, I'll get seasick. I just found out that I got an internship at Woods Hole Institute that involves collecting mussel specimens off the coast of Massachusetts. Seasickness here I come!

Critical Thinking

57. Oscar Wilde once said, "Few parents nowadays pay any regard to what their children say to them. The old-fashioned respect for the young is fast dying out." This statement can be translated to an argument, as shown next.

If parents respected their children, then parents would listen to them.

Parents do not listen to their children.

∴ Parents do not respect their children.

Using a truth table, determine whether the argument is valid or invalid.

58. Winston Churchill once said, "If you have an important point to make, don't try to be subtle or clever. Use a pile driver. Hit the point once. Then come back and hit it again. Then a third time—a tremendous wack!" This statement can be translated to an argument as shown.

If you have an important point to make, then you should not be subtle and you should not be clever.

You are not being subtle and you are not being clever.

∴ You will make your point.

Using a truth table, determine whether the argument is valid or invalid.

59. Make up your own example for each of the four common valid argument forms discussed in Section 3-4. Use topics that have some relevance to your life.

60. Make up your own example for each of the four common fallacies discussed in Section 3-4 (including the one in the sidelight on page 135). Use topics that have some relevance to your life.

61. The law of detachment is sometimes given the Latin name *modus ponens*. Look up the literal translation of that phrase on the Internet and describe how it applies.

62. The law of contraposition is also known by a Latin name, *modus tollens*. Look up the literal translation of that phrase and explain how it applies.

63. Write the argument labeled 1 on page 132 in symbols and make a truth table for it. Is the argument valid? Is the conclusion a true or false statement? What can you conclude?

64. Repeat Exercise 63 for the argument labeled 2 on page 132.

Section 3-5 Euler Circles

LEARNING OBJECTIVES

☐ 1. Define *syllogism*.

☐ 2. Use Euler circles to decide if an argument is valid.

Abraham Lincoln once said, "You can fool some of the people all of the time, and all of the people some of the time, but you cannot fool all of the people all of the time." Lincoln was a really smart guy—he understood the power of logical arguments and the fact that cleverly crafted phrases could be an effective tool in the art of persuasion. What's interesting about this quote from our perspective is the liberal use of the quantifiers *some* and *all*. In this section, we will study a particular type of argument that uses these quantifiers, along with *no* or *none*. A technique developed by Leonhard Euler way back in the 1700s is a useful method for analyzing these arguments and testing their validity.

TABLE 3-6	Types of Statements Illustrated by Euler Circles	

Type	General Form	Example
Universal affirmative	All *A* is *B*	All chickens have wings.
Universal negative	No *A* is *B*	No horses have wings.
Particular affirmative	Some *A* is *B*	Some horses are black.
Particular negative	Some *A* is not *B*	Some horses are not black.

Math Note

The "some" quantifier doesn't necessarily mean that "all" is not a more accurate description of a situation. For example, if I say "Some nursing jobs pay over $40,000," it's entirely possible that ALL of them actually do. When you read a statement like "Some horses are black," you can't assume that there are some that are not black.

Euler circles are diagrams similar to Venn diagrams. We will use them to study arguments using four types of statements. The statement types are listed in Table 3-6, and the Euler circle that illustrates each is shown in Figure 3-1.

Each statement can be represented by a specific diagram. The universal affirmative "All *A* is *B*" means that every member of set *A* is also a member of set *B*. For example, the statement "All chickens have wings" means that the set of all chickens is a subset of the set of animals that have wings. This is illustrated in Figure 3-1(a).

The universal negative "No *A* is *B*" means that no member of set *A* is a member of set *B*. In other words, set *A* and set *B* are *disjoint sets*. For example, "No horses have wings" means that the set of all horses and the set of all animals with wings are disjoint (nonintersecting): see Figure 3-1(b).

The particular affirmative "Some *A* is *B*" means that there is at least one member of set *A* that is also a member of set *B*. For example, the statement "Some horses are black" means that there is at least one horse that is a member of the set of black animals. The × in Figure 3-1(c) means that there is at least one black horse.

The particular negative "Some *A* is not *B*" means that there is at least one member of set *A* that is not a member of set *B*. For example, the statement "Some horses are not black" means that there is at least one horse that does not belong to the set of black animals. The diagram for the particular negative is shown in Figure 3-1(d). The × is placed in circle *A* but not in circle *B*. The × in this example means that there exists at least one horse that is some color other than black.

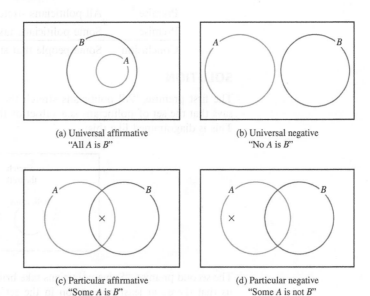

(a) Universal affirmative
"All *A* is *B*"

(b) Universal negative
"No *A* is *B*"

(c) Particular affirmative
"Some *A* is *B*"

(d) Particular negative
"Some *A* is not *B*"

Figure 3-1

 1. Define *syllogism*.

Many of the arguments we studied in Section 3-4 consisted of two premises and a conclusion. This type of argument is called a **syllogism**. We will use Euler circles to test the validity of syllogisms involving the statement types in Table 3-6. Here's a simple example:

Premise	All politicians stretch the truth.
Premise	Some politicians take bribes.
Conclusion	Some people that stretch the truth take bribes.

Remember that we are not concerned with whether the conclusion is true or false, but only whether the conclusion logically follows from the premises. If it does, the argument is valid. If not, the argument is invalid.

Euler Circle Method for Testing the Validity of an Argument

To decide if an argument is valid, diagram both premises in the same figure. If the conclusion is shown in the figure, the argument is valid. But if the premises can be diagrammed so that a different conclusion can be shown, the argument is invalid.

In many cases, the premises can be diagrammed more than one way. Our job will be to find every way the premises can possibly be diagrammed, and see if they match the conclusion. If even one diagram contradicts the conclusion, it's possible to get a different conclusion from the premises, and we've proved that the argument is invalid.

The examples in this section illustrate how we can decide if an argument is valid using Euler circles.

EXAMPLE 1   Using Euler Circles to Decide If an Argument Is Valid

Use Euler circles to decide if the argument is valid.

Premise	All politicians stretch the truth.
Premise	Some politicians take bribes.
Conclusion	Some people that stretch the truth take bribes.

SOLUTION

The first premise, "All politicians stretch the truth," is the universal affirmative; it says that the set of politicians is a subset of the set of people who stretch the truth. This is diagrammed like this:

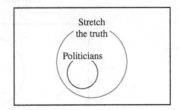

The second premise, "Some politicians take bribes," is the particular affirmative; it tells us that there's at least one person in the set of politicians that's also in the set of people who take bribes. So we need to put an $\times$ in the intersection of the "politicians"

circle and the "take bribes" circle; this can be done by either putting the entire "take bribes" circle inside the "stretch the truth" circle, or by having the "take bribes" circle go outside the "stretch the truth" circle.

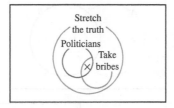
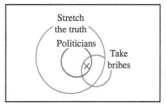

The conclusion of the argument is that some people that stretch the truth take bribes. For this to be valid, every possible diagram of the premises has to have at least one object in the set of people that stretch the truth that's also in the set of people that take bribes. The × in each diagram shows that this is the case, so the argument is valid.

▼ **Try This One 1**

Use Euler circles to decide if the argument is valid.

All college students buy textbooks.
Some book dealers buy textbooks.
Therefore, some college students are book dealers.

It isn't necessary to use actual subjects such as crooked politicians and truth-stretchers in syllogisms. Arguments can use letters to represent the various sets, as shown in Example 2.

EXAMPLE 2   Using Euler Circles to Decide If an Argument Is Valid

Use Euler circles to decide if the argument is valid.

Some A is not B.
All C is B.
∴ Some A is C.

SOLUTION

The first premise, "Some A is not B," is diagrammed by drawing circles for A and B with at least one element in A that is not in B.

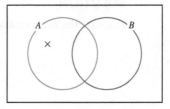

The second premise, "All C is B," is diagrammed by placing circle C inside circle B. This can be done in three different ways: the circle for C has to live entirely inside the circle for *B*. It can either intersect partially with the circle for *A*, live completely inside it, or miss it entirely.

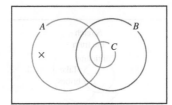 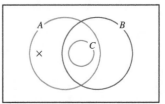

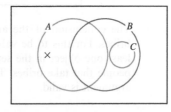

The third diagram shows that the argument is invalid. It matches both premises, but there are no members of *A* that are also in *C*, so it contradicts the conclusion "Some *A* is *C*."

▼ **Try This One 2**

Use Euler circles to decide if the argument is valid.

Some *A* is *B*.
Some *A* is not *C*.
∴ Some *B* is not *C*.

Let's try one more specific example.

| EXAMPLE 3 | **Using Euler Circles to Decide If an Argument Is Valid** |

Use Euler circles to decide if the argument is valid.

No criminal is admirable.
Some athletes are not criminals.
∴ Some admirable people are athletes.

SOLUTION

Diagram the first premise, "No criminal is admirable."

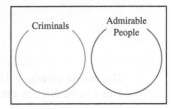

144   **Chapter 3**   Logic

We can add the second premise, "Some athletes are not criminals," in at least two different ways:

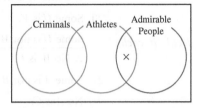 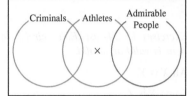

In the first diagram, the conclusion appears to be valid: some athletes are admirable. But the second diagram doesn't support that conclusion, so the argument is invalid.

☑ 2. Use Euler circles to decide if an argument is valid.

▼ Try This One 3

Use Euler circles to decide if the argument is valid.

All cruise directors have degrees in hospitality management.

No one with a degree in hospitality management services cabins.

∴ No cruise directors service cabins.

Remember that Euler circles can be useful for certain types of arguments, but they're definitely not a substitute for truth tables. Euler circles are a convenient way to evaluate syllogisms made up of special types of statements involving quantifiers; truth tables work for arguments in general. In Exercises 47 and 48, we'll see how truth tables can be used in place of Euler circles.

Answers to Try This One

1   Invalid   **3**   Valid

2   Invalid

EXERCISE SET 3-5

Writing Exercises

1. Name and give an example of each of the four types of statements that can be diagrammed with Euler circles.
2. Explain how to decide whether an argument is valid or invalid after drawing Euler circles.
3. What is a syllogism?
4. How do Euler circles differ from Venn diagrams?

Computational Exercises

For Exercises 5–14, draw an Euler circle diagram for each statement.

5. Some environmentalists ride motorcycles.
6. No hybrid cars cost less than $26,000.
7. Some people do not go to college.
8. No textbooks are perfect. (Not even this one.)
9. Some law enforcement officers are women.
10. Some fad diets do not result in weight loss.

11. Some laws in the United States are laws in Mexico.
12. Some lobbyists do not offer bribes to politicians.
13. No cheeseburgers are low in fat.
14. Some politicians are crooks.

For Exercises 15–24, use Euler circles to decide if each argument is valid or invalid.

15. All *X* is *Y*.

    Some *Y* is *Z*.

    ∴ Some *X* is *Z*.

16. Some *A* is not *B*.

    No *B* is *C*.

    ∴ Some *A* is not *C*.

17. Some *P* is *Q*.

    No *Q* is *R*.

    ∴ Some *P* is not *R*.

18. All *S* is *T*.

    No *S* is *R*.

    ∴ Some *T* is *R*.

19. No *M* is *N*.

    No *N* is *O*.

    ∴ Some *M* is not *O*.

20. Some *U* is *V*.

    Some *U* is not *W*.

    ∴ No *W* is *U*.

21. Some *A* is not *B*.

    No *A* is *C*.

    ∴ Some *A* is not *C*.

22. All *P* is *Q*.

    All *Q* is *R*.

    ∴ All *P* is *R*.

23. No *S* is *T*.

    No *T* is *R*.

    ∴ No *S* is *R*.

24. Some *M* is *N*.

    Some *N* is *O*.

    ∴ Some *M* is *O*.

Applications in Our World

For Exercises 25–42, use Euler circles to decide if the argument is valid.

25. All phones are communication devices.

    Some communication devices are inexpensive.

    ∴ Some phones are inexpensive.

26. Some students are overachievers.

    No overachiever is lazy.

    ∴ Some students are not lazy.

27. Some dietitians are overweight.

    No personal trainers are overweight.

    ∴ No personal trainers are dietitians.

28. Some protesters are angry.

    Some protesters are not civil.

    ∴ Some civil people are not angry.

29. Some teachers are underpaid.

    Nobody that's underpaid reports complete satisfaction with their job.

    ∴ Some teachers are not completely satisfied with their job.

30. Some Democrats vote for Independents.

    Some people that vote for Independents are not politically active.

    ∴ Some Democrats are not politically active.

31. Some biologists are park rangers.

    No biologist is a rodeo clown.

    ∴ No park rangers are rodeo clowns.

32. Some CEOs are women.

    Some women are tech-savvy.

    ∴ Some CEOs are not tech-savvy.

33. Some juices have antioxidants.

    Some fruits have antioxidants.

    ∴ No juices are fruits.

34. Some theater majors perform in musicals.

    No art appreciation majors perform in musicals.

    ∴ No theater majors are art appreciation majors.

35. Some nurses have RN degrees.
    All nurses went to college.

    All people that went to college have high school diplomas.

    ∴ Some people with high school diplomas went to college.

36. All students text message during class.
    Some students in class take notes.

    All students who take notes in class pass the test.

    ∴ Some students pass the test.

146   **Chapter 3** Logic

37. Some birds can talk.
Some animals that can talk can also moo.

All cows can moo.

∴ Some cows can talk.

38. All cars use gasoline.
All things that use gasoline emit carbon dioxide.

Some cars have four doors.

∴ Some things with four doors emit carbon dioxide.

39. Every police officer carries a gun, and some people that carry guns cannot be trusted. So it's clear to me that some police officers can't be trusted.

40. I've seen bosses that don't treat their employees well. Everyone I know has a boss, so some of them don't get treated well.

41. All of the teams in the NCAA tournament won more games than they lost this year, and some of them won at least two-thirds of their games. So all of the teams that won more than two-thirds of their games are playing in the NCAA tournament.

42. Some of the people that got flu shots this year got the flu anyhow. Nobody in my family got a flu shot this year, so I'm sure that none of us will get the flu.

Critical Thinking

For Exercises 43–46, write a conclusion so that the argument is valid. Use Euler circles.

43. All *A* is *B*.

All *B* is *C*.

∴

44. No *M* is *P*.

All *S* is *M*.

∴

45. All calculators can add.

No adding machines can make breakfast.

∴

46. Some people are prejudiced.

All people have brains.

∴

47. Here's a guide for translating the types of statements studied with Euler circles into statements using connectives so that we can use truth tables to evaluate the same arguments. For two sets *A* and *B*, let *p* = "the object belongs to set *A*", and *q* = "the object belongs to set *B*." Then "All *A* is *B*" can be translated as $p \rightarrow \sim q$; "No *A* is *B*" can be translated as $p \rightarrow \sim q$; "Some *A* is *B*" translates to $p \wedge q$; and "Some *A* is not *B*" translates to $p \wedge \sim q$. Use these to translate the arguments in Examples 1 and 3 in this section into symbols, like we did in Section 3-4.

48. Use your answers from Problem 47 to decide if each argument is valid. Did your results match the results of Examples 1 and 3? If not, try again!

CHAPTER **3**   # Summary

Section	Important Terms	Important Ideas
3-1	Statement Simple statement Compound statement Connective Conjunction Disjunction Conditional Biconditional Negation	**Formal symbolic logic** is based on statements. A statement is a sentence that is either true or false but not both. A simple statement contains only one idea. A compound statement is formed by joining two or more simple statements with connectives. The four basic connectives are the conjunction (which uses the word *and* and the symbol ∧), the disjunction (which uses the word *or* and the symbol ∨), the conditional (which uses the words *if . . . then* and the symbol →), and the biconditional (which uses the words *if and only if* and the symbol ↔). The symbol for negation is ~. Statements are usually written using logical symbols and letters of the alphabet to represent simple statements. This removes the actual topic from our study of the argument and makes it less likely that we will be influenced by emotion or personal opinions.
3-2	Truth table	**Truth Tables** can be used to decide if compound statements are true or false based on the truth value of the simple statements that make them up. This is largely based on knowing how to evaluate the truth values associated with connectives. A conjunction $p \wedge q$ is true only when both p and q are true; a disjunction $p \vee q$ is true as long as at least one of p or q is true; a conditional $p \rightarrow q$ is true unless p is true and q is false; a biconditional $p \leftrightarrow q$ is true when p and q have the same truth value.
3-3	Tautology Self-contradiction Logically equivalent statements Converse Inverse Contrapositive De Morgan's laws Antecedent Consequent	**A statement** that is always true is called a tautology. A statement that is always false is called a self-contradiction. Two statements that have the same truth values are said to be logically equivalent. De Morgan's laws are used to find the negation of a conjunction or disjunction. From the conditional statement, three other statements can be made: the converse, the inverse, and the contrapositive. Of these three, only the contrapositive is logically equivalent to the original conditional statement.
3-4	Argument Premise Conclusion	**A logical argument** consists of two parts: a set of premises, and a conclusion based on those premises. Premises are statements that are offered as supporting evidence for the conclusion. An argument is called valid when the conclusion follows necessarily from the premises. If not, it is called invalid. Truth tables can be used to decide if a given argument is valid. We write a conditional statement where the antecedent is the conjunction of all premises and the consequent is the conclusion of the argument. If that conditional statement is a tautology, then the argument is valid. Otherwise, it is invalid.
3-5	Syllogism Euler circles Universal affirmative Universal negative Particular affirmative Particular negative	**Euler circles** are diagrams similar to Venn diagrams that can be used to decide if certain types of arguments are valid. This type of argument involves statements of four forms: all *A* is *B*, No *A* is *B*, Some *A* is *B*, and Some *A* is not *B*.

148   **Chapter 3**   Logic

MATH IN ▶ Mind Control REVISITED

All of the arguments listed are invalid except the last one. If you were to write that argument using connectives, it would be "A school like Butler makes it to the Final Four → toga party on the moon; Butler made the Final Four; therefore toga party on the moon." Of course, this conclusion is false (no matter how cool it sounds), but this is because the first premise is false, not because the argument isn't valid.

The first argument is basically "Fire → smoke, so smoke → fire." This is the fallacy of the converse. So is the second: money → happiness, so happiness → money. The third argument looks like this: being in SEC → good enough for bowl, so not being in SEC → not good enough for bowl. This is the fallacy of the inverse. The fourth argument is classical circular reasoning (see the Sidelight on p. 135). The fifth is another fallacy of the inverse: weapons of mass destruction → war, so no weapons of mass destruction → not war.

Review Exercises

Section 3-1

For Exercises 1–5, decide whether the sentence is a statement.

1. Let's go with the flow.
2. Medical assistants report a high level of job satisfaction.
3. That politician's ideas are crazy.
4. Ignorance is always a choice.
5. Are we there yet?

In Exercises 6–12, decide if the statement is simple or compound. If it's compound, classify it as a conjunction, disjunction, conditional, or biconditional.

6. I'm majoring in communications and public relations.
7. The fine arts are widely supported by public grants.
8. If we hadn't found the obstruction in time, the patient probably would have died.
9. Defendants are convicted if and only if the jury agrees on their guilt unanimously.
10. Anthropology is the study of an obscure animal known as the anthrop.
11. I'm going to pass this final or change my major.
12. We should call a tree surgeon if our prized buckeye tree loses any more leaves.

For Exercises 13–18, write the negation of the statement.

13. The cell phone is out of juice.
14. No people who live in glass houses throw stones.
15. Some failing students can learn new study methods.
16. There is a printer that has no ink.
17. All SUVs are gas guzzlers.
18. The tires on that hybrid are black.

For Exercises 19–28, let p = "It is ambitious" and let q = "It is worthwhile." Write each statement in symbols.

19. It is ambitious and worthwhile.
20. If it is worthwhile, then it is ambitious.
21. It is worthwhile if and only if it is ambitious.
22. It is worthwhile and not ambitious.
23. If it is not ambitious, then it is not worthwhile.
24. It is not true that it is worthwhile and ambitious.

25. It is not true that if it is ambitious, then it is worthwhile.
26. It is not worthwhile if and only if it is not ambitious.
27. It is not true that it is not worthwhile.
28. It is neither ambitious nor worthwhile.

For Exercises 29–33, let p = "It is cool." Let q = "It is cloudy." Write each statement in words.

29. $p \vee \sim q$
30. $q \rightarrow p$
31. $p \leftrightarrow q$
32. $(p \vee q) \rightarrow p$
33. $\sim(\sim p \vee q)$

Section 3-2

34. True or false: a conditional statement is true unless the consequent is false.
35. True or false: a disjunction is true only if one of the two simple statements involved is true.

For Exercises 36–43, construct a truth table for each statement.

36. $p \leftrightarrow \sim q$
37. $\sim p \rightarrow (\sim q \vee p)$
38. $(p \rightarrow q) \wedge \sim q$
39. $\sim p \vee (\sim q \rightarrow p)$
40. $\sim q \leftrightarrow (p \rightarrow q)$
41. $(p \rightarrow \sim q) \vee r$
42. $(p \vee \sim q) \wedge r$
43. $r \rightarrow (\sim p \vee q)$

For Exercises 44–47, use the truth value of each simple statement to determine the truth value of the compound statement. You may need to use the Internet as a resource.

44. *p*: the population of the United States surpassed 400 million in 2012.
    q: the United States was the third most populous country in the world in 2012.
    Statement: $p \rightarrow q$
45. *p*: gas prices remained near historic highs into 2012.
    q: more hybrid cars and light trucks were put into production for the 2012 model year.
    Statement: $p \wedge q$
46. *p*: Mitt Romney was a Presidential candidate in 2012.
    q: Charlie Sheen was a Presidential candidate in 2012.
    r: Romney won the Republican nomination in 2012.
    Statement: $(p \vee q) \rightarrow r$

47. p: attending college costs thousands of dollars.
    q: lack of education does not lead to lower salaries.
    r: the average college graduate will make back more than they paid for school.
    Statement: $(p \land \sim q) \leftrightarrow r$

Section 3-3

48. Write an example of a conditional statement $p \rightarrow q$ that has a different truth value than its converse. Then explain why you can't do that for the contrapositive.

For Exercises 49–53, decide if the statement is a tautology, self-contradiction, or neither.

49. $p \rightarrow (p \lor q)$
50. $(p \rightarrow q) \rightarrow (p \lor q)$
51. $(p \land \sim q) \leftrightarrow q \land \sim p$
52. $q \rightarrow p \lor \sim p$
53. $(\sim q \lor p) \land q$

For Exercises 54–56, decide if the two statements are logically equivalent.

54. $\sim(p \rightarrow q);\ \sim p \land \sim q$
55. $\sim p \lor q;\ \sim(p \leftrightarrow q)$
56. $(\sim p \land q) \lor r;\ (\sim p \lor r) \land (q \lor r)$

For Exercises 57–60, use De Morgan's laws to write the negation of each statement.

57. Social work is lucrative or fulfilling.
58. We will increase sales or our profit margin will go down.
59. The signature is not authentic and the check is not valid.
60. It is not strenuous and I am tired.

For Exercises 61 and 62, assign a letter to each simple statement and write the compound statement in symbols.

61. I will be happy only if I get rich.
62. Having a good career is sufficient for a fulfilling life.

For Exercises 63–65, write the converse, inverse, and contrapositive of the statement.

63. If gas prices go any higher, I will start riding my bike to work.
64. If I don't pass this class, my parents will kill me.
65. The patient will get an MRI only if the X-rays are inconclusive.

Section 3-4

For Exercises 66–69, use truth tables to decide if each argument is valid or invalid.

66. $p \rightarrow \sim q$
    $\sim q \leftrightarrow \sim p$
    $\therefore p$

67. $\sim q \lor p$
    $p \land q$
    $\therefore \sim q \leftrightarrow p$

68. $\sim p \lor q$
    $q \lor \sim r$
    $\therefore q \rightarrow (\sim p \land \sim r)$

69. $\sim r \rightarrow \sim p$
    $\sim q \lor \sim r$
    $\therefore p \leftrightarrow q$

For Exercises 70–73, write the argument in symbols; then use a truth table to decide if the argument is valid.

70. I'm going to Wal-Mart and McDonald's.
    If I go to McDonald's, I will get the sweet tea.
    $\therefore$ I did not get sweet tea and go to Wal-Mart.

71. If we don't hire two more workers, the union will strike.
    If the union strikes, our profit will not increase.
    We hired two more workers.
    $\therefore$ Our profit will not increase.

72. Whenever I show my clients a new workout routine, they end up getting in better shape. T.J. is chunkier than ever, so obviously I didn't show him a new routine.

73. I won't go check on my bacteria experiment today if I'm not finished with my paper. I finished my paper, so either I didn't check on my bacteria experiment or I went bowling.

For Exercises 74 and 75, use the commonly used forms of arguments from Section 3-4 to decide if the argument is valid.

74. If it is early, I will get tickets to the comedy club.
    It is not early.
    $\therefore$ I will not get tickets to the comedy club.

75. If pigs fly, then I'm a monkey's uncle.
    Pigs fly or birds don't sing.
    Birds do sing.
    $\therefore$ I'm a monkey's uncle.

Section 3-5

For Exercises 76–80, use Euler circles to determine whether the argument is valid or invalid.

76. No A is B.
    Some B is C.
    $\therefore$ No A is C

77. Some A is not C.
    Some B is not C.
    $\therefore$ Some A is not B.

78. All money is green.
    All grass is green.
    $\therefore$ Grass is money.

79. No psychologists write prescriptions.
    Some psychiatrists write prescriptions.
    $\therefore$ No psychiatrists are psychologists.

80. Some policemen are college grads, and all college grads expect to make at least $35,000 per year, so some policemen expect to make $35,000 or greater.

Chapter Test

1. True or false: an argument can only be valid if its conclusion is true.
2. True or false: the last column in a truth table used to decide if an argument is valid represents a conditional statement.
3. Explain why we use letters to represent statements when studying arguments in logic.

150   **Chapter 3** Logic

4. Decide if each sentence is a statement.

   (a) My degree is in microbiology.
   (b) The capital of California is Paris.
   (c) Hang in there, man.
   (d) A career in law enforcement is WAY better than a career in teaching.

For Exercises 5–8, write the negation of the statement.

5. The image is uploading to my online bio.
6. All men have goatees.
7. Some students ride a bike to school.
8. No nursing majors have trouble finding jobs.

For Exercises 9–14, let p = "It is warm." Let q = "It is sunny." Write each statement in symbols.

9. It is warm and sunny.
10. If it is sunny, then it is warm.
11. It is warm if and only if it is sunny.
12. It is warm or sunny.
13. It is false that it is not warm and sunny.
14. It is not sunny, and it is not warm.

In Exercises 15–18, let p = "Congress is in session" and q = "My representative is in Aruba." Write each statement in words.

15. $p \wedge \sim q$
16. $q \to p$
17. $(p \vee q) \to p$
18. $\sim(\sim p \vee q)$

For Exercises 19–22, construct a truth table for each statement.

19. $p \to \sim q$
20. $(p \to \sim q) \wedge r$
21. $(\sim q \vee p) \wedge p$
22. $p \to (\sim q \vee r)$

For Exercises 23–25, decide if each statement is a tautology, self-contradiction, or neither.

23. $(p \wedge q) \wedge \sim p$
24. $(p \vee q) \to (p \to q)$
25. $\sim(p \wedge q) \vee p$

26. Are the two statements logically equivalent?
    $(p \vee q) \wedge r; (p \wedge r) \vee (q \wedge r)$
27. Write the converse, inverse, and contrapositive for the statement "If I exercise regularly, then I will be healthy." Which are equivalent to the original statement?
28. Use De Morgan's laws to write the negation of the compound statement.
    (a) It is not cold and it is snowing.
    (b) I am hungry or thirsty.

For Exercises 29 and 30, use truth tables to determine the validity of each argument.

29. $\sim q \vee p$
    $\underline{p \vee q}$
    $\therefore \sim q \to p$

30. $p \to q$
    $\underline{\sim q \vee \sim r}$
    $\therefore q \leftrightarrow (\sim p \wedge \sim r)$

For Exercises 31 and 32, decide if the argument is valid or invalid by using the given forms of valid arguments and fallacies.

31. If I finish my paper early, I will have my professor proofread it.
    I have my professor proofread my paper.

    $\therefore$ I finish my paper early.

32. If Starbucks isn't too busy, I'll study there, but if Starbucks is too busy, I'll study at the library. If I don't end up studying at Starbucks, you can find me at the library.

For Exercises 33 and 34, use Euler circles to determine whether the argument is valid or invalid.

33. No B is A.
    Some A is C.

    $\therefore$ No B is C.

34. Some of the arts are inaccessible to the general public.
    All pursuits that are inaccessible need public funding.

    $\therefore$ Some of the arts need public funding.

Projects

1. Politicians argue in favor of positions all the time. An informed voter doesn't vote for a candidate because of the candidate's party, gender, race, or how good they look on TV—an informed voter listens to the candidates' positions and evaluates them.

   Do a Google search for the text of a speech by each of the main candidates in the 2012 Presidential election. Then find at least three logical arguments within the text, write the arguments in symbols, and use truth tables or commonly used argument forms to analyze the arguments, and see if they are valid.

2. Electric circuits are designed using truth tables. A circuit consists of switches. Two switches wired in *series* can be

represented as $p \wedge q$. Two switches wired in *parallel* can be represented as $p \vee q$.

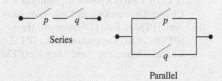

Series

Parallel

In a series, circuit electricity will flow only when both switches p and q are closed. In a parallel circuit, electricity will flow when one or the other or both switches are closed. In a truth table, T represents a closed switch and F represents an open switch. So the truth table for $p \wedge q$ shows electricity flowing only when both switches are closed.

	Truth table				Circuit	
p	q	$p \wedge q$		p	q	$p \wedge q$
T	T	T		closed	closed	current
T	F	F		closed	open	no current
F	T	F		open	closed	no current
F	F	F		open	open	no current

Also, when switch p is closed, switch $\sim p$ will be open and vice versa, and p and $\sim p$ are different switches. Using this knowledge, design a circuit for a hall light that has switches at both ends of the hall so that the light can be turned on or off from either switch.

3. One of the biggest benefits to studying formal logic is generally improving your ability to think logically, even if you're not using the specific methods we studied in this chapter. The ability to think logically is an important part of almost all standardized tests. In particular, the Law School Admissions Test (LSAT) is well known for featuring logic puzzles like the following. How logically can you think now that you've completed this chapter?

A therapist is scheduling her sessions for an upcoming day when she plans to see seven patients, plus take an hour to grab a salad and run some errands. All of the patients are being treated for either depression or posttraumatic stress. Of course, all of the patients will be scheduled for a separate session. In addition:

- The therapist likes to separate out conditions, so none of the patients suffering from posttraumatic stress will be scheduled consecutively.
- Jyoti will be scheduled before both Henry and Paul.
- Juan, who suffers from posttraumatic stress, absolutely needs the third appointment of the day.
- Henry is also being treated for posttraumatic stress.
- Jyoti is not being treated for posttraumatic stress only if Paul is not being treated for depression.
- Paul can't make the seventh and final appointment.

(a) Which of the following could be a complete list of the appointment order and respective conditions from earliest to latest?
   (i) Jyoti (PTSD), Mariska (Depression), Juan (PTSD), Paul (Depression), Henry (PTSD), Chanel (Depression), and Jake (Depression)
   (ii) Jyoti (PTSD), Paul (Depression), Henry (PTSD), Jake (Depression), Juan (PTSD), Chanel (Depression), and Mariska (PTSD)

   (iii) Henry (PTSD), Jyoti (Depression), Juan (PTSD), Mariska (Depression), Jake (Depression), Paul (PTSD), and Chanel (Depression)
   (iv) Chanel (Depression), Jyoti (Depression), Juan (PTSD), Mariska (Depression), Henry (PTSD), Jake (Depression), and Paul (PTSD)
   (v) Mariska (PTSD), Jyoti (Depression), Juan (PTSD), Jake (Depression), Paul (Depression), Henry (PTSD), Chanel (Depression)

(b) What's the smallest possible number of patients with appointments before Henry?

(c) If Jyoti has the second appointment, which of the following has to be true?
   (i) Jake's and Juan's appointments are not consecutive.
   (ii) Mariska is scheduled before Paul.
   (iii) Henry has the last appointment of the day.
   (iv) The first patient of the day suffers from PTSD.
   (v) Exactly four of the patients suffer from PTSD.

(d) Each one of the following statements must be false EXCEPT:
   (i) Exactly five of the patients suffer from depression.
   (ii) Exactly three of the patients with appointments after Juan have PTSD.
   (iii) Jyoti arrives second, and Henry arrives fifth.
   (iv) Jyoti suffers from depression, and Jake from PTSD.
   (v) There are three appointments between Juan and Paul, regardless of which has the earlier appointment.

(e) If Henry doesn't have the last appointment, then which one of the following CANNOT be true?
   (i) Chanel arrives before Mariska.
   (ii) Exactly four of the patients have PTSD.
   (iii) Paul arrives before Juan.
   (iv) Jake is being treated for depression.
   (v) Jyoti is being treated for depression.

(f) If Chanel is scheduled after Jake but before Mariska, then which one of the following statements, if true, would provide enough information to determine the patient's exact order of arrival and condition each is being treated for?
   (i) Chanel is scheduled fourth, and exactly three of the patients have PTSD.
   (ii) Chanel is scheduled sixth, and exactly four of the patients have PTSD.
   (iii) Jake is scheduled second, and exactly four of the patients have depression.
   (iv) Jyoti is scheduled fourth, and no more than three of the patients have depression.
   (v) Jyoti is scheduled first, and exactly three of the patients have depression.

Topics in Algebra

CHAPTER 6

Topics in Algebra

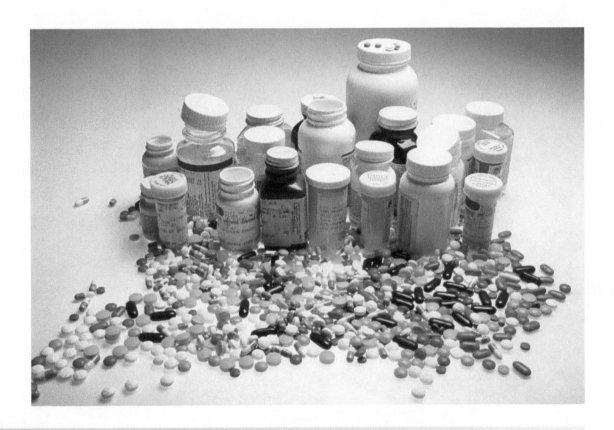

Outline

6-1   The Fundamentals of Algebra   **6-5**   Solving Linear Inequalities

6-2   Solving Linear Equations   **6-6**   Solving Quadratic Equations

6-3   Applications of Linear Equations   Summary

6-4   Ratio, Proportion, and Variation

MATH IN ▶ Drug Administration

Have you ever looked at the dosage information on a bottle of aspirin and thought "It just doesn't seem reasonable to recommend the same dosage for all adults"? People come in all shapes and sizes, and the effect of a certain dosage is in large part dependent on the size of the individual. If a 105-pound woman and her 230-pound husband both take two aspirin the morning after their wedding reception, she is in effect getting more than twice as much medicine as he is.

Because there's a lot of variation in the world, the study of algebra was created, based on a brilliantly simple idea: using a symbol, rather than a number, to represent a quantity that can change. Since the word "vary" is a synonym for change, we call such a symbol a *variable*. The use of variables is the thing that distinguishes algebra from arithmetic and makes it extremely useful to describe phenomena in a world in which very few things stay the same for very long. An understanding of the basics of algebra is, in a very real sense, the gateway to higher mathematics and its applications. Simply put, you can only go so far with just arithmetic. To model real situations, expressions involving variables are almost always required.

In this chapter, you will be introduced to the fundamental ideas of algebra: variables, expressions, equations, and inequalities. We're setting the groundwork for a lot of the math that will follow in the book, but we will always keep an eye on how the fundamentals of algebra can be applied to situations in our world, like dosage calculations. You're accustomed to losing points when you make a mistake in a calculation, but outside the classroom, the stakes can be a LOT higher.

The wrong dose of aspirin might upset your stomach, but more serious drugs carry with them more serious consequences. In many cases, an incorrect dosage could lead to death. Using the skills you learn in the chapter, you should be able to answer the following questions.

Suppose that a new pain-killing drug is being tested for safety and effectiveness in a variety of people. The recommended dosage for an average 170-pound man is 400 mg. The manufacturer claims that the minimum effective dose for a person of that size is 250 mg, and that anything over 1,500 mg could be lethal. Two of the patients in the test are a 275-pound college football player recovering from a major injury, and a 65-pound girl being treated for sickle-cell disease. According to the manufacturer, dosages for this drug are proportional to body weight.

- What would the recommended dosage be for each patient?
- If the medications are mixed up and the recommended dosage for the football player is given to the child, is she in danger of dying?
- Would the child's recommended dosage be at all effective for the football player?

For many medications, the effective dosage depends not just on body weight but also on body surface area, which accounts for the overall size of the patient. We'll study this slightly more complicated approach to dosage briefly in Problem 97 of Section 6-1, then in more depth in Project 3 at the end of this chapter.

For answers, see Math in Drug Administration Revisited on page 361

Section 6-1   The Fundamentals of Algebra

LEARNING OBJECTIVES

☐ 1. Identify terms and coefficients.

☐ 2. Simplify algebraic expressions.

☐ 3. Evaluate algebraic expressions.

☐ 4. Apply evaluating expressions in our world.

In the movie "The Shawshank Redemption," there's a character who is released from prison after being locked away for a very long time. The first thing that jumped out at him after going back out into the world was how quickly everything and everyone seemed to move. In a letter back to his friends in prison, he wrote "The world went and got itself in a big damn hurry."

Things do change very quickly in our modern world, and those who can't adapt to change get left behind. We have seen that arithmetic is a very valuable tool in our world, but working only with numbers has one main limitation: a number is what it is, and it can't change. That might be the world's shortest explanation of the value of algebra—in the study of algebra we use *variables* to represent quantities that change (or *vary*). That gives us the flexibility to model far more things in our changing world than when we strictly use fixed numbers. So it's only reasonable that our coverage of the fundamentals of algebra begins with a look at variables.

Basic Definitions

Algebra is a branch of mathematics that generalizes the concepts of arithmetic by applying them to quantities that are allowed to vary.

> A **variable**, usually represented by a letter, is a quantity that can change. It represents unknown values in a situation.

There's no reason we HAVE TO use letters to represent quantities that vary—it's just convenient to do so. If you want, you could use a smiley face, a flower, a picture of your mom, whatever. We'll use letters though because we don't know what your mom looks like.

For example, we can write the formula distance = rate × time as $d = rt$. Then the letters d, r, and t are all variables. This allows us to describe a relationship between these quantities not just for a specific distance, rate, and time, but a wide variety of them.

The right side of the equation $d = rt$ is an example of an algebraic expression.

> An **algebraic expression** is a combination of variables, numbers, operation symbols, and grouping symbols.

Math Note

An algebraic expression does *not* have an equal sign in it; $d = rt$ is an *equation*, not an expression.

Some examples of algebraic expressions are

$$3x + 2 \qquad 8x^2 \qquad 111 \qquad \frac{9}{5}C + 32 \qquad 7(2y^2 - 5)$$

Algebraic expressions are made up of one or more *terms*. Terms are the pieces in an expression that are separated by addition or subtraction signs. In the expression $8x^2 + 6x - 3$, each of $8x^2$, $6x$, and -3 is a term. The expression 111 has just one term, namely 111.

Every term has a **numerical coefficient**, or just coefficient. This is the number part of a term, like the 8 in $8x^2$. Terms also may or may not have variables in them; the term -3 in the preceding paragraph doesn't have a variable. For the term $-17x^2y$, -17 is the coefficient, and x and y are the variables.

EXAMPLE 1   Identifying Terms and Coefficients

> **Math Note**
>
> In the expression in Example 1, the negative sign in front of 3 is considered to be part of the term. We could write the expression as
>
> $$-8y + \frac{5}{2}x^3 + xy + (-3)$$

Identify the terms of the algebraic expression, and the coefficient for each term.

$$-8y + \frac{5}{2}x^3 + xy - 3$$

SOLUTION

The expression has four terms: $-8y$, which has coefficient -8; $\frac{5}{2}x^3$, which has coefficient $\frac{5}{2}$; xy, which has coefficient 1; and -3, which has coefficient -3. (When no number appears in a term, as in xy, the coefficient is 1; we just don't need to write it.)

☑ 1. Identify terms and coefficients.

> ▼ **Try This One 1**
>
> Identify the terms of the algebraic expression, and the coefficient for each term.
>
> $$3x^2y - \frac{1}{2}y^3 + \sqrt{3}x - y + 10$$

The Distributive Property

The distributive property, which we studied in Chapter 5, is used very often in working with algebraic expressions. (Recall that the distributive property is $a(b + c) = ab + ac$ for any numbers a, b, and c.) Using new terminology from this section, the distributive property tells us that when an expression with more than one term in parentheses is multiplied by a term outside the parentheses, the term outside can be distributed to each term inside. This is illustrated in Example 2.

EXAMPLE 2   Using the Distributive Property

> **Math Note**
>
> When the term being distributed is negative, notice that the sign of *every* original term inside the parentheses changes. Not doing so is one of the most commonly made mistakes in all of math, so be especially careful not to make it!

Use the distributive property to multiply out the parentheses.

(a) $5(3x + 7)$ (b) $-3(6A - 7B + 10)$

SOLUTION

(a) Distributing the 5 to each term inside the parentheses, we get

$$5(3x + 7) = 5 \cdot 3x + 5 \cdot 7 = (5 \cdot 3)x + 35 = 15x + 35$$

Note the use of the associative property in deciding that $5 \cdot 3x$ is $15x$.

(b) This time we have to be careful because the term we're distributing is negative.

$$-3(6A - 7B + 10) = -3 \cdot 6A - (-3) \cdot 7B + (-3) \cdot 10 = -18A + 21B - 30$$

▼ **Try This One 2**

Use the distributive property to multiply out the parentheses.

(a) $7(4x - 20)$ (b) $-5(3x - 7y + 18)$

Simplifying Algebraic Expressions

When two terms have the same variables with the same exponents, we will call them **like terms**. For example, $3x$ and $-5x$ are like terms, but $3x$ and $-5x^2$ are not. Table 6-1 shows some examples of like and unlike terms.

TABLE 6-1   **Like Terms and Unlike Terms**

Like Terms		Unlike Terms	
$6x$	$-10x$	$6x$	$-10x^2$
$8x^3$	$6x^3$	$8x^3$	$6y^3$
$2x^2y$	$-5x^2y$	$2x^2y$	$-5xy^2$
5	12	x	5

> **Math Note**
>
> Here's an easy way to tell if two terms are like: cover up the coefficients. If the things left over are perfectly identical, the terms are like. If they're different in any way, the terms are not like.

Like terms can be added or subtracted by using the reverse of the distributive property. For example,

$$3x + 5x = (3 + 5)x = 8x$$

$$-2x^2y + 3x^2y + 9x^2y = (-2 + 3 + 9)x^2y = 10x^2y$$

Unlike terms cannot be added or subtracted since the distributive property does not apply.

In other words, to add or subtract like terms (i.e., combine like terms), add or subtract the numerical coefficients of the like terms. Unlike terms cannot be combined by addition or subtraction.

It's a little bit silly, but effective, to think of the variable parts of terms as objects, say bunny rabbits. In that case, 3 bunny rabbits plus 5 bunny rabbits is 8 bunny rabbits—you're just adding the numbers. But 3 bunny rabbits plus 5 teddy bears isn't 8 anything—bunny rabbits and teddy bears are not like objects, so you can't add them.

EXAMPLE 3   **Combining Like Terms**

Combine like terms, if possible.

(a) $9x - 20x$ (b) $3x^2 + 8x^2 - 2x^2$ (c) $6x + 8x^2$

SOLUTION

(a) $9x - 20x = (9 - 20)x = -11x$ (Found by subtracting $9 - 20$)

(b) $3x^2 + 8x^2 - 2x^2 = (3 + 8 - 2)x^2 = 9x^2$ (Found by adding and subtracting $3 + 8 - 2$)

(c) $6x + 8x^2$ (These terms cannot be combined since they are not like terms.)

▼ **Try This One 3**

Combine like terms for each, if possible.

(a) $12y^2 - 18y^2$ (b) $7xy + 9xy - 11xy$ (c) $10z^2 + 10$

Algebraic expressions can have any number of terms. The phrase "to simplify an expression" means to find any terms that are like and combine them as in Example 3. For example, in the expression $-6x + 3y - 12 + 8y - 2x + 10$, $-6x$ and $-2x$ are like terms that combine to give $-8x$; $3y$ and $8y$ are like terms that combine to give $11y$; and -12 and 10 are like terms that combine to give -2. So the simplified version of the expression is $-8x + 11y - 2$. (The order of terms is not important.)

EXAMPLE 4   **Combining Like Terms**

Simplify each expression.

(a) $9x - 7y + 18 - 27 + 6y - 10x$
(b) $3x^3 + 4x^2 - 6x + 10 - 7x^2 + 4x^3 + 2x - 6$

SOLUTION

(a) Combine like terms: $9x - 10x = -x$

$$-7y + 6y = -y$$
$$18 - 27 = -9$$

The answer is $-x - y - 9$.

(b) Combine like terms: $3x^3 + 4x^3 = 7x^3$

$$4x^2 - 7x^2 = -3x^2$$
$$-6x + 2x = -4x$$
$$10 - 6 = 4$$

The answer is $7x^3 - 3x^2 - 4x + 4$.

▼ **Try This One 4**

Simplify each expression.

(a) $2x - 6 + 3y - 7x + 8y - 12$
(b) $9y^3 + 7y - 2y^2 + 6 - 8 + 8y^3 - 7y + 12y^2$
(c) $3a - 2b + 4c - 7a + 3b + 2c$

When an algebraic expression has parentheses, it can be simplified by combining the two skills we've already practiced in this section: multiplying out the parentheses using the distributive property, and combining like terms.

| EXAMPLE 5 | **Simplifying an Algebraic Expression** |

Simplify the expression $8(3x^2 + 5) + 3(2 - x) - (5x^2 + x)$.

SOLUTION

First, we multiply out the parentheses. We can think of the last set as $-1(5x^2 + x)$.

$$8(3x^2 + 5) = 24x^2 + 40$$
$$3(2 - x) = 6 - 3x$$
$$-1(5x^2 + x) = -5x^2 - x$$

Now we combine like terms:

$$24x^2 - 5x^2 - 3x - x + 40 + 6 = 19x^2 - 4x + 46$$

> *Math Note*
>
> A negative sign outside parentheses changes the sign of every term inside. For example,
> $-(3x - 2) = -3x + 2$

☑ 2. Simplify algebraic expressions.

▼ **Try This One 5**

Simplify each expression.

(a) $5(7y + 10) - (4y + 8)$ (b) $2z + 5 - 3(4 - 2z^2) + 10(z^2 + z)$

Evaluating Algebraic Expressions

Algebraic expressions almost always contain variables, which can be any number. But when we substitute numbers in for the variables, the result is an arithmetic problem. Finding the value of this problem is called *evaluating* the expression. This is illustrated in Example 6.

| EXAMPLE 6 | **Evaluating an Expression** |

Evaluate $9x - 3$ when $x = 5$.

SOLUTION

Substitute 5 for the variable x, then perform the calculation:

$$9x - 3 = 9(5) - 3 \quad \textit{Multiply first.}$$
$$= 45 - 3 \quad \textit{Subtract.}$$
$$= 42$$

The value of $9x - 3$ when $x = 5$ is 42.

▼ **Try This One 6**

Evaluate each expression.

(a) $9x - 17$ when $x = 3$.   (b) $2x^2 - 3x + 5$ when $x = -10$.

Expressions with more than one variable are evaluated in the same way.

Sidelight A BRIEF HISTORY OF ALGEBRA

Algebra had its beginnings when people attempted to solve mathematical riddles. One of the earliest books which contained algebraic problems (i.e., riddles) was a collection of 85 problems copied by an Egyptian priest, Ahmes, around 1650 BCE. This manuscript later became known as the *Rhind Papyrus*. We referred to this document when studying the Egyptian numeration system in Section 4-1.

The next important development in algebraic thinking came around 250 CE, when a famous mathematician named Diophantus wrote a book called *Arithmetica,* which contained about 130 algebraic problems and a number of algebraic principles called theorems. *Arithmetica* contained problems that were solved using first-degree and second-degree equations in one unknown. Diophantus studied mathematics in Alexandria in northern Egypt where Euclid and Hypatia had also lived.

Diophantus is known as the "Father of Algebra" because he was the first mathematician to use symbols to represent mathematical concepts. Prior to Diophantus, all mathematical concepts were written out in words.

A Persian mathematician, Al-khwārizmī, wrote a book on algebra, and when it was translated into Latin, the word "al-jabr," which later became "algebra," was used in the title of the translation. The word means the science of reduction and cancellation.

One of the first mathematicians to realize the existence of negative numbers was Leonardo de Pisa, called Fibonacci (1170–1250 CE), who used them to solve financial problems. The use of the plus sign (+) and minus sign (−) first appeared in print in an arithmetic textbook written by Johann Widman in 1489. Prior to this, plus and minus signs were used by merchants to mark bales or barrels that were weighed at warehouses and compared to a standard weight. If the barrels were heavier than the standard weight, they were marked with a plus sign. If they weighed less than the standard weight, they were marked with a minus sign.

In 1494, a Franciscan friar, Luca Pacioli, published a book called *Summa de Arithmetica,* which contained all the known algebra to date. A French mathematician, François Vieta (1540–1603), was the first person to use letters to represent quantities. He used vowels for variables or unknowns and consonants for constants or knowns.

René Descartes in 1637 used a variation of Vieta's symbolization. He used the first letters of the alphabet to represent constants or knowns and the letters at the end of the alphabet to represent variables or unknowns. When an equation had one unknown, Descartes used the letter "x" to represent it. Descartes also used the letters "x" and "y" to represent the coordinates of a point.

You probably had no idea that the algebra you studied in high school was the product of 3,500 years of study!

EXAMPLE 7 **Evaluating an Expression with Two Variables**

Evaluate $5x^2 - 7y + 2$ when $x = -3$ and $y = 6$.

SOLUTION

Substitute -3 for x and 6 for y in the expression, and then use order of operations to perform the calculation.

$$5x^2 - 7y + 2 = 5(-3)^2 - 7(6) + 2 \quad \textit{Exponent first.}$$
$$= 5(9) - 7(6) + 2 \quad \textit{Multiply twice.}$$
$$= 45 - 42 + 2 \quad \textit{Add and Subtract.}$$
$$= 5$$

The value of $5x^2 - 7y + 2$ when $x = -3$ and $y = 6$ is 5.

▼ **Try This One 7**

Evaluate $6x + 8y - 15$ when $x = -5$ and $y = 7$.

☑ 3. Evaluate algebraic expressions.

Algebraic expressions have a practically endless supply of applications in our world. In the remainder of the section, we'll look at just a few examples.

As you look over these examples, and practice application problems in the exercises, try to focus on the fact that *this is the real point of algebra*! Too often, students fall into the "who cares what x is?" trap in algebra. The reason we learn to work with variables, expressions, and equations is so we can use algebra to answer questions about real situations.

EXAMPLE 8   Finding Commission on Sales

A salesperson at a popular clothing boutique gets a $600 monthly salary and a 10% commission on everything she sells. The expression $0.10x + 600$ describes the amount of money she earns each month, where x represents the dollar amount of sales. If she had net sales of $13,240 in July, how much did she earn?

SOLUTION

Since we were told that x represents monthly sales, and that her sales for July were $13,240, we substitute 13,240 in for x, then simplify.

$$0.10(13,240) + 600 = 1,324 + 600$$
$$= 1,924$$

The salesperson earned $1,924 in July.

Calculator Guide

Graphing calculators can be used to evaluate expressions. To perform the evaluation in Example 8, use the following keystrokes:

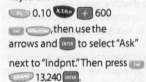 0.10 X,T,θ,n + 600

2nd WINDOW, then use the arrows and ENTER to select "Ask"

next to "Indpnt." Then press 2nd GRAPH 13,240 ENTER.

▼ Try This One 8

The salesperson in Example 8 is considering a job at a different store that pays a $400 salary per month, but a 15% commission, so that the amount she would earn is given by $0.15x + 400$, where x is the dollar amount of sales. Would she earn more or less on her July sales? By how much?

EXAMPLE 9   Computing Total Cost Including Tax

The state of Florida has a sales tax of 6%.

(a) Write an expression for the total cost of an item purchased in Florida, including sales tax. The variable should represent the cost of the item before tax.
(b) John bought an iPhone at a store in Hollywood, Florida. The price was $349. What was the total cost John paid, including tax?

SOLUTION

(a) We'll use the variable x to represent the cost of the item before tax. The sales tax will be 6% of x, or $0.06x$. That makes the total cost $x + 0.06x$, which simplifies to $1.06x$.
(b) Substitute 349 in for x: $1.06(349) = \$369.94$.

▼ **Try This One 9**

The sales tax in Georgia is only 4%. How much money would John have saved if he bought the iPhone at the same chain store in Georgia instead of Florida?

EXAMPLE 10   **Computing a Discount Price**

> *Math Note*
>
> When we found the discount price in Example 10, we decided that 40% is $0.4x$ (where x is the selling price), and subtracted that from x to get $0.6x$. We could also have noticed that taking 40% off results in the price being 60% of what it was originally, which would get us directly to $0.6x$. Clever!

While shopping at her favorite department store, Carmen found a dress she's been hoping to buy on the 40%-off clearance rack.

(a) Write an algebraic expression representing the new price of the dress before tax, then one for the total price including tax. Use 6% as the sales tax rate.

(b) If the original price of the dress was $59, find the discounted price, and the total amount that Carmen would pay including tax.

SOLUTION

(a) Let x represent the original price of the dress. Then the amount of the discount is 40% of x, or $0.4x$. So the sale price is $x - 0.4x$, which simplifies to $0.6x$. With a sales tax rate of 6%, the total cost will be

$$\underset{\substack{\textit{Discount} \\ \textit{price}}}{0.6x} \quad + \quad \underset{\substack{\textit{6% Sales} \\ \textit{tax}}}{0.06(0.6x)} = 0.6x + 0.036x = 0.636x$$

(b) In our expressions in part (a), the variable x represented the original price of the dress, so we substitute 59 in for x. The discount price is $0.6(59) = \$35.40$, and the total cost including tax is $0.636(59) = \$37.52$.

▼ **Try This One 10**

A sporting goods store in Cincinnati is having a going-out-of-business sale. Bad for them, good for me. All items are 70% off. Write an algebraic expression describing the sale price of items before tax, and one for the total price including tax. (The sales tax rate in Cincy is 6.5%.) Finally, find the discount and total prices if I buy a golf club that originally sold for $180 along with a dozen golf balls that were originally $24.99.

Formulas are used in almost any area where numbers can describe some quantity. A formula is an equation, usually with more than one variable, that allows you to calculate some quantity of interest. For example, you probably recognize the equation $A = lw$ as the formula for calculating the area of a rectangle. You can use the same procedure used to evaluate expressions to get information from a formula, as in Example 11.

EXAMPLE 11   **Using the Formula for Distance**

The distance in miles a car travels is given by the formula $d = rt$, where r is the rate (or speed) in miles per hour and t is the time in hours. How far will a car travel in 6 hours at a rate of 55 miles per hour?

Math Note

Formulas can be evaluated using units in addition to numbers. For example, in the previous problem, if the units were included, the formula would look like this:

$$d = \frac{55 \text{ miles}}{\text{hour}} \cdot \frac{6 \text{ hours}}{1}$$

$$= 330 \text{ miles}$$

The hours divide out, leaving behind miles.

☑ 4. Apply evaluating expressions in our world.

SOLUTION

In the formula $d = rt$, substitute 55 for r and 6 for t and evaluate.

$$d = rt$$
$$d = 55(6)$$
$$d = 330$$

The car will cover 330 miles in 6 hours.

▼ Try This One 11

In Canada and in other countries where the metric system is used, the temperature is given in Celsius instead of Fahrenheit. If the temperature in Montreal is 26°C, find the corresponding Fahrenheit temperature. The formula is $F = \frac{9}{5}C + 32$.

Answers to Try This One

1	Term	$3x^2y$	$-\frac{1}{2}y^3$	$\sqrt{3x}$	$-y$	10
	Coefficient	3	$-\frac{1}{2}$	$\sqrt{3}$	-1	10

2 (a) $28x - 140$
   (b) $-15x + 35y - 90$

3 (a) $-6y^2$
   (b) $5xy$
   (c) Cannot be combined

4 (a) $-5x + 11y - 18$
   (b) $17y^3 + 10y^2 - 2$
   (c) $-4a + b + 6c$

5 (a) $31y + 42$
   (b) $16z^2 + 12z - 7$

6 (a) 10
   (b) 235

7 11

8 $462 more

9 $6.98

10 $0.3x$; $0.3195x$; $61.50; $65.49

11 78.8°F

EXERCISE SET 6-1

Writing Exercises

1. If someone said to you "a variable is a letter," how would you explain to them that they're incorrect?
2. Students often use the terms "expression" and "equation" interchangeably. Explain why that's a bad idea.
3. Explain the connection between terms, coefficients, and algebraic expressions.
4. What does it mean to evaluate an algebraic expression? What do you need to be given in order to do so?
5. What does it mean to simplify an expression?
6. How does the distributive property come into play when simplifying expressions?
7. What's meant by the term *formula*?
8. Give at least three examples of quantities you're aware of that can be calculated using a formula.

Computational Exercises

For Exercises 9–42, simplify the expression.

9. $5x + 12x - 6x$
10. $3x^2 + 8x^2 - 15x^2$
11. $4y - 10y - 12y$
12. $8A - 15A + 2A$
13. $3p + 2q - 7 + 6p - 3q - 10$
14. $5x - 8y + 9 + 4y - 27 + 2x$
15. $8x^2 + 6x - 10 + 15 - 7x + 3x^2$
16. $-9x^2 - 2x - 7 + 3 - 5x + 21x$
17. $5(6x - 7)$
18. $9(3x + 8)$
19. $-4(12x - 10)$
20. $-8(4m + 7)$
21. $-7(3x + 8) - 5x + 6$
22. $-10(4x + 11) - 15x + 19$
23. $8(6 - 2x^2) - 3(7x - 1) + x^2$
24. $-3(8y^2 - 2y) + 16y^2 - 9(2y + 7)$
25. $4x - 2 - (x + 3) + 11(2x - 4y)$
26. $3(x - 2) - (x + 4) + 30(-y - x)$
27. $3(4 - x^2) - 2(5x + 7) + x^2$
28. $-2(3y^2 + y) + 5y^2 - 7(y + 2)$
29. $7x^2y + 8xy^2 - 9 + 10xy^2 - 11x^2y$
30. $-2ab + 5a^2b + 8ab - 11b^2 + 14a^2b$
31. $\frac{5}{2}(2m - 7) + 8m + \frac{17}{2}$
32. $4k - \frac{2}{3} + \frac{5}{3}(3k + 4)$
33. $\frac{15}{4}yz + \frac{1}{4}(3 - yz) - \frac{3}{2}$
34. $\frac{5}{8}ab + \frac{11}{8}(2 - ab) + \frac{9}{4}$
35. $\frac{7}{2}(6m - 4) + 10m + \frac{13}{2}$
36. $5k - \frac{3}{4} + \frac{7}{4}(2k + 10)$
37. $\frac{12}{5}(5 - 2xz) + \frac{3}{4}xz - \frac{3}{2}$
38. $\frac{9}{8}(2ab + 4) - \frac{11}{8}(5 - 6ab)$
39. $0.6(8 + tz) - 10(6tz - 9)$
40. $-12.2(rs + 7) + 0.5(8 - rs)$
41. $0.5(3 + tz) - 0.25(tz + 6)$
42. $-0.4(rs - 5) + 0.3(2 + tz)$

For Exercises 43–66, evaluate the expression for the given value or values of the variable.

43. $5x - 7$ when $x = 18$
44. $-3x + 8$ when $x = 5$
45. $3x^2 + 2x - 6$ when $x = 5$

46. $8x^2 - 7x + 4$ when $x = 16$
47. $9r^2 - 5r - 10$ when $r = -7$
48. $14x^2 - 6x + 30$ when $x = -7$
49. $3x^2 - 2y^2 + 6x$ when $x = -8$ and $y = 2$
50. $5x^2 - 7x + 2y^2$ when $x = -1$ and $y = 5$
51. $13y^2 - 6x^2 + 7y - 6x + 1$ when $x = -5$ and $y = 9$
52. $5x^2 - 4x + 3 - 2y$ when $x = 7$ and $y = -3$
53. $9x^2 + 7y^2 + 6x + 2y + 5$ when $x = 1$ and $y = 5$
54. $10y^3 + 10y^2 + 7x - 6$ when $x = -3$ and $y = 10$
55. $y + \frac{2x}{5}$ when $x = 6$ and $y = -2$
56. $5x - \frac{4y}{7}$ when $x = 7$ and $y = 3$
57. $8x^2 - \frac{5}{2y}$ when $x = 4$ and $y = 6$
58. $6x^2 - \frac{10}{3y}$ when $x = -5$ and $y = 15$
59. $4x^2 - 3x + 10$ for $x = -\frac{3}{2}$
60. $-3 - 4y - 5y^2$ for $y = \frac{11}{5}$
61. $\frac{t - 7}{t + 5}$ for $t = 5\frac{2}{3}$
62. $\frac{7 - 3x}{2x + 4}$ for $x = -3\frac{1}{2}$
63. $4rs + 6s^2 - 2r$ when $r = 1.7$ and $s = 2.2$
64. $3x^2 + 3y^2 - 6xy$ when $x = 2.4$ and $y = -1.9$
65. $8st + 5s^2 - 3t^2$ when $t = -2.5$ and $s = 0.5$
66. $x^2 + y^2 - 2xy$ when $x = 1.5$ and $y = -0.5$

For Exercises 67–76, evaluate each formula.

67. $A = 2\pi rh$ when $\pi \approx 3.14$, $r = 6$ in., and $h = 10$ in.
68. $P = 2l + 2w$ when $l = 10$ feet and $w = 5$ feet
69. $A = P(1 + rt)$ when $P = \$5,000$, $r = 0.07$ per year, and $t = 3$ years
70. $S = \frac{1}{2}gt^2$ when $g = 32$ ft/sec^2 and $t = 20$ seconds
71. $V = \frac{4}{3}\pi r^3$ when $r = 4$ mm and $\pi \approx 3.14$
72. $S = 4\pi r^2$ when $r = 7$ and $\pi \approx 3.14$
73. $FV = P(1 + r)^n$ when $P = \$20,000$, $r = 0.06$, and $n = 8$
74. $v = V + gt$ when $V = 50$, $g = -32$, and $t = 8.5$
75. $SA = 2\pi rh + 2\pi r^2$ when $\pi \approx 3.14$, $r = \frac{11}{2}$, and $h = 12$
76. $T = 2\pi\sqrt{\dfrac{L}{g}}$ when $\pi \approx 3.14$, $L = 10$, and $g = 32$

Applications in Our World

77. The simple interest (I) on a certain amount of money (p) that is invested at a specified interest rate (r) for a specific period of time (t) can be found by the formula $I = prt$. Find the interest on a principal of $500 invested at 5% yearly for 4 years.

78. For a group project in economics class, four students find that the average hourly salary for administrative assistants in a nearby city can be estimated using the equation $11.2 + 1.88x + 0.547y$, where x is the number of years of experience on the job and y is the number of years of college completed. Find the expected salary for an admin that completed 4 years of college and has worked at his company for 5 years.

79. For a manufacturing company, finding the number of defective items they are likely to produce is really important. A study at a plant that produces microchips for use in smart phones indicates that the number of defective items produced by any given worker can be estimated by the expression $2.2x - 0.6y + 9.6$, where x is the number of hours worked in that shift, and y is the number of chips produced. Who is likely to produce more defective chips: a worker that makes 40 chips in a seven hour shift, or one that makes 46 chips in a 10-hour shift? By how much?

80. Two of the key factors in determining the value of a home are the square footage inside the home and the size of the property the home sits on. In one upscale seaside community, the price of a home (in thousands of dollars) on the market can be predicted by the formula $122.56x + 0.223y + 57.3$, where x is the number of acres the home sits on and y is the square footage of the house. Which would be expected to cost more: a 3,600 square foot house with 5.5 acres of land or a 5,800 square foot house with 1.8 acres? By how much?

81. Find the electric current, I, delivered by battery cells connected in a series given by the formula $I = \frac{nE}{R} + nr$ when $n = 4$, $E = 2$ volts, $R = 12$ ohms, and $r = 0.2$ ohms.

82. The kinetic energy (KE) in ergs of an object is given by the formula $KE = \frac{mv^2}{2}$ where m is the mass of the object and v is the velocity. Find the kinetic energy when $m = 30$ g and $v = 200$ cm/s.

83. The heat energy from electricity is given by the formula $E = 0.238I^2Rt$. Find E when the current $I = 25$ amps, the resistance $R = 12$ ohms, and the time $t = 175$ s.

84. The future value (FV) of a compound interest investment (P) at a specific interest rate (r) for a specific number of periods, n, is found by the formula $FV = P(1 + r)^n$. Find the future value of $9,000 invested at 8% compounded annually for 6 years.

85. Use Einstein's mass-energy equivalence formula $E = mc^2$ to find how many joules of energy E are equivalent to an object with a mass $m = 2$ kg that is moving at the speed of light $c = 300,000$ km/s.

86. The effective interest rate, which is the actual interest rate earned after interest is compounded N times a year, is given by the formula $r_{eff} = \left(1 + \frac{r}{N}\right)^N - 1$, and then that decimal is converted to a percentage. Find the effective interest rate for an account where the given interest rate is $r = 0.0625$ and the interest is compounded monthly ($N = 12$).

87. The M224 mortar is commonly used by U.S. infantry troops for shelling enemy positions. With a muzzle velocity of 940 feet per second, a mortar fired from an elevation of 200 feet at a 45 degree angle relative to the ground will have height $h = -16t^2 + 494t + 200$ t seconds after launch. Find the height of a mortar 10, 20, 30, and 40 seconds after it's launched.

88. The profit equation for a company can be found by taking its revenue (money coming in) and subtracting its costs (money going out). The revenue equation for a certain company is $R = 3.25x$ and the cost equation is $C = 1.15x + 500$, where x is the number of units sold. Find a formula from the profit equation and then find the profit made from selling 1,000 units.

89. Monique is a sales rep for a pharmaceutical company. She makes $1,200 per month in salary and a 12% commission on sales within her territory. The expression $0.12x + 1,200$ describes her monthly earnings, where x is the dollar amount of sales. Her sales for the first 3 months of 2014 were $19,400, $22,390, and $18,145. How much did she earn in those 3 months?

90. A beer vendor in a major-league baseball park gets paid $12 per game, plus 6% of beer sales. Her per-game pay is given by $12 + 0.06x$, where x is the dollar amount of beer sales. Over one big four-game series, she sold $490, $634, $590, and $432 in beer. How much money did she make total?

91. When Monique (Problem 89) was hired, she was given the option of her current salary structure or another plan that would pay her $2,000 monthly in base pay, but just 7% commission. Write an expression describing her monthly pay under this plan in terms of x, her sales in dollars. Then use your expression to decide if she would have made more or less during the three month period at the beginning of 2014 if she'd chosen this alternate plan. By how much?

92. The beer vendors at a different ballpark from the one in Problem 90 get $20 per game, but only 4% of their beer sales. Write an expression describing the per-game pay for a beer vendor at this park in terms of x, the beer sales in dollars. Would the vendor from Problem 90 have made more or less at the other park? By how much?

93. The state of Maine has a 5% sales tax. Write an expression for the total cost of an item bought in Maine including sales tax. The variable should represent the cost of the item before tax. Then use your expression to find the total cost, including tax, of a TV with a sale price of $1,199.

94. Some counties in California have a sales tax of 9.75%—ouch! Write an expression for the total cost of an item bought in one of those counties including sales tax. The variable should represent the cost of the item before tax. Then use your expression to find the total cost, including tax, of an Abercrombie shopping spree with items totaling $425.

95. The clearance rack at the Lacoste store near my house offers 35% off all items.
    (a) Write an algebraic expression representing the discount price of an item that originally cost x dollars, and an expression for the total cost including sales tax, which is 6.25% in my county.
    (b) The regular retail price of the classic Lacoste pique polo is $89.50. Find the discount price for one on the clearance rack, and the total cost with sales tax.

96. The bookstore at Enormous State U has a policy of marking up all items to 140% of the wholesale price.
    (a) Write an algebraic expression representing the retail price of an item that originally cost x dollars, and an expression for the total cost including sales tax of 5%.
    (b) If one student's book purchases for the semester cost the bookstore $330 wholesale, find the retail price and the total price including sales tax.

Critical Thinking

97. The amount of medication a person receives is sometimes based on what is called *body surface area* (BSA) in square meters (m²). The formula for BSA is $\text{BSA} = \sqrt{(\text{weight in kg}) \times (\text{height in cm}/3{,}600)}$. If an order of medication is 50 mg/m², how much medication should be given to a person who weighs 88 kg and has a height of 150 cm?

98. A track with straightaways of length x yards and width y yards has half-circles at the end of a rectangle, as shown in the diagram. The perimeter of a half-circle is $P = \pi r$, where r is the radius, which is half the distance across the circle.

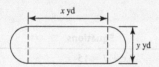

(a) Write an expression describing the distance around the track in terms of x and y.
(b) One track in this shape has straightaway length 110 yards and width 50 yards, while another has length 200 yards and width 75 yards. How much longer is a 12-lap race around the larger track?

99. An efficiency consultant informs the CEO of Bosman Automotive Manufacturing that the weekly cost of producing x alternators is given by the formula $C = -0.03x^2 + 42.7x + 633$. If the company is currently selling the alternators for $70 each, write and simplify a formula that describes the profit they will make from making and selling x alternators.

100. (a) Use your answer from Problem 99 to find the profit for 0, 100, 200, 300, 400, and 500 alternators.
     (b) Find the average profit per alternator sold at each of those production levels, then describe any trends you notice.

101. At Bosman Automotive Manufacturing, the daily production of alternators during a typical month can be modeled using the equation $P_1 = -0.06x^2 + 1.8x + 61$, where x is days since the month began. The company is planning a large expansion: they will expand their current plant to triple production, and acquire a competitor with production equation $P_2 = -0.02x^2 + 0.74x + 40$. Write and simplify a formula that describes the company's production after the expansion.

102. (a) Use your answer from Problem 101 to find the new production for the 1st, 8th, 15th, 22nd, and 29th days of the month. Round to the nearest unit.
     (b) If the company continues to sell its product for $70, how much more revenue will it make for each of those days compared to previous levels of production? Again, round production to the nearest unit.

Section 6-2   Solving Linear Equations

In Section 6-1, we saw many situations in which algebraic expressions can help us find information in our world. But sometimes there's a little more work involved. In Example 9, we found the total cost of an iPhone including tax. But what if we knew the total cost, and wanted to find the price before tax? In that case, the formula we set up would look like $1.06x = 369.94$, and we would be interested in finding the value of x that makes the equation true.

    The truth is that very often when you are using a formula to find some quantity of interest, the quantity you want to find is going to be mixed into the equation, like the original price in the example above. This requires the ability to solve equations, which is probably the most useful skill in algebra.

LEARNING OBJECTIVES

- ☐ 1. Decide if a number is a solution of an equation.
- ☐ 2. Identify linear equations.
- ☐ 3. Solve general linear equations.
- ☐ 4. Solve linear equations containing fractions.
- ☐ 5. Solve formulas for one specific variable.
- ☐ 6. Decide if an equation is an identity or a contradiction.

Basic Definitions

> An **equation** is a statement that two algebraic expressions are equal.

It's absolutely crucial that you understand the difference between an equation and an expression, because there are some things that can be done to equations, but not expressions. Table 6-2 reviews the distinction between equations and expressions.

    For most equations, if you substitute in some values of the variable the equation will be a true statement, and for other values it will be false.

Math Note

Equations can have any number of solutions. Some have one, some have two, some have many, and some have none at all.

> A **solution** of an equation is a value of the variable that makes the equation a true statement when substituted into the equation. **Solving** an equation means finding *every* solution of the equation. We call the set of all solutions the **solution set**, or simply the **solution** of an equation.

For example, $x = 2$ is one solution of the equation $x^2 - 4 = 0$, because $(2)^2 - 4 = 0$ is a true statement. But $x = 2$ is not **the** solution, because $x = -2$ is a solution as well. The solution set is actually $\{-2, 2\}$.

TABLE 6-2	**Expressions and Equations**

Expressions	Equations
$5x + 7$	$5x + 7 = 15$
$3x + 4y + 7$	$3x + 4y + 7 = 10$
$8 + 5$	$8 + 5 = 13x$
$4(x + 6)$	$4(x + 6) = 20x - 7$

EXAMPLE 1	**Identifying Solutions of an Equation**

Decide if the given value is a solution of the equation.

(a) $4(x - 1) = 8$; $x = 2$
(b) $x + 7 = 2x - 1$; $x = 8$
(c) $2y^2 = 200$; $y = -10$

SOLUTION

(a) Substituting 2 in for x we get:
$$4(2 - 1) = 8$$
$$4(1) = 8$$
$$4 = 8$$

This is not true, so $x = 2$ is not a solution of the equation.

(b) Substituting 8 in for x we get:
$$8 + 7 = 2(8) - 1$$
$$15 = 16 - 1$$
$$15 = 15$$

This is true, so $x = 8$ is a solution of the equation.

(c) Substituting in -10 for y, we get:
$$2(-10)^2 = 200 \quad (-10)^2 = 100, \text{ not } -100!$$
$$2 \cdot 100 = 200$$
$$200 = 200$$

This is true, so $y = -10$ is a solution of the equation.

▢ 1. Decide if a number is a solution of an equation.

> ### ▼ Try This One 1
>
> Decide if the given value is a solution of the equation.
>
> (a) $3(t - 4) = 5t$; $t = -6$
> (b) $x^2 + x = 12$; $x = 3$
> (c) $7y + 3 = 10y - 4$; $y = 2$

We will begin our study of solving equations by working with a special type. *Linear equations* are equations in which the variable appears only to the first power. Here's a formal definition:

> A **linear equation in one variable** is an equation that can be written in the form $Ax + B = 0$, where A and B are real numbers, and A is not zero.

For example, $2x + 3 = 7$ is a linear equation. Certainly, it fits our informal definition because the only variable that appears has exponent 1. It also fits the formal definition because it can be rewritten as $2x - 4 = 0$ (we will see shortly how to do so). In that form, it fits the formal definition with $A = 2$ and $B = -4$.

EXAMPLE 2	**Identifying Linear Equations**

Decide which of the equations are linear equations.

(a) $2(x - 3) = 3x + 2$ (c) $\frac{1}{2}t - 3^2 = 10$

(b) $y^2 - 4 = 0$ (d) $x(x + 3) = 4$

Math Note

Part (d) of Example 2 shows that it's usually a good idea to simplify both sides of an equation before deciding if it is or is not linear.

SOLUTIONS

(a) This is a linear equation: the variable appears only to the first power.
(b) This is not a linear equation: the variable has exponent 2.
(c) This is a linear equation. Don't let the fraction, or the exponent on 3 fool you! The variable has exponent 1.
(d) This is not a linear equation. It looks like it at first, because both xs have exponent 1. But the left side can be simplified to $x^2 + 3x$, so we see that x has exponent two.

> ### ▼ Try This One 2
>
> Decide which of the equations are linear equations.
>
> (a) $3z + 7 = z^3$ (c) $2x = x(4 - x)$
> (b) $7x - 4 = 11$ (d) $19(2y - 7) = 5(3y + 1)$

☑ 2. Identify linear equations.

Solving Basic Linear Equations

When two equations have the same solution set, we call them **equivalent equations**. The equations $x - 3 = 0$ and $x = 3$ are equivalent because in each case, the only number that makes them true is $x = 3$. Our strategy for solving linear equations will be to perform one or more steps that transforms the original equation into an equivalent one, until we get to the point where the solution set is obvious, like the equation $x = 3$.

We'll use two main tools to accomplish this. The first involves addition and subtraction.

> ### The Addition and Subtraction Properties of Equality
>
> You can add or subtract the same real number or algebraic expression to both sides of an equation without changing the solution set. In symbols, if $a = b$, then $a + c = b + c$ and $a - c = b - c$.

In Example 3, we'll see how to use these properties to solve simple linear equations.

EXAMPLE 3	**Solving Linear Equations Using the Addition and Subtraction Properties**

Math Note

When solving equations, make sure you add or subtract on *both sides* of the equation! Adding or subtracting on one side only will almost always change the solutions. That's bad.

Solve each equation, and check your answer.

(a) $x - 5 = 9$
(b) $y + 30 = 110$

SOLUTION

(a) The goal is to transform the equation into one whose solution is obvious. We can do this by isolating the variable, x, on the left side. To do so, we'll add 5 to both sides.

$$x - 5 = 9$$
$$x - 5 + 5 = 9 + 5$$
$$x = 14$$

The solution set is now obvious: it's {14}. **One of the great things about solving equations is that you can easily check your answer by substituting back into the original equation:**

Check: $14 - 5 = 9$
$9 = 9$ ✓   *The equation is true, so 14 is a solution.*

(b) This time, to isolate the variable, we subtract 30 from both sides.

$$y + 30 = 110$$
$$y + 30 - 30 = 110 - 30$$
$$y = 80$$

The solution set is {80}.

Check: $80 + 30 = 110$
$$110 = 110 \checkmark$$

▼ Try This One **3**

Solve each equation, and check your answer.

(a) $y + 25 = 70$ (b) $x - 13 = 20$

When solving an equation where the coefficient of the variable is not 1, we'll need one of the next two properties.

The Multiplication and Division Properties of Equality

You can multiply or divide both sides of an equation by the same *nonzero* real number without changing the solution set. In symbols, if $a = b$, then $a \cdot c = b \cdot c$ and $\frac{a}{c} = \frac{b}{c}$ as long as $c \neq 0$.

EXAMPLE 4   ## Solving Linear Equations Using the Multiplication and Division Properties

Math Note

The properties we're using to solve equations don't say you can do *anything you want* to both sides of an equation. They say you can add, subtract, multiply, or divide by the same number on both sides (except zero when multiplying or dividing).

Solve each equation, and check your answer.

(a) $\frac{t}{6} = 3$

(b) $5x = 30$

SOLUTION

(a) This time, to isolate the variable, we need to multiply both sides of the equation by 6.

$$\frac{t}{6} = 3 \qquad \textit{Multiply both sides by 6.}$$
$$\frac{t}{6} \cdot 6 = 3 \cdot 6 \qquad \textit{Simplify.}$$
$$t = 18$$

The solution set is {18}.

Check: $\dfrac{18}{6} = 3$

$$3 = 3 \checkmark$$

(b) The variable is multiplied by 5, so we can isolate x by dividing both sides by 5 (or multiplying both sides by $\frac{1}{5}$).

$$5x = 30 \qquad \textit{Divide both sides by 5.}$$

$$\frac{5x}{5} = \frac{30}{5} \qquad \textit{Simplify.}$$

$$x = 6$$

Check: $5 \cdot 6 = 30$

$30 = 30$ ✓

▼ **Try This One 4**

Solve each equation, and check your answer.

(a) $11z = 121$ (b) $\frac{x}{7} = -4$

Solving General Linear Equations

So far, we've seen how to solve simple linear equations. Any linear equation can be solved using the procedure listed below.

Procedure for Solving Linear Equations

Step 1 Simplify the expressions on both sides of the equation by distributing and combining like terms.

Step 2 Use the addition and/or subtraction property of equality to move all the variable terms to one side of the equation and all the constant terms to the opposite side of the equation.

Step 3 Combine like terms.

Step 4 Use the multiplication or division property of equality to eliminate the numerical coefficient and solve for the variable.

The next three examples illustrate this general procedure. At the risk of being overly dramatic, in a very real sense the procedures we're learning here are the core skills needed to solve almost all of the equations you'll encounter in algebra. If you don't practice and get really good at solving these equations, any algebra beyond this point will be like going to a stick fight and leaving your stick at home.

EXAMPLE 5   Solving a General Linear Equation

Solve the equation $5x + 9 = 29$, and check your answer.

SOLUTION

$$5x + 9 = 29 \qquad \textit{Subtract 9 from both sides of the equation.}$$

$$5x + 9 - 9 = 29 - 9 \qquad \textit{Combine like terms.}$$

$$5x = 20 \qquad \textit{Divide both sides by 5.}$$

$$\frac{5x}{5} = \frac{20}{5}$$

$$x = 4, \text{ or the solution set is } \{4\}$$

Check: $5x + 9 = 29$

$5(4) + 9 \stackrel{?}{=} 29$

$29 = 29$ ✓

▼ **Try This One 5**

Solve the equation $3x - 25 = 8$, and check your answer.

| EXAMPLE 6 | **Solving a General Linear Equation** |

Solve $6x - 10 = 4x + 8$, and check your answer.

SOLUTION

Math Note

Example 6 illustrates a good strategy for solving linear equations: put all terms with the variable on one side and all terms without the variable on the other. Then you can multiply or divide to isolate the variable, leaving an equation with an obvious solution.

$6x - 10 = 4x + 8$ *Subtract 4x from both sides of the equation.*

$6x - 4x - 10 = 4x - 4x + 8$ *Combine like terms.*

$2x - 10 = 8$ *Add 10 to both sides of the equation.*

$2x - 10 + 10 = 8 + 10$ *Combine like terms.*

$2x = 18$ *Divide both sides by 2.*

$\dfrac{2x}{2} = \dfrac{18}{2}$

$x = 9$, or the solution set is $\{9\}$

Check: $6x - 10 = 4x + 8$

$6(9) - 10 \stackrel{?}{=} 4(9) + 8$

$54 - 10 \stackrel{?}{=} 36 + 8$

$44 = 44$ ✓

▼ **Try This One 6**

Solve the equation $8x - 27 = 3x + 33$, and check your answer.

| EXAMPLE 7 | **Solving a General Linear Equation** |

Solve $3(2x + 5) - 10 = 3x - 10$, and check your answer.

SOLUTION

First, we simplify the left side, then proceed as usual.

$3(2x + 5) - 10 = 3x - 10$ *Multiply out parentheses.*

$6x + 15 - 10 = 3x - 10$ *Combine like terms.*

$$6x + 5 = 3x - 10 \qquad \text{Subtract } 3x \text{ from both sides.}$$
$$6x - 3x + 5 = 3x - 3x - 10 \qquad \text{Combine like terms.}$$
$$3x + 5 = -10 \qquad \text{Subtract } 5 \text{ from both sides.}$$
$$3x + 5 - 5 = -10 - 5 \qquad \text{Combine like terms.}$$
$$3x = -15 \qquad \text{Divide both sides by } 3.$$
$$\frac{3x}{3} = \frac{-15}{3}$$
$$x = -5, \text{ or the solution set is } \{-5\}$$

Check:

$$3(2x + 5) - 10 = 3x - 10$$
$$3(2 \cdot (-5) + 5) - 10 \overset{?}{=} 3(-5) - 10$$
$$3(-10 + 5) - 10 \overset{?}{=} -15 - 10$$
$$3(-5) - 10 \overset{?}{=} -25$$
$$-15 - 10 = -25$$
$$-25 = -25 \checkmark$$

> **Math Note**
>
> It's very important that, when checking your solution, you substitute back into the *original equation*. If you use one of the later equations you wrote and made a mistake in the very first step, a wrong answer might appear to be a correct answer.

☑ 3. Solve general linear equations.

> **▼ Try This One 7**
>
> Solve each equation, and check your answer.
>
> (a) $2(x - 7) + 5 = 3x - 10$ \qquad (b) $-5(2x - 8) + 6 = 4x - 32$

Solving Equations Containing Fractions

Suppose you were given a choice on a test between solving these two equations:

$$6x + 4 = x - 7 \qquad \frac{3x}{2} + 1 = \frac{x}{4} - \frac{7}{4}$$

> **Math Note**
>
> If you need a review of finding least common denominators, you can refer to the procedure for finding least common multiples on page 216.

If you're like pretty much everyone on the planet, you'd choose the first: it just looks easier because there are no fractions. Actually, these are the same equation in different forms. The good news is that there's a simple procedure that will turn *any* equation with fractions into one with no fractions at all. You just need to find the least common denominator of all fractions that appear in the equation, and multiply every single term on each side of the equation by the LCD. If there are any fractions left after doing so, you made a mistake! In the remaining examples in this section, we'll leave the checking to you.

EXAMPLE 8   Solving a Linear Equation Containing Fractions

Solve the equation $\frac{2x}{3} + \frac{x}{5} = \frac{26}{3}$.

SOLUTION

The least common denominator of fractions with denominators 3 and 5 is 15. So the first step is to multiply every term in the equation by 15.

$$\frac{2x}{3} + \frac{x}{5} = \frac{26}{3}$$ *Multiply every term on each side by 15.*

$$15 \cdot \frac{2x}{3} + 15 \cdot \frac{x}{5} = 15 \cdot \frac{26}{3}$$ *Simplify fractions.*

$$5 \cdot 2x + 3 \cdot x = 5 \cdot 26$$ *Multiply.*

$$10x + 3x = 130$$ *Combine like terms.*

$$13x = 130$$ *Divide both sides by 13.*

$$\frac{13x}{13} = \frac{130}{13}$$ *Simplify.*

$$x = 10, \text{ or the solution set is } \{10\}$$

▼ **Try This One 8**

Solve the equation $\frac{3x}{2} + 1 = \frac{x}{4} - \frac{7}{4}$.

EXAMPLE 9   **Solving a Linear Equation Containing Fractions**

Solve the equation $\frac{2x - 3}{3} + \frac{5x}{2} = \frac{x}{2} - 4$.

SOLUTION

The least common denominator is 6, so we begin by multiplying every term on each side by 6.

Math Note

Make sure you multiply *every* term on each side by the LCD, not just the ones that are fractions.

$$6 \cdot \frac{2x - 3}{3} + 6 \cdot \frac{5x}{2} = 6 \cdot \frac{x}{2} - 6 \cdot 4$$ *Simplify fractions.*

$$2(2x - 3) + 3 \cdot 5x = 3x - 24$$ *Multiply.*

$$4x - 6 + 15x = 3x - 24$$ *Combine like terms.*

$$19x - 6 = 3x - 24$$ *Subtract 3x from both sides.*

$$19x - 6 - 3x = 3x - 24 - 3x$$ *Combine like terms.*

$$16x - 6 = -24$$ *Add 6 to both sides.*

$$16x - 6 + 6 = -24 + 6$$ *Simplify.*

$$16x = -18$$ *Divide both sides by 16.*

$$\frac{16x}{16} = \frac{-18}{16}$$ *Simplify.*

$$x = -\frac{18}{16} = -\frac{9}{8}, \text{ or the solution set is } \left\{-\frac{9}{8}\right\}$$

▼ **Try This One 9**

☑ 4. Solve linear equations containing fractions.

Solve the equation $\frac{2(x - 3)}{5} - \frac{x}{3} = \frac{3x - 1}{5} - 2$.

Solving a Formula for a Specific Variable

Most formulas contain more than one variable, and it's often helpful to rearrange a formula so that the quantity you want to find is isolated on one side. For example, the formula $A = \frac{t_1 + t_2 + t_3}{3}$ is used to find the average of three test scores. A common use of this formula is to figure out what score you'd need on the third test to reach an average you're shooting for. In that case, it would be convenient to solve the equation for t_3, treating the other variables like they're numbers. That would give you a formula for finding the scores needed on test three to reach a variety of different average scores.

EXAMPLE 10   **Solving an Average Score Formula for One Test Score**

Solve the formula $A = \dfrac{t_1 + t_2 + t_3}{3}$ for the third test score, t_3.

SOLUTION

$$A = \frac{t_1 + t_2 + t_3}{3} \qquad \textit{Multiply both sides by 3.}$$

$$3A = 3 \cdot \frac{t_1 + t_2 + t_3}{3} \qquad \textit{Simplify.}$$

$$3A = t_1 + t_2 + t_3 \qquad \textit{Subtract } t_1 \textit{ and } t_2 \textit{ from both sides.}$$

$$3A - t_1 - t_2 = t_1 + t_2 + t_3 - t_1 - t_2 \qquad \textit{Simplify.}$$

$$3A - t_1 - t_2 = t_3$$

The formula for the third test score is $t_3 = 3A - t_1 - t_2$.

▼ **Try This One 10**

The formula for the area of a trapezoid is $A = \dfrac{1}{2} b(h_1 + h_2)$. Solve this formula for b.

EXAMPLE 11   **Finding a Formula for Temperature in Celsius**

The formula $F = \frac{9}{5}C + 32$ gives the Fahrenheit equivalent for a temperature in Celsius. Transform this into a formula for calculating the Celsius temperature C.

SOLUTION

$$F = \frac{9}{5}C + 32 \qquad \textit{Multiply both sides by 5.}$$

$$5F = 5 \cdot \frac{9}{5}C + 5 \cdot 32 \qquad \textit{Simplify.}$$

$$5F = 9C + 160 \qquad \textit{Subtract 160 from both sides.}$$

$$5F - 160 = 9C + 160 - 160 \qquad \textit{Combine like terms.}$$

$$5F - 160 = 9C \qquad \textit{Divide both sides by 9.}$$

$$\frac{5}{9}F - \frac{160}{9} = \frac{9C}{9} \qquad \textit{Simplify.}$$

$$\frac{5}{9}F - \frac{160}{9} = C$$

The formula for Celsius temperature is $C = \dfrac{5}{9}F - \dfrac{160}{9}$.

☑ 5. Solve formulas for one specific variable.

▼ Try This One 11

The formula $A = P(1 + rt)$ can be used to calculate the amount in an interest-bearing account. Transform this into a formula for calculating the interest rate r.

Contradictions and Identities

Not every equation has a solution. For example, it's easy to see that the equation $x = x + 1$ is never true no matter what number you choose for x: you can't add one to a number and have it result in the original number. An equation like this is called a *contradiction*. Let's see what happens if we apply our procedure for solving to this equation:

$$x = x + 1 \qquad \textit{Subtract x from both sides.}$$
$$x - x = x - x + 1 \qquad \textit{Simplify.}$$
$$0 = 1$$

Since the final equation is always a false statement, the same is true for the original equation. Formally,

> A **contradiction** is an equation with no solution.

Informally, a contradiction is an equation that when solved results in a false statement. The solution set of a contradiction is the empty set, { } or ∅.

On the other hand, there are equations in one variable with infinitely many solutions. These equations are called *identities*.

> An **identity** is an equation that is true for any value of the variable for which both sides are defined.

Math Note

If you really pay attention, you can notice that this equation is always true from the third line:
$10x + 6 = 10x + 6$.

When you solve an equation that is an identity, the final equation will be a statement that is always true as in the following example:

$$2(5x + 8) - 10 = 10x + 6 \qquad \textit{Distribute.}$$
$$10x + 16 - 10 = 10x + 6 \qquad \textit{Simplify.}$$
$$10x + 6 = 10x + 6 \qquad \textit{Subtract 10x from both sides.}$$
$$10x - 10x + 6 = 10x - 10 + 6 \qquad \textit{Simplify.}$$
$$6 = 6$$

In this case every real number is a solution to the equation so the solution set is $\{x \mid x$ is a real number$\}$.

In summary, if the variable is eliminated when solving an equation and the resulting equation is false then the equation is a contradiction and the solution set is the empty set. If the variable is eliminated and the resulting equation is true, then the equation is an identity and the solution set is the set of all real numbers.

EXAMPLE 12   Recognizing Identities and Contradictions

Decide if the equation is an identity or a contradiction, and write the solution set.

(a) $3(x - 6) + 2x = 5x - 18$ (b) $6x - 4 + 2x = 8x - 10$

SOLUTION

(a) $3(x - 6) + 2x = 5x - 18$

$\quad 3x - 18 + 2x = 5x - 18$

$\qquad 5x - 18 = 5x - 18$

$\qquad\qquad -18 = -18$

Since the resulting equation is true, it is an identity and the solution set is $\{x \mid x \text{ is a real number}\}$.

(b) $6x - 4 + 2x = 8x - 10$

$\qquad 8x - 4 = 8x - 10$

$\quad 8x - 8x - 4 = 8x - 8x - 10$

$\qquad\qquad -4 = -10$

Since the resulting equation is false, it's a contradiction, and the solution set is $\varnothing$.

▼ Try This One 12

☑ 6. Decide if an equation is an identity or a contradiction.

Decide if the equation is an identity or a contradiction, and write the solution set.

(a) $13x - 6 = 2(5x + 4) + 3x$ 　　　(b) $5(x + 6) - 5x = 30$

Answers to Try This One

1 (a) Yes 　(b) Yes 　(c) No

2 (b) and (d) are linear

3 (a) $\{45\}$ 　(b) $\{33\}$

4 (a) $\{11\}$ 　(b) $\{-28\}$

5 $\{11\}$

6 $\{12\}$

7 (a) $\{1\}$ 　(b) $\left\{\dfrac{39}{7}\right\}$

8 $\left\{-\dfrac{11}{5}\right\}$

9 $\left\{\dfrac{15}{8}\right\}$

10 $b = \dfrac{2A}{h_1 + h_2}$

11 $r = \dfrac{A}{Pt} - \dfrac{1}{t}$ 　or 　$r = \dfrac{1}{t}\left(\dfrac{A}{P} - 1\right)$

12 (a) contradiction; $\varnothing$
　　(b) identity; $\{x \mid x \text{ is a real number}\}$

EXERCISE SET 6-2

Writing Exercises

1. How can you tell when an equation is a linear equation?
2. What role does simplifying sometimes play in recognizing a linear equation?
3. Explain what it means to solve an equation. Why is that not the same thing as "find a solution"?
4. List the steps for solving a general linear equation in your own words.
5. What's the best way to begin solving an equation that contains fractions?
6. When does an equation have an empty solution set?
7. Why is it sometimes useful to solve a formula for one of the variables?
8. Explain what an identity is, and how to recognize one when solving equations.

Computational Exercises

In Exercises 9–16, state whether the equation is a linear equation in one variable or not.

9. $3x(2 - x) = x - 3$

10. $4x^2 = 5(x - 2)$

11. $7x = 3(x + 3)$

12. $9x - 7 + 2x = 3$

13. $\dfrac{5}{x} + x = 3x$

14. $\dfrac{2}{5}x - \dfrac{3}{x} = 4$

15. $7(x - 3) = 2x$

16. $\dfrac{1}{3}x = 7$

In Exercises 17–24, decide if the given value is a solution to the equation.

17. $x^2 = 1; x = -1$

18. $3x - 2 = 7; x = 3$

19. $4(x - 1) = 3x; x = -3$

20. $\dfrac{2}{3}x = 3(x - 2); x = 3$

21. $3(x + 2)^2 = 12; x = 0$

22. $2(x + 3) - 4 = 3x + 3; x = -1$

23. $\dfrac{2x + 3}{2} - 6 = 11 - \dfrac{4}{x}; x = 8$

24. $\dfrac{24}{3y} + 5 = \dfrac{-3y + 7}{3} - 3; y = -3$

For Exercises 25–70, solve each equation.

25. $x + 6 = 32$

26. $7 + x = 43$

27. $36 = x - 9$

28. $-5 = y - 2$

29. $9x = 27$

30. $6x = 42$

31. $-3z = 36$

32. $-42 = -7z$

33. $6x + 12 = 48$

34. $10x - 30 = -5$

35. $-5x + 25 = -55$

36. $-3x + 18 = 42$

37. $2t + 10 = 4t - 30$

38. $5t - 6 = 2t - 24$

39. $-6x + 15 = 4x - 25$

40. $9 - 2x = 7 - x$

41. $3(x + 2) = 26$

42. $7(x - 3) = 42$

43. $6 + 3(x - 5) = 2(x - 3)$

44. $-2(4x - 7) = 3x - 8$

45. $12(x - 2) - 10(x + 7) = 14$

46. $-2x + 3 + 4(x - 6) = 18$

47. $6(3x - 11) - 4(3x - 1) = 8x - 12(4 - 5x)$

48. $21y - (2y - 3) = 7(9 - 5y) - 6(8 - 4y)$

49. $3t - 12(3 + t) - 4t = -(5 - t) - (7 - t)$

50. $2(3x + 4) - 5(6x - 7) = 8(9x - 10) - 11(12x + 13)$

51. $\dfrac{5}{6}x = 30$

52. $-\dfrac{1}{4}x = 2$

53. $\dfrac{3}{4}x + 2 = 21$

54. $\dfrac{1}{8}x - 10 = -16$

55. $\dfrac{5z}{6} + \dfrac{z}{3} = 30$

56. $\dfrac{3t}{4} + \dfrac{7t}{2} = 18$

57. $\dfrac{11}{12} - \dfrac{x}{4} = \dfrac{x}{3} + \dfrac{5}{6}$

58. $\dfrac{4x}{6} + \dfrac{x}{5} = \dfrac{2}{3} - \dfrac{x}{5}$

59. $\dfrac{7x}{3} + 5 = \dfrac{4x}{8} + 10$

60. $\dfrac{3x}{2} + \dfrac{1}{2} = \dfrac{4x}{5} + \dfrac{3}{5}$

61. $\dfrac{x}{6} + \dfrac{3x}{2} = \dfrac{4}{5} - \dfrac{2x}{15}$

62. $\dfrac{5}{12} - \dfrac{1}{3}x = \dfrac{2}{3}x - \dfrac{7}{6}$

63. $\dfrac{4x}{6} + \dfrac{2x}{7} = 3 + \dfrac{3x}{4}$

64. $\dfrac{4x - 1}{6} + 5 = \dfrac{x}{4}$

65. $\dfrac{x + 2}{2} + \dfrac{1}{4} = \dfrac{3x}{2} - 1$

66. $\dfrac{x + 3}{2} + \dfrac{3}{4} = \dfrac{3x}{2} - 1$

67. $\dfrac{3}{5} = \dfrac{2(x - 3)}{3} + \dfrac{x}{5}$

68. $\dfrac{x}{3} + \dfrac{5(x - 1)}{4} = \dfrac{3x}{4} - 1$

69. $\dfrac{x}{4} + \dfrac{3(x - 1)}{4} = \dfrac{2x}{3} - 6$

70. $\dfrac{y - 2}{3} + \dfrac{2y + 1}{6} = y - \dfrac{y + 4}{8}$

For Exercises 71–76, solve each equation for the specified variable.

71. $3x + 8 = 2y + 4$ for y

72. $5y = 3x + 2$ for x

73. $2 + 5x - 7y = 18$ for x

74. $5y - 3x + 2 = 10$ for y

75. $7x + 2y = 9$ for y

76. $3y + 6 = 2x + 8$ for x

For Exercises 77–84, indicate whether the equation is an identity or a contradiction and give the solution set.

77. $8x - 5 + 2x = 10x - 10 + 5$

78. $3x + 7 - x = 2x + 21$

79. $5(x - 3) + 2 = 5x - 8$

80. $4(x + 2) + 6 = 2x + 2x + 14$

81. $3x - 2 = 5(x - 3) - 2x$

82. $4x + 3(x - 2) = 7(x - 2) + 8$

83. $\dfrac{-2(y + 4)}{3} = -\dfrac{39}{9} - \dfrac{2y - 5}{3}$

84. $\dfrac{2}{3}x = \dfrac{4x - 2}{6}$

Applications in Our World

85. The electrical resistance for a conductor can be found by the formula $R = \frac{KL}{d^2}$. Solve the formula for L.

86. The illumination of a light can be found by the formula $I = \frac{C}{D^2}$. Solve the formula for C.

87. The volume of a cylinder can be found by the formula $V = \pi r^2 h$. Solve the formula for h.

88. The formula for the perimeter of a rectangle is $P = 2l + 2w$. Solve the formula for w.

89. The formula for the volume of a rectangular solid is $V = lwh$. Solve the formula for h.

90. The formula for converting mass to energy is $E = mc^2$. Solve the formula for m.

91. The formula for the distance traveled during an acceleration period is $d = \frac{1}{2}at^2$. Solve the formula for a.

92. The formula for earned run average in baseball is $E = \frac{R}{I} \times 9$. Solve the formula for I.

93. The formula for slugging percentage in baseball is $P = \frac{S + 2D + 3T + 4H}{A}$. Solve the formula for H.

94. The formula for the area of a triangle is $A = \frac{1}{2}bh$. Solve the formula for h.

95. The formula for the average a of two numbers b and c is $a = \frac{b + c}{2}$. Solve for b.

96. The centripetal force of an object can be found by using the formula $F = \frac{mv^2}{r}$. Solve the formula for r.

Exercises 97–100 use the following formula: the cost of a cell phone plan is given by the formula $C = 0.035m + 45$, where C is the cost per month, m is the number of minutes used per month, and $\$45$ is the basic monthly charge.

97. What is the cost if you use 300 minutes per month?

98. What is the cost if you use 1,000 minutes per month?

99. How many minutes would you get to talk per month if you want the total bill to be $100?

100. How many minutes would you get to talk per month if you want the total bill to be $150?

Exercises 101–104 use the following formula: the grade for Steve's English class can be calculated if he takes the sum of his three essay scores and divides that total by 3, as in the formula $G = (E1 + E2 + E3)/3$. Say he got an 80 on the first essay, E1, and he got a 95 on the second essay, E2.

101. What is his grade G if he gets a 70 on his third essay?

102. What is his grade G if he gets an 87 on his third essay?

103. What does he need to score on his third essay to get an overall grade of 80?

104. What does he need to score on his third essay to get an overall grade of 90?

Exercises 105–108 use the following formula: the power of a circuit can be computed by the formula $P = V^2/R$,

where P is the power in watts, V is the voltage, and R is the resistance in ohms.

105. For a 25-volt circuit, find the power for a resistance of 10 ohms.

106. For a 50-volt circuit, find the power for a resistance of 25 ohms.

107. For a 30-volt circuit, find the resistance in ohms for 100 watts of power.

108. For a 20-volt circuit, find the resistance in ohms for 250 watts of power.

109. The bar graph below shows the average grade point averages for all students at a group of 38 public colleges for 4 different school years. The equation $G = 2.84 + 0.01x$ can be used to approximate the average GPA, where x represents the number of years after 1990 that the school year began.

    (a) How do values from the equation compare to actual values from the graph?

    (b) If the trend described by the given equation continues, in what year will the average GPA reach 3.3? What about 3.5?

    (c) Does this information mean that students are getting smarter? Discuss some possible interpretations.

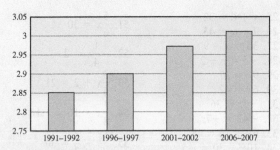

Source: gradeinflation.com

110. The bar graph on the next page shows the average grade point averages for all students at a group of 19 private colleges for 4 different school years. The equation $G = 3.08 + 0.014x$ can be used to approximate the average GPA, where x represents the number of years after 1990 that the school year began.

    (a) How do values from the equation compare to actual values from the graph?

    (b) If the trend described by the given equation continues, in what year will the average GPA reach 3.6? What about 3.8?

    (c) Does this information mean that professors' grading standards are getting easier? Discuss some possible interpretations.

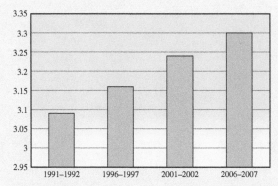

Source: gradeinflation.com

111. The total number of inmates held in adult correctional facilities in the United States for 1990–2010 can be approximated by the equation $P = 46,619x + 820,755$, where x represents years after 1990. (*Source:* The World Almanac and Book of Facts, 2010)

(a) Find the approximate number of inmates in 1990, then find how long it took for that number to double.

(b) If the trend continues, in what year will the number of inmates reach 3 million?

(c) Does this information mean that crime is increasing? Discuss some possible interpretations.

112. The equation $y = 617x + 7,782$ can be used to approximate the average annual tuition at 4-year colleges and universities in the United States for the period from 2001–2002 to 2008–2009. (*Source:* National Center for Education Statistics) The variable x represents years after the 2001–2002 school year.

(a) Find the approximate tuition in the 2001–2002 school year, then find how long it took for tuition to increase by 50%.

(b) If the trend continues, in what year will average tuition reach $15,000?

Critical Thinking

113. Fact: You can solve linear equations using only the addition and multiplication properties of equality. Explain why.

114. Explain why you can't multiply both sides of an equation by zero when solving. If your answer doesn't focus on what it means for a number to be a solution of an equation, it probably stinks.

115. Review your answer to Exercise 114, then explain why you can't multiply or divide both sides of an equation by an expression containing the variable.

116. Describe a method for easily writing an equation that is an identity and an equation that is a contradiction.

117. For the equation in Example 8, try to solve without multiplying both sides by the LCD. Instead, get a common denominator and perform the addition on the left side, then solve using the usual procedure. Did you get the same answer? Explain why multiplying both sides by the LCD is a much more efficient way to solve equations with fractions.

118. Check that $y = 5$ is a solution to the equation below by substituting it in for the variable. Does that mean that the solution set is {5}? Why or why not?

$$7(2y - 3) = -2(y + 1) + 16y - 19$$

Section 6-3 Applications of Linear Equations

LEARNING OBJECTIVES

☐ 1. Translate verbal expressions into mathematical symbols.

☐ 2. Solve problems using linear equations.

Two of the most common questions that students ask when learning about solving equations are "When would I ever *use* this?" and "Who cares what *x* is?" (If you want to drive your professor up the wall, ask these questions at least once a day.) Nobody will claim that you will solve multiple equations every day once you leave the hallowed halls of college. But the fact is that solving equations is a topic that is widely applied to almost every area of study. And even if it weren't, the problem-solving skills that you learn and hone while solving applied problems are among the best "brain exercise" you can get. And what could possibly be more useful to your education than training your brain to work better?

So in this section, we will solve problems that relate to issues in our world. In most cases, the plan is to write an equation that describes a situation, then solve that equation to find some quantity of interest. And even if you don't find the situations applicable to your life, keep the bigger picture in mind: you'll be practicing useful problem-solving skills with every question.

In the box below, we've outlined a general strategy for attacking word problems using algebra. If you look close enough, you'll notice that our strategy is based on Polya's problem-solving strategy that we studied in Chapter 1, with a few elaborations matching this specific type of problem.

A General Procedure for Solving Word Problems Using Equations

Step 1 Read the problem carefully, but *don't read it all at once without doing anything!* As you're reading, write down any information provided by the problem that seems relevant. This will at least get you started. Make sure you carefully note what it is you're being asked to find. Draw a diagram if the situation calls for one.

Step 2 Assign a variable to an unknown quantity in the problem. Most of the time, the variable should represent the quantity you're being asked to find.

Step 3 Write an equation based on the information given in the problem. Remember, an equation is a statement that two quantities are equal, so keep an eye out for statements in the problem indicating two different ways to express the same quantity.

Step 4 Solve the equation.

Step 5 Make sure that you answer the question! The best approach is to reread the question, then write your answer in sentence form.

Step 6 Check to see if your solution makes sense based on the original wording of the problem.

The step that almost everyone finds most challenging is Step 3. In order to write an equation that describes a situation, you have to translate verbal statements into mathematical symbols. For example, the verbal statement "six more than three times some number" can be written in symbols as "$6 + 3x$" or "$3x + 6$." A careful read of Table 6-3 will help get you started on these types of translations. The table is also very useful to refer back to as you work on problems.

TABLE 6-3   Common Phrases That Represent Operations

Phrases that represent addition

6 more than a number	$6 + x$
A number increased by 8	$x + 8$
5 added to a number	$5 + x$
The sum of a number and 17	$x + 17$

Phrases that represent subtraction

18 decreased by a number	$18 - x$
6.5 less than a number	$x - 6.5$
3 subtracted from a number	$x - 3$
The difference between a number and 5	$x - 5$

Phrases that represent multiplication

8 times a number	$8x$
Twice a number	$2x$
A number multiplied by 4	$4x$
The product of a number and 19	$19x$
$\frac{2}{3}$ of a number	$\frac{2}{3}x$

Phrases that represent division

A number divided by 5	$x \div 5$
35 divided by a number	$35 \div x$
The quotient of a number and 6	$x \div 6$

EXAMPLE 1   Translating Verbal Statements into Symbols

Translate each verbal statement into symbols.

(a) 14 times a number
(b) A number divided by 7
(c) 10 more than the product of 8 and a number
(d) 3 less than 4 times a number
(e) 6 times the sum of a number and 18

SOLUTION

(a) Using variable x to represent the unspecified number, we can write this as $14x$.
(b) $\dfrac{x}{7}$
(c) $10 + 8x$
(d) It might help to reword this as 3 subtracted from 4 times a number: $4x - 3$
(e) Parentheses are required here because the multiplication is 6 times the sum: $6(x + 18)$

> *Math Note*
>
> The actual letter you choose for a variable is unimportant. You can choose any letter (or other symbol) you like.

☑ 1. Translate verbal expressions into mathematical symbols.

▼ **Try This One 1**

Translate each verbal statement into symbols.

(a) 100 divided by a number
(b) 5 more than the product of a number and 7
(c) The difference between 25 and a number
(d) The product of 8 and the difference of a number and 4

Solving Word Problems

We'll begin our study of solving word problems with a basic translation problem. It's not terribly realistic, but gives you a start on the basic steps for solving.

EXAMPLE 2   Solving a Basic Translation Problem

If 8 times a number plus 3 is 27, find the number.

SOLUTION

> *Math Note*
>
> When translating a statement into an equation, the word "is" usually indicates where the equal sign should go.

Step 1 Write the relevant information:

$$8 \text{ times a number plus 3 is 27}$$

Identify what we're asked to find: that unknown number.

Step 2 Use variable x to represent the unknown number.

Step 3 Translate the relevant information into an equation:

$$8 \text{ times a number plus 3 is 27}$$
$$8x \quad + \quad 3 = 27$$

Step 4 Solve the equation:

$$8x + 3 = 27 \qquad \textit{Subtract 3 from both sides.}$$
$$8x + 3 - 3 = 27 - 3 \qquad \textit{Simplify.}$$
$$8x = 24 \qquad \textit{Divide both sides by 8.}$$
$$\frac{8x}{8} = \frac{24}{8} \qquad \textit{Simplify.}$$
$$x = 3$$

Math Note

When checking your answer to a word problem, don't just substitute it into the equation you wrote—if you wrote the wrong equation, you won't know. Instead, check that it matches the verbal description of the problem.

Step 5 Answer the question: the requested number is 3.

Step 6 Check: 8 times 3 is 24, and when you add 3, you get 27. This matches the description of the problem.

▼ **Try This One 2**

Ten less than twice a number is 42. Find the number.

In the next example, see if you can recognize the similarity to the abstract problem in Example 2.

EXAMPLE 3   **A Problem Involving Contract Negotiations**

Two basketball teams are interested in signing a free-agent player. An inside source informs the general manager of one team that the other has made an offer, and the player's agent said "Double that and add an extra million per year, and you're in our league." According to a published report, the player is seeking a contract of $18 million per year. What was the rival team's offer?

SOLUTION

Step 1 Relevant information: twice the offer plus 1 million is 18 million. We're asked to find the offer.

Step 2 Use the variable x to represent the offer. Since the numbers are in millions, we'll let x stand for the offer in million dollar units—that will keep the arithmetic simpler.

Step 3 Translate the relevant information into an equation:

Twice the offer plus	one	is	eighteen.
$2x$ +	1	=	18

Step 4 Solve the equation:

$$2x + 1 = 18 \qquad \textit{Subtract 1 from both sides.}$$
$$2x + 1 - 1 = 18 - 1 \qquad \textit{Simplify.}$$
$$2x = 17 \qquad \textit{Divide both sides by 2.}$$
$$x = \frac{17}{2} \text{ or } 8.5$$

Math Note

Remember, we're using million dollar units, so 1 million and 18 million are represented by 1 and 18.

Step 5 Answer the question: the team's offer was $8.5 million. Only $8.5 million? That's an insult!

Step 6 Check: doubling $8.5 million gives $17 million, and adding 1 million more makes it $18 million as required.

▼ **Try This One 3**

A teacher with a fondness for joking around with students tells one that if he doubled his score on the last test and subtracted 12%, he would have just barely gotten an A. The syllabus says that the minimum cutoff for A is 92%. What was the student's score?

Sometimes when there are two unknowns in a word problem, one unknown can be represented in terms of the other. For example, if I know that one number is 5 more than another number, then the first number can be represented by x and the second number can be represented by $x + 5$. Example 4 uses this idea.

EXAMPLE 4   An Application to Home Improvement

Pat and Ron are planning to build a deck off the back of their house, and they buy some plans from the Internet. The plans can be customized to the required deck height, which in this case will be 92 inches. They call for support posts of two different heights. The taller ones are 8 inches longer than the shorter ones, and the plans say that the sum of the lengths should be the height of the deck. How long should the support posts be cut?

SOLUTION

Step 1 Relevant information: the posts are 8 inches different in length, and the lengths should add to 92 inches.

Step 2 We'll call the length of the shorter posts x. The other posts are 8 inches longer, so they must be $x + 8$.

Step 3 Translate the relevant information into an equation:
Length of shorter post + length of longer post is 92.

$$x \qquad + \qquad x + 8 \qquad = 92$$

Step 4 Solve the equation:
$$x + x + 8 = 92$$
$$2x + 8 = 92$$
$$2x = 84$$
$$x = 42$$

Step 5 Answer the question: this is where it becomes really important to reread the original question. We were asked to find *two* lengths, so $x = 42$ isn't a valid answer. We used x to represent the length of the shorter posts, and found that it's 42 in. The longer posts are supposed to be 8 in. longer, so the two lengths are 42 in. and 50 in.

Step 6 Check: the two lengths are definitely separated by 8 inches and 42 inches + 50 inches = 92 inches, as required.

> ### ▼ Try This One 4
> The railings for the deck in Example 4 have three different lengths of board. The shortest is 10 inches less than the next shortest, which is 14 inches shorter than the longest. Their combined length is supposed to match the overall length of the deck, which in this case is 20 feet. How long should each piece be?

Math Note

We could also call the length of the longer posts x; in that case, the shorter ones would have length $x - 8$.

EXAMPLE 5   An Application Involving Money

Math Note

In this case, we could have used a variable like q to represent the number of quarters, but then the number of dollar bills would be $\frac{q}{3}$, and we'd be introducing fractions. So it's simpler to use $d =$ the number of dollar bills.

After a busy Friday evening, the tip jar at an off-campus bar is stuffed full of dollar bills and quarters. The tradition is that the bartenders split the dollars, while the barbacks split the quarters. There's $245 in the jar, with three times as many quarters as dollar bills (college students aren't known to be the best tippers in the universe). How much money goes to the bartenders, and how much to the barbacks?

SOLUTION

Step 1 Relevant information: three times as many quarters as dollar bills, and the total value is $245.

Step 2 Use variable d to represent the number of dollar bills. Then $3d$ is the number of quarters (because there are three times as many).

322   **Chapter 6**   Topics in Algebra

Step 3   Translate the relevant information into an equation: the value in dollars of the quarters is the number of quarters ($3d$) times $0.25. The value of the dollar bills is the number of them (d).

Total value is $245.

$$0.25(3d) + d = 245$$

Step 4   Solve the equation:

$0.25(3d) + d = 245$	*Multiply.*
$0.75d + d = 245$	*Combine like terms.*
$1.75d = 245$	*Divide both sides by 1.75.*
$d = \dfrac{245}{1.75} = 140$	

Step 5   Answer the question: there are 140 dollar bills, so the bartenders split $140. Three times as many quarters is 420 quarters; multiply by $0.25 to get $105 to be split by the barbacks.

Step 6   Check: 420 quarters is three times as many as 140 dollar bills, and $140 + $105 = $245. Sounds like a winner to me.

☑ 2. Solve problems using linear equations.

▼ **Try This One 5**

Corrine collected $137 in tips during a Friday evening shift waiting tables, split among one- and five-dollar bills. She got 53 more singles than fives. How many of each did she get?

As you work the exercises, keep in mind that one of the main goals is to practice organized thinking and problem-solving skills. You shouldn't worry too much about how realistic or interesting you think the situations are—focus on the process of setting up and solving the equations. But if you find the situations interesting and relevant, feel free to send some cash to the authors.

Answers to Try This One

1   (a) $\dfrac{100}{x}$ (b) $5 + 7x$ (c) $25 - x$ (d) $8(x - 4)$

2   26

3   52% (ouch!)

4 $68\frac{2}{3}$ in., $78\frac{2}{3}$ in., $92\frac{2}{3}$ in.

5   67 singles and 14 fives

EXERCISE SET **6-3**

Writing Exercises

1. Write some reasons why it's a bad idea to read an entire word problem without writing down any information.
2. Write some reasons why it's a great idea to write your answer to a word problem in the form of a sentence.
3. What's the difference between checking your answer when solving an equation, and checking your answer when solving a word problem?
4. How do you choose what the variable in a word problem should represent?

Computational Exercises

For Exercises 5–24, write each phrase in symbols.

5. 3 less than a number
6. A number decreased by 17
7. A number increased by 9
8. 6 increased by a number
9. 11 decreased by a number
10. 8 more than a number
11. 6 subtracted from a number
12. 7 times a number
13. One-half a number added to that number
14. 5 more than 3 times a number
15. The quotient of 3 times a number and 6
16. 4 less than 6 times a number
17. The quotient of a number and 14
18. The product of 7 and a number, all subtracted from 10.
19. Triple the sum of a number and pi.
20. One-fourth the difference of 12 and a number.
21. Three times a number subtracted from the quotient of twice that number and the sum of that number and 8.
22. The sum of 146 and the product of a number raised to the third power and 18.
23. The square of the sum formed from adding five times a number to three times a different number.

24. The square root of the difference between half a number and two-thirds of a different number.

For Exercises 25–34, solve each.

25. Six times a certain number plus the number is equal to 56. Find the number.
26. The sum of a number and the number plus 2 is equal to 20. Find the number.
27. Twice a number is 32 less than 4 times the number. Find the number.
28. The larger of two numbers is 10 more than the smaller number. The sum of the numbers is 42. Find the numbers.
29. The difference of two numbers is 6. The sum of the numbers is 28. Find the numbers.
30. Five times a number is equal to the number increased by 12. Find the number.
31. Twice a number is 24 less than 4 times the number. Find the number.
32. The difference between one-half a number and the number is 8. Find the number.
33. Twelve more than a number is divided by 2. The result is 20. Find the number.
34. Eighteen less than a number is tripled, and the result is 10 more than the number. Find the number.

Applications in Our World

35. A math class containing 57 students was divided into two sections. One section has three more students than the other. How many students were in each section?
36. In 2011, the Coca-Cola company and PepsiCo had combined revenues of $101.6 billion, with PepsiCo revenues $31.4 billion higher. Find the revenue for each company.
37. The cost, including sales tax, of a Ford Focus SE is $19,392.70. If the sales tax is 6%, find the cost of the car before the tax was added.
38. During the first day of a heat wave, an emergency room had three times as many patients as the day before. There were 48 patients seen total over the 2-day period. How many patients visited the E.R. on each day?
39. Three students that share a townhouse find that their electric bill for October is $2.32 less than the September bill. The total of both bills is $119.48, and each bill is split evenly among the roommates. How much did each owe in September?
40. If Marita invested half of her money at 8% and half at 6% and received $210 simple interest, find the total amount of money invested.
41. A basketball team played 32 games and won 4 more games than it lost. Find the number of games the team won.

42. The enrollment of students in evening classes at a local university decreased by 6% between the years of 2012 and 2013. If the total number of students attending evening classes in both years was 16,983, find how many students enrolled in evening classes in each of those years.
43. If a television set is marked $\frac{1}{3}$ off and sells for $180, what was the original price?
44. A carpenter wanted to cut a 6-foot board into three pieces so that each piece is 6 inches longer than the preceding one. Find the length of each piece.
45. The Halloween Association reported that last year, Americans spent $0.68 billion more on candy than costumes for Halloween. If the total spent by Americans for both items was $3.18 billion, how much did Americans spend on each item?
46. In a charity triathlon, Mark ran half the distance and swam a quarter of the distance. When he took a quick break to get a drink of Gatorade, he was just starting to bike the remaining 15 miles. What was the total distance of the race?
47. A nurse is told to give a patient recovering from surgery a total of 21 units of a potent antibiotic over 3 days. The dosage should be cut in half the second day, then in half again for the third day. How many units should she administer on the first day?

324   **Chapter 6**   Topics in Algebra

48. An investor flips a house, selling it for $82,000. If her profit was 20%, how much did she pay for the house originally?

49. A father left $\frac{1}{2}$ of his estate to his son, $\frac{1}{3}$ of his estate to his granddaughter, and the remaining $6,000 to charity. What was his total estate?

50. In 2011, there were 92 female officials in Congress, and there were 58 more female members of the House of Representatives than female senators. Find the number of females in each house of Congress.

51. While shopping on BlueFly.com, Juanita notices a special where if she buys two items, the third will be half off. She buys one item, then another item that is half of that amount, and then a third item that is a quarter of the original item amount. The discount she is given is half off the cheapest item. She ends up spending $65 on the order (neglect taxes). What is the price of the first item she bought?

52. There were five winning lottery tickets for a total jackpot of $24 million. Three of the winners won twice as much as the other two. How much did each of the two that won the least get?

53. In Mary's purse, there are $3.15 worth of nickels and dimes. There are 5 times as many nickels as dimes. The vending machine is only taking dimes, and Mary needs 10 dimes for her purchase. Does Mary have enough dimes?

54. If the perimeter of a triangular flower bed is 15 feet with two sides the same length and the third side 3 feet longer, what are the measures of the three sides of the flower bed?

55. Last semester, Marcus's tuition bill was 12% cheaper than this semester's tuition bill of $640. How much did Marcus pay for tuition last semester?

56. Jane and her two friends will rent an apartment for $875 a month, but Jane will pay double what each friend does because she will have her own bedroom. How much will Jane pay a month?

57. In the 2012 Illinois Republican presidential primary, 839,238 votes were cast for the top three candidates. Mitt Romney got 107,704 more votes than Rick Santorum, who got 236,959 more votes than Ron Paul. What percentage of the ballots cast for the top three candidates did each receive?

58. Three sisters inherited $100,000 from a rich uncle. The uncle's favorite niece got twice as much as his second favorite niece and the second favorite niece got twice as much as the least favorite niece. How much did the favorite niece get?

59. A bounty hunter makes a base monthly salary of $1,700, plus $900 for every bail-jumper he brings in. Write an algebraic expression that describes his monthly earnings, using a variable that stands for the number of fugitives he captures. Then use your equation to find how many fugitives he needs to average per month in order to make $60,000 per year.

60. A telemarketer is paid $3.70 per hour, plus $0.30 for every caller she keeps on the line for at least a minute. Write an algebraic expression describing her hourly earnings, using a variable that stands for the number of callers she keeps on the line for at least a minute. Then use your equation to find how many callers she has to keep on the line for at least a minute over an 8-hour shift to make $104.

Critical Thinking

61. The temperature and the wind combine to cause body surfaces to lose heat. Meteorologists call this effect "the windchill factor." For example, if the actual temperature outside is 10°F and the wind speed is 20 miles per hour, it will feel like it is −20°F outside, so −20°F is called the windchill. When it is 25°F outside and the wind speed is 40 miles per hour, it will feel like it is −35°F outside. From the information given, write a linear equation for determining the windchill using the actual temperature and the wind speed. Then use your equation to find the windchill factor on a day with temperature 30°F and 18 mile per hour winds.

62. Suppose your roommate brags that he made $250 in singles and fives one night waiting tables, and that he collected four times as many one-dollar bills as five-dollar bills. How can you tell that he's not telling the exact truth?

63. The prevailing winds for air travel in the United States typically blow from west to east, slowing down travel to the west considerably. Last year, I flew from Cincinnati to Salt Lake City, a distance of 1,447 miles from east to west. The return flight took three-fourths as long as the flight out west. If the average speed of the plane in still air is 422 mph, what was the wind speed? (Assume it was the same for both flights.)

(*Hint:* Use a variable to represent what you're asked to find, and fill in the following chart. The information will help you to write an equation.)

	Distance	Speed	Time
Cincinnati → Salt Lake			
Salt Lake → Cincinnati			

64. In an attempt to conserve energy (and, let's be honest, save some cash), Bob decides to ride his bike to work every day. He starts out by riding a half mile uphill, which slows him down by 4 miles per hour.

The rest of the ride is a mile downhill, which speeds him up by 5 miles per hour. After several days, he notices that when he reaches the top of the hill, he's exactly halfway there if you measure in terms of time. How fast would Bob be riding if the trip were on level ground? (*Hint:* Make a table similar to the one in Problem 63.)

65. Winona has two jobs: one pays $11.25 per hour, and the other pays $9.50 per hour plus an average of 60% of the hourly pay in tips and bonuses. Each pay period, 22% of her total pay goes to taxes.
    (a)   Write and simplify an equation that describes Winona's total take-home pay in terms of the number of hours worked at the first job and the number of hours worked at the second.
    (b)   If Winona is committed to work 30 hours per week at the first job, how many hours per week would she need to work at the second job if she needs her biweekly take-home pay to be $800?

66. Refer to Problem 65. If Winona decides that she'll work exactly 45 hours per week total and is not committed to a certain number of hours at either job, how many hours should she work at each job to earn $1,000 in take-home pay every two weeks? What about $1,200?

Section 6-4   Ratio, Proportion, and Variation

LEARNING OBJECTIVES

☐ 1. Write ratios in fraction form.

☐ 2. Solve proportions.

☐ 3. Solve problems using proportions.

☐ 4. Solve problems using direct variation.

☐ 5. Solve problems using inverse variation.

The most obvious way to compare the sizes of two numbers is to subtract them. But is that the *best* way? Suppose you're comparing the cost of an item at two different stores, and you find that the item is a dollar more at Target than at Wal-Mart. If that item is a bottle of Coke, and the prices are $1 and $2, that dollar difference is significant. But if the item is a 50-inch flat-screen TV and the prices are $1,201 and $1,200, would you really care? It's essentially the same price. If you *divide* the prices rather than subtract them, however, something interesting happens:

$$\text{Coke: } \frac{\$2}{\$1} = 2$$

$$\text{TV: } \frac{\$1,201}{\$1,200} = 1.0008$$

Do you see the point? For the Coke, a dollar more is twice as much—kind of a big deal. For the TV, when you divide the prices, you essentially get 1, meaning the two prices are pretty much the same. The most meaningful way to compare the sizes of two numbers is to divide them, forming what we called a *ratio* in Section 5-3.

Ratios

A **ratio** is a comparison of two quantities using division.

For example, in the fourth quarter of 2011, 58% of tablet computers sold worldwide were iPads and 42% were some other model, so we would say that the ratio of iPads sold to other tablets was 58 to 42.

For two nonzero numbers, *a* and *b*, the **ratio of *a* to *b*** is written as *a:b* (read *a* to *b*) or $\frac{a}{b}$.

Ratios can be written using either a colon or a fraction as shown in the definition, but in math we'll typically use the fraction so that we can do arithmetic with ratios.

| EXAMPLE 1 | **Writing Ratios** |

Math Note

To set up a correct ratio, whatever number comes first in the ratio statement should be placed in the numerator of the fraction and whatever number comes second in the ratio statement should be placed in the denominator of the fraction.

According to the Sporting Goods Manufacturers' Association, 95.1 million Americans participate in recreational swimming, 56.2 million Americans participate in recreational biking, 52.6 million Americans participate in bowling, and 44.5 million Americans participate in freshwater fishing. Find each:

(a) The ratio of recreational swimmers to recreational bikers
(b) The ratio of people who fish to people who bowl

SOLUTION

(a) $\dfrac{\text{Number of swimmers}}{\text{Number of bikers}} = \dfrac{95.1}{56.2}$

(b) $\dfrac{\text{Number of people who fish}}{\text{Number of people who bowl}} = \dfrac{44.5}{52.6}$

> ▼ **Try This One 1**
>
> From 1969 through 1977, there were 24 teams in Major League Baseball, and only 4 made the playoffs each year. Now, there are 30 teams, and 10 make the playoffs. Find the ratio of teams making the playoffs to those not making the playoffs in 1969 and today.

Since ratios can be expressed as fractions, they can be simplified by reducing the fraction. For example, the ratio of 10 to 15 is written 10:15 or $\frac{10}{15}$ and the fraction $\frac{10}{15}$ can be reduced to $\frac{2}{3}$. So the ratio 10:15 is the same as 2:3.

Sometimes ratios can be written as fractions where the numerator and the denominator have the same units of measure. In such cases, it is necessary to make the units match as shown in Example 2.

| EXAMPLE 2 | **Writing a Ratio Involving Units** |

Math Note

We could have written 18 inches as $\frac{3}{2}$ feet in Example 2, and the ratio would have been $\dfrac{3/2 \text{ feet}}{2 \text{ feet}}$, which also simplifies to $\frac{3}{4}$.

Find the ratio of 18 inches to 2 feet.

SOLUTION

It's tempting to simply write $\frac{18}{2}$, but this is deceiving—it makes it seem like 18 inches is 9 times as much as 2 feet, which is of course silly. Instead, to make the ratio meaningful, we want the units to be the same. Since 1 foot is 12 inches, 2 feet is 24 inches. So the ratio is

$$\frac{18 \text{ inches}}{24 \text{ inches}}$$

Now we can reduce. The unit inches divides out, and we're left with

$$\frac{18}{24} = \frac{3 \cdot 6}{4 \cdot 6} = \frac{3}{4}$$

The ratio of 18 inches to 2 feet is $\frac{3}{4}$.

> ▼ **Try This One 2**
>
> Find the ratio of 40 ounces to 2 pounds. (There are 16 ounces in 1 pound.)

☑ 1. Write ratios in fraction form.

Proportions

When two ratios are equal, they can be written as a *proportion*.

> A **proportion** is an equation in which two ratios are stated to be equal.

For example, the ratios 4:7 and 8:14 are equal; this fact can be expressed as a proportion:

$$\frac{4}{7} = \frac{8}{14}$$

Two fractions, $\frac{a}{b}$ and $\frac{c}{d}$, are equal if $ad = bc$. (This will be shown in Exercise 57.) The product of the numerator of one fraction and the denominator of the other fraction is called a cross product. For example, $\frac{3}{4} = \frac{6}{8}$ since $3 \cdot 8 = 4 \cdot 6$, or $24 = 24$.

This tells us that two ratios form a proportion if the cross products of their numerators and denominators are equal. For example, the two ratios $\frac{5}{6}$ and $\frac{15}{18}$ can be written as a proportion since

$$\frac{5}{6} \diagdown\!\!\!\!\diagup \frac{15}{18} \qquad \textit{This is called cross multiplying.}$$

$$5 \cdot 18 = 6 \cdot 15$$

$$90 = 90$$

So we can write 5:6 = 15:18, or $\frac{5}{6} = \frac{15}{18}$.

EXAMPLE 3   **Deciding if a Proportion Is True**

Math Note

Cross multiplying is a really convenient procedure for working with proportions, but there's a catch: it ONLY works when the equation in question looks like single fraction = single fraction. Don't try to apply cross multiplying to any equation that's not of that form.

Decide if each proportion is true or false.

(a) $\dfrac{3}{5} = \dfrac{9}{15}$ (b) $\dfrac{5}{3} = \dfrac{7}{2}$ (c) $\dfrac{14}{16} = \dfrac{7}{8}$

SOLUTION

In each case, we will cross multiply and see if the two products are equal.

(a) $3 \cdot 15 = 45$; $5 \cdot 9 = 45$ The proportion is true.
(b) $5 \cdot 2 = 10$; $3 \cdot 7 = 21$ The proportion is false.
(c) $14 \cdot 8 = 112$; $16 \cdot 7 = 112$ The proportion is true.

▼ **Try This One 3**

Decide if each proportion is true or false.

(a) $\dfrac{2}{9} = \dfrac{6}{25}$ (b) $\dfrac{5}{2} = \dfrac{25}{4}$ (c) $\dfrac{11}{2} = \dfrac{55}{10}$

If there is an unknown value in a proportion, we can solve for the unknown value by cross multiplying as shown in Examples 4 and 5.

EXAMPLE 4   **Solving a Proportion**

Solve the proportion for *x*.

$$\frac{12}{48} = \frac{3}{x}$$

The height of the people and the statue are in proportion. If we know the ratio of the heights and the height of the people, we can find the height of the statue.

SOLUTION

We begin by cross multiplying.

$$\frac{12}{48} \diagdown\!\!\!\!\!\diagup \frac{3}{x} \qquad \textit{Cross multiply.}$$

$$12x = 3 \cdot 48$$

$$12x = 144 \qquad \textit{Divide both sides by 12.}$$

$$\frac{12x}{12} = \frac{144}{12} \qquad \textit{Simplify.}$$

$$x = 12$$

Check: $$\frac{12}{48} \overset{?}{=} \frac{3}{12}$$

$$\frac{1}{4} \overset{?}{=} \frac{1}{4} \checkmark$$

▼ **Try This One 4**

Solve the proportion: $\dfrac{x}{7} = \dfrac{22}{25}$

EXAMPLE 5	**Solving a Proportion**

Solve the proportion. $\dfrac{x-5}{10} = \dfrac{x+2}{20}$

SOLUTION

$$\frac{x-5}{10} \diagdown\!\!\!\!\!\diagup \frac{x+2}{20} \qquad \textit{Cross multiply.}$$

$$20(x-5) = 10(x+2) \qquad \textit{Multiply out parentheses.}$$

$$20x - 100 = 10x + 20 \qquad \textit{Subtract 10x from both sides.}$$

$$10x - 100 = 20 \qquad \textit{Add 100 to both sides.}$$

$$10x = 120 \qquad \textit{Divide both sides by 10.}$$

$$x = 12$$

Check: $$\frac{x-5}{10} = \frac{x+2}{20}$$

$$\frac{12-5}{10} \overset{?}{=} \frac{12+2}{20}$$

$$\frac{7}{10} \overset{?}{=} \frac{14}{20}$$

$$\frac{7}{10} = \frac{7}{10} \checkmark$$

▼ **Try This One 5**

Solve the proportion: $\dfrac{x+6}{15} = \dfrac{x-2}{5}$

☑ 2. Solve proportions.

Applications of Proportions

Proportions have been around for a really long time in one form or another—a written record of their use goes back at least to 400 BCE or so, but most math historians feel that the idea is almost as old as formal numeric thought. This is because they're very useful in solving problems in our world. Example 6 illustrates a procedure that works well for problems where ratios are provided in some way.

EXAMPLE 6   **Applying Proportions to Fuel Consumption**

While on a spring break trip, a group of friends burns 12 gallons of gas in the first 228 miles, then stops to refuel. If they have 380 miles yet to drive, and the SUV has a 21-gallon tank, can they make it without refueling again?

SOLUTION

Step 1 *Identify the ratio statement.* The ratio the problem gives us is 12 gallons of gas to drive 228 miles.

Step 2 *Write the ratio as a fraction.* The ratio is $\dfrac{12 \text{ gallons}}{228 \text{ miles}}$.

Step 3 *Set up the proportion.* We need to find the number of gallons of gas needed to drive 380 miles, so we'll call that x. The ratio we already have is gallons compared to miles, so the second ratio in our proportion should be as well. We have x gallons, and 380 miles, so the proportion is

$$\frac{12 \text{ gallons}}{228 \text{ miles}} = \frac{x \text{ gallons}}{380 \text{ miles}}$$

Step 4 Solve the proportion.

$$\frac{12}{228} = \frac{x}{380} \qquad \textit{Cross multiply.}$$

$$\frac{12}{228} \bowtie \frac{x}{380}$$

$$228x = 12 \cdot 380 \qquad \textit{Simplify.}$$

$$228x = 4{,}560 \qquad \textit{Divide both sides by 228.}$$

$$\frac{228x}{228} = \frac{4{,}560}{228}$$

$$x = 20$$

> **Math Note**
>
> When setting up a proportion, be sure to put like quantities in the numerators and like quantities in the denominators. In Example 6, gallons were placed in the numerators and miles in the denominators.

Step 5 *Answer the question.* The SUV will burn 20 gallons of gas to cover the last 380 miles, so they can make it without stopping.

▼ Try This One 6

In 2012, roughly 13 of every 100 people in the United States were African-American. A marketing company wants to select a group of 250 people that accurately reflects the racial makeup of the country. How many African-Americans should be included?

In order to decide that a certain species is endangered, biologists have to know how many individuals are in a population. But how do they do that? It's actually an interesting application of proportions illustrated in Example 7.

EXAMPLE 7	**Applying Proportions to Wildlife Population**

As part of a research project, a biology class plans to estimate the number of fish living in a lake thought to be polluted. They catch a sample of 35 fish, tag them, and release them back into the lake. A week later, they catch 80 fish and find that 5 of them are tagged. About how many fish live in the lake?

SOLUTION

Step 1 *Identify the ratio statement.* Five of 80 fish caught were tagged.

Step 2 *Write the ratio as a fraction.* $\dfrac{5 \text{ tagged}}{80 \text{ total}}$

Step 3 *Set up the proportion.* We want to know the number of fish in the lake, so call that x. The comparison in the lake overall is $\dfrac{35 \text{ tagged}}{x \text{ total}}$, so the proportion is

$$\frac{5 \text{ tagged}}{80 \text{ total}} = \frac{35 \text{ tagged}}{x \text{ total}}$$

Step 4 *Solve the proportion.*

$$\frac{5}{80} = \frac{35}{x}$$
$$5x = 35 \cdot 80$$
$$5x = 2{,}800$$
$$x = \frac{2{,}800}{5} = 560$$

Step 5 *Answer the question.* There are about 560 fish in the lake.

☑ 3. Solve problems using proportions.

▼ Try This One 7

The staff biologists at a wildlife preserve tagged 74 protected woodpeckers shortly after hatching season. In midsummer, 30 of the birds were caught and 16 were tagged. Estimate the total population of these woodpeckers in the preserve.

Sidelight **PROPORTIONS IN MY WORLD**

Proportions are a topic that it's easy to write application problems about because they're useful in a wide variety of everyday settings. In fact, I just used a proportion yesterday in my car. I have one of those cool touch screen systems with GPS,

entertainment options and so forth, and you can upload a picture to be the background for the home screen. The catch is that the screen resolution is 800 × 384 pixels, and to make a picture display right, it should be cropped to make it fit.

But it doesn't have to be exactly those dimensions—it just needs to have the same ratio of width to length. So the picture I wanted to use had a width of 1,164 pixels, and I had to figure out the height it should be cropped to. How did I do it? Using a proportion. The ratio of width to height needed to be the same as it is for the 800 × 384 screen, so I got

$$\frac{800}{384} = \frac{1{,}164}{x}$$

The solution, 559 (rounded), told me the number of pixels to crop to, and I think the result looks pretty darn good. Yay proportions.

Variation

Two quantities are often related in such a way that if one goes up, the other does too, and if one goes down, the other goes down as well. For example, if you have a job that pays $95 a day, the amount you make goes up or down depending on how many days you work. This is an example of what is called **direct variation**. In this case, we can write a ratio statement based on the pay: $\frac{\$95}{1\,\text{day}}$. We could then use this to write an equation that describes your total pay depending on how many days you work: $y = \frac{\$95}{1\,\text{day}} \cdot x$ days, or just $y = 95x$.

> A quantity y is said to **vary directly** with x if there is some nonzero constant k so that $y = kx$. The constant k is called the **constant of proportionality**.

EXAMPLE 8   **Using Direct Variation to Find Wages**

Suppose you earn $95 per day. Write a variation equation that describes total pay in terms of days worked, and use it to find your total pay if you work 6 days and if you work 15 days.

SOLUTION

Let y = the total amount earned
     x = the number of days you work
     k = $95 per day (as we saw above)
Then $y = 95x$ is the variation equation.
For $x = 6$ days: $y = 95 \cdot 6 = \$570$
For $x = 15$ days: $y = 95 \cdot 15 = \$1,425$

▼ Try This One 8

A 6-month-old Labrador puppy gets $4\frac{1}{2}$ cups of food per day. Write a variation equation that describes how many cups of food she eats in terms of days, then use it to find how much she eats in 6 days and in 2 weeks.

When two quantities vary directly, if we know the size of each for some specific case, we can use that information to find the constant of proportionality. That gives us the equation of variation, which we can then use to solve problems.

EXAMPLE 9   **Using Direct Variation to Find a Weight**

When utility cables are strung above ground, the weight is an important consideration. The weight of a certain type of cable varies directly with its length. If 20 feet of cable weighs 4 pounds, find k and determine the weight of 75 feet of cable.

SOLUTION

Step 1 Write the equation of variation.

$$y = kx \quad \text{where } y = \text{the weight}$$
$$x = \text{length of cable in feet}$$
$$k = \text{the constant}$$
$$4\,\text{lb} = k \cdot 20\,\text{ft}$$

Step 2 Solve for k.

$$4\,\text{lb} = k \cdot 20\,\text{ft} \quad \textit{Divide both sides by 20 ft.}$$

$$\frac{4\,\text{lb}}{20\,\text{ft}} = \frac{k \cdot 20\,\text{ft}}{20\,\text{ft}}$$

$$k = 0.2\,\text{lb/ft}$$

Now we know that the equation of variation can be written as $y = 0.2x$.

Step 3 Solve the problem for the new values of x and y using $k = 0.2$.

$$y = 0.2x \quad \textit{Substitute } x = 75$$

$$y = 0.2 \cdot 75$$

$$y = 15\,\text{pounds}$$

So 75 feet of cable will weigh 15 pounds.

> ### ▼ Try This One 9
>
> The weight (in pounds) of a hollow statue varies directly with the square of its height (in feet); i.e., $y = kx^2$, where y = the weight and x = the height. If a statue that's $4\frac{1}{2}$ feet tall weighs 12 pounds, find the weight of a statue that's 10 feet tall.

☑ 4. Solve problems using direct variation.

A quantity can also vary *inversely* with another quantity. For example, the time it takes to drive a certain distance to a vacation home varies inversely with the rate of speed of the automobile. That is, if you drive on average 55 miles per hour as opposed to 40 miles per hour, you'll get there in less time. In short the higher the speed, the lower the time. This is an example of **inverse variation**.

> A quantity y is said to **vary inversely** with x if there is some nonzero constant k such that $y = \frac{k}{x}$.

EXAMPLE 10   Using Inverse Variation to Find Driving Time

The time it takes to drive a certain distance varies inversely with the speed, and the constant of proportionality is the distance. A family has a vacation cabin that is 378 miles from their residence. Write a variation equation describing driving time in terms of speed. Then use it to find the time it takes to drive that distance if they take the freeway and average 60 miles per hour, and if they take the scenic route and average 35 miles per hour.

SOLUTION

Let y = the time it takes to drive the distance
$\quad x$ = the average speed
$\quad k$ = 378 miles (the distance)

Then the variation equation is $y = \dfrac{k}{x}$ or $y = \dfrac{378}{x}$.

If they average 60 miles per hour:

$$y = \frac{378}{60} = 6.3\,\text{hours}$$

If they average 35 miles per hour:

$$y = \frac{378}{35} = 10.8 \text{ hours}$$

I vote for the freeway.

▼ **Try This One 10**

A student lives 120 miles from the college she attends. Write a variation equation describing the time it takes to drive home for a weekend in terms of speed. Then use it to find driving time if she averages 72 miles per hour and manages to not get pulled over by the state patrol.

EXAMPLE 11 **Applying Inverse Variation to Construction**

In construction, the strength of a support beam varies inversely with the cube of its length. If a 12-foot beam can support 1,800 pounds, how many pounds can a 15-foot beam support?

SOLUTION

Step 1 *Write the variation equation.* Let

y = strength of the beam in pounds it can support

x = length of the beam

k = the constant of proportionality

The variation equation is $y = \frac{k}{x^3}$, since y varies inversely with the cube of x.

Step 2 Find k.

$$y = \frac{k}{x^3} \quad \textit{Substitute } y = 1,800 \textit{ and } x = 12$$

$$1,800 = \frac{k}{12^3} \quad \textit{Solve for k.}$$

$$1,800 = \frac{k}{1,728}$$

$$k = 1,800 \cdot 1,728 = 3,110,400$$

Step 3 *Substitute in the given value for x.* In this case, the given length is 15.

$$y = \frac{3,110,400}{x^3}$$

$$y = \frac{3,110,400}{15^3} = 921.6$$

A 15-foot beam can support 921.6 pounds.

---

5. Solve problems using inverse variation.

▼ **Try This One 11**

If the temperature of a gas is held constant, the pressure the gas exerts on a container varies inversely with its volume. If a gas has a volume of 38 cubic inches and exerts a pressure of 8 pounds per square inch, find the volume when the pressure is 64 pounds per square inch.

Answers to Try This One

1   In 1969: $\dfrac{4}{20}$; Today: $\dfrac{10}{20}$

2 $\dfrac{5}{4}$

3   (a) False   (c) False   (b) True

4 $x = \dfrac{154}{25}$

5 $x = 6$

6   Either 32 or 33

7   139 woodpeckers

8 $y = \dfrac{9}{2}x$; In 6 days: 27 cups; In 2 weeks: 63 cups

9 $59\dfrac{7}{27}$ lb

10 $y = \dfrac{120}{x}$; about 1.7 hours

11   4.75 cubic inches

EXERCISE SET 6-4

Writing Exercises

1. Write an example of a ratio in an applied situation.
2. What's the difference between a ratio and a proportion?
3. Write an example of two quantities that vary directly in an applied situation.
4. Write an example of two quantities that vary inversely in an applied situation.
5. Describe the procedure for solving a proportion.
6. What is the constant of proportionality in a variation problem?

Computational Exercises

For Exercises 7–16, write each ratio statement as a fraction and reduce to lowest terms if possible.

7. 18 to 28
8. 5 to 12
9. 14:32
10. 40:75
11. 12 cents to 15 cents
12. 18 inches to 42 inches
13. 3 weeks to 8 weeks
14. 2 pounds to 12 ounces
15. 5 feet to 30 inches
16. 12 years to 2 decades

For Exercises 17–26, solve each proportion.

17. $\dfrac{3}{x} = \dfrac{14}{45}$

18. $\dfrac{x}{2} = \dfrac{18}{6}$

19. $\dfrac{5}{6} = \dfrac{x}{42}$

20. $\dfrac{9}{8} = \dfrac{45}{x}$

21. $\dfrac{x-6}{12} = \dfrac{1}{3}$

22. $\dfrac{x+3}{5} = \dfrac{35}{25}$

23. $\dfrac{2}{x-3} = \dfrac{5}{x+8}$

24. $\dfrac{4}{x-3} = \dfrac{16}{x-2}$

25. $\dfrac{x-3}{4} = \dfrac{x+6}{20}$

26. $\dfrac{x}{10} = \dfrac{x-2}{20}$

Applications in Our World

27. The Information Resources Institute reports that one out of every five people who buy ice cream buys vanilla ice cream. If a store sells 75 ice cream cones in one day, about how many will be vanilla?
28. The U.S. Department of Agriculture reported that 57 out of every 100 milk drinkers drink skim milk. If a storeowner orders 25 gallons of milk, how many should be skim?
29. Under normal conditions, 1.5 feet of snow will melt into 2 inches of water. After a monster snowstorm, there were 3.5 feet of snow. How many inches of water will there be when the snow melts?
30. The Travel Industry Association of America reports that 4 out of every 35 people who travel do so by air. If there are 180 students who are traveling for spring break, how many of them will fly?
31. A gallon of paint will cover 640 square feet of wall space. If I plan to paint a room whose walls measure 2,560 square feet, how many gallons of paint will I need?

32. The American Dietetic Association reported that 31 out of every 100 people want to lose weight. If 384 students were surveyed at random in the student union, how many would want to lose weight?

33. The U.S. Census Bureau reported that 9 out of every 20 joggers are female. On a trail, there were 230 joggers on July 4. Approximately how many were female?

34. Angel took a 2-year lease on a new car and after 8 months of driving, he'd put 6,600 miles on it. The lease allows 10,000 miles per year. If his driving habits stay consistent, will he stay under the allotted mileage for 2 years? By how much?

35. Out of every 80 iPods sold by a discount website, 3 were returned as defective. If the website sold 1,000 iPods this holiday season, how many should they expect will be returned as defective?

36. The American Dietetic Association states that 11 out of every 25 people do not eat breakfast. If there are 175 students in a large lecture hall, about how many of them did not eat breakfast?

37. Mark is interested in measuring the height of a tree in his yard. He measures the length of the tree's shadow at 18 feet at the same time his own shadow is 3 feet 6 inches. If Mark is 5″10″, how tall is the tree?

38. An online photo printing service will put any photo you like on a commemorative baseball. The preferred dimensions for photo uploads are 640 × 480 pixels. Quan wants to have her son's little league photo put on a ball. The file she has is 1,100 pixels wide. To what height should she crop it so that the proportions fit the requirements?

39. A small college has 1,200 students and 80 professors. The college is planning to increase enrollment to 1,500 students next year. How many new professors should be hired, assuming they want to maintain the same ratio?

40. The taxes on a house assessed at $64,000 are $1,600 a year. If the assessment is raised to $80,000 and the tax rate did not change, how much would the taxes be now?

41. According to a poll conducted by the Pew Research Center in early 2011, for every 69 people who could correctly identify the religion practiced by the president of the United States, there were 131 who could not. At that time there were about 235 million adult Americans. How many could not identify the president's religion?

42. Based on a combination of worldwide surveys conducted from 2008 to 2010 and reported at gallup.com, for every 29 people who would be happy to stay in the country they live in, 71 would prefer to move to another country. Among those who would prefer to move, 24 of 71 say they would like to move to the United States. The two next-highest proportions were for Canada and Great Britain, each at 7 of 71.

(a) Based on these numbers, if a random sample of 1 million people was chosen from around the globe, how many would like to move to the United States?

(b) How many more would like to move to the United States than Canada and the UK combined?

43. According to a poll conducted by the Gallup Corporation in March 2011, the metropolitan areas with the highest and lowest proportions of obese adults were Evansville, IN-KY, and Boulder, CO, respectively. In Evansville, for every 311 people who were not obese, there were 189 who were. In Boulder, for every 16 obese people, there were 109 who were not obese. At that time, the estimated populations were 358,676 for Evansville and 303,482 for Boulder. How many more obese people were there in the Evansville area than in the Boulder area?

44. A Gallup survey showed that in March 2011, 8 of every 25 employers in the United States were adding more workers to their workforce, 9 of 50 were reducing their workforce, and 1 of 2 were keeping it the same.

(a) If there were 1,250 employers in one metropolitan area, and those who were hiring planned to hire an average of seven new employees, how many new jobs were about to become available?

(b) If the employers who were cutting their workforce in that area were planning on letting go an average of nine workers, what would the net change in jobs for the area be?

45. The amount of simple interest on a specific amount of money varies directly with the time the money is kept in a savings account when the interest rate is constant. Find the amount of interest on a $5,000 savings account, if the interest rate is 6%, and the money has been invested for 4 years.

46. The number of tickets purchased for a prize varies directly with the amount of the prize. For a prize of $1,000, 250 tickets are purchased. Find the approximate number of tickets that will be purchased on a prize worth $5,000.

Use the following information for Exercises 47–50. If everyone had the same body proportions, your weight in pounds would vary directly with the cube of your height in feet. According to Wikipedia, the most recent statistics available in 2012 indicated that the average height and weight for an adult male in the United States is 5 feet 9.4 inches and 191 lb. Use this information to write a variation equation, then use it to find the weight that each of the following famous athletes would be if they had the same body type as the average male.

47. Basketball player Lebron James: 6'8" (Actual weight is 250 lb.)
48. Basketball player Yao Ming: 7'6" (Actual weight is 310 lb.)
49. Jockey Pat Day: 4'11" (Actual weight is 105 lb.)
50. Football player Tom Brady: 6'4" (Actual weight is 225 lb.)
51. Under certain conditions, the pressure of a gas varies inversely with its volume. If a gas with a volume of 20 cubic inches has 36 pounds of pressure, find the amount of pressure 30 cubic inches of gas is under.
52. The strength of a particular beam varies inversely with the square of its length. If a 10-foot beam can support 500 pounds, how many pounds can a 12-foot beam support?
53. In karate, the force needed to break a board varies inversely with the length of the board. If it takes 5 lb of force to break a board that is 3 feet long, how many pounds of force will it take to break a board that is 5 feet long?
54. The weight of a body varies inversely with the square of the distance from the center of the earth. If the radius of the earth is 4,000 miles, how much would a 150-lb woman weigh 500 miles above the surface of the earth?
55. The time to complete a project is inversely proportional to the number of people who are working on the project. A class project can be completed by 3 students in 20 days. In order to finish the project in 5 days, how many more students should the group add?
56. The intensity of sound varies inversely as the square of the distance from the source. A sound with an intensity of 300 watts/m^2 is heard from 20 feet away from a speaker. What is the intensity of the sound 50 feet away from the same speaker?

Critical Thinking

57. Starting with the equation $\frac{a}{b} = \frac{c}{d}$, find the LCD and multiply both sides by it. Make sure you simplify fractions. This proves something that's very important in working with proportions. What is it?
58. Write the generic variation equations for direct and inverse proportionality. Now fill in the blanks in the next two sentences, and explain how you can deduce your answer from the equations.

    When a quantity goes up in proportion to another going up, this is _____ variation. When a quantity goes down in proportion to another going up, this is _____ variation.

Stores are required by law to display unit prices. A unit price is the ratio of the total price to the number of units. For Exercises 59–64, decide which is a better buy. These prices were obtained from actual foods.

59. Flour: 10 pounds for $3.39 or 25 pounds for $7.49
60. Candy: 20 ounces for $1.50 or 24 ounces for $1.75
61. Potato sticks: 7 ounces for $1.99 or 1.5 ounces for $0.50
62. Cookies: 7 ounces for $0.99 or 14 ounces for $1.50
63. Coffee: 11.5 ounces for $2.75 or 34.5 ounces for $7.49
64. Beggin' Strips dog treats: $11.20 for 1.4 pounds, $2.75 for 8 ounces.
65. If a varies directly with the square of b, and b in turn varies inversely with d:
    (a) Give a verbal description of the variation of a with respect to d.
    (b) If a is 90 when d is 5, find a when d is 9.
    (c) Given the information in (b), can you find b? Why or why not?
66. If x varies inversely with the cube of y, and y in turn varies inversely with the square root of z:
    (a) Give a verbal description of the variation of x with respect to z.
    (b) If x is 14 when z is 4, find x when z is 16.
    (c) If x is 20 when y is 2 and y is 16 when z is 4, find x when z is 100.

In Exercises 67–70, decide if the two quantities are likely to vary directly or inversely, and explain your answer.

67. (a) The amount of time you spend on Facebook and your GPA
    (b) The square footage of an apartment and the monthly rent
68. (a) The outdoor temperature and the total weight of clothing you wear
    (b) The number of miles you run per week and your weight
69. (a) The age of your car and the total cost of maintaining it
    (b) The crime rate in a given area and the rate of unemployment in that area
70. (a) The distance you drive in an hour and a half, and your average speed
    (b) The magnitude of an earthquake and the cost of property damage that it causes

Section 6-5   Solving Linear Inequalities

LEARNING OBJECTIVES

☐ 1. Graph solution sets for simple inequalities.

☐ 2. Solve linear inequalities in one variable.

☐ 3. Solve three-part linear inequalities.

☐ 4. Solve problems using inequalities.

We have seen that solving linear equations is a very useful tool in solving problems from a wide variety of areas. But think about the following situation: you've finished school and are looking for a real job. As you nervously wait for your big interview, you decide not to be too demanding, but that the minimum compensation you're willing to accept in salary and benefits is $40,000 per year. Nobody has ever gone into an interview and said "I want 40k and I won't accept a penny more!" Of course, you would be perfectly happy with any amount over $40,000 as well.

This is where inequalities can be more useful than equations. Rather than describing your salary requirement as $S = 40,000$, it would be more sensible to describe it as $S \geq 40,000$. Inequalities are custom-built to describe situations where a range of possible outcomes is acceptable. The main goal of this section is to learn how to solve linear inequalities. But first, we should get comfortable with the terminology and the notation that we'll be using.

Recall that a linear equation in one variable was defined to be an equation of the form $Ax + B = 0$. The statement $3x + 4 < 0$ is an example of a linear inequality in one variable.

> A **linear inequality in one variable** is a statement that can be written in any of the following four forms: $Ax + B < 0$, $Ax + B > 0$, $Ax + B \leq 0$, or $Ax + B \geq 0$. In each case, B can be any real number, and A can be any real number except zero.

Just like equations, the simple way to recognize a linear inequality is that the variable appears only to the first power. To **solve** a linear inequality means to find the set of all numbers that make the inequality a true statement when substituted in for the variable. That set is called the **solution set** for the inequality. Finding the graphs of solution sets to very basic inequalities will help us become familiar with the concept of inequalities.

Graphing Inequalities on a Number Line

Math Note

This simple example illustrates a really important point: equations typically have a small handful of solutions, but the solutions to inequalities are almost always entire intervals of numbers, like the set of all numbers 5 or greater.

For an inequality of the form $x \geq 5$, the solution set is obvious: every real number that's 5 or larger. We can represent this solution set on a number line like this:

To show that the number 5 is included in the solution set, a *solid* or *closed circle* (•) is used. On the other hand, the solution set for the inequality $x > 5$ includes all real numbers greater than 5, but the actual number 5 is not in the solution set. The graph for the solution set of $x > 5$ looks like this:

To show that the number 5 is not included in the solution set, an *open circle* (○) is used.

If the inequality is of the form $x \leq 5$, the solution set is every real number that's 5 or smaller, represented like this:

Again, the closed circle indicates that 5 is included. For $x < 5$, an open circle indicates that only the numbers to the left of 5 on the number line are in the solution set:

If the set you want to describe has only one boundary, like the set of salaries that are \$40,000 or greater, inequalities like these are fine. But what if the range of numbers has a boundary on each end, like "I plan to spend between \$400 and \$600 on a tablet computer"? If we use S to represent the amount you plan to spend, we could write this as two separate inequalities: $S \geq 400$ *and* $S \leq 600$. But it's more efficient to write it this way: $400 \leq S \leq 600$. We call this a **three-part inequality**, and it's the type of inequality we'll use to represent an interval between two numbers. The graph for this set looks like:

A summary of simple inequalities and the graphs of their solution sets is shown in Table 6-4.

TABLE 6-4   Graphs of Solution Sets for Linear Inequalities

	For any real numbers a and b	
Inequality	**Graph**	**Solution set**
$x \geq a$		$\{x \mid x \geq a\}$
$x > a$		$\{x \mid x > a\}$
$x \leq a$		$\{x \mid x \leq a\}$
$x < a$		$\{x \mid x < a\}$
$a \leq x \leq b$		$\{x \mid a \leq x \leq b\}$
$a < x < b$		$\{x \mid a < x < b\}$
$a < x \leq b$		$\{x \mid a < x \leq b\}$
$a \leq x < b$		$\{x \mid a \leq x < b\}$

EXAMPLE 1   Graphing Solution Sets for Simple Inequalities

Graph the solution set for each inequality.

(a) $x \leq 10$ (b) $y > -4$ (c) $-30 < x \leq 50$

SOLUTIONS

(a)

(b)

(c)

▼ **Try This One 1**

Graph the solution set for each inequality.

(a) $y < -2$ (b) $x \geq 20$ (c) $-9 \leq t < -4$

1. Graph solution sets for simple inequalities.

Solving Linear Inequalities in One Variable

Since we're now really good at solving linear equations in one variable, the obvious question is "Can we solve inequalities the same way?" The answer, sadly, is no. But all is not lost—a better answer might be "almost." We will be able to use the technique we used for solving linear equations, with one important difference.

Our procedure for solving equations was based on the addition, subtraction, multiplication, and division properties of equality. So we begin with similar properties for inequalities.

The Addition and Subtraction Properties for Inequalities

You can add or subtract the same real number or algebraic expression to both sides of an inequality without changing the solution set. In symbols, if $a < b$, then $a + c < b + c, a - c < b - c$, and the same is true for the inequality symbols $\leq$, $>$, and $\geq$.

This is the analog of half of what we needed to solve linear equations. The other half was the multiplication and division properties of equality, and that's where things get interesting.

Consider the inequality $3 < 5$, which obviously is true. What if we multiply both sides by the same number?

Multiply by positive 4	Multiply by negative 4
$4 \cdot 3 \overset{?}{<} 4 \cdot 5$	$-4 \cdot 3 \overset{?}{<} -4 \cdot 5$
$12 \overset{?}{<} 20$	$-12 \overset{?}{<} -20$
Still true	False!

But if we reverse the inequality symbol when we multiply by -4, we get $-12 > -20$, which *is* true. This hints at the multiplication and division properties we need.

The Multiplication and Division Properties for Inequalities

- If you multiply or divide both sides of an inequality by the same *positive* real number, it does not change the solution set. In symbols, if $a < b$ and $c > 0$, then $a \cdot c < b \cdot c, \frac{a}{c} < \frac{b}{c}$, and the same is true for the inequality symbols $\leq$, $>$, and $\geq$.

- If you multiply or divide both sides of an inequality by the same *negative* real number, the direction of the inequality symbol is reversed. In symbols, if $a < b$ and $c < 0$, then $a \cdot c > b \cdot c, \frac{a}{c} > \frac{b}{c}$, and the analogous result is true for the inequality symbols $\leq$, $>$, and $\geq$.

The bottom line is that this gives us a simple procedure for solving linear inequalities:

Procedure for Solving Linear Inequalities

To solve a linear inequality, proceed in the same way you solve a linear equation except that when multiplying or dividing by a *negative* number, you have to reverse the inequality symbol.

Math Note

Reversing an inequality means that $\geq$ becomes $\leq$, $>$ becomes $<$, $\leq$ becomes $\geq$, and $<$ becomes $>$.

| EXAMPLE 2 | **Solving a Linear Inequality** |

Solve and graph the solution set for $5x - 9 \geq 21$.

SOLUTION

Math Note

An inequality can't be checked for the exact answer like an equation can; however, an approximate check can be made by picking some number in the solution set for x, substituting it into the inequality and seeing if the inequality is true.

In Example 2, try $x = 8$. (You can choose any value for x as long as it's 6 or larger.)

$$5x - 9 \geq 21$$
$$5(8) - 9 \overset{?}{\geq} 21$$
$$40 - 9 \overset{?}{\geq} 21$$
$$31 \geq 21 \quad \text{True}$$

$$5x - 9 \geq 21 \qquad \textit{Add 9 to both sides.}$$
$$5x - 9 + 9 \geq 21 + 9$$
$$5x \geq 30 \qquad \textit{Divide both sides by 5.}$$
$$\frac{5x}{5} \geq \frac{30}{5}$$
$$x \geq 6$$

The solution set is $\{x \mid x \geq 6\}$. The graph of the solution set is

▼ **Try This One 2**

Solve and graph the solution set for $7x + 29 \geq 1$.

| EXAMPLE 3 | **Solving a Linear Inequality** |

Solve and graph the solution set for $16 - 3x > 40$.

SOLUTION

$$16 - 3x > 40 \qquad \textit{Subtract 16 from both sides.}$$
$$16 - 16 - 3x > 40 - 16$$
$$-3x > 24 \qquad \textit{Divide both sides by -3 and reverse the inequality sign.}$$
$$\frac{-3x}{-3} < \frac{24}{-3} \qquad \textit{Simplify.}$$
$$x < -8$$

The solution set is $\{x \mid x < -8\}$ and the graph of the solution set is

CAUTION

Students (and even instructors!) will often divide both sides of an inequality by just writing the division in the previous step, rather than rewriting both sides. If we did that in Example 3, we'd turn $-3x > 24$ into

$$\frac{-3x}{-3} > \frac{24}{-3}$$

by just writing in the divisions. But this is a really bad idea, because the inequality we end up with is NOT equivalent to the original inequality—the sign goes in the wrong direction. Don't put off changing the direction of the inequality: do it AS SOON as you multiply or divide both sides by a negative number.

▼ **Try This One 3**

Solve and graph the solution set for $14 - 7x < 56$.

Checking answers is always a good idea, but it's an especially good idea to check your answer when you reverse the inequality sign. Also, be careful about the number you choose to test. For example, if your answer is $x \leq 8$, testing $x = 8$ would be a bad choice because it will make the inequality true even if $x \geq 8$ is the right solution set! Checking with $x = 6$ would be a much better choice.

EXAMPLE 4	**Solving a Linear Inequality**

Solve and graph the solution set for $4(x + 3) < 2x - 26$.

SOLUTION

$$4(x + 3) < 2x - 26 \qquad \textit{Multiply out parentheses.}$$
$$4x + 12 < 2x - 26 \qquad \textit{Subtract 2x from both sides.}$$
$$4x - 2x + 12 < 2x - 2x - 26$$
$$2x + 12 < -26 \qquad \textit{Subtract 12 from both sides.}$$
$$2x + 12 - 12 < -26 - 12$$
$$2x < -38 \qquad \textit{Divide both sides by 2.}$$
$$\frac{2x}{2} < \frac{-38}{2}$$
$$x < -19$$

The solution set is $\{x \mid x < -19\}$ and the graph is

$$\xleftarrow{\quad} \underset{-20 \quad -19 \quad -18}{} {\quad}$$

▼ **Try This One 4**

Solve and graph the solution set for $6(2x - 7) \leq 3x + 8$.

☑ 2. Solve linear inequalities in one variable.

When solving a three-part inequality, the goal is to isolate the variable in the middle. Make sure that whatever you do to one part of the inequality, you do to all three.

EXAMPLE 5	**Solving a Three-Part Linear Inequality**

Solve and graph the solution set for $-4 < 3 - 2y \leq 9$.

SOLUTION

$$-4 < 3 - 2y \leq 9 \qquad \textit{Subtract 3 from all three parts.}$$
$$-4 - 3 < 3 - 2y - 3 \leq 9 - 3$$
$$-7 < -2y \leq 6 \qquad \textit{Divide all three parts by } -2; \textit{ reverse both}$$
$$\qquad\qquad\qquad\qquad\qquad \textit{inequality symbols.}$$
$$\frac{-7}{-2} > y \geq \frac{6}{-2}$$
$$\frac{7}{2} > y \geq -3 \text{ or } -3 \leq y < \frac{7}{2}$$

The solution set is $\left\{y \mid -3 \le y < \dfrac{7}{2}\right\}$ and the graph is

$$\begin{array}{c} \xleftarrow{\quad\quad} \; | \quad \bullet \quad | \quad | \quad | \quad | \quad | \quad | \quad \circ \; | \; \xrightarrow{\quad\quad} \\ -4 \;\; -3 \;\; -2 \;\; -1 \;\;\; 0 \;\;\; 1 \;\;\; 2 \;\;\; 3\;\tfrac{7}{2}\;4 \end{array}$$

3. Solve three-part linear inequalities.

▼ **Try This One 5**

Solve and graph the solution set for $-10 \le 8 - x < 4$.

Applications of Inequalities

As we indicated at the beginning of the chapter, there are many situations where we're interested in some quantity being at least a certain amount, or at most a certain amount. In such situations, a couple of which are illustrated in Examples 6 and 7, inequalities are a natural fit. We'll proceed using the same problem-solving steps we used in Section 6-3. Table 6-5 is a handy reference for translating common phrases into inequality form.

| **TABLE 6-5** | **Common Phrases Used in Inequality Word Problems** |

>	<
Greater than	Less than
Above	Below
Higher than	Lower than
Longer than	Shorter than
Larger than	Smaller than
Increased	Decreased

≥	≤
Greater than or equal to	Less than or equal to
At least	At most
Not less than	Not more than

| **EXAMPLE 6** | **Applying Inequalities to Vacation Planning** |

With the stress of finals behind you, you decide to plan a vacation to relax a little bit. After poking around on the Internet, you find a room in the area you want to visit for $65 per night. Some quick estimating leads you to conclude that you'll need at least $250 for gas, food, beverages, and entertainment expenses. Upon checking your bank balance, you decide that you can afford to spend at most $600 on the trip. How many nights can you stay?

SOLUTION

Step 1 Relevant information: lodging is $65 per night, other expenses are $250, maximum you can spend is $600. We're asked to find the number of nights.

Step 2 Use variable n to represent the number of nights.

Step 3 Translate the relevant information into an inequality.

$65 × number of nights + other expenses is no more than $600

$$65 \times \quad n \quad + \quad 250 \quad \le \quad 600$$

Step 4 Solve the inequality.

$$65n + 250 \leq 600$$
$$65n \leq 350$$
$$n \leq \frac{350}{65} \approx 5.4$$

Step 5 Answer the question. Staying 5.4 nights doesn't make sense, so you could stay at most 5 nights.

Step 6 Check: Will 5 nights work?

$$\$65 \times 5 \text{ nights} + \$250 = \$325 + \$250 = \$575 \quad \textit{Less than } \$600$$

▼ Try This One 6

Philip doesn't want to look like a cheapskate, so he plans to spend at least $200 on his girlfriend for Christmas. He's already bought her a necklace for $135, and plans to buy some $15 iTunes gift cards as well. What's the smallest number he can buy?

EXAMPLE 7   **Applying Inequalities to the Cost of Buying Food**

Mike is planning to buy lunch for himself and some coworkers. He decides to buy cheeseburgers and fries from the value menu—the burgers are $1 each, and the fries cost $0.80. He also needs to pay 5% of the total in sales tax. What is the largest number of items he can buy if he wants to buy the same number of burgers as fries, and he only has $10 to spend?

SOLUTION

Step 1 Relevant information: burgers are $1 each, fries are $0.80 each; 5% sales tax; same number of burgers and fries; maximum cost $10.

Step 2 We can use variable x to represent both the number of burgers and the number of fries because those numbers are equal.

Step 3 $\$1 \cdot x$ is the total cost of burgers, and $\$0.80x$ is the total cost of fries. The tax is 5% of their sum, which is $0.05(x + 0.80x)$ dollars. That makes the total cost $x + 0.80x + 0.05(x + 0.80x)$, which must be less than or equal to 10. The inequality is

$$\underset{\substack{\textit{Cost of} \\ \textit{burgers}}}{x} \quad + \quad \underset{\substack{\textit{Cost of} \\ \textit{fries}}}{0.8x} \quad + \quad \underset{\textit{Tax}}{0.05(x + 0.80x)} \quad \leq \quad 10$$

Step 4

$$x + 0.80x + 0.05(x + 0.80x) \leq 10$$
$$x + 0.80x + 0.05x + 0.04x \leq 10$$
$$1.89x \leq 10$$
$$x \leq \frac{10}{1.89} \approx 5.29$$

Step 5 Mike can't buy 5.29 burgers, so we round down to 5. He can buy at most 5 burgers and 5 fries.

344   **Chapter 6**   Topics in Algebra

☑ 4. Solve problems using inequalities.

Step 6 Use $x = 5$ to check:

5 hamburgers cost $5 \times \$1.00 = \$5.00$

5 fries cost $5 \times \$0.80 =$ $+\ 4.00$

Total cost of food 9.00

Tax: $0.05 \times 9.00 = 0.45$ $+\ 0.45$

Total bill 9.45 *Less than $10*

▼ Try This One 7

Maureen plans to buy a computer and monitor. She wants to spend at most $1,000. She finds that there is a 10% rebate on all computers purchased at a certain store. If the monitor costs $100 (no rebate), what is the most she can pay for the computer? (Ignore the sales tax.)

Answers to Try This One

1 (a) ⟵─┼─┼─┼─┼─┼─┼─┼─┼─⟶
         -7 -6 -5 -4 -3 -2 -1 0 1

(b) ⟵─┼─┼─┼─┼─┼─┼─┼─┼─⟶
     -10 0 10 20 30 40 50 60 70

(c) ⟵─┼─┼─┼─┼─┼─┼─┼─┼─⟶
     -10 -9 -8 -7 -6 -5 -4 -3 -2

2 $\{x \mid x \geq -4\}$;

⟵─┼─┼─┼─┼─┼─┼─┼─⟶
-6 -5 -4 -3 -2 -1 0 1 2

3 $\{x \mid x > -6\}$ ⟵─┼─────┼─⟶
                         -6 0

4 $\{x \mid x \leq 5\frac{5}{9}\}$ ⟵─┼─┼─┼─⟶
                                        4 5 6 ($5\frac{5}{9}$)

5 $\{x \mid 4 < x \leq 18\}$;

⟵─┼─┼─┼─┼─┼─┼─┼─┼─┼─⟶
4 6 8 10 12 14 16 18 20

6 5

7 $\$1,000$

EXERCISE SET 6-5

Writing Exercises

1. What is the difference between the solution set of an inequality and the solution set of an equation?
2. What's the biggest difference between solving linear inequalities and solving linear equations?
3. Write a situation in our world where an inequality would be useful.
4. What does it mean to graph the solution set of an inequality?

Computational Exercises

For Exercises 5–14, show the solutions using a graph.

5. $x \geq 3$
6. $x < -2$
7. $y < -40$
8. $y \geq 0$
9. $x \leq -9$
10. $x \leq 120$
11. $-3 < t < 7$
12. $4 \leq t \leq 10$
13. $25 < x \leq 50$
14. $-300 \leq x < 0$

For Exercises 15–58, solve each inequality and graph the solution set on a number line.

15. $x + 6 < 11$
16. $x - 2 \leq 15$
17. $3y \geq 18$
18. $5y < 30$
19. $7 - x > 42$
20. $9 - x \leq 20$
21. $\frac{2}{3}x < 18$
22. $\frac{3}{4}x \geq 36$

23. $-10t < 30$

24. $-25t \geq 100$

25. $2z + 8 \geq 32$

26. $5z - 6 < 39$

27. $-3x + 12 \leq 36$

28. $5 - 2x > 25$

29. $6(x - 12) \leq 54$

30. $-3(2x + 7) < -16$

31. $-5(3 - y) \leq 27$

32. $9(4y - 1) > 71$

33. $11 - \frac{7}{2}y \geq 3$

34. $18 < 4 - \frac{11}{4}t$

35. $3(x + 1) - 10 < 2x + 7$

36. $4(n - 8) - 2n < -22$

37. $9 - 5(n + 6) \geq 32$

38. $18 - 6(x + 2) < 41$

39. $6(2x + 3) \geq 5(2x - 15)$

40. $-2\left(\frac{13}{2} + 3x\right) \geq \frac{3}{4}x + 2$

41. $\frac{5}{3}y + 12 \leq 6 - 12\left(\frac{11}{6} + 2y\right)$

42. $3x + 6 < -8x + 7$

43. $5.4 - 3.1x \geq 8 + 5.9x$

44. $2z - 11.9 < 6.3z - 4.2$

45. $-3(1.5t + 4.1) + 3 \leq 2t - 4.7$

46. $9.8 - 7(6.5x + 4) > 3.2 - x$

47. $3 \leq x + 10 < 18$

48. $-5 < 11 + y \leq -1$

49. $-8 < 3y + 1 < 10$

50. $3 \leq 2x - 7 \leq 11$

51. $-5 < -4z \leq 20$

52. $3 \leq -2x < 4$

53. $0 < 5(3 - 2x) < 25$

54. $-30 \leq -2(2t + 4) \leq 44$

55. $-8 < \frac{11}{4}y - 10 \leq \frac{1}{2}$

56. $\frac{4}{3} \leq 5 + \frac{23}{9}z < 9$

57. $-8 \leq 3 - \frac{2}{5}(x - 10) \leq 4$

58. $9 < 4 - \frac{9}{4}(2y - 20) < 10$

Applications in Our World

The list shown here represents the average number of tornados per year for the given states. Let x represent the average number of tornados per year. For Exercises 59–64, write the name or names of the states that are described by the solution to the inequality.

State	Average number of tornados per year
Texas	168
Florida	79
Kansas	75
Colorado	58
West Virginia	30
Missouri	26
Pennsylvania	22
California	14
Maryland	11
Arizona	5
Delaware	2
Maine	1

Source: *USA TODAY*

59. $x \geq 58$

60. $x < 22$

61. $26 \leq x < 58$

62. $2 < x \leq 22$

63. $11 \leq x \leq 30$

64. $30 < x < 168$

Write each statement in Exercises 65–70 as an inequality. State what the variable you choose represents.

65. I spend at least 6 hours a week working out.

66. I spend no more than 2 hours a day on Facebook.

67. As long as tuition is under $6,500, I can stay in school next year.

68. If I make over $2,200 this summer I can study abroad next spring.

69. The lowest test score in a class was 46%, and the highest was 98%.

70. The shortest baseball game of the year was 111 minutes and the longest was 326 minutes.

71. Mary is in the market for a good used car and can afford to spend at most $8,000. The sales tax rate in her county is 7%, and title and license plate fees come to $120. When she starts talking price at the car lot, the salesperson says that the asking price for the car she wants is $7,800. How much does Mary have to get them to shave off the price for her to be able to afford the car?

72. Paula and Melinda are considering selling their house, which they paid $150,000 for, but they'll only do so if they make at least a 10% profit. They'll have to pay 7% of the selling price in commission to their real estate agent, as well as $1,000 in closing costs. A potential buyer has offered $163,000 for the home. How much will they need to raise that offer for Paula and Melinda to consider accepting it?

73. Bill has three test grades of 95, 84, and 85 so far. If the final examination, still to come, counts for two test scores, what is the lowest he can score on the final exam and still get an A for the course? He needs at least 450 points for an A.

74. In order to get a C for her sociology course, Betsy needs at least a 70% average. On exam 1 she scored 78% and on exam 2 she scored 68%. What is the lowest score she can get on the last exam?

75. A health care researcher needs to hire volunteers for a study testing a new experimental therapy for rheumatoid arthritis. She receives a grant from a local hospital that allows her to pay up to $3,500 to the volunteers, but 12% of what she pays will go to a marketing service that locates volunteers. The study

requires 20 volunteers, all of whom will get the same fee. How much can the researcher offer to each volunteer?

76. In Beth's Greek mythology course, quizzes are worth 25% of the grade, tests are worth 60% of the grade, and the final exam is worth 15% of the grade. If Beth has an 82% quiz average and a 76% test average, what grade will she need on the final exam to get a B in the course with at least an 80% overall average?

77. When renting a car for her trip, Janice has the option of paying $0.32 a mile plus putting $25 down (option A) or she can pay $0.40 a mile (option B). What is the least amount of miles Janice can drive to make option A the cheaper option?

78. A foster-care facility houses children that have been removed from high-risk homes temporarily while permanent housing is located. The county pays the facility a weekly fee of $730 for each child under the age of 7 they take in, and $500 for each child between 7 and 18. The facility currently has four children under the age of 7, which is the largest number they have accommodations for. What's the smallest number of children between 7 and 18 they would need to take in to reach a weekly payment of $4,100?

79. Alana's using a pay-as-you-go phone with a monthly access fee of $18.83, and a flat per-minute rate of $0.033. If she were willing to sign a contract with a national carrier, she'd get unlimited minutes for $50 per month total. What range of minutes used will make the pay-as-you-go plan cheaper?

80. Dave works at the mall part-time for $9 per hour and notices that 20% of his check is deducted for taxes. If he wants to take home at least $200 per week, how many hours does he have to work?

81. Shelly has saved $10,000 to put down on her first house. She wants to make a down payment of 8% of the purchase price of the house and she was told it would cost 5% of the purchase price for closing costs and legal fees. What is the maximum price of house she can afford?

82. Amy spends $300 a month on bills, $600 a month on food and gas, $350 for her car, and $125 for her car insurance. If she makes $2,250 a month but wants to put 10% of the remaining money into her savings account, what is the most she can spend on her monthly rent?

83. A furniture designer for IKEA is planning a new shelving unit with shelves that are one-third as wide as the height of the unit. There will be four horizontal shelves with two vertical risers. To stay within budget the unit should use no more than 22 feet of wood. What are possible ranges of height that fit all of those criteria? What range do you think is reasonable?

84. Hideo can select from two salary plans. Plan A will pay him $20 per hour plus a $100 weekly bonus and Plan B will pay him $25 per hour. How many hours should Hideo work so that he earns the most from Plan B?

85. On his first four tests, Alon got 65%, 72%, 85%, and 90%. He wants a B in the course, which would mean his overall average would have to be between 80% and 89%. What range of scores can Alon get on his last test so he can get a B in the course?

86. On Molly's new diet, she is supposed to eat a lunch that is between 300 and 500 calories. She selects a yogurt for 100 calories and a half a bagel for 135 calories. How many calories could a third item contain so she remains on her diet?

87. Adrian spends a third of his week sleeping, 10 hours a week in class, 25 hours a week studying, 5 hours a week traveling, and 20 hours a week socializing. He also works part time at the campus café. Altogether, Adrian spends between 136 and 146 hours a week for all of those activities. How many hours a week does Adrian work?

88. Hannah wants to invest a certain amount of money into various accounts. She wants to invest 20% into Fund A and 15% into Fund B and then take half of the remainder and put it into Fund C. The amount left is between $1,000 and $1,500. How much money did Hannah start with?

Critical Thinking

89. It turns out that it's possible to solve two-part linear inequalities without ever having to worry about changing the direction of an inequality symbol. Why? How can you arrange the procedure for solving linear inequalities to make sure of it?

90. In the definition of linear inequality on page 337, why do we disallow $A = 0$?

91. All of the three-part inequalities we solved had the variable in the middle. First, explain what issues we'd run into solving a three-part inequality that had the variable in the first or third part. Then write about the case where the variable appears in both of the first and third parts.

92. Refer to Problem 91. Think about the types of application problems that result in three-part inequalities, and explain why we would mostly be interested in ones that have the variable only in the middle.

93. Write a verbal statement about something in your life that could be described using an inequality with $>$ or $\geq$, then write the inequality. Make sure you write what the variable you chose represents.

94. Write a verbal statement about something in your life that could be described using an inequality with $<$ or $\leq$, then write the inequality. Make sure you write

what the variable you chose represents. (Turning your inequality from Problem 93 around backwards is clearly cheating.)

95. Write a verbal statement about something in your life that could be described using a three-part inequality, then write the inequality. Make sure you write what the variable you choose represents.

96. I claim that you can tell that the following inequality has no solution without doing any work. How?

$$4 \leq 3 - \frac{5}{4}(x - 7) < 1$$

Section 6-6   Solving Quadratic Equations

LEARNING OBJECTIVES

☐ 1. Identify the standard form of a quadratic equation.

☐ 2. Multiply binomials using FOIL.

☐ 3. Factor trinomials.

☐ 4. Solve quadratic equations using factoring.

☐ 5. Solve quadratic equations using the quadratic formula.

☐ 6. Solve problems using quadratic equations.

The main theme of our study of linear equations and inequalities is that they can help us to solve a wide variety of problems in our world. But there are many other types of equations, and not every problem that applies to solving equations can be solved with linear equations. For example, the motion of objects (including bungee jumpers and other objects that are out of their minds) through the air can be described by equations where the highest power of the variable is 2. We call such equations *quadratic*, and studying them in this section will greatly expand the types of problems we can solve using equations.

Quadratic Equations

A **quadratic equation** is any equation that can be written in the form $ax^2 + bx + c = 0$, where a, b, and c are real numbers, and a is not zero. When written this way, a quadratic equation is in **standard form**.

To write a quadratic equation in standard form, we arrange it so that zero is on the right side of the equation, the term with exponent 2 comes first on the left side, followed by the term with exponent 1 (if there is one) and then the constant (numeric) term. This is illustrated in Example 1.

348   **Chapter 6**   Topics in Algebra

| EXAMPLE 1 | **Writing a Quadratic Equation in Standard Form** |

Write each equation in standard form and identify a, b, and c.

(a) $7 + 9x^2 = 3x$
(b) $4x - 15 = 3x^2$
(c) $5x^2 = 25$

SOLUTION

(a) $7 + 9x^2 = 3x$ *Subtract 3x from both sides; rearrange.*
         $9x^2 - 3x + 7 = 0$

Now we use the definition of standard form: a is the coefficient of x^2, b is the coefficient of x, and c is the constant term, so we get $a = 9$, $b = -3$, and $c = 7$.

(b) $4x - 15 = 3x^2$ *Subtract 3x² from both sides.*
      $-3x^2 + 4x - 15 = 0$
      $a = -3$, $b = 4$, $c = -15$

Notice that if we wanted to, we could multiply both sides of the equation in standard form by -1, giving us the equivalent equation $3x^2 - 4x + 15 = 0$. In this case, $a = 3$, $b = -4$, and $c = 15$.

(c) $5x^2 = 25$ *Subtract 25 from both sides.*
         $5x^2 - 25 = 0$
         $a = 5$, $b = 0$, $c = -25$

> ### Math Note
> Every quadratic equation with variable x has to have an x^2 term, or it isn't quadratic after all. But quadratic equations may or may not have an x term or a constant term.
>
> For the equation $x^2 - 6 = 0$, $a = 1$, $b = 0$, and $c = -6$. For the equation $2x^2 - 10x = 0$, $a = 2$, $b = -10$, and $c = 0$.

☑ 1. Identify the standard form of a quadratic equation

▼ **Try This One** **1**

Write each quadratic equation in standard form and identify a, b, and c.

(a) $6 + 8x - x^2 = 0$
(b) $-6x^2 = 5$
(c) $4x + 5x^2 = 0$

Multiplying Binomials

> ### Math Note
> It's not clear what multiplying binomials has to do with the topic of this section, which is solving quadratic equations. Hang in there, and we'll see in a while why this skill is so important.

Before we tackle solving quadratic equations, we need some background information. A **binomial** is an algebraic expression with two terms in which any variable has a whole number exponent. Some examples of binomials are

$$x - 5 \quad 2x + 3 \quad -6x^2 + 4$$

There is a clever method for multiplying two binomials known as the FOIL method. **F** represents the product of the *first* terms of the binomial. **O** represents the product of the *outer* terms. **I** represents the product of the *inner* terms. **L** represents the product of the *last* terms of the binomials.

The product of two binomials using the FOIL method is

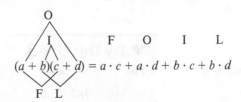

$$(a + b)(c + d) = a \cdot c + a \cdot d + b \cdot c + b \cdot d$$

Examples 2 and 3 show how to multiply binomials using the FOIL method.

EXAMPLE 2   Multiplying Binomials Using FOIL

Multiply $(x - 8)(x + 3)$.

SOLUTION

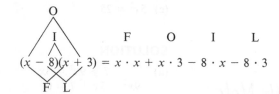

$$(x - 8)(x + 3) = x \cdot x + x \cdot 3 - 8 \cdot x - 8 \cdot 3$$

Math Note

When performing the individual multiplications in the FOIL method, don't forget to consider the sign of each term! In Example 2, the inner terms are not 8 and *x*, they're NEGATIVE 8 and *x*.

Multiply the *first* terms: $x \cdot x = x^2$
Multiply the *outer* terms: $x \cdot 3 = 3x$ *These two are like terms.*
Multiply the *inner* terms: $-8 \cdot x = -8x$
Multiply the *last* terms: $(-8) \cdot (+3) = -24$

Notice that $3x$ and $-8x$ are like terms that when combined equal $-5x$. So the product is $x^2 - 5x - 24$.

▼ **Try This One 2**

Multiply $(x + 7)(x + 9)$.

EXAMPLE 3   Multiplying Binomials Using FOIL

Multiply $(2x - 5)(3x - 8)$.

SOLUTION

$$(2x - 5)(3x - 8) = 2x \cdot 3x - 2x \cdot 8 - 5 \cdot 3x - 5(-8)$$

$$= 6x^2 - 16x - 15x + 40 \quad \text{Combine like terms.}$$
$$= 6x^2 - 31x + 40$$

The product is $6x^2 - 31x + 40$.

▼ **Try This One 3**

☑ 2. Multiply binomials using FOIL.

Find each product.

(a) $(4x - 9)(2x + 5)$
(b) $(3x - 8)(5x - 2)$

Factoring Trinomials

When a quadratic equation is written in standard form, there are three terms on the left side if none of the coefficients are zero. Three-term expressions like this are called **trinomials**, and you may have noticed that the result of each example of using FOIL in Examples 2 and 3 fit that form. It's important that you're really good at using FOIL, because one of our methods for solving quadratic equations will involve performing FOIL in reverse, a process we call *factoring*.

In Chapter 5, we called the process of writing a number as a product **factoring**. The same can often be done to algebraic expressions. Take another look at the result of Example 2:

$$(x - 8)(x + 3) = x^2 - 5x - 24$$

If we read this equation from right to left, it's an example of factoring, because we start with the trinomial $x^2 - 5x - 24$ and write it as a product of two factors: $x - 8$ and $x + 3$.

The key to being able to factor trinomials is recognizing where each term in the trinomial in the equation above comes from. The x^2 comes from multiplying the first terms of the two factors, x and x. The constant term, -24, comes from multiplying the last two numbers of the two factors, -8 and 3. And the x term comes from combining the products of the outsides and insides. In essence, we will reverse the process of FOIL to factor. It's easiest to describe the process using some examples.

> ### Math Note
>
> Factoring is one of the most important techniques in algebra. Simply put, you won't get very far without being good at it. And the only way to get good at factoring is to really understand what factoring means: it's simply writing an expression as a product. Try to keep that in mind as you practice factoring.

EXAMPLE 4   **Factoring a Trinomial with $a = 1$**

Factor $x^2 + 10x + 16$.

SOLUTION

Step 1 The factored form will be the product of two binomials; the first term of each is x (since the product of the firsts must be x^2).

$$x^2 + 10x + 16 = (x \quad)(x \quad)$$

Step 2 Write all pairs of factors of the constant term. One of these pairs must be the product of the last terms inside the parentheses. In this case, they are $1 \cdot 16$, $2 \cdot 8$, and $4 \cdot 4$.

Step 3 Set up the factorization with each possible pair of last terms, found in Step 2. Then find the product of outside and inside terms for each possibility.

$1 \cdot 16$: $(x \quad 1)(x \quad 16)$ Outsides: $16x$ Insides: x
$2 \cdot 8$: $(x \quad 2)(x \quad 8)$ Outsides: $8x$ Insides: $2x$
$4 \cdot 4$: $(x \quad 4)(x \quad 4)$ Outsides: $4x$ Insides: $4x$

Step 4 Find a sum or difference of the outsides and insides that yields the x term in the trinomial. In this case, we need $10x$, and $8x + 2x = 10x$. That tells us that the two last terms we need are $+8$ and $+2$, and the trinomial factors as

$$x^2 + 10x + 16 = (x + 2)(x + 8)$$

Check, using FOIL:

$$(x + 2)(x + 8) = x^2 + 8x + 2x + 16 = x^2 + 10x + 16$$

▼ **Try This One 4**

Factor $x^2 + 13x + 36$.

EXAMPLE 5   **Factoring a Trinomial with $a = 1$**

Factor $x^2 - 7x + 12$.

SOLUTION

Step 1 Write as the product of two binomials with first term x.

$$x^2 - 7x + 12 = (x \quad)(x \quad)$$

Step 2 The pairs of factors of the constant term are $1 \cdot 12$, $2 \cdot 6$, and $3 \cdot 4$.

Step 3 Possible factorizations:

$(x \quad 1)(x \quad 12)$	Outsides: $12x$	Insides: x
$(x \quad 2)(x \quad 6)$	Outsides: $6x$	Insides: $2x$
$(x \quad 3)(x \quad 4)$	Outsides: $4x$	Insides: $3x$

Step 4 The pair of outsides and insides that yields middle term $-7x$ is $4x$ and $3x$, if both are negative: $-4x - 3x = -7x$. Also, $(-4)(-3) = 12$, which is the correct constant term. So the factors are

$$x^2 - 7x + 12 = (x - 3)(x - 4)$$

Check:

$$(x - 3)(x - 4) = x^2 - 4x - 3x + 12 = x^2 - 7x + 12$$

> **Math Note**
>
> Notice that if the constant term is positive and the x term is negative, both factors of the constant term have to be negative.

▼ **Try This One 5**

Factor $x^2 - 12x + 20$.

EXAMPLE 6   **Factoring a Trinomial with $a = 1$**

Factor $x^2 - 2x - 8$.

SOLUTION

Step 1 Write as the product of two binomials with first term x.

$$x^2 - 2x - 8 = (x \quad)(x \quad)$$

Step 2 The pairs of factors of the constant term are $1 \cdot 8$ and $2 \cdot 4$.

Step 3 Possible factorizations:

$(x \quad 1)(x \quad 8)$	Outsides: $8x$	Insides: x
$(x \quad 2)(x \quad 4)$	Outsides: $4x$	Insides: $2x$

> **Math Note**
>
> Notice that if the constant term is negative, one factor of the constant is negative, and the other is positive.

Step 4 The pair of outsides and insides that yields middle term $-2x$ is $-4x$ and $2x$: $-4x + 2x = -2x$. Also, $(-4)(2) = -8$, which is the correct constant term. So the factors are

$$x^2 - 2x - 8 = (x + 2)(x - 4)$$

Check: $(x + 2)(x - 4) = x^2 - 4x + 2x - 8 = x^2 - 2x - 8$

▼ Try This One 6

Factor each trinomial:

(a) $x^2 - 3x - 40$ (b) $x^2 + x - 30$

Factoring Trinomials with $a \neq 1$

Step one was the same in each factoring example up to this point because the product of the first terms was always just $x \cdot x$. But that won't be the case if the coefficient of x^2 isn't 1, as in the next two examples. The good news, though, is that the same procedure still works.

EXAMPLE 7   **Factoring a Trinomial with $a \neq 1$**

Factor $3x^2 - 4x - 15$.

SOLUTION

Step 1 Write as the product of two binomials; the product of the first terms has to be $3x^2$, so they are $3x$ and x.

$$3x^2 - 4x - 15 = (3x \quad)(x \quad)$$

Step 2 The pairs of factors of the constant term are $1 \cdot 15$ and $3 \cdot 5$.

Step 3 Possible factorizations (important note: this time the order matters, so we have to write the possible combinations in both orders):

$(3x \quad 1)(x \quad 15)$	Outsides: $45x$	Insides: x
$(3x \quad 15)(x \quad 1)$	Outsides: $3x$	Insides: $15x$
$(3x \quad 3)(x \quad 5)$	Outsides: $15x$	Insides: $3x$
$(3x \quad 5)(x \quad 3)$	Outsides: $9x$	Insides: $5x$

Step 4 The pair of outsides and insides that yields middle term $-4x$ is $-9x$ and $5x$: $-9x + 5x = -4x$. This comes from factors 5 and -3, and $(5)(-3) = -15$, which is the correct constant term. So the factors are

$$3x^2 - 4x - 15 = (3x + 5)(x - 3)$$

Check: $(3x + 5)(x - 3) = 3x^2 - 9x + 5x - 15 = 3x^2 - 4x - 15$

> **Math Note**
>
> With enough practice, you'll eventually be able to try the possibilities mentally, rather than on paper. But we suggest you write them out until you're really comfortable with the process.

▼ Try This One 7

Factor $3x^2 - 11x + 6$.

The most challenging problems are ones where the coefficient of x^2 has more than one pair of factors, as in Example 8.

EXAMPLE 8	Factoring a Trinomial with $a \neq 1$

Factor $14x^2 - 33x + 10$.

SOLUTION

Step 1 Write as the product of two binomials; the product of the first terms has to be $14x^2$, so they can be $14x$ and x, or $7x$ and $2x$.

$$14x^2 - 33x + 10 = (14x \quad)(x \quad) \quad \text{or} \quad (7x \quad)(2x \quad)$$

Step 2 The pairs of factors of the constant term are $1 \cdot 10$ and $2 \cdot 5$.

Step 3 We'll start trying the combinations, starting with $14x$ and x as first terms:

> $(14x \quad 10)(x \quad 1)$ Outsides: $14x$ Insides: $10x$ *Can't get $-33x$*
> $(14x \quad 1)(x \quad 10)$ Outsides: $140x$ Insides: x *Can't get $-33x$*
> $(14x \quad 5)(x \quad 2)$ Outsides: $28x$ Insides: $5x$

Step 4 We haven't written all the combinations, but at this point we can stop. With factors $(14x - 5)$ and $(x - 2)$, we'll get outsides $-28x$ and insides $-5x$, which gives us the $-33x$ we need.

$$14x^2 - 33x + 10 = (14x - 5)(x - 2)$$

Check:

$$(14x - 5)(x - 2) = 14x^2 - 28x - 5x + 10 = 14x^2 - 33x + 10$$

> ▼ **Try This One 8**
>
> Factor $6x^2 + 25x + 21$.

☑ 3. Factor trinomials

Math Note

If you exhaust all of the possible combinations and don't find one that works, then the trinomial cannot be factored using integers, and we call it **prime**.

Math Note

The fact that the product of two numbers can only be zero if at least one of the two is zero is called the **zero product property**.

Solving Quadratic Equations Using Factoring

We come now to the main point of factoring: it's easy to find the solutions to a quadratic equation if the left side is factored. Here's why: consider the equation $(x - 3)(x + 2) = 0$. This is a statement that the product of two numbers, one named $x - 3$, and the other $x + 2$, is zero. But the only way a product can be zero is if one of the two factors is zero. (If you don't believe it, try to find two nonzero numbers with product zero!)

So from $(x - 3)(x + 2) = 0$, we conclude that either $x - 3 = 0$ or $x + 2 = 0$. This leaves us with two easy linear equations to solve, giving us $x = 3$ or $x = -2$. Now we have a general procedure, which will be demonstrated in Examples 9 and 10:

Procedure for Solving Quadratic Equations by Factoring

Step 1 Write the quadratic equation in standard form. That is, rearrange so that zero is on one side.

Step 2 Factor the left side.

Step 3 Set both factors equal to zero. This results in two simple equations.

Step 4 Solve each equation.

354 **Chapter 6** Topics in Algebra

| **EXAMPLE 9** | **Solving a Quadratic Equation Using Factoring** |

Solve $x^2 - 13x = -36$.

SOLUTION

Step 1 $x^2 - 13x + 36 = 0$ *Write in standard form.*

Step 2 $(x - 9)(x - 4) = 0$ *Factor the left side.*

Step 3 $x - 9 = 0$ or $x - 4 = 0$ *Set both factors equal to zero.*

Step 4
$$
\begin{array}{c|c}
x - 9 = 0 & x - 4 = 0 \\
x - 9 + 9 = 0 + 9 & x - 4 + 4 = 0 + 4 \\
x = 9 & x = 4
\end{array}
$$
    Solve each equation.

The solution set is $\{9, 4\}$.

    The solutions can be checked by substituting the values into the original equation, as shown.

$$
\begin{array}{cc}
\text{For } x = 9, & \text{For } x = 4, \\
x^2 - 13x = -36 & x^2 - 13x = -36 \\
9^2 - 13(9) \overset{?}{=} -36 & 4^2 - 13(4) \overset{?}{=} -36 \\
81 - 117 \overset{?}{=} -36 & 16 - 52 \overset{?}{=} -36 \\
-36 = -36 & -36 = -36
\end{array}
$$

▼ **Try This One 9**

Solve $x^2 + 6 = -7x$.

| **EXAMPLE 10** | **Solving a Quadratic Equation Using Factoring** |

Solve $6x^2 - 6 = -5x$.

SOLUTION

Step 1 $6x^2 + 5x - 6 = 0$ *Write in standard form.*

Step 2 $(3x - 2)(2x + 3) = 0$ *Factor.*

Step 3 $3x - 2 = 0$ $2x + 3 = 0$ *Set each factor equal to 0.*

Step 4
$$
\begin{array}{c|c}
3x - 2 = 0 & 2x + 3 = 0 \\
3x - 2 + 2 = 0 + 2 & 2x + 3 - 3 = 0 - 3 \\
3x = 2 & 2x = -3 \\
\dfrac{3x}{3} = \dfrac{2}{3} & \dfrac{2x}{2} = \dfrac{-3}{2} \\
x = \dfrac{2}{3} & x = -\dfrac{3}{2}
\end{array}
$$
    Solve each equation.

The solution set is $\left\{ \dfrac{2}{3}, -\dfrac{3}{2} \right\}$. We'll leave the check to you.

▼ **Try This One 10**

Solve $6x^2 - 11x = 2$ using factoring.

☑ 4. Solve quadratic equations using factoring.

Solving Quadratic Equations Using the Quadratic Formula

Factoring is a very useful tool for solving quadratic equations, but it's not the only one we need. There are plenty of trinomials that can't be factored using integers, and plenty of others that can be factored, but the size of the coefficients makes factoring impractical. Just when things look bad, along comes a formula to save the day, providing solutions to quadratic equations where factoring doesn't help.

The Quadratic Formula

The formula

$$x = \frac{-b \pm \sqrt{b^2 - 4ac}}{2a}$$

is called the **quadratic formula**. It provides the solutions for any quadratic equation written in standard form, $ax^2 + bx + c = 0$ with $a \neq 0$.

The good thing about this formula is that there's no algebraic manipulation involved: you simply substitute in the appropriate values for a, b, and c, then use order of operations to simplify the solutions.

EXAMPLE 11   **Using the Quadratic Formula**

Solve $2x^2 - x - 8 = 0$ using the quadratic formula.

SOLUTION

Identify a, b, and c. (The equation is already in standard form.)

$$a = 2, b = -1, \text{ and } c = -8$$

Substitute into the quadratic formula.

$$x = \frac{-b \pm \sqrt{b^2 - 4ac}}{2a}$$

$$= \frac{-(-1) \pm \sqrt{(-1)^2 - 4(2)(-8)}}{2(2)}$$

$$= \frac{1 \pm \sqrt{1 + 64}}{4}$$

$$x = \frac{1 + \sqrt{65}}{4} \quad \text{or} \quad x = \frac{1 - \sqrt{65}}{4} \quad \textit{Exact solutions}$$

$$\approx 2.266 \qquad\qquad \approx -1.766 \quad \textit{Decimal approximations}$$

$$\{2.266, -1.766\}$$

> **Math Note**
>
> To use the quadratic formula, you need to identify the coefficients a, b, and c, and you can't do that correctly unless the equation is written in standard form first. Also, don't forget to include negative signs when appropriate when identifying a, b, and c.

▼ **Try This One 11**

Solve $3x^2 - 5x + 1 = 0$ using the quadratic formula.

When solutions found using the quadratic formula are left in radical form, they are exact; decimal equivalents are usually approximate values. The exact solutions can sometimes be simplified; for example,

$$\frac{9 \pm \sqrt{27}}{6} = \frac{9 \pm \sqrt{9 \cdot 3}}{6} = \frac{9 \pm 3\sqrt{3}}{6} = \frac{3^1(3 \pm \sqrt{3})}{2\cancel{6}} = \frac{3 \pm \sqrt{3}}{2}$$

First $\sqrt{27}$ was simplified to $3\sqrt{3}$ and a 3 was factored out of the numerator. Finally, a factor of 3 was divided out of the numerator and denominator.

EXAMPLE 12   Using the Quadratic Formula

Solve $5 = 5y^2 + 8y$ using the quadratic formula.

SOLUTION

Before identifying a, b, and c, we need to rewrite the equation in standard form by subtracting $5y^2$ and $8y$ from both sides.

$$-5y^2 - 8y + 5 = 0 \qquad a = -5, b = -8, c = 5$$

Make sure to use variable y in the solution!

$$
\begin{aligned}
y &= \frac{-b \pm \sqrt{b^2 - 4ac}}{2a} \\[2mm]
&= \frac{-(-8) \pm \sqrt{(-8)^2 - 4(-5)(5)}}{2(-5)} \\[2mm]
&= \frac{8 \pm \sqrt{64 + 100}}{-10} \\[2mm]
&= \frac{8 \pm \sqrt{164}}{-10} \\[2mm]
&= \frac{8 \pm 2\sqrt{41}}{-10} \\[2mm]
&= \frac{2(4 \pm \sqrt{41})}{-10} \\[2mm]
&= \frac{4 + \sqrt{41}}{-5}, \frac{4 - \sqrt{41}}{-5}
\end{aligned}
$$

$\sqrt{164} = \sqrt{4} \cdot \sqrt{41} = 2\sqrt{41}$

Factor 2 out of numerator.

Divide numerator and denominator by 2.

The solution set is $\left\{\frac{4 + \sqrt{41}}{-5}, \frac{4 - \sqrt{41}}{-5}\right\}$. To two decimal places, the decimal approximations are $\{-2.08, 0.48\}$.

Calculator Guide

To find decimal approximations for $\frac{4 + \sqrt{41}}{-5}$:

Standard Scientific Calculator

(4 + 41 √) ÷ 5

± =

Standard Graphing Calculator

(4 + √ 41)) ÷

(−) 5 ENTER

The second close parenthesis after 41 is needed if your calculator automatically puts in an open parenthesis when you push the √ button.

▼ Try This One   12

Solve each quadratic equation using the quadratic formula.

(a) $3x^2 - 3x = 1$ (b) $x = x^2 - 13$

☑ 5. Solve quadratic equations using the quadratic formula.

In Problems 86–89, we'll learn everything there is to know about the significance of the stuff under the radical sign in the quadratic formula. For now, we'll just point out that if that number ends up being negative, the equation has no real solutions. We won't study equations like that in this book, but they do have some very real applications. Which brings us to the last important topic in this chapter.

Applications of Quadratic Equations

Quadratic equations can be used to solve many problems in our world using the problem-solving procedure we developed in Section 6-3.

EXAMPLE 13   Applying Quadratic Equations to Home Projects

There is a wide variety of plans available on the Internet for do-it-yourself furniture projects. One plan for making a rectangular picnic table allows you to choose the size you want, but requires the length to be 2 feet more than the width. If you want to build a table with 20 square feet of tabletop space, what dimensions should you choose?

SOLUTION

There are two things that can change in this problem: the width and the length. We should choose our variable to represent one of those variable quantities; let's say x = the width. The length is 2 feet more, so $x + 2$ is the length. Since the area of a rectangle is length times width, we can set up an equation:

Length	times	Width	is	Area
$(x + 2)$	$\times$	x	$=$	20

Now we solve:

$$(x + 2)x = 20 \qquad \textit{Distribute.}$$
$$x^2 + 2x = 20 \qquad \textit{Subtract 20 from both sides.}$$
$$x^2 + 2x - 20 = 0 \qquad \textit{Left side doesn't factor: use quadratic formula with } a = 1, b = 2, c = -20.$$
$$x = \frac{-2 \pm \sqrt{2^2 - 4(1)(-20)}}{2(1)}$$
$$= \frac{-2 \pm \sqrt{84}}{2} \approx 3.56, -5.56$$

The negative answer can't be a length, so we ignore it; the width we want is 3.56 feet (which is about 3′7″), making the length about 5′7″.

Check: 3.56 feet × 5.56 feet = 19.8 square feet, with the difference coming from rounding error.

> **Math Note**
>
> An exact answer, like
> $$\frac{-2 \pm \sqrt{84}}{2}$$
> is very nice, but in applied situations, we usually prefer a decimal approximation.
>
> If I ask you to cut a board to length
> $$\frac{-2 \pm \sqrt{84}}{2} \text{ feet, I'm}$$
> guessing
> you won't have much success without converting to a decimal.

6. Solve problems using quadratic equations.

▼ Try This One 13

The formula for the distance that an object falls freely to the ground is $d = rt + 16t^2$, where:

d is the distance it falls (in feet);
r is the rate at which the object starts to fall; and
t is the number of seconds the object falls.

If you toss a tennis ball downward from the top of the Sony Building in New York City (576 feet tall) with an initial speed of 6 feet per second, how long will it take to reach the ground? (*Legal note*: if you actually do this, you'll get arrested.)

Answers to Try This One

1 (a) $-x^2 + 8x + 6 = 0$; $a = -1$; $b = 8$; $c = 6$ or
  $x^2 - 8x - 6 = 0$; $a = 1$; $b = -8$; $c = -6$
  (b) $-6x^2 - 5 = 0$; $a = -6$; $b = 0$; $c = -5$ or
  $6x^2 + 5 = 0$; $a = 6$; $b = 0$; $c = 5$
  (c) $5x^2 + 4x = 0$; $a = 5$; $b = 4$; $c = 0$

2 $x^2 + 16x + 63$

3 (a) $8x^2 + 2x - 45$ (b) $15x^2 - 46x + 16$

4 $(x + 9)(x + 4)$

5 $(x - 10)(x - 2)$

6 (a) $(x - 8)(x + 5)$ (b) $(x + 6)(x - 5)$

7 $(3x - 2)(x - 3)$

8 $(6x + 7)(x + 3)$

9 $\{-1, -6\}$

10 $\left\{2, -\dfrac{1}{6}\right\}$

11 $\dfrac{5 \pm \sqrt{13}}{6} \approx \{1.43, 0.23\}$

12 (a) $\dfrac{3 \pm \sqrt{21}}{6} \approx \{1.26, -0.26\}$

  (b) $\dfrac{1 \pm \sqrt{53}}{2} \approx \{4.14, -3.14\}$

13 About 5.8 seconds

EXERCISE SET 6-6

Writing Exercises

1. Describe the process we use to multiply two binomial expressions.
2. What does it mean to factor an expression?
3. Describe the steps we use to factor a trinomial.
4. Why is factoring useful in solving quadratic equations?
5. Since we first learned to solve quadratic equations using factoring, why do we need the quadratic formula as well?
6. If you had to choose only one of solving by factoring and solving using the quadratic formula, which would you choose? Why?

Computational Exercises

For Exercises 7–12, write the equation in standard form and identify a, b, and c.

7. $2x + 3x^2 = 5$
8. $4 - 2x^2 = 7x$
9. $10 = 30x^2$
10. $-8 = -4x^2$
11. $-5x = 2x^2$
12. $100x = -50x^2$

For Exercises 13–22, use the FOIL method to multiply the two binomials.

13. $(x + 7)(x + 9)$
14. $(x - 8)(x - 12)$
15. $(y - 7)(y - 10)$
16. $(y + 4)(y + 2)$
17. $(x - 15)(x + 8)$
18. $(x + 10)(x - 3)$
19. $(2x - 7)(7x - 9)$
20. $(4x - 1)(4x - 1)$
21. $(5z + 7)(3z - 8)$
22. $(2t - 5)(3t + 8)$

For Exercises 23–42, solve each quadratic equation by factoring.

23. $x^2 + x - 12 = 0$
24. $x^2 - 3x - 10 = 0$
25. $t^2 - 14t = 51$
26. $y^2 - y = 20$
27. $x^2 + 24x = 81$
28. $x^2 - 12x = 64$
29. $y^2 + 15 = 8y$
30. $z^2 + 20 - 12z = 0$
31. $2x^2 - x - 21 = 0$
32. $5x^2 + 27x - 18 = 0$
33. $6x^2 - x - 12 = 0$
34. $4x^2 + 13x - 12 = 0$
35. $6m^2 - 12 = m$
36. $10k^2 + 21k = 10$
37. $5x^2 - 18 = 27x$
38. $6x^2 + 6 = 13x$
39. $\frac{1}{2}x^2 + \frac{1}{2}x - 3 = 0$
40. $\frac{1}{3}x^2 + 2x + \frac{5}{3} = 0$
41. $\frac{9}{4}y = -1 - \frac{1}{2}y^2$
42. $1 = \frac{1}{2}t^2 - \frac{7}{6}t$

For Exercises 43–62, solve each quadratic equation using the quadratic formula.

43. $3x^2 + x - 1 = 0$
44. $4x^2 - 7x = 2$
45. $2x^2 - 5x = 12$
46. $x^2 + 5x - 12 = 0$
47. $18y^2 + 42y = 31$
48. $120 = 8t + 27t^2$
49. $21x^2 - 50 = 2 - 79x$
50. $150y + 40 = -50y^2 - 32$
51. $x^2 + 5x = 3$
52. $6x - 1 = 4x^2$
53. $\frac{1}{3}y^2 = 7y - 10$
54. $\frac{5}{2} + y = 4y^2$
55. $\frac{7}{5}x - \frac{1}{2}x^2 = -3$
56. $-1 + \frac{11}{3}x^2 = \frac{1}{5}x$
57. $0.2x^2 + 1.2 = -1.3x$
58. $4.5x = x^2 + 1.1$
59. $2.3 - 1.6z = z^2$
60. $2.3t^2 - 4.5 = 6.7t$
61. $\sqrt{3}x^2 + 8 = 5\sqrt{11}x$
62. $-8x = 7\sqrt{2} - \sqrt{21}x^2$

63. The product of two consecutive even integers is 288. Find the numbers. (*Hint:* Consecutive even integers can be written as x and $x + 2$.)

64. The product of two consecutive integers is 156. Find the numbers. (*Hint:* Consecutive integers can be written as x and $x + 1$.)

Applications in Our World

65. How long will it take an object to hit the ground if it is dropped from a height of 1,296 feet? (Use $d = rt + 16t^2$.) Assume the object initially is held still.

66. A clothing designer wants a distinctive triangular tag on all of her designs, with height 6 inches more than the base. The manufacturer will allow 8 square inches for the overall size. Find the dimensions. (The area of a triangle is $A = \frac{1}{2}bh$.)

67. Mama Mia's Pizzeria offers two different sizes of pizza. The boxes they're delivered in are square and have a combined base area of 356 square inches. The smaller one has sides that are 6 inches shorter than the bigger one. Assuming that the boxes are made so that the pizza just fits, what are the diameters of the two pizza sizes?

68. An urban hospital is adding one new nurse practitioner and one new registered nurse to the staff each month. There are five more RNs than LPNs right now, and the product of the total number of each is three times what it was 5 months ago. How many LPNs are on staff right now?

69. To form part of a garden sculpture, an artist cuts a 20-foot wire into two pieces, and then bends each piece to form a square. The product of the lengths of one side of each square is 6 feet^2. What is the area of the larger square that is formed? (Use the formula $A = s^2$.)

70. A marketing manager for a publishing company has a 6 foot by 8 foot banner to be used when setting up booths at educational conferences. She decides to add more zing to the booth by increasing the square footage by 50%, and plans to accomplish this by increasing each of the dimensions by the same amount. What will the new dimensions be?

71. The profit for a company that produces custom gift baskets can be modeled by the equation $P = -2x^2 + 20x + 2,400$, where x is the number of gift baskets produced per month. How many gift baskets does the company have to sell to break even (no profit but no loss)?

72. A rectangular piece of cardboard has a length that is quadruple its width. When 2-inch squares are cut out of the four corners of the cardboard and the flaps are folded to form a box without a top, the box has a volume of 32 cubic inches. What is the length and width of the piece of cardboard? (The volume of a rectangular box is the product of length, width, and height.)

73. An interior designer plans to put a large rug in the reception area at a counselor's office. The room is three times as long as it is wide. The designer wants a $1\frac{1}{2}$-foot border of wood floor around the rug on all sides, and the budget allows for 105 square feet of rug. What should the dimensions of the rug be?

74. A hamburger wrapper is thrown from a sixth floor dorm window, and its motion can be modeled by the equation $h = -3t^2 + 3t + 60$, where h is the height in feet and t is the time in seconds. How long will it take for the wrapper to hit the ground?

75. A rectangular piece of land that is 30 feet by 20 feet is being sectioned off in the middle of campus to create a September 11 memorial monument. The developers would like to create a monument in the center that is 144 square feet, with a walkway border that is a uniform width. How wide should the walkway border be?

76. Dom and Sally conduct an experiment for extra credit in their math class. Standing on a 160-foot tall building, Sally drops her pencil over the edge at the same time Dom throws his pencil straight down with an initial velocity of 48 m/s. The motion of Sally's pencil can be modeled by the equation $h = -16t^2 + 160$ and the motion of Dom's pencil can be modeled by the equation $h = -16t^2 - 48t + 160$, where h is the height of the pencil and t is the time in seconds. By how many seconds does Dom's pencil beat Sally's to the ground below?

77. The distance it takes a particular type of car to stop is a function of the speed it is traveling (in miles per hour) when the brakes are applied and can be modeled by the equation $y = 0.07x^2 - 0.514x + 23$. When the distance this car takes to stop is 40 feet, find the speed the car is traveling when the brakes are applied.

78. The surface area A of a cylinder is given by the formula $A = 2\pi rh + 2\pi r^2$. Fizzy-Up, the manufacturer of a leading energy drink, uses 60π square inches of aluminum sheets for each can. If the height of each can is 7 inches, what is the radius of the can?

The Pythagorean theorem is a formula describing the relationship among the side lengths of a right triangle (a triangle with a 90 degree angle). If a and b represent the two shorter sides, and c is the longest side, then $a^2 + b^2 = c^2$. Use this formula for Exercises 79–82.

79. Two search planes are scrambled when a private jet carrying a well-known actor disappears from radar.

360   **Chapter 6**   Topics in Algebra

One flies directly north from the originating airport at 120 mph, while the other flies east at 140 mph. They'll lose radio contact when they're 215 miles apart. How long does it take for that to happen?

80. When a 20-foot ladder is leaned against a perpendicular wall, the distance from the base of the wall to the bottom of the ladder is 7 feet less than the height the ladder reaches up the wall. How far away from the wall is the bottom?

81. A kite is flying on 584 feet of string. Its vertical distance from the ground is 12 feet more than its horizontal distance from the person flying the kite. Assuming the string is being held at ground level, find the horizontal distance from the person and the vertical distance from the ground.

82. The roads Akani has to drive from home to school, school to work, and then work to home form a right triangle. She drives 7 more miles from school to work than from home to school. The distance from work to home is 13 miles. What is the round-trip distance Akani drives from home to school to work to home?

Critical Thinking

83. It can be shown using algebra that $2 = 1$. Incorrect algebra, that is. Look at the "proof" and find the error.

Let $x = 1$, then multiply both sides by x:
$x^2 = x$, then subtract one from each side:
$x^2 - 1 = x - 1$, then factor the left side:
$(x + 1)(x - 1) = x - 1$; divide both sides by $x - 1$:

$$(x + 1)\frac{(x - 1)}{(x - 1)} = \frac{(x - 1)}{(x - 1)}$$

$$x + 1 = 1;$$

substitute 1 for x:

$$1 + 1 = 1$$
$$2 = 1$$

84. Early in Section 6-6, we saw that the generic formula for multiplying two binomials using FOIL is

$$(a + b)(c + d) = a \cdot c + a \cdot d + b \cdot c + b \cdot d$$

Show that this is really just two consecutive applications of the distributive property. (*Hint:* Begin by treating the expression $(a + b)$ as if it were a single number.

85. Pick out three quadratic equations that were solved in this section using factoring, then rework them using the quadratic formula. What can you say about the expression under the radical sign in the quadratic formula, $b^2 - 4ac$, whenever the equation can be solved using factoring?

*Speaking of $b^2 - 4ac$, in the quadratic formula the expression under the radical is called the **discriminant**. In Questions 86–89, we'll see if we can figure out why.*

86. (a) Explain why the equation $2y^2 - 3y + 4 = 0$ has no real solutions. (*Hint:* Try to solve using the quadratic formula.)

   (b) What can you conclude about the solution to a quadratic equation when the discriminant is negative?

87. (a) Solve the equation $4x^2 - 20x + 25 = 0$ using whatever method you prefer, then find the discriminant.

   (b) What can you conclude about the solution to a quadratic equation when the discriminant is zero?

88. (a) Solve each equation using the quadratic formula:
   $5t^2 - t - 2 = 0$ $2y^2 + y - 15 = 0$
   $7x^2 + 13x - 2 = 0$

   (b) What is the value of the discriminant for each equation? How many solutions does each have?

   (c) Describe the solutions to each equation in terms of the sets of numbers we studied in Sections 5-3 and 5-4.

89. (a) Try to solve each of the equations in Exercise 88 using factoring. What do you notice? Based on this result, develop a criterion using the discriminant to decide if a quadratic expression does or does not factor.

   (b) Based on your results from Exercises 86–88 and part (a), fill in the chart below.

If the discriminant is…	Description of solutions
Negative	
Zero	
Positive	
A perfect square	

   (c) Why do you think the expression $b^2 - 4ac$ is called the discriminant?

90. From the Sidelight on page 248: if you divide a line into two parts so that the ratio of the longer part to the smaller is the same as the ratio of the total length to the longer part, that ratio is called the **golden ratio**. If the smaller part is length b and the longer is length a, this description gives us the proportion $\frac{a}{b} = \frac{a + b}{a}$.

   (a) Solve that proportion for a, treating b like it's just a number. The result will be an expression with b in it.

   (b) Write the golden ratio as a/b, substituting your solution from part (a) in for letter a. (Choose the positive answer because a has to be positive, as a length.) Then simplify the fraction to get the exact value of the golden ratio supplied in the Sidelight.

CHAPTER **6**   # Summary

Section	Important Terms	Important Ideas
6-1	Variable Algebraic expression Distributive property Like terms Evaluate Formula	**Algebra involves** the use of expressions and equations that contain a variable, which is a symbol that represents an unknown quantity that can change. Expressions can be simplified by using the distributive property and combining like terms. Expressions can be evaluated by substituting the values for the variables and using the order of operations to simplify the expression. Many problems in our world can be solved by using specific formulas that apply to a given situation.
6-2	Equation Solution Linear equation Solution set Equivalent equations Contradiction Identity	**An equation** is a statement that two algebraic expressions are equal. To solve an equation means to find all values of the variable that make the equation a true statement. We solve linear equations using the addition, subtraction, multiplication, and division properties of equality. The solutions to an equation can be checked by substituting them back in for the variable.
6-3		**Many** problems in our world can be solved by writing an appropriate equation that describes a problem and then solving the equation.
6-4	Ratio Proportion Cross multiply Direct variation Inverse variation	**The most efficient** way to compare the sizes of two quantities is to divide them, forming a ratio. A proportion is a statement that two ratios are equal; proportions come in handy in solving a ton of problems in our world.
6-5	Linear inequality Three-part inequality	**Inequalities** are similar to equations but use an inequality sign instead of an equal sign. Linear inequalities can be solved by using the same principles as equations with one exception: if you multiply or divide both sides of the inequality by a negative number, the inequality sign must be reversed. Inequalities are useful in solving problems that have an entire range of acceptable outcomes.
6-6	Quadratic equation Standard form Binomial FOIL method Trinomial Factoring Quadratic formula	**An equation** is called a quadratic equation when the largest exponent of the variable is 2. Some quadratic equations can be solved by factoring, which means writing an expression as a product. When one side of a quadratic equation can't be factored, the quadratic formula can be used. Quadratic equations can also be used to solve many problems in our world.

MATH IN ▶ Drug Administration REVISITED

Using proportions, comparing the amount of drug in milligrams to the weight of the patient in pounds, you can find that the recommended dosage for the football player is 647 mg, and for the child is 153 mg. The potentially lethal dose for the child is 573 mg, so the player's dose could kill her. The minimum dose for the football player is 404 mg, so the child's dose would do him absolutely no good.

362   **Chapter 6**   Topics in Algebra

Review Exercises

Section 6-1

For Exercises 1–7, simplify each algebraic expression.

1. $6x + 3y - 10 + 2y - 8x + 3$
2. $4x - 9 - 2x + 7y - 3y + 16$
3. $5(x - 6) + 2(x - 3)$
4. $-9(2x + 4) - 3(x - 2)$
5. $6x + 7 - 3(2x - 8) + 3x$
6. $-3y(7 - 2y) + 4y^2 - 10(y^3 - 5y^2 + 10)$
7. $4 - \dfrac{3}{2}(2t - 8) + 5\left(\dfrac{t}{2} + \dfrac{3}{4}\right)$

For Exercises 8–12, evaluate each algebraic expression or formula.

8. $2x^2 + 5x - 3$ when $x = 6$
9. $6(x - 8) - 10$ when $x = -2$
10. $\dfrac{4x^2 - 12}{x + 5}$ when $x = -3$
11. $d = rt$ when $r = 8$ and $t = 15$
12. $A = P(1 + rt)$ when $P = 3,000$, $r = 0.08$, and $t = 5$

Section 6-2

For Exercises 13–21, solve each equation.

13. $4x + 8 = -32$
14. $8y - 3 = 6y + 37$
15. $5(x + 9) = -20$
16. $3(z - 6) = 33$
17. $6(t + 8) - 4t = 3t - 19$
18. $9(2x - 4) = 15x - 27$
19. $\dfrac{3x}{2} + 2 = \dfrac{5x}{3}$
20. $\dfrac{y - 2}{3} + 2y = \dfrac{5}{3}$
21. $\dfrac{2x + 1}{4} + \dfrac{x}{8} = \dfrac{5}{4}$

For Exercises 22–27, solve for the specified variable.

22. $3x + 3y = 12$; solve for y
23. $P = a + b + c$; solve for c
24. $I = prt$; solve for r
25. $\dfrac{1}{x} = \dfrac{1}{y} - \dfrac{1}{z}$; solve for y
26. $P = 2L + 2W$; solve for W
27. $A = \dfrac{1}{2}bh$; solve for h

Section 6-3

For Exercises 28–31, write each statement in symbols.

28. 8 times a number decreased by 4
29. 3 added to four times a number
30. The product of 6 and the sum of one-half and a number
31. Three-fourths subtracted from the quotient of 18 and five times a number
32. Cindy is making the drive home for Thanksgiving, which takes 8 hours round trip. With the holiday traffic, she averages 40 miles per hour on the way home and 50

miles per hour back to school. Find the time it took her to get home and the time it took her to get back to school. (Use the formula distance = rate × time).

33. The health food store sells mixed soy nuts for $1.20 a pound and Asian trail mix for $1.80 a pound. If the store sold 2 more pounds of Asian trail mix than soy nuts and the total sales were $21.60 for these items for the day, how many pounds of each did the store sell?

34. The manager of a concert venue is adding up the proceeds from a Friday night show. Tickets sold for $8, $10, and $12 depending on where the seats were. Twice as many $8 seats were sold as $10, and 10 more $12 seats were sold than $10. The total proceeds were $3,122. How many of each type of ticket were sold?

35. A patient that returned from Jamaica with a great tan and a tropical foodborne illness is given an aggressive course of antibiotics. A total of 5,000 milligrams is to be taken over 5 days, with the amount for each of the third, fourth, and fifth days half as much as the amount for each of the first 2 days. How much should be taken on the first day? *Note*: That patient was me.

36. In a department store Juaquin notices a jacket that he wanted to buy on the "60% off" rack. If the original price of the jacket was $75 before sales tax, what is the sale price of the jacket before sales tax?

37. At one county detention facility, inmates convicted of petty larceny receive a 30-day sentence, those convicted of DUI get 6 days, and simple assault results in 45 days. At one point, there were twice as many larceny inmates as assault, and three times as many DUI inmates as larceny. Collectively, the prisoners at that point were serving 423 days in jail. How many DUI inmates were there at that time?

38. At a New Year's Eve party in a certain restaurant the cost was $60 per couple. If more than 50 couples attend, the restaurant agreed to drop the price by 50 cents a couple for each couple in excess of 50. If 76 couples attended the party, what was the cost per couple?

Section 6-4

For Exercises 39–42, write each ratio as a fraction.

39. 82 miles to 15 gallons of gasoline
40. 16 ounces cost $2.37
41. 4 months to 2 years
42. 18 minutes to 2 hours

For Exercises 43–45, solve each proportion.

43. $\dfrac{2}{x} = \dfrac{14}{63}$
44. $\dfrac{y - 3}{8} = \dfrac{40}{23}$
45. $\dfrac{120}{x + 30} = \dfrac{51}{2x - 3}$

46. If you burn 90 calories when exercising for 12 minutes, how many calories will you burn when exercising for 30 minutes?

47. The U.S. Center for Disease Control reported that 4 out of 10 people with incomes between $15,000 and $24,999

exercise regularly. About how many people exercise regularly in a group of 85 people who are in that income bracket?

48. In his will, a man's estate was divided according to a ratio of three parts for his wife and two parts for his son. If his estate amounted to $280,000, how much did each receive?

49. A professor states that if a student misses a unit test (worth 30 points), he will use the score on the final exam (100 points), proportionally reduced, for the score on the unit test. If a student scored 85 on the final exam, what would be the student's score on the unit test?

50. The cost of building a deck varies directly with the area of the deck. If a 6-foot by 9-foot deck costs $2,160, find the cost of building a 9-foot by 12-foot deck.

51. The amount of paint needed to paint a spherical object varies directly with the square of the diameter. If 3 pints of paint are needed to paint a model of Mercury with a diameter of 36 inches, how much paint will be needed to paint a model of Earth with a diameter of 60 inches?

52. The amount of amperage in amps of electricity passing through a wire varies inversely with the resistance in ohms of the wire when the potential remains the same. If the resistance is 20 ohms when the amperage is 10 amps, find the amperage when the resistance is 45 ohms.

53. The cost of producing an item varies inversely with the square root of the number of items produced. Find the cost of producing 1,600 items if the cost of producing 900 items is $600.

Section 6-5

For Exercises 54–60, solve each inequality.

54. $3x + 6 \leq 2x - 14$
55. $4 - 5y < -31$
56. $4(x - 6) > 3(x - 15)$
57. $2x + 7 \leq 6(2x + 9) - 20$
58. $\frac{11}{3}y - 9 > 4y + \frac{1}{2}$
59. $-9 < 9 - 3x \leq 20$
60. $2 \leq \frac{4 - 3t}{5} \leq 3$

61. A new health club is offering a special initiation fee of $74.99, plus a monthly membership fee of $32.50. While recovering from an injury suffered in a car accident, Tomas is allotted $1,000 for recovery services from his insurance company, with the stipulation that at least half has to be spent on health club membership. What is the range of months that Tomas can join for?

62. Cat manages the office for a biotech startup in Mason, Ohio. When the company moves to a shiny new facility, $2,300 is budgeted for live plants to decorate the offices. A plant service will choose appropriate plants and install them in the facility for $68.95 per plant. How many plants can Cat order?

Section 6-6

For Exercises 63–67, solve each equation by factoring.

63. $x^2 + 11x - 26 = 0$
64. $z^2 - 4z - 21 = 0$
65. $2x^2 + 5x = 3$
66. $2 = y + 3y^2$
67. $\frac{x^2}{2} + \frac{9}{4} = \frac{9x}{4}$

For Exercises 68–73, solve each equation using the quadratic formula.

68. $x^2 - 5x = 7$
69. $5t^2 - 7t - 4 = 0$
70. $8x^2 + 14x + 4 = 0$
71. $9x^2 - 12x = 7$
72. $4k^2 - 5 = -14k$
73. $\frac{3}{5}y - 9 = -\frac{11}{2}y^2$

74. If the product of two consecutive numbers is 132, find the numbers.

75. How long will it take a dropped object to fall a distance of 1,024 feet? Use $d = rt + 16t^2$.

76. The athletic department at a community college is planning to fence off a large rectangular parcel of land adjacent to the main parking area for intramural fields. The side that meets the parking lot will be left open, so fencing is needed on just three sides. The length of fence parallel to the parking lot will be 120 feet longer than the other sides, and the total area of the field is 85,000 square feet. Find the amount of fence that is needed.

Chapter Test ────────────────────────────────

For Exercises 1 and 2, simplify.

1. $3x - 7y + 2x - 3y + 5$
2. $5(x^2 - 6) + 2x - 10 - x(11 - 8x)$

For Exercises 3 and 4, evaluate.

3. $3x^2 - 2x + 6$ when $x = -5$
4. $E = 0.2381I^2Rt$ when $I = 30$, $R = 5$, and $t = 80$

For Exercises 5–7, solve the equation.

5. $3x - 5(2x + 10) = -59$
6. $2(y - 6) = 7 + 4(y + 16)$

7. $\frac{2t - 9}{5} + 6t = \frac{3}{10}t - \frac{2}{5}$

8. Solve: $F = \frac{mv^2}{r}$ for r

9. Solve for y: $3x + 2y = 10$

For Exercises 10–12, solve the inequality.

10. $2(y - 3) < 5y + 12$
11. $8x - \frac{17}{2} \geq \frac{3x}{4} - 2(x + 1)$
12. $-90 < 4 - (9 - 2y) \leq 136$

For Exercises 13 and 14, solve the proportion.

13. $\dfrac{x}{9} = \dfrac{16}{36}$

14. $\dfrac{3}{7} = \dfrac{20}{x-4}$

For Exercises 15 and 16, find the product.

15. $(x-8)(2x+3)$
16. $(3x-5)(4x-7)$

For Exercises 17–19, solve by factoring.

17. $x^2 - 14x - 51 = 0$
18. $t^2 + 12t - 40 = -27$
19. $6x^2 + x = 12$

For Exercises 20 and 21, solve using the quadratic formula.

20. $3x^2 - x - 1 = 0$
21. $\dfrac{5y^2}{2} + y = \dfrac{3}{2}$

22. A person has invested part of $5,000 in stocks paying a 4% dividend and the rest in stocks paying a 6% dividend. If the total of the dividends was $270, how much did the person invest in each stock?

23. A marketing company bought high-capacity flash drives for six new employees at a cost of $400. How much would it cost them to buy the same drives for the entire existing sales force of 37 people?

24. If you can bike 2 miles in $12\frac{1}{2}$ minutes, how many hours will it take to bike 210 miles without counting rest stops?

25. The number of vibrations per second of a metal string varies directly with the square root of the tension when all other factors remain unchanged. Find the number of vibrations per second of a string under a tension of 64 pounds when a string under a tension of 25 pounds makes 125 vibrations per second.

26. The number of hours it takes to do a certain job varies inversely with the number of people working on the job. If it takes 12 people 8 hours to build a front porch on a Habitat for Humanity house, how many hours will it take 8 people to build a porch?

27. The product of two consecutive even numbers is 624. Find the numbers. (*Hint:* Consecutive even numbers can be represented by x and $x + 2$.)

28. A board game is played on a rectangular board whose area is 96 square inches. If the length is 4 inches longer than the width, find its dimensions.

Projects

1. We studied two methods for solving quadratic equations in Chapter 6: factoring and the quadratic formula. The biggest advantage of the quadratic formula is that it works on *every* quadratic equation, not just the ones that factor. But is it always the best choice?

   (a) Solve the equation $x^2 + x - 6 = 0$ using factoring. Use a stopwatch or timer to time how long it takes, then check your solution.

   (b) Solve the same equation, this time using the quadratic formula. Again, time yourself, and note whether you got the correct solution.

   (c) Repeat parts *a* and *b* for each of the equations below.

   $$x^2 - 3x - 4 = 0$$
   $$2x^2 - x - 15 = 0$$
   $$3x^2 - 20x - 7 = 0$$

   (d) Compute your average time for each method on all four equations, then calculate the percentage of problems that you got right using each method. Which method overall would you say was more efficient, and why?

   (e) Repeat parts (a) through (d) for the four equations below.

   $$x^2 - 2x - 80 = 0$$
   $$4x^2 + 26x - 48 = 0$$
   $$6x^2 - 55x - 50 = 0$$
   $$2x^2 + 12x - 144 = 0$$

   (f) Was your decision on which method is more efficient different for the second group of equations? Write a general conclusion about the value of each method based on all of your results.

2. An interesting method for solving quadratic equations was developed in India about 1,400 years ago. The steps are
   1. Move the constant term to the right side of the equation.
   2. Multiply each term in the equation by four times the coefficient of the x^2 term.
   3. Square the coefficient of the original x term and add it to both sides of the equation.
   4. Take the square root of both sides. (*Hint*: Factor the left side first.)
   5. Set the left side of the equation equal to the positive square root of the number on the right side and solve for x.
   6. Set the left side of the equation equal to the negative square root of the number on the right side of the equation and solve for x.

   (a) Use the method to solve each equation.
       (i) $x^2 - 2x - 13 = 0$
       (ii) $4x^2 - 4x + 3 = 0$
       (iii) $x^2 + 12x - 64 = 0$
       (iv) $2x^2 - 3x - 5 = 0$

   (b) Do you find this method to be more or less effective than the ones we studied in Chapter 6?

   (c) The thing that makes this method work is that you can find the square root of the expression on the left side because it factors as a perfect square. Will it always work out that way for any quadratic equation? Describe what it is about the process specifically that justifies your answer.

   (d) We know that not every quadratic equation has real solutions. What will go wrong in this process if you try it on an equation with no solutions? If you can't figure it out, try some examples!

3. We started Chapter 6 by talking about drug dosage as it relates to the size of a patient. While some doses are based on body weight, it's more common to base them on a patient's body surface area, or BSA. This is the area of all of your body's skin if you could take it off and stretch it flat. While doing so would result in a very accurate reading for BSA, it would also render the patient deceased, which makes any dosage kind of pointless (and that doesn't even consider the legal and moral ramifications).

The point is that it's not terribly easy to measure a living person's BSA, and a wide variety of formulas has been developed to estimate this important number. In this project, your task is to rework the questions in the chapter opener on page 291 using the BSA for each patient, rather than strictly their weight. Here's some extra information you need:

- The football player is 6′4″, while the child is 4′5″.
- The recommended dose for an average man with BSA of 1.9 square meters is 400 mg.
- The minimum effective dose for that size is 250 mg, and anything over 1,500 mg could be lethal.

Use each of the BSA formulas listed, and compare the amount of medication that would be prescribed based on each. How widely do the amounts vary for different formulas? Write a short report discussing this variation and decide if there's one formula that you think is most useful based on ease of use and calculated result. Finally, discuss whether or not you think that it's really possible to get a good measure of body surface area using only height and weight.

(*Note*: to convert height in inches to centimeters (cm), multiply by 2.54; to convert weight in pounds to kilograms (kg), divide by 2.2.) All formulas provide BSA in square meters; all heights are in cm, and all weights are in kg.

(a) The Mosteller formula: $\text{BSA} = \sqrt{\dfrac{\text{Height} \times \text{Weight}}{3,600}}$

(b) The DuBois formula:
$\text{BSA} = 0.007184 \times \text{Height}^{0.725} \times \text{Weight}^{0.425}$

(c) The Haycock formula:
$\text{BSA} = 0.024265 \times \text{Height}^{0.3964} \times \text{Weight}^{0.5378}$

(d) The Gehan/George formula:
$\text{BSA} = 0.0235 \times \text{Height}^{0.42246} \times \text{Weight}^{0.51456}$

(e) The Boyd formula:

$$\text{BSA} = \frac{\text{Height}^{0.3} \times \text{Weight}^{\{0.6157 - [0.00816474 \ln (\text{Weight})]\}}}{30.03316}$$

(*Note*: "ln" represents the natural log function, which we'll encounter in Chapters 7 and 8. You can calculate it using the "LN" key on a calculator.)

Consumer Math

CHAPTER **8**

Consumer Math

Outline

8-1   Percents

8-2   Simple Interest

8-3   Compound Interest

8-4   Installment Buying

8-5   Student Loans and Home Buying

8-6   Investing in Stocks and Bonds

Summary

MATH IN ▶ Student Loans

"If you think education is expensive, try the cost of ignorance." This famous quote comes from Dr. Derek Bok, the former president of Harvard University. There are many nuanced interpretations of exactly what Dr. Bok was trying to say, but if you think of it strictly in terms of financial costs, it says that your earning power increases dramatically as you attain more education. This isn't a cliché or a myth: this table is based on cold, hard facts.

Education level	Median salary in 2011
Less than high school diploma	$23,452
High school diploma	$33,176
Some college	$37,388
Associate degree	$39,936
Bachelor's degree	$54,756
Master's degree	$65,676
Professional or doctoral degree	$86,580

Source: Bureau of Labor Statistics

The downside is that college is expensive and costs continue to rise at a rate far greater than inflation. According to *Money* magazine, between 1985 and 2005, the price of average consumer goods in the United States went up by 108%. Ouch. But during the same period, college costs went up by 439%! The truth is that a pretty small percentage of families have the means to pay all of the costs associated with college, meaning that student loans are a reality for an increasing segment of the population. Even the most optimistic students worry about whether or not they'll be able to afford college, and how much debt they'll run up while earning a degree.

This might lead you to come to a larger realization: long ago, survival depended on overcoming physical challenges that modern humans can only imagine, but today, survival is more about navigating the waters of the modern financial system. There are over 300 million people in the United States, and at any given time, it seems like half of them are trying to figure out a way to separate you from your hard-earned money. That's why this chapter is all about different aspects of our financial system that are particularly important to the average adult. Success in

this chapter will help you to become a more well-informed consumer, which makes it less likely that those 150 million people will succeed in getting your cash.

We begin with a thorough look at percentages, which play a big role in almost all areas of consumer math. Then we'll study loans and investments, two topics of particular interest in the current financial climate. The goal is to help you take the guesswork out of financial planning, so that rather than hoping you're doing the right things for your future, you can be sure that you are.

Now to return to the original issue: how much debt can you incur while paying for an education? In a 2012 survey, the College Board reported that a "moderate" college budget for an in-state public 4-year college for the 2011–2012 academic year averaged $21,447. (This takes into account tuition, fees, and other living expenses.) Let's study the ramifications of this frightening statistic.

1. How much would it cost to attain a 4-year degree with this budget?
2. If you are able to obtain grants and scholarships to pay for 25% of these costs and can also pay $5,000 per year out of pocket, how much money would you have to borrow to cover the rest?
3. If you obtain a federal student loan with an interest rate of 6.8% and a term of 10 years for the amount in Question 2, what will your monthly payment be upon graduation if you pay interest on the loan while still in school? How much total will you pay in interest?
4. Repeat Question 3 if you capitalize the interest on your loan.
5. Based on the median salaries in the table, how long would you have to work after obtaining a bachelor's degree to make back the total amount spent on student loan payments and the amount paid out of pocket? (Use the loan with interest capitalized, and don't forget to factor in how much you would have been able to make without going to college at all!)

For answers, see Math in Student Loans Revisited on page 512.

Section 8-1   Percents

LEARNING OBJECTIVES

☐ 1. Convert between percent, decimal, and fraction form.

☐ 2. Perform calculations involving percents.

☐ 3. Solve problems involving percents.

☐ 4. Find percent increase or decrease.

☐ 5. Evaluate the validity of claims based on percents.

Have you ever been shopping, come across a clearance rack that said something like "40% off lowest ticketed price," and had to ask someone what the discounted price of a certain item would be? If so, you're certainly not alone. Any math teacher will tell you that people ask them questions like that all of the time.

Percents are a math topic with a huge number of applications to everyday life, so they should be high on our priority list if we're trying to learn about math in our world. In this section, we'll learn about percents: what they really mean, how to use them in calculations, and even how they can be deceptively misused.

The word "percent" can be translated literally as "per hundred."

Percent means hundredths, or per hundred. That is, $1\% = \dfrac{1}{100}$.

For example, the International Mass Retail Association reported that 20% of adults plan to buy Valentine's Day cards next year. Of those who plan to buy them, 36% of women and 26% of men plan to buy romantic cards. This tells us that 20 out of every 100 adults plan to buy a card. Also, 26 out of 100 men who buy a card will choose a romantic one, and 36 out of 100 women will do so.

Percent Conversions

To work with percents in calculations, we will need to convert them to either decimal or fractional form. But to interpret the answers to calculations, we will want to convert them back into percents.

Converting Percents to Decimals

In order to change a percent to a decimal, drop the % sign and move the decimal point two places to the left.

EXAMPLE 1   Changing Percents to Decimals

Change each percent to a decimal.

(a) 84%   (c) 37.5%

(b) 5%   (d) 172%

SOLUTION

(Drop the % sign and move the decimal point two places to the left.)

(a) $84\% = 84.\% = 0.84\% = 0.84$ *Put decimal point in if necessary.*

(b) $5\% = 5.\% = 0.05\% = 0.05$

(c) $37.5\% = 0.375\% = 0.375$

(d) $172\% = 172.\% = 1.72\% = 1.72$

Math Note

Moving the decimal point two places to the left is the same as dividing by 100.

▼ **Try This One** **1**

Change each percent to a decimal.

(a) 62.5%   (b) 3%   (c) 250%

Converting Percents to Fractions

A percent can be converted to a fraction by dropping the percent sign and using the percent number as the numerator of a fraction whose denominator is 100.

Be sure to reduce fractions to lowest terms when possible.

EXAMPLE 2   **Changing Percents to Fractions**

Change each percent to a fraction.

(a) 42%   (c) $37\frac{1}{2}\%$

(b) 6%   (d) 15.8%

SOLUTION

(a) $42\% = \dfrac{42}{100} = \dfrac{21 \cdot 2}{50 \cdot 2} = \dfrac{21}{50}$

(b) $6\% = \dfrac{6}{100} = \dfrac{3 \cdot 2}{50 \cdot 2} = \dfrac{3}{50}$

(c) When converting fractional or decimal percents, it might be helpful to multiply by some number over itself to clear fractions or decimals. In this case, multiplying by $\frac{2}{2}$ is helpful:

$$\dfrac{37\frac{1}{2}}{100} \times \dfrac{2}{2} = \dfrac{75}{200} = \dfrac{25 \cdot 3}{25 \cdot 8} = \dfrac{3}{8}$$

(d) $15.8\% = \dfrac{15.8}{100} = \dfrac{15.8}{100} \cdot \dfrac{10}{10} = \dfrac{158}{1,000} = \dfrac{79 \cdot 2}{500 \cdot 2} = \dfrac{79}{500}$

▼ **Try This One** **2**

Change each percent to a fraction.

(a) 90%   (b) 16.5%   (c) 130%

Converting a Decimal to a Percent

To change a decimal to a percent, move the decimal point two places to the right and add a percent sign.

EXAMPLE 3   **Changing Decimals to Percents**

Change each decimal to a percent.

(a) 0.74   (b) 0.05   (c) 1.327   (d) 5.463

Math Note

Moving the decimal point two places to the right is the same as multiplying by 100.

SOLUTION

(a) $0.74 = 074.\% = 74\%$

(b) $0.05 = 005.\% = 5\%$

(c) $1.327 = 132.7\% = 132.7\%$

(d) $5.463 = 546.3\% = 546.3\%$

▼ **Try This One 3**

Change each decimal to a percent.

(a) 0.974   (b) 0.04   (c) 3.75

Changing a Fraction to a Percent

To change a fraction to a percent, first change the fraction to a decimal, then change the decimal to a percent.

EXAMPLE 4   Changing Fractions to Percents

Convert each fraction to a percent.

(a) $\frac{7}{8}$ (b) $\frac{3}{4}$ (c) $\frac{5}{6}$ (d) $1\frac{1}{2}$

Math Note

Recall that to change a fraction to a decimal, we divide the numerator by the denominator.

SOLUTION

(a) $\frac{7}{8} = 7 \div 8 = 0.875 = 87.5\%$ *Decimal moved two places right*

(b) $\frac{3}{4} = 3 \div 4 = 0.75 = 75\%$

(c) $\frac{5}{6} = 0.83\overline{3} = 83.\overline{3}\%$

(d) $1\frac{1}{2} = 1.5 = 150\%$

Calculator Guide

Calculators come in very handy when converting fractions to percents. For $\frac{5}{6}$:

Standard Scientific Calculator

5 ÷ 6 × 100 =

Standard Graphing Calculator

5 ÷ 6 × 100 ENTER

In each case, the display will show something like 83.3333333333. You can write this as 83.$\overline{3}$%, with the line representing the fact that 3 repeats. Better still, you might recognize that this can be written as 83$\frac{1}{3}$%.

☑ 1. Convert between percent, decimal, and fraction form.

▼ **Try This One 4**

Change each fraction to a percent.

(a) $\frac{5}{16}$ (b) $\frac{7}{9}$ (c) $1\frac{3}{4}$

Problems Involving Percents

The most common calculations involving percents involve finding a percentage of some quantity. To understand how to do so, consider the following example. You probably know that 50% of 10 is 5. Let's rewrite that statement, then turn it into a calculation:

50% of 10 is 5

0.5 × 10 = 5

When writing a percentage statement in symbols, the word "of" becomes multiplication, and the word "is" becomes an equal sign. Also, we must change the percent into decimal or fractional form. The next three examples show how to use this procedure to set up calculations.

| EXAMPLE 5 | **Finding a Certain Percentage of a Whole** |

According to minoritynurse.com, just 5.8% of all registered nurses in the United States are men. The average hospital in 2012 had 335 registered nurses. How many would likely be male?

SOLUTION

First, write 5.8% in decimal form, as 0.058. The question is "what is 5.8% of 335?" which we translate into symbols:

$$5.8\% \text{ of } 335 \text{ is } \underline{\hspace{2cm}}$$
$$0.058 \times 335 = 19.43$$

You can't have 0.43 nurses, so we interpret the answer as 19 male nurses at an average hospital.

▼ **Try This One 5**

In 2011, 13.2% of registered nurses had at least a master's degree. If 430 nurses attend a professional conference, how many would be likely to have at least a master's degree?

| CAUTION | In calculations with percents, it's very common for the result to contain digits after a decimal point, like 19.43 in Example 5. You should always think about what quantity your answer represents to decide if it's appropriate to round to the nearest whole number. |

| EXAMPLE 6 | **Finding a Percentage from a Discount** |

Cat finds the perfect dress at Macy's, with a selling price of $79. She has two coupons to choose from: one offers $15 off any purchase of $50 or more, the other offers 20% off any item. Which is the better choice?

SOLUTION

The question really asks if the $15 discount is more or less than 20%, so we need to answer this question:

$$15 \text{ is what percent of } 79?$$
$$15 = \qquad x \qquad \times 79 \qquad x \text{ is the percent in decimal form.}$$

This is the equation $79x = 15$, which we can solve for x.

$$79x = 15 \qquad \qquad \textit{Divide both sides by 79.}$$
$$x = \frac{15}{79} \approx 0.19$$

The decimal 0.19 corresponds to 19%, so the 20% off coupon will be a little better.

▼ **Try This One 6**

In 2012, 22 out of 50 states had a population of 5 million or higher. What percent is that?

Sidelight **MONEY, BANKS, AND CREDIT CARDS**

Long before money existed, people bartered for goods and services. For example, if you needed the roof of your hut fixed, you might pay the repair person two chickens. The first known coins were made over 2,500 years ago in Western Turkey. They consisted of a mixture of gold and silver and were stamped to guarantee uniformity. These coins were first accepted by the merchants of the area. Also around that time, coins were made in India and China.

Paper money was first made in China about 1,400 years ago; however, when Marco Polo brought the idea to Europe, it was rejected by the people. It wasn't until the 1600s that banks in Europe began to issue paper money to their depositors and borrowers.

In the United States, early settlers used tobacco, beaver skins, and foreign coins as currency. A popular coin was the Spanish dollar, called "pieces of eight." For purchases of less than one dollar, the coin was cut into eight pieces. Each piece was called a "bit" and was worth $12\frac{1}{2}$ cents. Hence 25 cents became known as "two bits," 50 cents as "four bits," etc.

During the Revolutionary War, the Continental Congress authorized the printing of paper money to pay war debts. The government printed more money than it could back up with gold and silver, and the dollar became virtually worthless. The phrase "not worth a Continental dollar" is still used today.

The U.S. Mint opened on April 2, 1792, in Washington, D.C., to mint coins. Gold was used for the $10.00, $5.00, and $2.50 coins. Silver was used for the $1.00, $0.50, $0.25, $0.10, and the $0.05 coins, and copper was used for the 1 cent and $\frac{1}{2}$ cent.

Most paper money was issued by state banks until 1863 when Congress established national banks to issue currency notes. In 1913, the Federal Reserve System was established to issue notes, which became our standard currency.

Banking began in ancient Babylon about 2000 BCE when people kept their money in temples. They thought that if the temples were robbed, the gods would punish the robbers. In medieval times, money was kept in vaults in castles and protected by the armies of the nobles. The Banco di San Giorgio, established in 1407 in Genoa, Italy was the first bank in the modern banking system ("modern" being a bit of a stretch in this case). The first bank in the United States was the Bank of North America, established in 1781 in Philadelphia.

Credit cards were first issued by large hotels in the early 1900s. These cards were considered to be prestigious and were issued only to customers who spent a lot of money at the hotel. Department stores and gasoline companies began to issue credit cards around 1915. During World War II, the United States forbade the use of credit cards, but by the early 1950s banks began issuing credit cards that could be used at multiple locations. Finally, in the late 1960s, banks agreed to sponsor credit cards with national name brands. These became our modern Master Card, Visa, American Express, and Discover cards, giving everyone the opportunity to spend more than they can afford to.

EXAMPLE 7   **Finding a Whole Amount Based on a Percentage**

A medium-sized company reported that it had to cut its work force back to 70% of what it was last year. If it has 63 workers now, how many did it have a year ago?

SOLUTION

Convert 70% to a decimal: 70% = 0.70. Now write as a question and translate to symbols:

$$70\% \text{ of what number is } 63?$$
$$0.70 \times x = 63$$

This gives us the equation $0.70x = 63$, which we solve for x.

$$0.70x = 63 \qquad \textit{Divide both sides by 0.70.}$$
$$\frac{0.70x}{0.70} = \frac{63}{0.70}$$
$$x = 90$$

The company had 90 workers a year ago.

2. Perform calculations involving percents.

▼ **Try This One 7**

After a really rotten year in 2012, a baseball team won 120% as many games in 2013, which was 84 games. How many games did they win in 2012?

Applications of Percents

Many aspects of consumer mathematics deal with finding parts of a whole. For example, you may want to leave a 15% tip, you may want to figure out a 33% markup, or you may want to calculate an 8% commission on sales. Some applications are shown in Examples 8 through 10.

EXAMPLE 8   **Calculating Sales Tax**

> **Math Note**
>
> In Example 8, you can find the total cost by multiplying the cost by 1.07 (i.e., 107%). This represents the 100% cost of the item plus 7% more for tax. 1.07($89.95) = $96.25 (rounded).

The sales tax in Allegheny County, Pennsylvania, is 7%. What is the tax on a calculator that costs $89.95? What is the total amount paid?

SOLUTION

Find 7% of $89.95: Write 7% as 0.07 in decimal form, then multiply.
$$0.07 \times \$89.95 = \$6.30 \text{ (rounded)}$$
The sales tax is $6.30. The total amount paid is
$$\$89.95 + \$6.30 = \$96.25$$

▼ **Try This One 8**

The sales tax in Atlanta, Georgia, is 8%. Find the amount of tax and the total cost of a portable DVD player on sale for $149.

EXAMPLE 9   **Calculating Cost of Sale from Commission**

A real estate agent receives a 7% commission on all home sales. How expensive was a home if she received a commission of $5,775.00?

SOLUTION

In this case, the problem can be written as $5,775.00 is 7% of what number?

$$\$5,775 \text{ is } 7\% \text{ of } x$$
$$5,775 = 0.07 \times x \qquad \textit{Divide both sides by 0.07.}$$
$$\frac{5,775}{0.07} = \frac{0.07 \times x}{0.07}$$
$$82,500 = x$$

The home was purchased for $82,500.00.

---

3. Solve problems involving percents.

▼ **Try This One 9**

A sales clerk receives a 9% commission on all sales. Find the total sales the clerk made if his commission was $486.00.

Sometimes it's useful to find the percent increase or the percent decrease in a specific situation. In this case, we can use the following method.

Procedure for Finding Percent Increase or Decrease

Step 1 Find the amount of the increase or the decrease.

Step 2 Make a fraction as shown:

$$\frac{\text{Amount of increase}}{\text{Original amount}} \quad \text{or} \quad \frac{\text{Amount of decrease}}{\text{Original amount}}$$

Step 3 Change the fraction to a percent.

EXAMPLE 10   **Finding a Percent Change**

A large latte at the Caffeine Connection sells at a regular price of $3.50. Today it is on sale for $3.00. Find the percent decrease in the price.

SOLUTION

The original price is $3.50.

Step 1 Find the amount of decrease. $3.50 − $3.00 = $0.50.

Step 2 Make a fraction as shown

$$\frac{\text{Amount of decrease}}{\text{Original price}} = \frac{\$0.50}{\$3.50}$$

Step 3 Change the fraction to a percent.

$$\frac{0.50}{3.50} \approx 0.1428 = 14.3\% \,(\text{rounded})$$

The decrease in price is 14.3%.

> *Math Note*
>
> When finding percent increase or decrease, make sure you divide by the *original* amount, not the ending amount.

▼ **Try This One 10**

In 2012 the population of the town of Oak Creek was 23,258. In 2013, the population increased to 23,632. Find the percent increase in the population.

☑ 4. Find percent increase or decrease.

Percent increase or decrease is often misused, sometimes intentionally, sometimes not. In Example 11, we'll look at a common deceptive use of percents in advertising.

EXAMPLE 11   **Recognizing Misuse of Percents in Advertising**

A department store advertised that certain merchandise was reduced 25%. Also, an additional 10% discount card would be given to the first 200 people who entered the store on a specific day. The advertisement then stated that this amounted to a 35% reduction in the price of an item. Is the advertiser being honest?

SOLUTION

Let's say that an item was originally priced at $50.00. (*Note:* any price can be used.) First find the discount amount.

$$\begin{aligned} \text{Discount} &= \text{rate} \times \text{selling price} \\ &= 25\% \times \$50.00 \\ &= 0.25 \times \$50.00 \\ &= \$12.50 \end{aligned}$$

Then find the reduced price.

$$\text{Reduced price} = \text{original price} - \text{discount}$$
$$= \$50.00 - \$12.50$$
$$= \$37.50$$

Next find 10% of the reduced price.

$$\text{Discount} = \text{rate} \times \text{reduced price}$$
$$= 10\% \times \$37.50$$
$$= \$3.75$$

Find the second reduced price.

$$\text{Reduced price} = \$37.50 - \$3.75$$
$$= \$33.75$$

Now find the percent of the total reduction.

$$\frac{\text{Reduction}}{\text{Original price}} = \frac{\$12.50 + \$3.75}{\$50.00} = \frac{16.25}{50.00} = 0.325 = 32.5\%$$

The total percent of the reduction was 32.5%, and not 35% as advertised.

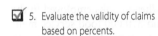

5. Evaluate the validity of claims based on percents.

▼ **Try This One 11**

A department store offered a 20% discount on all television sets. They also stated that the fist 50 customers would receive an additional 5% discount. Find the total percent discount. You can use any selling price for the televisions.

Answers to Try This One

1 (a) 0.625   (b) 0.03   (c) 2.50

2 (a) $\frac{9}{10}$ (b) $\frac{33}{200}$ (c) $\frac{13}{10}$

3 (a) 97.4%   (b) 4%   (c) 375%

4 (a) 31.25%   (b) 77.$\overline{7}$%   (c) 175%

5   57

6   44%

7   70

8   Tax: $11.92; total cost: $160.92

9   $5,400

10   1.6%

11   24%

EXERCISE SET 8-1

Writing Exercises

1. What exactly does the word "percent" mean?
2. Explain how to change percents into decimal and fraction form.
3. Explain how to change decimals and fractions into percent form.
4. Explain how the word "of" plays an important role in calculations involving percents.

5. How do you find the percent increase or decrease of a quantity?
6. Is it possible to have more than 100% of a quantity? Explain.

Computational Exercises

For Exercises 7–18, express each as a percent.

7. 0.63	10. 0.0872	13. $\frac{1}{5}$	16. $\frac{1}{6}$
8. 0.87	11. 1.56	14. $\frac{5}{8}$	17. $1\frac{1}{4}$
9. 0.025	12. 3.875	15. $\frac{2}{3}$	18. $2\frac{3}{8}$

For Exercises 19–28, express each as a decimal.

19. 18%	22. 2%	25. 320%	28. $20\frac{1}{3}$%
20. 23%	23. 62.5%	26. 275%	
21. 6%	24. 75.6%	27. $66\frac{2}{3}$%	

For Exercises 29–36, express each as a fraction or mixed number.

29. 24%	31. 236%	33. $\frac{1}{2}$%	35. $16\frac{2}{3}$%
30. 36%	32. 520%	34. $12\frac{1}{2}$%	36. $4\frac{1}{6}$%

Applications in Our World

37. Find the sales tax and total cost of a laser printer that costs $299.99. The tax rate is 5%.

38. Find the sales tax and total cost of an espresso machine that costs $59.95. The tax rate is 7%.

39. Find the sales tax and total cost of a Sony Playstation that costs $249.99. The tax rate is 6%.

40. Find the sales tax and total cost of a wireless mouse that costs $19.99. The tax rate is 4.5%.

41. A diamond ring was reduced from $999.99 to $399.99. Find the percent reduction in the price.

42. An MP3 player was reduced from $109.99 to $99.99. Find the percent reduction in price.

43. A 20-inch flat panel computer monitor is on sale for $249.99. It was reduced $80.00 from the original price. Find the percent reduction in price.

44. The sale price of a spring break vacation package was $179.99, and the travel agent said by booking early, you saved $20. Find the percent reduction in price.

45. You've had your eye on a luggage set that sells for $159.99, waiting for a sale. Finally, success! To make room for next year's model, the price has been reduced by 40%. You also have a 20% off coupon you can use on top of that. How much will you pay, not including tax?

46. Some really nice beach towels that usually sell for $24.99 each are on sale over Memorial Day weekend at 25% off. In addition, the store has distributed a coupon good for an additional 10% off your entire purchase. How much will it cost to buy four towels, not including tax?

47. If a sales clerk receives a 7% commission on all sales, find the commission the clerk receives on the sale of a computer system costing $1,799.99.

48. If the commission for selling a 70-inch high-definition television set is 12%, find the commission on a television set that costs $2,499.99.

49. Milo receives a commission of 6% on all sales. If his commission on a sale was $75.36, find the cost of the item he sold.

50. The sales tax in Pennsylvania is 6%. If the tax on an item is $96, find the cost of the item.

51. In the 1995–96 academic year, there were 86,087 bachelor's degrees awarded by American colleges in health professions and related clinical sciences. That number fell to 71,261 for the 2002–3 school year, then rose all the way to 120,488 in 2008–9. How much greater was the percent increase from 2003 to 2009 than the percent decrease from 1996 to 2003?

52. According to the U.S. Bureau of Labor Statistics, there were 100,600 chefs/head cooks employed in the United States in 2010 and 320,600 food service managers. Those numbers were projected to decrease to 99,800 and 310,000 by 2020. Which job was facing the larger percent decrease? By how much?

53. You saved $200 on your new laptop because you bought it online. If this was a 25% savings from the original price, find the original cost of the laptop.

54. The average teachers' and superintendents' salaries in a school district in western Pennsylvania was $50,480. Five years later, the new average was $54,747. Find the percent increase.

55. According to CTIA—The Wireless Association, in 2000, there were 109.5 million cell phone subscribers in the United States. That number rose to 207.9 million in 2005 and 300.5 million in 2010. Find the actual change in number of subscribers and the percent change for each 5-year period. What can you conclude?

56. Based on statistics from UNAIDS.org, in 2001, there were 3.8 million people living with HIV in south and southeast Asia and 1.2 million in North America. By 2009, those numbers had grown to 4.1 million and 1.5 million. Find the actual change in number of people living with HIV and the percent change for each region. What can you conclude?

57. The website forsalebyowner.com reported that total real estate commissions in 2007 were $55 billion, an increase of $19 billion over the year 2000. Commissions then decreased to $44.3 billion in 2009. Find the percent increase from 2000 to 2007 and the percent decrease from 2007 to 2009. Then find the average percent change per year for each period.

58. According to the Institute of Education Sciences, the average cost of tuition, room and board, and fees at public 4-year universities was $8,653 in the 2000–2001 academic year, $12,797 for 2006–7, and $15,014 for 2009–10. Find the percent increase from 2001 to 2007 and from 2007 to 2010. Then find the average percent change per year for each period.

59. You buy $129 in clothes at a department store. You can choose between coupons that offer $20 off your entire purchase or 25% off. Which will save you more money? By how much?

60. While shopping at Nordstrom, you pick out two pairs of jeans at $49 each and a pair of shoes on sale for $39. Then you splurge on a $95 sweater. You have two coupons but can only use one. The first offers 40% off any single item. The second offers 15% off your entire purchase. Which is the better choice?

61. The Hawaii department of labor issued a press release at the beginning of 2011 stating that it projected "green jobs" (jobs related to renewable energy and energy efficiency) to increase by 26% between 2010 and 2012. Green jobs in the private sector in Hawaii were estimated at 11,145 in 2010, accounting for 2.4% of total private employment.

    (a) How many total jobs were there in the private sector in Hawaii in 2010?

    (b) How many green jobs in the private sector were expected by 2012?

    (c) If the overall job market was projected to increase by 4.3%, what percentage of total private-sector jobs was projected to be green by 2012?

62. The U.S. Department of Housing and Urban Development issued a report in early 2011 reporting some grim numbers on the housing industry. There were 523,000 building permits issued for single-family homes in 2010, but that number was projected to decrease by 27.0% in 2011. Construction was expected to start on 375,000 new homes in 2011, which would represent a 28.8% decrease from 2010. Also, in the 12-month period through January 2011, 298,000 new homes were sold, but this represented just 66.0% of new homes completed.

    (a) How many fewer permits were expected to be issued for single-family homes in 2011 compared to 2010?

    (b) How many fewer new homes were started in 2011 compared to 2010?

    (c) How many new homes were completed in the 12-month period through January 2011, and how did that compare to the number of new homes started in 2010?

The graph shown here, based on information from Zillow.com, displays the estimated value of my house (red) and the average for all houses in my town (green) for the period from mid-2006 to April 1, 2011. The marks on the graph occur on April 1 of each year. Use the graph to answer Exercises 63–66.

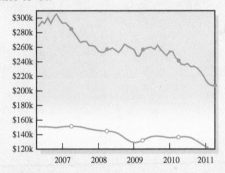

63. Find the percent decrease in the value of my house from April 1, 2007, to April 1, 2011. Then find the percent decrease in the average price of all houses in my town over the same period. Use $120,000 as the average for April 1, 2011.

64. Find the percent change for both my home and the average home in my town for each 1-year period starting on April 1, 2007.

65. If the market turned around and my house started gaining value at 6% each year, how many years would it take to get back to the highest value on the chart? Repeat for the town average.

66. Find the sum of the yearly changes for both my home and all homes in my town. How do the results compare to the answers for Exercise 65? What can you conclude?

Critical Thinking

67. A store has a sale with 30% off every item. When you enter the store, you receive a coupon that states that you receive an additional 20% off. Is this equal to a 50% discount? Explain your answer.

68. You purchase a stock at $100 per share. It drops 30% the next day; however, a week later, it increases in value by 30%. If you sell it, will you break even? Explain your answer.

69. Suppose a friend planning a shopping spree on the day after Thanksgiving tells you he plans to buy a 65-inch plasma TV, and you say "There's no way you can afford that!" He then tells you that the store is offering 50% off any one item, and he has an Internet coupon good for 50% off any price, even a discounted one. So that's 100% off, and he'll get it for free! Explain why your friend will come home very disappointed.

70. A store that used to sell a grill for $90 now offers it at $60, and advertises "33% off our best-selling grill!" An amusement park used to have 60 rides, and now

boasts 90 rides, claiming "50% more rides this year!" Which one of them is lying?

71. While grocery shopping last week, I saw this claim on a package of some product: "NOW 20% MORE!" Sounds nice, right? Explain why this claim is completely meaningless.

Another common gimmick is for companies to make a big deal about lowering the price on a product, but fail to mention that they also lowered the size of the package. A famous example is ice cream. Large name brands for many years came in half-gallons, which contained 64 ounces of creamy goodness. Starting in 2007, some brands kept the shape of the cartons the same, and the price by the way, but reduced the size to 56 ounces, and then again

a couple of years later to 48 ounces. Let's say that the original half-gallon was priced at $4.

72. By what percent was the size reduced the first time?

73. At $4 for 56 ounces, how much would you have to pay to get 64 ounces of ice cream?

74. Use your answer from Problem 73 to find what the effective percent increase in price was.

75. Repeat Problems 72–74 for the reduction in size from 56 to 48 ounces.

76. Repeat Problems 72–74 for the overall reduction in size from 64 to 48 ounces. How do the results compare to a combination of the results for the two smaller reductions?

Section 8-2   Simple Interest

LEARNING OBJECTIVES

☐ 1. Compute simple interest and future value.

☐ 2. Compute principal, rate, or time.

☐ 3. Compute interest using the Banker's rule.

☐ 4. Compute the true rate for a discounted loan.

The topic of the next two sections is of interest to anyone who plans to buy a house or a car, have a credit card, invest money, have a savings account—in short, pretty much everyone. This interesting topic is interest—a description of how fees are calculated when money is borrowed, and how your money grows when you save. Unless you don't mind being separated from your hard-earned money, this is a topic you should be eager to understand well.

Interest is a fee paid for the use of money. For example, if you borrow money from a bank to buy a car, you must not only pay back the amount of money that you borrowed, but also an additional amount, called the interest, for the use of the bank's money. On the other hand, if you deposit money in a savings account, the bank will pay you interest for saving money since it will be using your money to provide loans, mortgages, etc. to people who are borrowing money. The stated rate of interest is generally given as a yearly percentage of the amount borrowed or deposited.

There are two kinds of interest. *Simple interest* is a one-time percent of an amount of money. *Compound interest* is a percentage of an original amount, as well as a percentage of the new amount including previously calculated interest. We'll study simple interest in this section, and compound interest in the next.

Simple Interest

In order to compute simple interest, we will need three pieces of information: the *principal*, the *rate*, and the *time*.

Interest (I) is the fee charged for the use of money.

Principal (P) is the amount of money borrowed or placed into a savings account.

Rate (r) is the percent of the principal paid for having money loaned, or earned for investing money. Unless indicated otherwise, rates are given as a percent for a term of 1 year.

Math Note

Remember: *P* (principal) is the beginning amount borrowed or invested, and *A* (future value) is the final amount repaid or accumulated.

Time (*t*) or **term** is the length of time that the money is being borrowed or invested. When the rate is given as a percent per year, time has to be written in years. **Future value** (*A*) is the amount of the loan or investment plus the interest paid or earned.

We can use what we know about percents to develop a formula for simple interest. Suppose someone offers to lend you $100 if you'll pay 5% interest per year. You accept, and pay them back after 3 years. How much would you owe? Since 5% of $100 is $5 ($0.05 \times \$100$), you'd owe $5 in interest for each year. Then we multiply by the number of years ($3 \times \$5$) to get $15 in interest, for a total amount of $115 that you owe.

What did we learn? The amount of interest is the interest rate *r* times the original amount *P* times the number of years passed *t*. And the future value *A* is the principal amount plus the interest.

Math Note

The formula $A = P(1 + rt)$ can be used to find future value without explicitly computing the interest first.

Formulas for Computing Simple Interest and Future Value
1. Interest = principal × rate × time:
$$I = Prt$$
2. Future value = principal + interest:
$$A = P + I \quad \text{or} \quad A = P(1 + rt)$$

EXAMPLE 1   **Computing Simple Interest**

Find the simple interest on a loan of $3,600 for 3 years at a rate of 8% per year.

SOLUTION

Change the rate to a decimal and substitute into the formula $I = Prt$:

$$8\% = 0.08$$
$$I = Prt$$
$$= (\$3,600)(0.08)(3)$$
$$= \$864$$

The interest on the loan is $864.

▼ **Try This One 1**

Find the simple interest on a $12,000 loan for 5 years at 7%.

EXAMPLE 2   **Finding Future Value**

Find the future value for the loan in Example 1.

SOLUTION

Substitute into the formula $A = P + I$
$$A = P + I$$
$$= \$3,600 + \$864$$
$$= \$4,464$$

The total amount of money to be paid back is $4,464.

ALTERNATE SOLUTION

Substitute into the formula $A = P(1 + rt)$
$$A = P(1 + rt)$$
$$= \$3,600(1 + 0.08 \cdot 3)$$
$$= \$4,464$$

> ▼ **Try This One 2**
>
> Find the future value of the loan in Try This One 1.

Since rates are typically given in terms of percent per year, when the time of a loan or investment is given in months, we need to divide the time by 12 to convert to years.

EXAMPLE 3   **Computing Simple Interest for a Term in Months**

To meet payroll during a down period, United Ceramics Inc. needed to borrow $2,000 at 4% simple interest for 3 months. Find the interest.

SOLUTION

Change 3 months to years by dividing by 12, and change the rate to a decimal. Substitute in the formula $I = Prt$.

$$I = (\$2,000)(0.04)\left(\frac{3}{12}\right) \qquad 4\% = 0.04$$

$$= \$20$$

The interest is $20.

---

1. Compute simple interest and future value.

> ▼ **Try This One 3**
>
> Marta needs some quick cash for books at the beginning of spring semester, so she borrows $600 at 11% simple interest for 2 months. How much interest will she pay?

Often, a simple interest loan is paid off in monthly installments. To find the monthly payment, divide the future value of the loan by the number of months in the term of the loan.

EXAMPLE 4   **Computing Monthly Payments**

Admiral Chauffeur Services borrowed $600 at 9% simple interest for $1\frac{1}{2}$ years to repair a limousine. Find the interest, future value, and the monthly payment.

SOLUTION

Step 1 Find the interest.

$$I = Prt$$
$$= (\$600)(0.09)\left(1\frac{1}{2}\right) \qquad 9\% = 0.09$$
$$= \$81$$

The interest is $81.

Step 2 Find the future value of the loan.

$$A = P + I$$
$$= \$600 + \$81$$
$$= \$681$$

Step 3 Divide the future value of the loan by the number of months. Since $1\frac{1}{2}$ years = 18 months, divide $681 by 18 to get $37.83. The monthly payment is $37.83.

▼ **Try This One 4**

The Lookout Restaurant took out a loan for $5,000. The simple interest rate was 6.5%, and the term of the loan was 3 years. Find the interest, future value, and monthly payment.

Finding the Principal, Rate, or Time

In addition to finding the interest and future value for a loan or investment, we can find the principal, the rate, and the time period by substituting into the formula $I = Prt$ and solving for the unknown.

Examples 5–7 show how to find the principal, rate, or time.

EXAMPLE 5   **Computing Principal**

Calculator Guide

In the calculation for Example 5, order of operations is very important. The parentheses are, too!

Standard Scientific Calculator

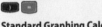
93.5 ÷ (.055 × 2
) =

Standard Graphing Calculator

93.5 ÷ (.055 × 2)
ENTER

Phillips Health and Beauty Spa is replacing one of its workstations. The interest on a loan secured by the spa was $93.50. The money was borrowed at 5.5% simple interest for 2 years. Find the principal.

SOLUTION

$$I = \$93.50, r = 5.5\% = 0.055, \text{ and } t = 2$$

$$I = Prt$$
$$\$93.50 = P(0.055)(2)$$ *Divide both sides*
$$\frac{\$93.50}{(0.055)(2)} = \frac{P(0.055)(2)}{(0.055)(2)}$$ *by (0.055)(2).*
$$P = \$850$$

The amount of the loan was $850.

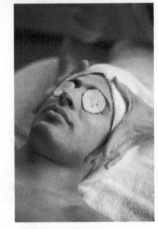

▼ **Try This One 5**

Find the principal on a savings account that paid $76.50 in simple interest at 6% over 3 years.

The same formulas can be used for investments as well. Example 6 shows this.

EXAMPLE 6   **Computing Interest Rate**

R & S Furnace Company invested $15,250 for 10 years and received $9,150 in simple interest. What was the rate that the investment paid?

SOLUTION

$$P = \$15,250, t = 10, \text{ and } I = \$9,150$$

$$I = Prt$$

$$\$9,150 = (\$15,250)(r)(10) \qquad \textit{Divide both sides by } (\$15,250)(10).$$

$$\frac{\$9,150}{(\$15,250)(10)} = \frac{(\$15,250)(r)(10)}{(\$15,250)(10)}$$

$$0.06 = r$$

$$r = 0.06 \text{ or } 6\%$$

The interest paid on the investment was 6%.

▼ **Try This One 6**

If you invest $8,000 for 30 months and receive $1,000 in simple interest, what was the rate?

CAUTION   Be sure to change the decimal to a percent since rates are given in percents.

EXAMPLE 7   **Computing the Term of a Loan**

Judi and Laura borrowed $4,500 at $8\frac{3}{4}\%$ to put in a hot tub. They had to pay $2,756.25 interest. Find the term of the loan and the monthly payment.

SOLUTION

$$P = \$4,500, r = 8\tfrac{3}{4}\% = 0.0875, \text{ and } I = \$2,756.25$$

$$I = Prt$$

$$\$2,756.25 = (\$4,500)(0.0875)t \qquad \textit{Divide both sides}$$

$$\frac{\$2,756.25}{(\$4,500)(0.0875)} = \frac{(\$4,500)(0.0875)t}{(\$4,500)(0.0875)} \qquad \textit{by } (\$4,500)(0.0875).$$

$$7 = t$$

The term of the loan was 7 years, which is 84 months. The total amount paid is the principal plus the interest:

$$\$4,500 + \$2,756.25 = \$7,256.25$$

Divide by 84 months to find the monthly payment:

$$\frac{\$7,256.25}{84} = \$86.38$$

☑ 2. Compute principal, rate, or time.

▼ Try This One 7

A pawn shop offers to finance a guitar costing $750 at 4% simple interest. The total interest charged will be $150. What is the term of the loan and the monthly payment?

The Banker's Rule

Simple interest for short term loans is sometimes computed in days. For example, the term of a loan may be 90 days. In this case, the time would be $\frac{90 \text{ days}}{365 \text{ days}} = \frac{90}{365}$ since there are 365 days in a year. However, many lending institutions use what is called the *Banker's rule*. The Banker's rule treats every month like it has 30 days, so it uses 360 days in a year. They claim that the computations are easier to do. When a lending institution uses 360 days instead of 365, how does that affect the amount of interest? For example, on a $5,000 loan at 8% for 90 days, the interest would be

$$I = Prt$$
$$= (\$5,000)(0.08)\left(\frac{90}{365}\right) \qquad 8\% = 0.08; \ 90 \text{ days is } \frac{90}{365} \text{ year.}$$
$$= \$98.63$$

Using the Banker's rule, the interest is

$$I = Prt$$
$$= (\$5,000)(0.08)\left(\frac{90}{360}\right) \qquad \textit{We used a 360 day year here.}$$
$$= \$100.00$$

We can see why this is called the Banker's rule and not the customer's rule!

EXAMPLE 8 **Using the Banker's Rule**

Find the simple interest on a $1,800 loan at 6% for 120 days. Use the Banker's rule.

SOLUTION

$$P = \$1,800, \ r = 6\% = 0.06, \ t = \frac{120}{360}$$
$$I = Prt$$
$$= (\$1,800)(0.06)\left(\frac{120}{360}\right) = \$36$$

The interest using the Banker's rule is $36.

Sidelight **AN OUTDATED RULE**

The Banker's rule is very old, and there was a time when it made sense. Originally, interest on savings and loans had to be calculated by hand, and standardizing every month to 30 days did in fact make the calculations a lot simpler. But those types of calculations haven't been done by hand for over 50 years, and in the age of computers, it's just plain silly to worry about how difficult it is to compute the interest. That's exactly why computers are called computers—they're really good at computing things! So why do some lenders still use the Banker's rule? Because they can, probably, and it makes them more money.

☑ 3. Compute interest using the
     Banker's rule.

▼ Try This One 8

Find the simple interest on a $2,200 loan at 7% interest for 100 days. Use the Banker's rule, then compare to the amount of interest using a 365-day year.

Discounted Loans

Sometimes the interest on a loan is paid upfront by deducting the amount of the interest from the amount the bank gives you. This type of loan is called a **discounted loan**. The interest that is deducted from the amount you receive is called the **discount**. Example 9 illustrates how it works.

EXAMPLE 9 — Finding the True Rate of a Discounted Loan

A student obtained a 2-year $4,000 loan for college tuition. The rate was 9% simple interest and the loan was a discounted loan.

(a) Find the discount.
(b) Find the amount of money the student received.
(c) Find the true interest rate.

SOLUTION

(a) The discount is the total interest for the loan.

$$P = \$4,000, r = 9\%, t = 2 \text{ years}$$
$$I = Prt$$
$$= (\$4,000)(0.09)(2) \qquad 9\% = 0.09$$
$$= \$720$$

The discount is $720.

(b) The student received $4,000 − $720 = $3,280.

(c) The true interest rate is calculated by finding the rate on a $3,280 loan with $720 interest.

$$I = Prt$$
$$\$720 = (\$3,280)r(2) \qquad \textit{Multiply.}$$
$$\$720 = \$6,560r \qquad \textit{Divide both sides by } \$6,560.$$
$$r = \frac{\$720}{\$6,560} = 0.1098 \text{ (rounded)}$$

The true interest rate is approximately 10.98%.

Sidelight **WHO GETS THE DISCOUNT?**

Everyone likes getting discounts, so "discounted loan" sounds great, right? This is just another way that lenders can take advantage of customers. Since you're paying the interest up front, out of the amount you're borrowing, the effect is that you're borrowing less money and paying the same amount of interest. As Example 9 shows, the actual interest rate you end up paying is quite a bit higher than the rate you're quoted. The only thing they're really "discounting" is your ability to make smart financial decisions. If you're ever offered a discounted loan, walk away immediately. Or run if you're wearing sneakers.

☑ 4. Compute the true rate for a discounted loan.

▼ Try This One 9

Mary Dixon obtained a $5,000 discounted loan for 3 years at 6% simple interest.

(a) Find the discount.
(b) Find the amount of money Mary received.
(c) Find the true interest rate.

Answers to Try This One

1	$4,200	**4**	$975, $5,975, $165.97	**7**	5 years; $15	**9**	(a) $900
							(b) $4,100
2	$16,200	**5**	$425	**8**	$42.78; $42.19		(c) 7.32%
3	$11	**6**	5%				

EXERCISE SET 8-2

Writing Exercises

1. Describe what interest is, and how simple interest is calculated.
2. What do the terms "principal" and "future value" refer to?
3. What is meant by the term of a loan?

4. How is the rate of a loan or a savings account typically described?
5. What is the Banker's rule? Does it help borrowers or lenders?
6. What does it mean for a loan to be discounted?

Computational Exercises

For Exercises 7–22, find the missing value.

Principal	Rate	Time	Simple Interest
7. $12,000	6%	2 years	
8. $6,150	0.25%	_____	$61.50
9. $154,625	4.75%	30 years	
10. $600	4%		$72
11. $7,300	_____	6 years	$1,927.20
12. $200	_____	3 years	$45
13. _____	9%	4 years	$354.60
14. _____	15%	7 years	$65,625
15. _____	1.16%	5 years	$464
16. $1,250	5%		$375
17. $15,600	1.8%	4.75 years	_____
18. $420	_____	30 months	$31
19. $1,975	7.2%	$3\frac{1}{2}$ years	_____
20. $325	_____	8 years	$156

Principal	Rate	Time	Simple Interest
21. $700	$6\frac{3}{4}$%	_____	$141.75
22. _____	5.6%	$3\frac{1}{2}$ years	$1,372

For Exercises 23–26, find the future value of the loan

23. $P = \$800$, $r = 4\%$, $t = 5$ years
24. $P = \$15,000$, $r = 9\%$, $t = 7$ years
25. $P = \$960$, $r = 2.28\%$, $t = 6\frac{1}{2}$ years
26. $P = \$1,350$, $r = 3.38\%$, $t = 4$ years

For Exercises 27–30, find the interest on each loan using the Banker's rule.

27. $P = \$2,200$, $r = 4.3\%$, $t = 30$ days
28. $P = \$550$, $r = 1.75\%$, $t = 135$ days
29. $P = \$1,750$, $r = 2.3\%$, $t = 45$ days
30. $P = \$660$, $r = 5.6\%$, $t = 225$ days

460   **Chapter 8** Consumer Math

For Exercises 31–34, the loans are discounted. For each exercise, find (a) the discount, (b) the amount of money received, and (c) the true interest rate.

31. $P = \$3,000$, $r = 8\%$, $t = 3$ years
32. $P = \$1,750$, $r = 4\frac{1}{2}\%$, $t = 6$ years

33. $P = \$6,000$, $r = 7\frac{1}{2}\%$, $t = 4.5$ years
34. $P = \$33,000$, $r = 3.6\%$, $t = 7$ years

Applications in Our World

For Exercises 35–68, all interest is simple interest.

35. In addition to working and her family's contribution, Jane had to borrow $8,000 over the course of 6 years to complete her education. The interest is $4,046.40. Find the rate.

36. Fred started a new e-Commerce business and borrowed $15,000 for 12 years to get the business up and running. The interest is $18,000. Find the rate.

37. To take advantage of a going-out-of-business sale, the College Corner Furniture Store had to borrow some money. It paid back a total of $150,000 on a 6-month loan at 12%. Find the principal.

38. To purchase two new copiers, a campus bookstore paid $1,350 interest on a 9% loan for 3 years. Find the principal.

39. To train employees to use new equipment, Williams Muffler Repair had to borrow $4,500.00 at $9\frac{1}{2}\%$. The company paid $1,282.50 in interest. Find the term of the loan.

40. Berger Car Rental borrowed $8,650.00 at 6.8% interest to cover the increasing cost of auto insurance. Find the term of the loan if the interest is $441.15.

41. To pay for new supplies, Jiffy Photo Company borrowed $9,325.00 at 8% and paid $3,170.50 in interest. Find the term of the loan.

42. Mary Beck earned $216 interest on a savings account at 8% over 2 years. Find the principal.

43. John White has savings of $4,300, which earned $9\frac{3}{4}\%$ interest for 5 years. Find the interest.

44. Ed Bland had savings of $816 invested at $4\frac{1}{2}\%$ for 3 years. Find the interest.

45. Matt's Appliance Store borrowed $6,200 for 3 years for repairs. The rate was 6%. Find the future value of the loan.

46. Adrienne's Pub borrowed $12,000 for 6 years at 9%. Find the future value of the loan.

47. Martin wants to buy a new bedroom set that costs $1,829 including tax. Unfortunately, he doesn't have $1,829, so he secures a 2-year loan from the furniture store at 11% interest to be repaid in 24 equal monthly installments. Find the monthly payment.

48. When Cecilia's car needs a new transmission, she's stuck with a bill for $1,800. The dealership offers her an 18-month loan at 12.9% interest to be repaid in 18 equal installments. Find the monthly payment.

49. To pay for a new roof on his home, Jin is offered a 10-year loan at 6% and a 5-year loan at 10%. If the roof cost $6,300:
    (a) Without doing any calculations, which loan sounds like the better deal to you? Why?
    (b) Find the monthly payment for each loan.
    (c) Which loan results in less total interest being paid? By how much?

50. Elena needs $530 to cover the cost of books for this semester and decides to borrow an extra 25% above that in case of unanticipated expenses. Find the monthly payment if she borrows that amount at 6.29% interest for $1\frac{1}{2}$ years.

Businesses that offer repayment plans for purchases are required by law to disclose the interest rate. But that doesn't mean they go out of their way to let you know what it is. You have to read all the paperwork. In Problems 51–54, find the interest rate for each purchase.

51. To finance a new laptop, Emilie is offered a 3-year payment plan with low monthly payments of $34.20. The cost of the laptop was $884.29 including tax.

52. For a new set of tires ($412.23 including tax), you're offered 18 payments of $28.80.

53. For a 312-square-foot family room, you choose carpet that costs $1.49 per square foot. The tax rate is 6.5%, and you're offered 24 payments of $27.41.

54. To fence their backyard, Juan and Cheryl choose fence at $8.49 per foot. They need 194 feet of fence, and the tax rate is 7.6%. The financing is for $2\frac{1}{2}$ years with monthly payments of $72.12.

55. Sally borrowed $600 for 90 days at 4%. Find the interest using the Banker's rule.

56. Harry borrowed $950 for 120 days at $6\frac{3}{4}\%$. Find the interest using the Banker's rule.

57. If you borrow $2,200 for college expenses at 7.2% interest for 2 years, and the lender uses the Banker's rule, how much more interest are you paying than if the lender used a 365-day year? (Ignore leap years.)

58. Repeat Problem 57 if the loan is for 5 years, then again for 10 years. What can you conclude?

59. The West Penn Finance group secured an $18,000 discounted loan to remodel its offices. The rate was 5% and the term was 6 years. Find
    (a) the discount.
    (b) the amount of money the group received.
    (c) the true interest rate.

60. The University Center obtained a $20,000 discounted loan for 3 years to remodel the student game room. The rate was 9%. Find
    (a) the discount.
    (b) the amount of money the center received.
    (c) the true interest rate.

61. Susan would like to buy a new car. Which loan would have the higher interest amount: a personal loan of $10,000 at 9% for 6 years or an auto loan of $10,000 at 8% for 60 months? Why?

62. Sea Drift Motel is converting its rooms into privately owned condominiums. The interest on a $1,000,000, 20-year construction loan is $98,000. What is the rate of interest? Does the rate seem unreasonable?

63. The Laurel Township Fire Department is deciding whether to purchase a new tanker truck or repair the one they now use. For a new truck loan, the interest rate on $25,000 is 18% for a 10-year period; to repair the existing truck, the department must borrow $18,000 at $12\frac{1}{2}$% for 8 years. Which loan is less expensive?

64. A local miniature golf course owner has to recarpet his fairways and replace the golf clubs his customers use. A bank will lend the owner the necessary $7,800 at 9.5% interest over 48 months. A savings and loan company will lend the owner $7,800 at 8.5% interest for 54 months. Which loan will be less expensive for the golf course owner to assume?

65. Suppose that you borrow $10,000 for school expenses at 6% interest for 5 years.
    (a) How much simple interest would you pay?
    (b) Suppose the bank splits the 5-year loan into five 1-year loans, so that the future value of the loan would be recalculated at the end of each 1-year period, with interest charged on the new amount for the next year. Fill in the table below, which will show the future value of the loan at the end of each 1-year period. Round to the nearest dollar.

End of year	1	2	3	4	5
Future value					

    (c) How much more interest would you end up paying with the loan being split this way?
    (d) Repeat parts (b) and (c) for the situation where the loan is split into two loans, each with length $2\frac{1}{2}$ years.

66. A local bank offers two choices for a certificate of deposit with a term of 4 years. In option 1, you get 4% simple interest for the entire term. In option 2, you get just 3.5% simple interest per year, but the CD is split into four separate 1-year CDs, similar to the loan in Exercise 65.
    (a) If you plan to invest $5,000, which CD is the better option? How much more will the better option be worth?
    (b) Would your answers to part (a) change if the amount you invest is $50,000? Why or why not?

Critical Thinking

67. As you know, when computing interest it's important to convert the interest rate, given as a percentage, to decimal form. But everyone makes mistakes, so occasionally you might forget to do that. If so, how can you tell? Try to repeat some of the problems from this section without converting the rate to decimal form, then explain how you could catch this mistake.

68. Suppose that when making a major purchase, you're offered a 10-year loan at 5% and a 5-year loan at 10%. You decide on what amount would constitute a "major purchase" for you.
    (a) Without doing any calculations, which sounds like the better deal to you? Why?

    (b) Find the total amount of interest paid on each loan.
    (c) Find the monthly payment for each.
    (d) Now discuss which loan you would prefer, considering as many aspects of the loan as you can think of.

69. Suppose that you have a choice of two loans: one at 5% simple interest for 6 years, and one at 6% simple interest for five years. Which will result in the smaller future value? Does it depend on the principal?

70. When a loan is discounted, is it better or worse for the borrower if the term is longer? Try some specific examples and make a conjecture.

462   **Chapter 8**   Consumer Math

Section 8-3   Compound Interest

LEARNING OBJECTIVES

☐ 1. Compute compound interest.

☐ 2. Find the time needed to reach an investment goal.

☐ 3. Compute the effective interest rate of an investment.

☐ 4. Compare the effective rate of two investments.

☐ 5. Find the future value of an annuity.

☐ 6. Compute the periodic payment needed to meet an investment goal.

If you think about simple interest over a long period of time, it doesn't sound like a great deal for the investor. Suppose you put $1,000 into an account that pays 5% simple interest, and you keep it untouched for 30 years. Each year, you're getting 5% of $1,000 in interest. But for all that time, the bank could have been increasing your money through loans and investments, and they're still paying interest only on the original amount.

This is where compound interest comes into play. It seems more fair for the bank to pay interest on the actual value of the account each year, not just the original amount. When interest is computed on the principal *and* any previously earned interest, it's called **compound interest**. Let's look at an example that compares simple and compound interest.

| EXAMPLE 1 | Comparing Simple and Compound Interest |

Suppose that $5,000 is invested for 3 years at 8%.

(a) Find the amount of simple interest.
(b) Find the compound interest if interest is calculated once per year.

SOLUTION

(a) Using the formula $I = Prt$ with $P = \$5,000$, $r = 0.08$, and $t = 3$, we get

$$I = \$5,000 \times 0.08 \times 3 = \$1,200 \quad \textit{Simple interest over 3 years}$$

(b) **First year** For the first year, we have $P = \$5,000$, $r = 0.08$ and $t = 1$:

$$I = Prt = \$5,000 \times 0.08 \times 1 = \$400$$

The interest for the first year is $400.
Second year At the beginning of the second year, the account now contains $5,400, so we use this as principal for the second year. The rate and time remain the same.

$$I = Prt = \$5,400 \times 0.08 \times 1 = \$432$$

The interest for the second year is $432.
Third year The principal is now $5,400 + $432 = $5,832.

$$I = Prt = \$5,832 \times 0.08 \times 1 = \$466.56$$

The interest for the third year is $466.56, and the total interest for three years is $400 + $432 + $466.56 = $1,298.56. This is almost a hundred dollars more than with simple interest.

▼ Try This One 1

For an investment of $100,000 at 6% interest for 4 years, find (a) the simple interest, and (b) the compound interest if interest is calculated once per year.

In Example 1, if we had been asked to find the future value rather than the interest, we could have used the formula $A = P(1 + rt)$ from Section 8.2. In that case, we'd get

$$A = 5,000(1 + 0.08) \quad \textit{First year}$$

This would be our new principal for the second year, so the future value after the second year would be

$$A = [5,000(1 + 0.08)](1 + 0.08) = 5,000(1 + 0.08)^2$$

This is now the principal for year three, so the final future value is

$$A = [5,000(1 + 0.08)^2](1 + 0.08) = 5,000(1 + 0.08)^3$$

Math Note

A savings account where the principal and interest can't be withdrawn for some fixed period of time without penalty is called a *certificate of deposit.*

Do you see the pattern? Each year adds another power of $(1 + 0.08)$, which is $(1 + r)$. So after t years, the future value is $A = P(1 + r)^t$. When interest is calculated once each year, we say that it is **compounded annually**. But in many cases, interest is computed more than once per year. It can be computed **semiannually** (twice a year), **quarterly** (four times a year), **monthly** (12 times a year), or even **daily** (365 times a year).

When the interest is calculated more than once per year, you don't get the entire percentage each time. If our $5,000 investment at 8% were compounded twice a year, we'd get $\frac{1}{2}$ of the interest, or 4%, each time. So when interest is compounded n times per year, the r in our calculation above becomes r/n, and the exponent t becomes nt (t years at n times per year). This gives us the most important formula in this section:

Math Note

When interest is compounded yearly, $n = 1$; semiannually, $n = 2$; quarterly, $n = 4$; and daily, $n = 365$.

Formula for Computing Compound Interest

$$A = P\left(1 + \frac{r}{n}\right)^{nt}$$

where A is the future value (principal + interest)

r is the yearly interest rate in decimal form

n is the number of times per year the interest is compounded

t is the term of the investment in years

EXAMPLE 2   Computing Compound Interest

Find the interest on $7,000 compounded quarterly at 3% for 5 years.

SOLUTION

Quarterly means 4 times a year, so $n = 4$.

Calculator Guide

To compute the future value in Example 2:

Standard Scientific Calculator

7000 × (1.0075) y^x

20 =

Standard Graphing Calculator

7000 (1.0075) ^

20 ENTER

The parentheses are critical.

$P = \$7,000$, $r = 3\% = 0.03$, $t = 5$

$$A = P\left(1 + \frac{r}{n}\right)^{nt}$$

$$= \$7,000\left(1 + \frac{0.03}{4}\right)^{4(5)}$$

$$= \$7,000(1.0075)^{20} \qquad \text{See Calculator Guide.}$$

$$= \$8,128.29$$

To find the interest, subtract the principal from the future value.

$$I = \$8,128.29 - \$7,000$$
$$= \$1,128.29$$

The interest is $1,128.29.

464   **Chapter 8**   Consumer Math

▼ Try This One 2

Find the interest on $600 compounded semiannually at 4.5% for 6 years.

EXAMPLE 3   **Computing Compound Interest**

Find the interest on $11,000 compounded daily at 5% for 6 years. Assume a 365-day year.

SOLUTION

$$P = \$11,000,\ r = 5\% = 0.05,\ n = 365,\ t = 6$$

$$A = P\left(1 + \frac{r}{n}\right)^{nt}$$

$$= \$11,000\left(1 + \frac{0.05}{365}\right)^{365(6)} \qquad \textit{See Calculator Guide.}$$

$$= \$14,848.14$$

To find the interest, subtract the principal from the future value.

$$I = \$14,848.14 - \$11,000$$
$$= \$3,848.14$$

The interest is $3,848.14.

Calculator Guide

The future value in Example 3 can be computed in one step using a graphing calculator, but should be done in stages with a scientific calculator:

Standard Scientific Calculator

1 [+] .05 [÷] 365 [=] y^x

2190 [=] [×] 11000

(Note that 365 × 6 must be calculated first.)

Standard Graphing Calculator

11000 [×] [(] 1 [+] .05 [÷]

365 [)] [^] [(] 365 [×]

6 [)] [ENTER]

☑ 1. Compute compound interest.

▼ Try This One 3

Find the interest on $50,000 compounded weekly at 7% for 20 years. Assume a 52-week year.

CAUTION

In Example 2, we simplified $1 + \frac{0.03}{4}$ to 1.0075 before calculating, but didn't do the same for $1 + \frac{0.05}{365}$ in Example 3. This is because the second number has a much longer decimal expansion, and would likely have required rounding. This affects the accuracy considerably. If you rework the calculation in Example 3, but round $1 + \frac{0.05}{365}$ to four decimal places, the result is $2,692.99, which is off by over a thousand dollars! We'll study the potential effects of rounding in Exercises 71 and 72.

Using the logarithms we studied in Section 7-6, we can solve the compound interest formula for t, which allows us to find the time needed to meet an investment goal, as in Example 4.

EXAMPLE 4   **Finding the Time Needed to Reach an Investment Goal**

If you want to save $5,000 before buying your first new car, and you have $3,000 right now to invest at 3% interest compounded monthly, how long will you have to wait?

SOLUTION

$$A = \$5,000,\ P = \$3,000,\ r = 3\% = 0.03,\ n = 12$$

$$A = P\left(1 + \frac{r}{n}\right)^{nt}$$

$$5,000 = 3,000\left(1 + \frac{0.03}{12}\right)^{12t}$$ *Divide both sides by 3,000.*

$$\frac{5,000}{3,000} = \left(1 + \frac{0.03}{12}\right)^{12t}$$ *Simplify.*

$$\frac{5}{3} = (1.0025)^{12t}$$ *Apply $\log_{1.0025}$ to both sides.*

$$\log_{1.0025}\frac{5}{3} = \log_{1.0025}(1.0025)^{12t}$$ *Simplify right side.*

$$\log_{1.0025}\frac{5}{3} = 12t$$ *Divide both sides by 12.*

$$t = \frac{\log_{1.0025}\frac{5}{3}}{12} = \frac{\log\left(\frac{5}{3}\right)}{\log 1.0025}\bigg/12 \approx 17$$ *Use change of base formula.*

Uh oh . . . better figure out a way to save more money unless you're okay with waiting for 17 years.

---

2. Find the time needed to reach an investment goal.

▼ Try This One 4

If you owe $1,400 on a high-interest credit card at 21% compounded monthly, how long will it take the amount you owe to double if you don't make any payments?

Effective Rate

As the number of times per year that interest is compounded goes up, the amount of interest does as well, but not by as much as you might think. For a $1,000 investment at 4% interest for 10 years, the difference between compounding yearly and compounding daily is only about $11. (We'll study the effects of more compounding periods in the Sidelight on page 469, and then in more depth in critical thinking Exercises 61–64.) Still, because of this relatively small difference, when interest is compounded more than once per year, the interest earned on a savings account is actually a bit higher than the stated rate.

For example, consider a savings account with a principal of $5,000 and an interest rate of 4% compounded semiannually. The interest is compounded twice a year at 2%. Using the formula shown in Example 2, the actual interest for one year is $202. The stated rate is 4%, but the actual rate can be found by dividing $202 by $5,000; it is 4.04%. This rate is called the *effective rate* or *annual yield*.

The **effective rate** (also known as the **annual yield**) is the simple interest rate which would yield the same future value over 1 year as the compound interest rate.

The next formula can be used to calculate the effective interest rate.

Formula for Effective Interest Rate

$$E = \left(1 + \frac{r}{n}\right)^n - 1$$

where

E = effective rate
n = number of periods per year the interest is calculated
r = interest rate per year (i.e., stated rate)

466   **Chapter 8** Consumer Math

The stated rate is also called the **nominal rate**.
Example 5 illustrates the use of this formula.

EXAMPLE 5   Finding Effective Interest Rate

Calculator Guide

To compute the effective
interest rate:

Standard Scientific Calculator

1 =

Standard Graphing Calculator

(1 + .04 ÷ 2) x²

= 1 ENTER

Find the effective interest rate when the stated rate is 4% and the interest is compounded semiannually.

SOLUTION

Let $r = 0.04$ (rate is 4%) and $n = 2$ (compounded semiannually) and then substitute into the formula.

$$E = \left(1 + \frac{r}{n}\right)^n - 1$$

$$= \left(1 + \frac{0.04}{2}\right)^2 - 1 \qquad See\ Calculator\ Guide.$$

$$= 0.0404 = 4.04\%$$

The effective rate is 4.04%. (This is the same rate that we calculated previously.)

▼ Try This One 5

Find the effective rate for a stated interest rate of 8% compounded quarterly.

 3. Compute the effective
interest rate of an
investment.

The effective rates of two savings accounts can be used to determine which account would be a better investment. The next example shows how to do this.

EXAMPLE 6   Comparing the Effective Rate of Two Investments

Which savings account is a better investment: 6.2% compounded daily or 6.25% compounded semiannually?

SOLUTION

Find the effective rates of both accounts and compare them.

6.2% daily	**6.25% semiannually**
$r = 0.062, n = 365$	$r = 0.0625, n = 2$
$E = \left(1 + \dfrac{r}{n}\right)^n - 1$	$E = \left(1 + \dfrac{r}{n}\right)^n - 1$
$= \left(1 + \dfrac{0.062}{365}\right)^{365} - 1$	$= \left(1 + \dfrac{0.0625}{2}\right)^2 - 1$
$\approx 0.0640 = 6.40\%$	$\approx 0.0635 = 6.35\%$

The 6.2% daily investment has a slightly better effective rate than 6.25% semiannually.

▼ Try This One 6

4. Compare the effective rate of
two investments.

Which is a better investment, 3% compounded monthly or 3.25% compounded semiannually?

Annuities

An **annuity** is a savings investment plan in which the investor makes a regular, fixed payment into a compound-interest account where the interest rate doesn't change during the term of the investment. This differs from a regular compound-interest account in that you don't invest an entire amount at the beginning of the investment period, but rather break the investment up into smaller payments. For example, you might pay $500 annually for 3 years into an account that yields 6% interest compounded annually. The total amount accumulated (payments plus interest) is called the **future value** of the annuity.

Annuities are often used by individuals or families to save money to pay for things like college expenses, vacations, home improvements, or (most commonly) retirement. Businesses and governments set up annuities to pay future expenses like business expansion, new equipment, and health care costs. The payments in a regular annuity are made at the end of each period.

Example 6 shows how an annuity works.

> **Math Note**
>
> A scary fact: in May of 2012, cnn.com reported on a study showing that over 47% of all working Americans at that time were currently not saving ANY money for retirement.

EXAMPLE 7   **Finding the Future Value of an Annuity**

Find the future value of an annuity where a $500 payment is made annually for 3 years at 6%.

SOLUTION

The interest rate is 6% and the payment is $500 each year for 3 years.

I. End of the first year $500 (payment)

II. End of the second year

The $500 collected 6% interest and a $500 payment is made; the value of the annuity at the end of the second year is

$500(0.06) =	$ 30	Interest
	$500	Principal paid at end of first year
	+$500	Payment at the end of the second year
	$1,030	

III. End of the third year

During the third year, the $1,030 earns 6% interest and a payment of $500 is made at the end of the third year. The annuity is worth

$1,030(0.06) =	$ 61.80	Interest
	$1,030.00	Principal at end of second year
	+$500.00	Payment at end of third year
	$1,591.80	

The future value of the annuity at the end of the three years is $1,591.80.

> ▼ **Try This One 7**
>
> Find the future value of an annuity where a $300 payment is made annually for 4 years at 9%.

Example 7 shows that an annuity really is just a series of compound-interest problems. But calculating each of those compound-interest problems one at a time can be pretty time-consuming for a long-term annuity. In many cases, annuities are used to save for retirement, and regular payments might be made for 30 years or more. Mix in the fact that the payments might be made monthly, and in that case you'd need over 360 separate compound interest calculations to find the future value! Who has time for that? To avoid this mess, the following formula can be used to find the future value of an annuity.

Formula for Finding the Future Value of an Annuity

$$A = \frac{R\left[\left(1 + \dfrac{r}{n}\right)^{nt} - 1\right]}{\dfrac{r}{n}}$$

where A is the future value of the annuity
R is the regular periodic payment
r is the annual interest rate
n is the number of payments made per year
t is the term of the annuity in years

CAUTION

You should be especially careful in using the annuity formula because it uses both capital R and lowercase r. The lowercase represents what it always does—annual interest rate. Think of the capital R as standing for "Regular" or "Recurring" payment.

EXAMPLE 8   **Finding the Future Value of an Annuity**

If you open an annuity with semiannual payments of $800 at 5% compounded semiannually for 4 years:

(a) Find the future value of the annuity.
(b) How much interest will you earn?
(c) How much money would you have to invest in a regular savings account at 5% compounded semiannually to get the same future value after 3 years? (Note that your first payment on the annuity is at the end of the first year, so that would be when you'd make the lump-sum investment, giving you just 3 years of interest.)

SOLUTION

$$R = \$800, \; r = 5\% = 0.05, \; n = 2 \text{ (semiannual)}, \; t = 4$$

(a) The calculations in the annuity formula are a little complicated, so we'll be especially careful to work in stages.

$$A = \frac{R\left[\left(1 + \dfrac{r}{n}\right)^{nt} - 1\right]}{\dfrac{r}{n}}$$

$$A = \frac{\$800\left[\left(1 + \dfrac{0.05}{2}\right)^{2(4)} - 1\right]}{\dfrac{0.05}{2}} = \frac{\$800[(1.025)^8 - 1]}{0.025} = \$6,988.89$$

The future value of the annuity at the end of 4 years is $6,988.89.

(b) You would have made eight payments of $800 (two each year for 4 years), so your total investment would be $6,400. The interest earned is $6,988.89 − $6,400 = $588.89.

(c) This is a compound interest problem with $r = 0.05$, $A = \$6{,}988.89$, $n = 2$, and $t = 3$; we need to solve for the principal.

$$A = P\left(1 + \frac{r}{n}\right)^{nt}$$

$$6{,}988.89 = P\left(1 + \frac{0.05}{2}\right)^{2(3)}$$

$$P = \frac{6{,}988.89}{(1.025)^6} = 6{,}026.50$$

You'd have to invest $6,026.50 at the end of the first year to get the same final amount.

▼ Try This One 8

(a) Find the future value of an annuity when the payment is $275 quarterly, the interest is 6.5% compounded quarterly, and the term is 6 years.

(b) Find the interest earned.

(c) How much would you have to invest at the end of the first year to get the same return over 5 years in a regular savings account at 6.5% compounded quarterly?

☑ 5. Find the future value of an annuity.

One way that annuities are commonly used is to save money for some specific future expense. In that case, you'd more than likely know what future value you're shooting for, and you'd be interested in finding the regular payment necessary to

Sidelight DOUBLING YOUR MONEY

People will often ask, "If I put my money in a savings account, how long will it take me to double it?" The answer, of course, depends on the interest rate. Bankers use a simple rule to find the answer in what is called the *rule of 72*.

All that is necessary to find the answer is to divide 72 by the current interest rate. For example, if the interest rate is 3%, then it will take you 72 ÷ 3 or 24 years. If the interest rate is 10%, it will take you 72 ÷ 10 or approximately 7.2 years.

There are several things to consider, though. First, the answer is only an approximation. Second, it is assumed that the interest is compounded yearly. When interest is compounded semiannually, quarterly, or daily, the answer found by the rule is less precise. Other simple rules can be used to find how to triple your money, quadruple your money, etc.

As you know, the higher the interest rate, the faster your money will grow. The growth rate of your money also depends on how often the interest rate is compounded. Usually, interest is compounded yearly (once a year), semiannually (two times a year), or quarterly (four times a year). There are two other ways to compound interest. They are daily (365 times a year) and continuously (all the time). You might think that interest compounded continuously will make you a lot of money, but in reality, continuous interest pays only slightly more money than daily interest. The comparison is shown in the chart.

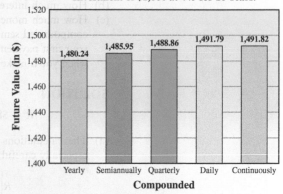

Investment of $1,000 at 4% for 10 Years.

Compounded	Future Value
Yearly	$1,480.24
Semiannually	$1,485.95
Quarterly	$1,488.86
Daily	$1,491.79
Continuously	$1,491.82

As you can see, you will earn only about 3 cents more from continuous interest than you would earn with daily compounding.

reach that goal. In that case, we can use the annuity formula and solve for the regular payment, as in Example 9.

EXAMPLE 9   **Finding the Monthly Payment for an Annuity**

Suppose you've always dreamed of opening your own tattoo parlor, and decide it's time to do something about it. A financial planner estimates that you would need a $35,000 initial investment to start the business, and you plan to save that amount over the course of 5 years by investing in an annuity that pays 7.5% compounded weekly. How much would you need to invest each week?

SOLUTION

We know the following values: $A = 35{,}000$, $r = 7.5\% = 0.075$, $t = 5$, and $n = 52$.

$$A = \frac{R\left[\left(1 + \frac{r}{n}\right)^{nt} - 1\right]}{\frac{r}{n}}$$

$$35{,}000 = \frac{R\left[\left(1 + \frac{0.075}{52}\right)^{52(5)} - 1\right]}{\frac{0.075}{52}} \quad \textit{Multiply both sides by } \frac{0.075}{52}.$$

$$35{,}000 \cdot \frac{0.075}{52} = R\left[\left(1 + \frac{0.075}{52}\right)^{52(5)} - 1\right] \quad \textit{Divide to isolate R.}$$

$$R = \frac{35{,}000\left(\frac{0.075}{52}\right)}{\left(1 + \frac{0.075}{52}\right)^{52(5)} - 1} \quad \textit{Reduce error by not rounding } \frac{0.075}{52}.$$

$$= \frac{\frac{2{,}625}{52}}{\left(1 + \frac{0.075}{52}\right)^{260} - 1} = 111.04$$

A payment of $111.04 per week would be necessary to save the required $35,000.

☑ 6. Compute the periodic payment needed to meet an investment goal.

▼ Try This One 9

Find the monthly payment needed to save a $6,000 down payment for a car in an annuity that pays 5.5% interest compounded monthly over 2 years.

Answers to Try This One

1	(a) $24,000	**5**	8.24%
	(b) $26,247.70	**6**	3.25% semiannually
2	$183.63	**7**	$1,371.94
3	$152,569.20	**8**	(a) $7,993.75 (b) $1,393.75 (c) $5,790.81
4	About 3.3 years	**9**	$237.07

EXERCISE SET 8-3

Writing Exercises

1. Describe the difference between simple interest and compound interest.
2. What does it mean to say that interest is compounded quarterly? What about compounded monthly?
3. What is the effective rate of an investment?
4. Describe how an annuity works.

5. What's the difference between an annuity and an investment using compound interest? What are the advantages of each?
6. Why does it make sense that the interest rate r is divided by n in the compound interest formula?

Computational Exercises

For Exercises 7–12, find the compound interest and future value for each.

Principal	Rate	Compounded	Time
7. $825	4%	Annually	10 years
8. $1,495	0.6%	Semiannually	11 years
9. $560	4.25%	Quarterly	3 years
10. $750	9%	Daily	1 year
11. $320	2.5%	Daily	$4\frac{1}{2}$ years
12. $115,000	4.19%	Weekly	32 years

For Exercises 13–16, find the future value of each annuity.

Payment	Rate	Compounded	Time
13. $430	7%	Annually	15 years
14. $8,000	1.61%	Semiannually	3 years
15. $2,750	0.34%	Quarterly	6 years
16. $3,500	1.73%	Quarterly	$8\frac{1}{2}$ years

For Exercises 17–20, find the periodic payment needed to attain the future value of each annuity.

Future Value	Rate	Compounded	Time
17. $7,200	3.1%	Quarterly	3 years
18. $27,500	5.3%	Monthly	8 years

Future Value	Rate	Compounded	Time
19. $1.1 million	7.2%	Monthly	28 years
20. $2.4 million	9.25%	Weekly	32 years

For Exercises 21–24, find the effective interest rate.

21. Rate: 6%   Compounded: Quarterly
22. Rate: 10%   Compounded: Semiannually
23. Rate: 6.5%   Compounded: Quarterly
24. Rate: 9.55%   Compounded: Semiannually

For Exercises 25–28, determine which is the better investment.

25. 4.5% compounded semiannually or 4.25% compounded quarterly.
26. 7% compounded monthly or 7.2% compounded semiannually.
27. 3% compounded daily or 3.1% compounded quarterly.
28. 5.74% compounded semiannually or 5.6% compounded daily.

Applications in Our World

29. A couple decides to set aside $5,000 in a savings account for a second honeymoon trip. It is compounded quarterly for 10 years at 9%. Find the amount of money they will have in 10 years.
30. In order to pay for college, the parents of a child invest $20,000 in a bond that pays 8% interest compounded semiannually. How much money will there be in 18 years?
31. A 25-year-old plans to retire at age 50. She decided to invest an inheritance of $60,000 at 7% interest compounded semiannually. How much will she have at age 50?
32. To pay for new machinery in 5 years, a company owner invests $10,000 at $7\frac{1}{2}$% compounded quarterly. How much money will be available in 5 years?
33. The Elders hope to accumulate $12,000 for a sunroom over the next 6 years. How much would they need to invest right now at 3.9% compounded quarterly to reach that goal?

34. A recent college grad accepts a job but plans to save money to go back to grad school in 6 years. She wants to have $22,000 saved at that point to help pay for school. How much would she have to invest right now at $5\frac{1}{4}$% compounded quarterly to reach that goal?
35. How much would you have to invest into a 5-year certificate of deposit paying 2.3% compounded weekly to make it worth $4,500 at the end of the term?
36. After the birth of their first child, the Bartons plan to set up an account to pay for her college education. The goal is to save $80,000 over the next 18 years, and their financial planner suggests a bond fund that historically pays 6.2% interest compounded monthly. How much should they put into the fund now?
37. After winning $73,000 on a game show, Jasmine invests the money in a fixed-rate account offering 7.2% interest compounded semiannually. How long will it take that amount to grow to $100,000?

38. Jamaal is offered a new job with a signing bonus of $17,000. After accepting the job, rather than spending the bonus, Jamaal decides to invest it with a long-term goal of turning it into $40,000 so he can take 6 months off and travel. If he finds an investment that pays 7.1% compounded daily, how long will it take to reach that goal?

39. How many years does it take an investment to double if the interest rate is 6.8% compounded annually? What if it's compounded daily?

40. If you have a $700 balance on a credit card that charges 18% interest compounded monthly, how long will it take that amount to reach $2,000 if you don't make any payments?

41. A husband and wife plan to save money for their daughter's college education in 4 years. They decide to purchase an annuity with a semiannual payment earning 7.5% compounded semiannually. Find the future value of the annuity in 4 years if the semiannual payment is $2,250.

42. A business owner decided to purchase an annuity to pay for new copy machines in 3 years. The payment is $600 quarterly at 8% interest compounded quarterly. Find the future value of the annuity in 3 years.

43. Find the future value of an annuity if you invest $200 quarterly for 20 years at 5% interest compounded quarterly.

44. The Washingtons decide to save money for a vacation in 2 years. They purchase an annuity with semiannual payments of $200 at 9% interest compounded semiannually. Find the amount of money they can spend for the vacation.

45. The owner of the Campus Café plans to open a second location on a satellite campus in 5 years. She buys an annuity that pays 10.5% interest compounded annually.
    (a) If the payment is $4,000 a year, find the future value of the annuity in 5 years.
    (b) How much more interest would be earned if the owner could invest the full amount paid into the annuity in a regular compound-interest account with the same terms for 4 years?

46. Titan Thigh, the owner of Work-it-out Fitness, wants to buy an annuity that pays 4% interest compounded quarterly for 4 years.
    (a) If the quarterly payment is $160, find the future value of the annuity.
    (b) How much more interest would be earned if the owner could invest the full amount paid into the annuity in a regular compound-interest account with the same terms for 3 years?

47. In order to plan for their retirement, a married couple decides to buy an annuity that pays 8% interest compounded semiannually.
    (a) If the semiannual payment is $2,000, how much will they have saved in 10 years?
    (b) Find the total interest earned.

(c) How much would this couple have to invest at the end of the first year to get the same return over 9 years in a regular savings account?

48. The Wash-n-Surf, an Internet café and laundromat, plans to replace two wash and surf hubs in 3 years.
    (a) If the owner buys an annuity at 6% interest compounded annually with an annual payment of $800, find the value of the annuity in 3 years.
    (b) Find the total interest earned.
    (c) How much would the owner have to invest at the end of the first year to get the same return over 2 years in a regular savings account?

49. Petty Marine Co. has a long-term plan to expand to a second location that's actually near some water, so they want to start a monthly annuity to save $150,000 in capital over 5 years. The best rate they can find is 7%. Find the monthly payment.

50. Suppose you plan to work right after you graduate, but still save money for grad school. You decide to save $10,000 before starting, and find a weekly annuity that pays 6.5% interest for 4 years. How much will you need to pay each week?

51. The Massive Chemical Corporation starts an annuity to pay for the huge government penalties they expect in 10 years when a pending case finally gets litigated. Their lead attorney informs them that they can expect a $4,000,000 fine. An investment house offers 11% interest on annuities of that size, compounded semiannually. What will the semiannual payment be on this annuity?

52. A 25-year-old decides that her goal is to retire at age 50 with at least $2,000,000 in savings. The company investment annuity offers 7.4% annual returns, compounded monthly. What amount will she need to invest each month?

53. If the Elders (Exercise 33) are also offered an annuity at 3.9% compounded monthly to save the $12,000 they need over 6 years, what would the monthly payments be? How much more would they end up contributing to the final amount?

54. If the college grad in Exercise 34 is also offered an annuity at $5\frac{1}{4}$% compounded quarterly to save the $22,000 she needs over 6 years, what would the quarterly payments be? How much more would she end up contributing to the final amount?

55. If you have $5,000 to invest and you're offered a 6-year investment at 4.5% paying simple interest, and the same rate and time with compound interest compounded daily, and you make the ridiculously bad choice of simple interest, how much money would you cost yourself?

56. Suppose you're offered the following three accounts to invest $10,000 for 10 years: 12% simple interest, 6% interest compounded monthly, and an annuity with quarterly payments of $250 at 8% interest compounded quarterly. Which is the best choice?

57. Which is a better way to invest $4,000 if the concern is simply the future value: a 3-year certificate of deposit paying 4.1% compounded quarterly, or a 3-year annuity that divides that $4,000 into 12 quarterly payments and pays 5.4% compounded quarterly?

58. Which investment results in a greater future value: a $30,000 investment into an account paying 3.8% interest compounded monthly for 4 years, or an annuity that divides the $30,000 into monthly payments for those 4 years and pays 5.9% interest compounded monthly?

59. Bill and Ted open an annuity with $80 monthly payments that pays 4.9% interest compounded monthly. How long will it take for the future value to reach $15,000?

60. How long will it take to accumulate $300,000 in an annuity that pays 7.2% compounded monthly if the monthly payment is $520?

Critical Thinking

In Problems 61–64, we'll study what happens to the compound interest formula when we keep compounding more and more often.

61. The compound interest formula is $A = P(1 + \frac{r}{n})^{nt}$, where n is the number of times per year that interest is compounded.

    (a) If we perform the algebraic substitution $u = \frac{n}{r}$, show that the compound interest formula becomes $A = P(1 + \frac{1}{u})^{urt}$, and then can be rewritten as $A = P[(1 + \frac{1}{u})^u]^{rt}$.

    (b) When the number of times per year that interest is compounded grows larger and larger, what happens to the expression we called u? (In this case, we say that n is *tending to infinity*.)

    (c) Using a calculator, fill in the table below. Round to three decimal places.

u	50	100	500	1,000	1,500	2,000	2,500
$\left(1 + \dfrac{1}{u}\right)^u$							

    What can you conclude about the value of $(1 + \frac{1}{u})^u$ as the number of times interest is compounded gets very large?

62. The number that you should have found in Exercise 61(c) is about 2.718, and is denoted e. (Actually, e is irrational, so its decimal equivalent neither terminates nor repeats: $e = 2.718...$) What is the result of the compound interest formula from Exercise 61(a) when the number of times interest is compounded tends to infinity? (In this case, we say that interest is **compounded continuously**. You can think of this as the interest being compounded every instant of every day.)

63. Use the formula $A = Pe^{rt}$ to find the future value after 20 years of a $5,000 account that earns 4% interest compounded continuously, then compare that to the future value of the same account if interest is compounded annually.

64. Now let's compare interest compounded continuously to simple interest. Suppose that $50,000 is invested in two accounts: one earns 6% simple interest, the other earns 6% compounded continuously. Fill in the table in the next column with the future value of each account after each term.

Years	5	10	15	20	25	30
6% simple interest						
6% compounded continuously						

65. An investor deposits $5,000 into an account paying 4% compounded semiannually. Two years later she deposited $2,000 into the same account. How much money was there at the end of 5 years?

66. Sam deposited $3,500 into a savings account paying 3% compounded quarterly. Two years later he withdrew $800. How much money was in the account at the end of 6 years?

67. Akish deposited $900 into a savings account paying 2% compounded quarterly. Two years later, she deposited $400 into the same account. One year after that, she withdrew $200. How much money was in the account at the end of 6 years?

68. Which account would draw more interest over 5 years: 12% simple interest or 7.5% interest compounded hourly? What about over 20 years?

69. What percent simple interest would be needed on a 10-year investment to have the same future value as one that pays 5% compounded monthly?

70. As you know, some years have 366 days. Does this have any significant effect on interest compounded daily? Do some sample calculations to compare a 365-day year to a 366-day year to decide.

71. As we pointed out in the Caution on page 464, rounding can cause significant error in the compound–interest formula. For $30,000 invested at 6% interest compounded weekly, the formula is $A = 30,000(1 + \frac{0.06}{52})^{52t}$, and the number in parentheses is 1.001153846 to nine decimal places.

    (a) Calculate the future value after 5 years without rounding at all: enter the calculation just as it looks above.

    (b) Now calculate the future value if you round the number in the parentheses to three decimal places. How inaccurate is the result?

72. Repeat Problem 71 with $t = 20$. Is the effect of rounding exaggerated as the term increases?

474   **Chapter 8** Consumer Math

Section 8-4   Installment Buying

A lot of people celebrate their college graduation by getting a new car. Unless you're very wealthy, you won't be plunking down a stack of crisp hundred dollar bills to make that happen—you'll need to get a loan. In this case, you'll be doing what is called **installment buying**. This is when an item is purchased and the buyer pays for it by making periodic partial payments, or installments.

There are natural advantages and disadvantages to installment buying. The most obvious advantage is that it allows you to buy an item that you don't have enough money to pay for, and use it while you're raising that money. The most obvious disadvantage is that you pay interest on the amount borrowed, so you end up paying more for the item—in some cases a *lot* more.

LEARNING OBJECTIVES

☐ 1. Find amount financed, total installment price, and finance charge for a fixed installment loan.

☐ 2. Use a table to find APR for a loan.

☐ 3. Compute unearned interest and payoff amount for a loan paid off early.

☐ 4. Compute credit card finance charges using the unpaid balance method.

☐ 5. Compute credit card finance charges using the average daily balance method.

☐ 6. Study the effects of making minimum payments.

Fixed Installment Loans

A **fixed installment loan** is a loan that is repaid in equal payments. Sometimes the buyer will pay part of the cost at the time of purchase. This is known as a **down payment**. The other terms used to describe installment loans are defined next.

> The **amount financed** is the amount a borrower will pay interest on.
>
> Amount financed = Price of item − Down payment
>
> The **total installment price** is the total amount of money the buyer will ultimately pay.
>
> Total installment price = Sum of all payments + Down payment
>
> The **finance charge** is the interest charged for borrowing the amount financed.
>
> Finance charge = Total installment price − Price of item

EXAMPLE 1   **Calculating Information About a Car Loan**

Cat bought a 2-year old Santa Fe for $12,260. Her down payment was $3,000, and she will have to pay $231.50 for 48 months. Find the amount financed, the total installment price, and the finance charge.

SOLUTION

Using the formulas in the box above:

$$\text{Amount financed} = \text{Cash price} - \text{Down payment}$$
$$= \$12,260 - \$3,000$$
$$= \$9,260$$

Since she paid $231.50 for 48 months and her down payment was $3,000,

$$\text{Total installment price} = \text{Total of monthly payments} + \text{Down payment}$$
$$= 48 \times \$231.50 + \$3,000 \quad \textit{48 payments at \$231.50.}$$
$$= \$14,112.00$$

Now we can find the finance charge:

$$\text{Finance charge} = \text{Total installment price} - \text{Cash price}$$
$$= \$14,112.00 - \$12,260.00$$
$$= \$1,852.00$$

Sidelight TO BUY OR TO LEASE? THAT IS THE QUESTION.

Obvious statement of the day: new cars are expensive. (And used ones aren't particularly cheap, either.) If you don't have a lot of money to make a down payment but you want that new-car smell, leasing may be the way to go. Like an auto loan, with a lease you're making regular equal payments to a financial insti-tution. The difference is simple: after making payments for a set number of months, you don't own the vehicle and you have to give it back. In essence, you're renting the car rather than buying it. So why would you want to do that? There are several reasons.

For one, many leases require little or even no down pay-ment, so you can get a new car without having to save a lot of money in advance. Second, lease payments are usually quite a bit less than those you'd have on a loan (as they should be, since you don't get to keep the car!). Third, most leases last for 2 or 3 years, allowing regular leasers to get a brand new car every

few years. And you do have the option of buying the car at a pre-arranged price after the term of the lease expires.

The biggest downside to leasing is obvious—you're paying for the car but you don't get to keep it. Also, most leases have mileage limits, and if you go over the number of miles you're allot-ted, you can end up paying a substantial penalty at the end of the lease. You may pay more for insurance with a leased car as well. In addition, you're committed to making payments for the life of the lease, so if you decide you don't like the car that much or your financial situation changes, you're pretty much out of luck.

Depending on what you're looking for and your financial situation, leasing might be the right thing for you. But make sure you understand all of the provisions before signing any-thing because leases are commitments that are *very* difficult to get out of.

The amount financed was $9,260.00; the total installment price was $14,112.00, and the finance charge was $1,852.00.

▼ Try This One 1

If you buy a used car for $8,200 with a down payment of $1,000 and 36 monthly payments of $270, find the amount financed, the total installment price, and the finance charge.

In some sense, an installment loan is the opposite of an annuity. You make equal regular payments, but instead of saving money for future use, you're paying off money that you borrowed to use at the beginning of the loan.

EXAMPLE 2   Computing a Monthly Payment

After a big promotion, a young couple bought $9,000 worth of furniture. The down payment was $1,000. The balance was financed for 3 years at 8% simple interest per year.

(a) Find the amount financed.
(b) Find the finance charge (interest).
(c) Find the total installment price.
(d) Find the monthly payment.

SOLUTION

(a) Amount financed = Price of item − Down payment

$$= \$9,000 - \$1,000 = \$8,000$$

(b) To find the finance charge, we use the simple interest formula:

$$I = Prt$$
$$= \$8,000 \times 0.08 \times 3 \quad \textit{8\% = 0.08}$$
$$= \$1,920$$

476   **Chapter 8**   Consumer Math

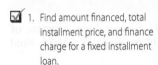
(c) In this case, the total installment price is simply the cost of the furniture plus the finance charge:

$$\text{Total installment price} = \$9{,}000 + \$1{,}920$$
$$= \$10{,}920$$

(d) To calculate the monthly payment, divide the amount financed plus the finance charge ($8,000 + $1,920) by the number of payments:

$$\text{Monthly payment} = \$9{,}920 \div 36$$
$$= \$275.56$$

In summary, the amount financed is $8,000, the finance charge is $1,920, the total installment price is $10,920, and the monthly payment is $275.56.

☑ 1. Find amount financed, total installment price, and finance charge for a fixed installment loan.

▼ Try This One 2

A graphic design pro buys a new iMac for $1,499 with a $200 down payment, and gets manufacturer financing for 5 years at 12% simple interest. Find (a) the amount financed, (b) the finance charge, (c) the total installment price, and (d) the monthly payment.

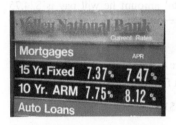

APR on a loan is similar to the effective rate on an investment, but may also factor in upfront fees.

Annual Percentage Rate

Many lenders add upfront fees to a loan and then spread them over the life of the loan. This has the effect of making the actual interest rate that a borrower pays higher than the quoted rate. Because this can get confusing, lenders are required by law to disclose an **annual percentage rate**, or APR, that reflects the true interest charged. This allows consumers to compare loans with different terms. The mathematical procedures for computing APR are extremely complicated, so tables have been compiled that help you to estimate APR for a loan. There is also a wide variety of APR calculators available online. A partial APR table is shown in Table 8-1. There are three steps required to find an APR from the table; they are listed at the top of the next page.

TABLE 8-1	APR Table

Annual Percentage Rate

Number of Payments	6.0%	6.5%	7.0%	7.5%	8.0%	8.5%	9.0%	9.5%	10.0%	10.5%	11.0%	11.5%	12.0%
	(Finance charge per $100 of amount financed)												
6	$1.76	$1.90	$2.05	$2.20	$2.35	$2.49	$2.64	$2.79	$2.94	$3.08	$3.23	$3.38	$3.53
12	3.28	3.56	3.83	4.11	4.39	4.66	4.94	5.22	5.50	5.78	6.06	6.34	6.62
18	4.82	5.22	5.63	6.04	6.45	6.86	7.28	7.69	8.10	8.52	8.93	9.35	9.77
24	6.37	6.91	7.45	8.00	8.54	9.09	9.64	10.19	10.75	11.30	11.86	12.42	12.98
30	7.94	8.61	9.30	9.98	10.66	11.35	12.04	12.74	13.43	14.13	14.83	15.54	16.24
36	9.52	10.34	11.16	11.98	12.81	13.64	14.48	15.32	16.16	17.01	17.86	18.71	19.57
48	12.73	13.83	14.94	16.06	17.18	18.31	19.45	20.59	21.74	22.90	24.06	25.23	26.40
60	16.00	17.40	18.81	20.23	21.66	23.10	24.55	26.01	27.48	28.96	30.45	31.96	33.47

> ### Using the APR Table
>
> **Step 1** Find the finance charge per $100 borrowed using the formula
>
> $$\frac{\text{Finance charge}}{\text{Amount financed}} \times \$100$$
>
> **Step 2** Find the row in the table marked with the number of payments and move to the right until you find the amount closest to the number from Step 1.
>
> **Step 3** The APR (to the nearest half percent) is at the top of the corresponding column.

EXAMPLE 3   Finding APR

Burk Carter bought a color laser printer for $600. He made a down payment of $50 and financed the rest for 2 years with a monthly payment of $24.75. Find the APR.

Math Note

In Example 3, we're fortunate to get a result that's exactly in the table. If that's not the case, you can estimate the APR pretty accurately by noting how far in between two consecutive entries in the table your result is.

If we had gotten $8.27, which is halfway between $8.00 and $8.54, we could conclude that the APR is 7.75%.

SOLUTION

Step 1 Find the finance charge per $100. The total amount he will pay is $24.75 per month × 24 payments, or $594. Since he financed $550, the finance charge is $594 − $550 = $44.

$$\text{Finance charge per \$100} = \frac{\text{Finance charge}}{\text{Amount financed}} \times \$100$$
$$= \frac{\$44}{\$550} \times \$100$$
$$= \$8$$

Step 2 Find the row for 24 payments and move across the row until you find the number closest to $8. In this case, it's exactly $8.

Step 3 Move to the top of the column to get the APR; it is 7.5%.

☑ 2. Use a table to find APR for a loan.

▼ Try This One 3

Darla Connor bought a Mercury Mariner for $19,900. Her down payment was $3,000. She financed the balance at $623 per month for 30 months. Find the APR.

One way to save money on a fixed installment loan is to pay it off early. This will allow a buyer to avoid paying the entire finance charge. The amount of the finance charge that is saved when a loan is paid off early is called **unearned interest**. There are two methods for calculating unearned interest, the **actuarial method** and the **rule of 78**. The actuarial method uses the APR table, and the following formula:

> *Math Note*
>
> The value *h* is found using Table 8-1: it is the entry in the row with the number of remaining payments and the column matching the loan's APR.

The Actuarial Method

$$u = \frac{kRh}{100 + h}$$

where   *u* = unearned interest
            k = number of payments remaining, excluding the current one
            R = monthly payment
            h = finance charge per $100 for a loan with the same APR and *k* monthly payments

EXAMPLE 4   Using the Actuarial Method

Our friend Burk from Example 3 decides to use part of his tax refund to pay off the full amount of his laser printer with his 12th payment. Find the unearned interest and the payoff amount.

SOLUTION

To use the formula for the actuarial method, we'll need values for *k*, *R*, and *h*. Half of the original 24 payments will remain, so *k* = 12. From Example 3, the monthly payment is $24.75 and the APR is 7.5%. Using Table 8-1, we find the row for 12 payments and the column for 7.5%; the intersection shows $4.11, so *h* = $4.11. Now we substitute those values into the formula:

$$u = \frac{kRh}{100 + h} \qquad k = 12,\ R = 24.75,\ h = 4.11$$

$$= \frac{(12)(24.75)(4.11)}{100 + 4.11} \qquad \textit{Multiply in the numerator, add in the denominator.}$$

$$= \frac{1{,}220.67}{104.11} \approx 11.72$$

The unearned interest is $11.72.

The payoff amount is the amount remaining on the loan minus unearned interest. At this point, Burk has made 11 payments, so there would be 13 remaining if he were not paying the loan off early.

$$\text{Payoff amount} = 13 \times \$24.75 - \$11.72$$
$$= \$310.03$$

With a payment of $310.03, Burk is the proud owner of a laser printer.

▼ Try This One 4

The buyer in Try This One 3 decided to pay off her car loan in 24 months instead of 30. Use the actuarial method to find the unearned interest and the payoff amount.

The next example will show how to find the unearned interest and payoff amount of a fixed installment loan using the rule of 78.

The Rule of 78

$$u = \frac{fk(k+1)}{n(n+1)}$$

where u = unearned interest
         f = finance charge
         k = number of remaining monthly payments
         n = original number of payments

Notice that the formula has the number of payments remaining in the numerator and the original number of payments in the denominator. That means as the number of remaining payments gets smaller, the unearned interest does as well. The reason it's not simply the proportion $u = \frac{fk}{n}$ is that the lenders collect more interest and less principal in the beginning of a loan.

EXAMPLE 5   Using the Rule of 78

Math Note

The reason that the rule of 78 is used is that the unearned interest for the last months of the loan is considerably smaller than the first months.

The interest saved during the last three months of a 12-month loan is $\frac{3}{78} + \frac{2}{78} + \frac{1}{78} = \frac{6}{78}$ of the total interest while the interest paid for the first three months is $\frac{12}{78} + \frac{11}{78} + \frac{10}{78} = \frac{33}{78}$ of the total interest.

Paying off a loan early feels pretty good, but if there aren't many payments left, it usually doesn't save that much money.

A \$5,000 car loan is to be paid off in 36 monthly installments of \$172. The borrower decides to pay off the loan after 24 payments have been made. Find the amount of interest saved by paying the loan off early. Use the rule of 78.

SOLUTION

Find the finance charge (i.e., total interest).

$172 \times 36 = \$6,192$ *\$172 × 36 payments*
$\$6,192 - \$5,000 = \$1,192$ *Total payments — Amount financed*

Substitute into the formula using $f = \$1,192$, $n = 36$, and $k = 36 - 24 = 12$.

$$u = \frac{fk(k+1)}{n(n+1)}$$
$$= \frac{1,192(12)(12+1)}{36(36+1)} = \frac{185,952}{1,332} \approx 139.60$$

By paying off the loan a year early, the borrower saved \$139.60.

▼ Try This One 5

A \$16,500 truck loan is to be paid off in 48 monthly installments of \$386.50. The borrower decides to pay off the loan after 40 payments have been made. Find the amount of interest saved. Use the rule of 78.

☑ 3. Compute unearned interest and payoff amount for a loan paid off early.

So far, we've covered examples of closed-ended credit; this is credit with a fixed number of payments and a specific payoff date. We turn our attention now to open-ended credit, where there is no fixed number of payments or payoff date. By far the most common example of this is credit cards. Since more and more people use credit cards for convenience, an understanding of open-ended credit is more important than ever.

480   **Chapter 8**   Consumer Math

The Unpaid Balance Method

With the **unpaid balance method**, interest is charged only on the balance from the previous month. Example 6 shows how to find the interest on the unpaid balance.

EXAMPLE 6   **Computing a Credit Card Finance Charge**

Math Note

The billing cycle for credit cards and loans can begin and end on any day of the month; however, for the examples given in this section, we will assume the cycle ends on the last day of the month.

For the month of April, Elliot had an unpaid balance of $356.75 at the beginning of the month and made purchases of $436.50. A payment of $200.00 was made during the month. The interest on the unpaid balance is 1.8% per month. Find the finance charge and the balance on May 1.

SOLUTION

Step 1 Find the finance charge on the unpaid balance using the simple interest formula with rate 1.8%.

$$I = Prt$$
$$= \$356.75 \times 0.018 \times 1 \quad \textit{1.8\% = 0.018}$$
$$= \$6.42 \text{ (rounded)}$$

The finance charge is $6.42.

(*Note:* since the interest rate is given per month, the time is always equal to 1 month.)

Step 2 To the unpaid balance, add the finance charge and the purchases for the month; then subtract the payment to get the new balance.

$$\text{New balance} = \$356.75 + \$6.42 + \$436.50 - \$200$$
$$= \$599.67$$

The new balance as of May 1 is $599.67.

▼ **Try This One 6**

For the month of January, Christina has an unpaid balance of $846.50 from December. Purchases for the month were $532.86 and a payment of $350.00 was made during the month. If the interest on the unpaid balance is 2% per month, find the finance charge and the balance on February 1.

☑ 4. Compute credit card finance charges using the unpaid balance method.

Average Daily Balance Method

Because a company that issues credit cards doesn't make as much money when users pay off the balance every month, they sometimes charge an annual fee for use of the card. Another way for them to make money from all users is to use the **average daily balance method** for computing the finance charge. In this method, the balance for each day of the month is used to compute an average daily balance, and interest is computed on that average. So in effect, consumers start paying interest on the day they make a purchase. Example 7 shows how to compute interest using this method.

Sidelight MONEY FOR NOTHING?

Since most credit card companies either use the unpaid balance method, or don't charge interest on new purchases, if you pay off the full balance each month, you never pay any interest. In essence, you're getting to use the bank's money for nothing! But don't shed any tears for the poor banks. They charge the merchant a fee for each transaction. Also, the freedom that comes from buying stuff and walking out the door without handing over any money makes it extremely difficult for people to spend only what they can afford, especially young people using credit cards for the first time. Consider the following statistics:

- 91% of college undergrads have at least one credit card.
- The average college senior will graduate with $4,100 in credit card debt in addition to any student loan debt.
- 58% of all credit card users carry a balance on their cards.
- Total credit card debt in the United States in 2011 was almost 900 *billion* dollars.
- The average credit card debt per borrower in 2011 was $5,100 and was rising, expected to reach $6,500 by 2013.

If you find yourself spending more than you can pay off, and having to keep a balance on your card, the best approach is probably the one pictured above.

EXAMPLE 7   Computing a Credit Card Finance Charge

Betty's credit card statement showed the following transactions during the month of August.

August 1	Previous balance	$165.50
August 7	Purchases	59.95
August 12	Purchases	23.75
August 18	Payment	75.00
August 24	Purchases	107.43

Find the average daily balance, the finance charge for the month, and the new balance on September 1. The interest rate is 1.5% per month on the average daily balance.

SOLUTION

Step 1 Find the balance as of each transaction.

August 1	$165.50
August 7	$165.50 + $59.95 = $225.45
August 12	$225.45 + $23.75 = $249.20
August 18	$249.20 − $75.00 = $174.20
August 24	$174.20 + $107.43 = $281.63

Step 2 Find the number of days for each balance.

Date	Balance	Days	Calculations
August 1	$165.50	6	$(7 - 1 = 6)$
August 7	$225.45	5	$(12 - 7 = 5)$
August 12	$249.20	6	$(18 - 12 = 6)$
August 18	$174.20	6	$(24 - 18 = 6)$
August 24	$281.63	8	$(31 - 24 + 1 = 8)$

Math Note

Since the transaction period starts on August 1 and ends on the last day of the month, which must be included, we had to add 1 to the last period of days in Step 2. The total number of days has to equal the number of days in the given month.

Step 3 Multiply each balance by the number of days, and add these products.

Date	Balance	Days	Calculations
August 1	$165.50	6	$165.50(6) = $993.00
August 7	$225.45	5	$225.45(5) = $1,127.25
August 12	$249.20	6	$249.20(6) = $1,495.20
August 18	$174.20	6	$174.20(6) = $1,045.20
August 24	$281.63	8	$281.63(8) = $2,253.04
		31	$6,913.69

Step 4 Divide the total by the number of days in the month to get the average daily balance.

$$\text{Average daily balance} = \frac{\$6,913.69}{31} \approx \$223.02$$

The average daily balance is $223.02.

Step 5 Find the finance charge. Multiply the average daily balance by the rate, which is 1.5%, or 0.015.

$$\text{Finance charge} = \$223.02 \times 0.015 \approx \$3.35$$

Step 6 Find the new balance. Add the finance charge to the balance as of the last transaction.

$$\text{New balance:} \quad \$281.63 + \$3.35 = \$284.98$$

The average daily balance is $223.02. The finance charge is $3.35, and the new balance is $284.98.

The procedure for finding the average daily balance is summarized next.

Procedure for the Average Daily Balance Method

Step 1 Find the balance as of each transaction.

Step 2 Find the number of days for each balance.

Step 3 Multiply the balances by the number of days and find the sum.

Step 4 Divide the sum by the number of days in the month.

Step 5 Find the finance charge (multiply the average daily balance by the monthly rate).

Step 6 Find the new balance (add the finance charge to the balance as of the last transaction).

▼ **Try This One 7**

5. Compute credit card finance charges using the average daily balance method.

A credit card statement for the month of November showed the following transactions.

November 1	Previous balance	$937.25
November 4	Purchases	$531.62
November 13	Payment	$400.00
November 20	Purchases	$89.95
November 28	Payment	$100.00

(a) Find the average daily balance.
(b) Find the finance charge. The interest rate is 1.9% per month on the average daily balance.
(c) Find the new balance on December 1.

It's definitely a good idea to check with your credit card company to see what method it uses for computing finance charges. If it uses average daily balance, you will end up paying interest even if you pay off the full amount each month. There's a lot of competition out there, so if that's the case, you can probably find another card with a better deal.

Each month when you get a credit card statement, there's a minimum payment that must be paid. Before 2003, these minimum payments had shrunk to the point that they didn't even cover the interest for the month, so if a cardholder paid just the minimum payment, the balance would continue to rise. In response to a public outcry, the federal government set new regulations in 2003 requiring credit card companies to set the minimum payment high enough that it covers the interest for the month, as well as part of the principal balance. (The exact minimum payment formula varies some from company to company.)

This is not to say that making minimum payments only is a good idea. If at all possible, you should always pay off the full amount each month. This is the only foolproof way to make sure that you don't get in the habit of spending more money than you can afford to. In Example 8, we'll look at how a credit card balance changes if only minimum payments are made.

EXAMPLE 8   Studying the Effect of Making Minimum Payments

Suppose you have a $2,300 balance on a credit card with an interest rate of 1.1% per month, and the minimum payment for any month is the amount of interest plus 1% of the principal balance. If you don't make any more purchases on that card and make the minimum payment for 6 months, how much will you pay down the balance?

SOLUTION

This sounds like we'll have to compute interest, but actually we won't since the minimum payment will cover the interest each month. In short, we'll be paying the interest each month plus 1% of the principal. So our balance will decrease by 1% each month.

Month 1: 1% of $2,300 = $23; new balance:
$$\$2,300 - \$23 = \$2,277$$

Month 2: 1% of $2,277 = $22.77; new balance:
$$\$2,277 - \$22.77 = \$2,254.23$$

Month 3: 1% of $2,254.23 = $22.54; new balance:
$$\$2,254.23 - \$22.54 = \$2,231.69$$

Month 4: 1% of $2,231.69 = $22.32; new balance:
$$\$2,231.69 - \$22.32 = \$2,209.37$$

Month 5: 1% of $2,209.37 = $22.09; new balance:
$$\$2,209.37 - \$22.09 = \$2,187.28$$

Month 6: 1% of $2,187.28 = $21.87; new balance:
$$\$2,187.28 - \$21.87 = \$2,165.41$$

> **Math Note**
>
> The terms of the credit card in Example 8 (1.1% interest per month, and a minimum payment equal to interest plus 1% of principal) represent industry averages in 2012.

So after 6 months, you would have paid off $2,300 − $2,165.41, or $134.59. If it seems like it would take you forever to pay off the full amount at that rate, you're pretty close. In Problems 63 and 64, we'll study some methods to simplify these calculations.

☑ 6. Study the effects of making minimum payments.

▼ Try This One 8

If the credit card company in Example 8 instead sets its minimum payment at interest plus 3% of the principal balance, how much more progress would you make after making minimum payments for 6 months?

Answers to Try This One

1. Amount financed, $7,200; total installment price, $10,720; finance charge, $2,520

2. (a) $1,299   (c) $2,278.40
   (b) $779.40   (d) $34.64

3. 8.0%

4. Unearned interest, $85.83; Payoff amount, $4,275.17

5. $62.82

6. Finance charge = $16.93; balance on Feb. 1 = $1,046.29

7. (a) $1,198.69
   (b) $22.78
   (c) $1,081.60

8. $249.57

EXERCISE SET 8-4

Writing Exercises

1. Explain what is meant by the term "installment loan."
2. What is a finance charge?
3. What is the difference between the purchase price of an item and the amount financed?
4. What is the difference between closed-ended credit and open-ended credit?
5. What is the annual percentage rate (APR) for a loan? Why is it typically different than the stated interest rate?
6. What is the difference between the unpaid balance method and the average daily balance method for computing interest? Which is better for the consumer?
7. How are minimum payments on credit cards calculated?
8. What's the difference between buying and leasing a car?

Applications in Our World

9. Mary Lee bought a stove for $460. She made a down payment of $60 and paid $42 a month for 10 months. Find the total installment price of the stove.
10. Martin Dennis bought a wide screen television for $1,720. He made a down payment of 15% and paid the balance over 18 months. The finance charge was 4% of the amount financed. Find the down payment and the installment price of the television and the monthly payment.
11. Joy Lansung bought a microwave oven for $375.00. She made a down payment of 15% and financed the rest for 12 months with payments of $27.25. Find the down payment and the total installment price of the oven.
12. Mary Scherer bought a wristwatch for $845.00. She made a down payment of $95.00 and financed the rest with six monthly payments of $128.75. Find the total installment price.
13. Hang Yo bought a treadmill for $925. He made a 20% down payment and financed the rest over 18 months. Find the monthly payment if the finance charge was 5% of the amount financed.
14. Stacie Howard bought a water softener for $550. She made a down payment of $75 and paid the balance off in 12 monthly payments. Find the monthly payment if the interest rate was 11%.

In Exercises 15–20, for the automotive loan, find the amount financed, the total installment price, and the finance charge.

15. Purchase price including taxes and fees: $14,295.41; down payment: $2,600; payments: $279.40 for 48 months.

16. Purchase price including taxes and fees: $22,152.37; down payment: $6,300; payments: $312.15 for 60 months.

17. Purchase price: $19,500; sales tax: 6.5%; license and title fees: $375; down payment: $3,500; payments: $390.25 for 60 months.

18. Purchase price: $6,052; sales tax: 8%; license and title fees: $260; down payment: $1,500; payments: $180.10 for 36 months.

19. Purchase price: $31,600; sales tax 5.5%; license and title fees: $410; money credited for trade-in (subtracted from price of vehicle before taxes): $12,400; payments: $471.22 for 48 months.

20. Purchase price: $20,600; sales tax 4.5%; license and title fees: $304; money credited for trade-in (subtracted from price of vehicle before taxes): $3,600; payments: $371.48 for 60 months.

21. Richard Johnston bought a 2014 GMC Terrain for $39,905. He made a down payment of $15,000 and paid $614 monthly for 4 years. Find the APR.

22. Jennifer Siegel bought a new Ford Focus for $14,400. She made a down payment of $4,000 and made monthly payments of $319 for 3 years. Find the APR.

23. Erin LaRochelle bought four comforter sets for $900. She made a down payment of $100 and paid off the balance in 12 monthly payments of $71.05. Find the APR.

24. Hector Rondón bought his wife a turquoise bracelet, earrings, and pendant for her birthday. He paid $1,125 for the set and had a down payment of $175. He paid the balance with 12 monthly payments of $84. Find the APR.

25. Matt Brawn bought a diamond engagement ring for $2,560. His down payment was $600, and he made 24 monthly payments of $90. Find the APR.

26. Mary Sinclair bought a preowned Corvette for $27,900.00. She made a down payment of $8,000.00 and financed the rest over 5 years with monthly payments of $389.50. Find the APR.

27. In Exercise 21, Richard was able to pay off his loan at the end of 30 months. Using the actuarial method, find the unearned interest and payoff amount.

28. In Exercise 22, Jennifer decided to pay off her loan at the end of 2 years. Using the actuarial method, find the unearned interest and payoff amount.

29. In Exercise 23, Erin decided to pay off her loan at the end of 6 months. Using the actuarial method, find the unearned interest and the payoff amount.

30. In Exercise 24, Hector was able to pay off his loan at the end of 6 months. Using the actuarial method, find the unearned interest and the payoff amount.

31. In Exercise 25, Matt was able to pay off his loan 6 months early. Using the actuarial method, find the unearned interest and the payoff amount.

32. In Exercise 26, Mary decided to pay off her loan 6 months early. Using the actuarial method, find the unearned interest and the payoff amount.

For Exercises 33–38, use the rule of 78.

33. A $4,200.00 loan is to be paid off in 36 monthly payments of $141.17. The borrower decides to pay off the loan after 20 payments have been made. Find the amount of interest saved.

34. Fred borrowed $150.00 for 1 year. His payments are $13.75 per month. If he decides to pay off the loan after 6 months, find the amount of interest that he will save.

35. Greentree Limousine Service borrowed $200.00 to repair a limousine. The loan was to be paid off in 18 monthly installments of $13.28. After a good season, they decide to pay off the loan early. If they pay off the loan after 10 payments, how much interest do they save?

36. Household Lighting Company borrowed $600 to purchase items from another store that was going out of business. The loan required 24 monthly payments of $29.50. After 18 payments were made, the company decided to pay off the loan. How much interest was saved?

37. Lydia needed to have her roof repaired. She borrowed $950 for 10 months. The monthly payments were $99.75 each. After seven payments, she decided to pay off the balance of the loan. How much interest did she save?

38. The owners of Scottdale Village Inn decided to remodel the dining room at a cost of $3,250. They borrowed the money for 1 year and repaid it in monthly payments of $292.50. After eight payments were made, the owners decided to pay off the loan. Find the interest saved.

39. Ticha is interested in a new Chevy Cruze and is given the option to lease or buy. If she buys, with a down payment of $4,000 the monthly payments will be $340.27 for 48 months. If she leases, with $1,000 up front, the monthly lease payment will be $199.
    (a) How much will Ticha pay total if she chooses the lease option?
    (b) How much more will she pay in the first 2 years if she chooses to buy instead?
    (c) Which option would you choose? Explain your answer.

40. Bui is checking out a Ford Explorer, which has a sticker price of $32,415. She's able to negotiate $3,000 off sticker price, and the tax rate is 6.5%.

License and title fees are $395. If she trades in her old minivan for $9,000 (deducted from the negotiated price before taxes), the monthly payment will be $500.95 for 60 months. She's also offered a lease with $2,900 down and payments of $429 for 36 months.

(a) How much will Bui pay total if she chooses the lease option?

(b) How much more will she pay in the first 3 years if she chooses to buy instead?

(c) How much interest will she pay if she buys?

(d) Which option would you choose? Explain your answer.

41. If the lender uses the rule of 78 rather than the actuarial method in Problem 27, does this benefit the borrower or the lender? What's the difference in unearned interest?

42. (a) If the lender uses the rule of 78 rather than the actuarial method in Problem 32, does this benefit the borrower or the lender? What's the difference in unearned interest?

(b) Based on Problems 41 and 42, which method for computing unearned interest appears to be better for the borrower? Does it matter how far from the end of the loan the payoff is made?

43. When the engine falls out of Rhonda's old car, it's time to shop for something newer. She is hoping to keep her monthly payment at $150, and the loan will be 6.2% simple interest.

(a) If Rhonda plans to make a down payment of $2,000 and finance her car for 48 months, what's the price of the most expensive car she can afford? (*Hint*: Let x = the price of the car and use the formulas on p. 474 and the simple interest formula to set up an equation.)

(b) How much does the highest price she can afford go up if she puts down $4,000?

44. Refer to Exercise 43. A salesman tries to convince Rhonda that she would be able to get a much better car if she raises the payment by just $30 per month.

(a) With her down payment of $2,000, how much higher is the maximum price she can shop for if she adds $30 to the monthly payment?

(b) How much more will Rhonda end up paying total if she goes with the $180 payment?

45. For the month of January, Juan had an unpaid balance on a credit card statement of $832.50 at the beginning of the month and made purchases of $675.00. A payment of $400.00 was made during the month. If the interest rate was 2% per month on the unpaid balance, find the finance charge and the new balance on February 1.

46. For the month of July, the unpaid balance on Sue's credit card statement was $1,131.63 at the beginning of the billing cycle. She made purchases of $512.58. She also made a payment of $750.00 during the month. If the interest rate was 1.75% per

month on the unpaid balance, determine the finance charge and the new balance on the first day of the August billing cycle.

47. Sam is redecorating his apartment. On the first day of his credit card billing cycle, his balance was $2,364.79. He has recently made purchases totaling $1,964.32. He was able to make a payment of $1,000.00 during this billing cycle. If his interest rate is 1.67% per month on the unpaid balance, what is the finance charge and what will Sam's new balance be on the first day of the next billing cycle?

48. Janine has recently accepted a position with an upscale clothing store. On the first day of her March credit card billing cycle, her unpaid balance was $678.34. She has made clothing purchases totaling $3,479.03. She was able to make one payment of $525.00 during the billing cycle. If the interest rate is 2.25% per month on the unpaid balance, find the finance charge and the new balance on the first day of the April billing cycle.

49. Joe's credit card statement on the first day of the May billing cycle shows a balance of $986.53. During this billing cycle, he charged $186.50 to his account and made a payment of $775.00. At 1.35% interest per month on the unpaid balance, what is the finance charge? Also, find the balance on the first day of the next billing cycle.

50. Frank's credit card statement shows a balance of $638.19 on the first day of the billing cycle. If he makes a payment of $475.00 and charges $317.98 during this billing period, what will his finance charge be (the interest rate is 1.50% of the unpaid balance per month)? What will his beginning balance be at the start of the next billing cycle?

51. Mary's credit card statement showed these transactions during September:

September 1	Previous balance	$627.75
September 10	Purchase	$87.95
September 15	Payment	$200.00
September 27	Purchases	$146.22

(a) Find the average daily balance.

(b) Find the finance charge for the month. The interest rate is 1.2% per month on the average daily balance.

(c) Find the new balance on October 1.

52. Pablo's credit card statement showed these transactions during March:

March 1	Previous balance	$2,162.56
March 3	Payment	$800.00
March 10	Purchases	$329.27
March 21	Payment	$500.00
March 29	Purchases	$197.26

(a) Find the average daily balance.

(b) Find the finance charge for the month. The interest rate is 2% per month on the average daily balance.

(c) Find the new balance on April 1.

53. Mike's credit card statement showed these transactions during the month of June:

June 1   Previous balance $157.95
June 5   Purchases $287.62
June 20   Payment $100.00

(a) Find the average daily balance.
(b) Find the finance charge for the month. The interest rate is 1.4% per month on the average daily balance.
(c) Find the new balance on July 1.

54. Charmaine's credit card statement showed these transactions during the month of December:

December 1   Previous balance $1,325.65
December 15   Purchases $287.62
December 16   Purchases $439.16
December 22   Payment $700.00

(a) Find the average daily balance.
(b) Find the finance charge for the month. The interest rate is 2% per month on the average daily balance.
(c) Find the new balance on January 1.

55. Ruth's credit card statement showed these transactions for the month of July:

July 1   Previous balance $65.00
July 2   Purchases $720.25
July 8   Payment $500.00
July 17   Payment $100.00
July 28   Purchases $343.97

(a) Find the average daily balance.
(b) Find the finance charge for the month. The interest rate is 1.1% per month.
(c) Find the new balance on August 1.

56. Tamera's credit card statement showed these transactions for the month of September:

September 1   Previous balance $50.00
September 13   Purchases $260.88

September 17   Payment $100.00
September 19   Purchases $324.15

(a) Find the average daily balance.
(b) Find the finance charge for the month. The interest rate is 1.9% per month on the average daily balance.
(c) Find the new balance on October 1.

57. Ellen has maxed out her credit card at $11,500 and vows not to make any other credit card purchases. Her credit card company charges 1.2% interest per month, and the minimum monthly payment is all interest due plus 2% of the principal balance. How much of the balance can Ellen pay down if she pays the minimum payment only for 4 months?

58. If you have $500 on a credit card at 1.4% per month, and the minimum payment is interest due plus 1% of the principal balance, what will the balance be after 6 months of payments?

59. (a) For the credit cards in Exercises 51, 53, and 55, find the new balance on the first of the month following the given purchases if the credit card company uses the unpaid balance method, rather than the average daily balance method. Assume that the monthly interest rate remains the same.
    (b) Calculate the difference in the amount each customer would owe with the two methods.
    (c) Under what circumstances does the unpaid balance method work out better for the consumer?

60. Repeat Exercise 59 parts (a) and (b) for the accounts in Exercises 52, 54, and 56. Does this help you draw any conclusions about when each method is better for the consumer?

Critical Thinking

We'll study student loans in depth in Section 8–5. Problems 61 and 62 provide a brief glimpse at some aspects of student loans.

61. In most cases, payments on student loans are deferred until the borrower graduates, although interest does get added to the principal while the student is in school. If Jaime takes out a student loan for $40,000 in 2012 at 4.5% simple interest and graduates in 4 years, find the monthly payment that would be required when he graduates if he plans to pay off the loan in 8 years after graduation.

62. Refer to Exercise 61. Rather than borrowing a lump sum at the beginning of college, Cheryl decides to borrow $10,000 each year at the beginning of the

school year. If these are treated as four individual loans at 4.5% simple interest, how much more or less would Cheryl owe at the end of four years compared to Jaime?

63. Find the principal on a loan at 8% for 4 years when the monthly payments are $100 per month.

64. A couple borrowed $800 for 1 year at 12% interest. Payments were made monthly. After eight payments were made, they decided to pay it off. Find the interest that was saved if it was computed equally over 12 months. Then find the interest saved using the rule of 78. Explain which is a better deal for the borrower.

65. In Example 8, we calculated the amount of progress that would be made in paying down a credit card

balance if only minimum payments are made. Since 1% of the balance will be paid off each month, 99% of the balance will remain. Use this fact to rework the calculations. How does it help?

66. Here's another approach to the calculation in Example 8. It's actually like a savings account with *negative* interest: instead of 1% of the amount being added each compounding period (month in this case), 1% is being *subtracted* from the amount. Use the compound interest formula with a principal balance of $2,300 and interest of -1% per month

compounded monthly for 6 months. How does the result compare to the calculations in Example 8?

67. Use the result of Problem 66 to find how many months it would take to reduce the balance to $500.

68. Use the result of Problem 66 to show that if the minimum monthly payments are always calculated the same way and the borrower never pays more than the minimum that the loan will technically never reach a zero balance. Then explain why that doesn't mean that realistically it won't ever be paid off.

Section 8-5 Student Loans and Home Buying

LEARNING OBJECTIVES

- ☐ 1. Compute the interest on a student loan.
- ☐ 2. Compute payments on a student loan.
- ☐ 3. Find a monthly mortgage payment using a payment table.
- ☐ 4. Find the total interest on a home loan.
- ☐ 5. Compare two mortgages with different lengths.
- ☐ 6. Find a monthly mortgage payment using a formula.
- ☐ 7. Make an amortization schedule for a home loan.

What do paying for college and paying for a home have in common? Simple: they both cost a LOT of money, which means the loans needed to obtain them tend to have much longer terms than loans for cars and other items. That alone makes them different from other types of loans, but there are other issues that make student loans and home loans worth studying separately.

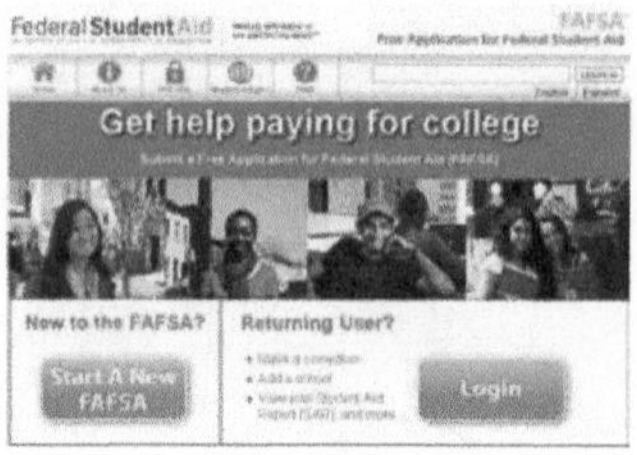

We'll begin with student loans, a topic of interest to more students today than ever before. In early 2012, fears arose that student loans would be the nexus of the next great financial crisis. An Associated Press story reported that for students in the class of 2010, average student loan debt at graduation for borrowers topped \$25,000, and total student loan debt was projected to pass a *trillion* dollars by the end of 2012. When it comes to credit card debt, the best advice is often "Don't." But that's not a viable option for college costs: as we pointed out in the chapter opener, the cost of NOT going to college is far more in the long run than the cost of attending.

That makes student loans a necessary evil for most folks, and if there's one common theme in this chapter, it's that understanding the nuances of the financial transactions you're likely to deal with makes you far less likely to end up in a bad situation.

There are three basic types of loans that most undergraduates might consider: federal loans made by the government, federal loans made by banks or other lenders but guaranteed by the government, and private loans. Every student's first choice should be the federal loans due to stability: the interest rates are fixed for the life of the loan and are regulated by congress, so you're unlikely to end up with a nasty surprise somewhere down the line. There are, however, limits on the amount that can be borrowed for one student through federal loan programs, and private loans might be the only alternative for an especially expensive education.

Other than the length of the loan, the big difference between student loans and other installment loans is that the payments are typically deferred until after graduation. This makes perfect sense, as in many cases students aren't working enough to make the money required to keep up with payments. So that's a pretty good deal. But it comes with a catch: in some cases, interest will accumulate on your loan while you're in school even though you're not making any payments. This can increase the principal balance considerably. The loan term can vary depending on the amount borrowed, but the standard term is 10 years, with payments deferred until 6 months after graduation.

Interest on student loans is simple interest: the interest accrues only on the principal balance, not on previously accrued interest. So while the student is still in school, the amount of interest that accrues each month remains constant. The interest is calculated using the simplified daily interest formula:

The Simplified Daily Interest Formula

$$\text{Annual interest} = \text{Principal balance} \times \text{interest rate}$$

$$\text{Daily interest amount} = \frac{\text{Principal balance} \times \text{interest rate}}{365.25}$$

$$\text{Monthly interest amount} = \text{Daily interest amount} \times \text{days in month}$$

EXAMPLE 1   Computing Interest on a Student Loan

If Sonia borrows \$6,500 to cover one-time college expenses in a federal student loan program at 6.8% interest:

(a) Find the monthly interest for 30- and 31-day months.
(b) How much interest will accrue while Sonia is still in school? Assume she starts school in August, graduates in May (3 years and 9 months later) and payments begin 6 months after graduation.

SOLUTION

(a) The daily interest is

$$\text{Daily interest} = \frac{\text{Balance} \times \text{interest}}{365.25} = \frac{\$6,500 \times 0.068}{365.25}$$
$$= \$1.21$$

In a 30-day month, the interest will be

$$30 \times \$1.21 = \$36.30$$

and in a 31-day month, it will be

$$31 \times \$1.21 = 37.51$$

(b) Interest will accrue for 4 years and 3 months. The 3 months are September, October, and November: two 30-day months, and one 31-day month. So the interest accrued is

$$4 \times \text{Balance} \times \text{rate} + 2(36.30) + 37.51$$
$$= 4(6,500)(0.068) + 72.60 + 37.51$$
$$= \$1,878.11$$

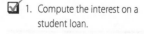

1. Compute the interest on a student loan.

▼ Try This One 1

Max borrows \$11,500 for her last 2 years of college, acquiring a federal student loan at 6.2% interest.

(a) Find the monthly interest for 30- and 31-day months.
(b) Find the amount of interest that accrues if she acquires the loan in August, graduates 2 years later, and payments begin 3 months later.

Math Note

The payment formula is very similar to the formula you would use to find the regular payments for an annuity. This makes sense because a loan of this nature is like a reverse annuity, where money is being paid down rather than accumulating. If the term isn't 10 years, the exponent is −12 times the number of years.

When interest is covered by the government while the borrower is still in school, a student loan is called **subsidized**. If interest is added to the principal while the borrower is in school the loan is called **unsubsidized**. For the loan in Example 1, the student would have saved $1,878.11 by acquiring a subsidized loan.

When monthly payments begin on a student loan, they're based on the principal balance at that point in time. These payments can be computed using the following formula:

Monthly Payments on a Student Loan

For a 10-year student loan with principal P and interest rate r (written as a decimal), the monthly payment R is given by

$$R = \frac{P \cdot \dfrac{r}{12}}{1 - \left(1 + \dfrac{r}{12}\right)^{-120}}$$

CAUTION   Obviously, the payment formula is pretty complicated. We will have to be extra careful in doing the calculations and take it in stages.

EXAMPLE 2   Finding the Monthly Payment on a Student Loan

Find the monthly payment on the loan in Example 1 if the term is 10 years.

SOLUTION

In Example 1, we found that the interest accrued before payments start is $1,878.11. Since the original loan amount was $6,500, the principal at the time payments begin is

$$\$6,500 + \$1,878.11 = \$8,378.11 = P$$

The interest rate is $r = 0.068$. Now we can find the payment:

Calculator Guide

The keystrokes for the final calculation in Example 2 are:

Standard Scientific Calculator

47.48 [÷] [(] 1 [−] 1.00566667

[yˣ] 120 [±] [)] [=]

Standard Graphing Calculator

47.48 [÷] [(] 1 [−] 1.00566667

[^] [(−)] 120 [)] [ENTER]

Like other interest formulas, the payment formula can be very sensitive to rounding.

$$R = \frac{P \cdot \dfrac{r}{12}}{1 - \left(1 + \dfrac{r}{12}\right)^{-120}}$$

$$R = \frac{8,378.11 \cdot \dfrac{0.068}{12}}{1 - \left(1 + \dfrac{0.068}{12}\right)^{-120}}$$ *Multiply in numerator*

$1 + \dfrac{0.068}{12} \approx 1.00566667$

$$= \frac{47.48}{1 - (1.00566667)^{-120}}$$ *See calculator guide.*

$$= \$96.42$$

▼ Try This One 2

Find the monthly payment on the loan in Try This One 1 if the term is ten years.

When interest on a student loan is not paid during college, we say that the interest is **capitalized**. As we've seen, when interest is capitalized, it adds to the principal balance, resulting in larger payments. When interest is not capitalized, payments must be made during college but only covering the amount of interest. Let's see how that would have affected the monthly payment on the loan in Example 2.

EXAMPLE 3   **Studying the Effects of Capitalizing Interest**

If interest on the loan in Examples 1 and 2 is not capitalized:

(a) Find the interest payment while Sonia is still in school.
(b) Find the payment on the loan when full payments begin.
(c) How much less would Sonia pay in total if she did not capitalize the interest?

SOLUTION

(a) We already did this in Example 1! The interest due each month will be the interest that accrues on the loan at the rate of $1.21 per day. So the student will owe that amount times the number of days in any given month.

(b) The principal remains $P = \$6,500$ since the interest is being paid while Sonia is still in school. The interest rate is $r = 0.068$.

$$R = \frac{P \cdot \dfrac{r}{12}}{1 - \left(1 + \dfrac{r}{12}\right)^{-120}}$$

$$R = \frac{\$6,500 \cdot \dfrac{0.068}{12}}{1 - \left(1 + \dfrac{0.068}{12}\right)^{-120}} = \$74.80$$

> **Math Note**
>
> When interest isn't capitalized, the payments can vary depending on what day of the month the payment is processed due to weekends or holidays, but it will always add up to the correct yearly amount.

(c) In Example 2, we found that when all interest is deferred, Sonia would make 120 payments of $96.42 for a total of $120 \times \$96.42 = \$11,570.40$. If the interest that accrued while Sonia was in school has already been paid, there would be 120 payments of $74.80, which totals $120 \times \$74.80 = \$8,976$. Adding the interest paid up front ($1,878.11), we get $10,854.11. By not capitalizing the interest, Sonia saved $\$11,570.40 - \$10,854.11 = \$716.29$ over the life of the loan.

☑ 2. Compute payments on a student loan.

▼ **Try This One 3**

If interest on the loan in Try This Ones 1 and 2 is not capitalized:

(a) Find the interest payment while Max is still in school.
(b) Find the payment on the loan when full payments begin.
(c) How much less would Max pay in total if she had not capitalized the interest?

Home Buying

For many people, the day they buy their first home is one of the proudest days of their life—and one of the scariest. There is nothing that compares to the feeling of looking at a house and knowing that it's all yours. But the buying process is tremendously intimidating. There are dozens of documents to sign, and the sheer numbers involved are enough to make almost everyone wonder if they're making a colossal mistake.

The most common home loans are paid over a 30-year span. That's a major commitment, and one that nobody should enter into without an understanding of the mathematics that go into the process. In the remainder of this section, we will study that math, hopefully helping you to become a well-informed home buyer.

Mortgages

A **mortgage** is a long-term loan where the lender has the right to seize the property purchased if the payments are not made. Homes are the most common items bought using mortgages. The most common mortgage term is 30 years, but they are widely available in terms from 15 to as many as 50 years.

There are several types of mortgages. A **fixed-rate mortgage** means that the rate of interest remains the same for the entire term of the loan. The payments (usually monthly) stay the same. An **adjustable-rate mortgage** means that the rate of interest may fluctuate (i.e., increase and decrease) during the period of the loan. Some lending institutions will allow you to make **graduated payments**. This means that even though the interest doesn't change for the period of the loan, you can make smaller payments in the first few years and larger payments at the end of the loan period.

Finding Monthly Payments and Total Interest

One way to find the monthly payments for a fixed-rate mortgage is to use a table like Table 8-2 below. The table displays the monthly payment required for each $1,000 of a mortgage.

TABLE 8-2	Monthly Payment per $1,000 of Mortgage (Includes Principal and Interest)

Math Note

The word "mortgage" comes from a combination of Old French words "mort" (dead) and "gage" (pledge). It is believed the intent was that the debtor pledged the property to secure the loan, and if he or she failed to pay, the property was taken, and was therefore "dead" to the debtor.

Rate (%)	Number of Years					
	15	20	25	30	35	40
3.5	$7.15	$5.80	$5.01	$4.49	$4.13	$3.87
4	7.40	6.06	5.28	4.77	4.43	4.18
4.5	7.65	6.33	5.56	5.07	4.73	4.50
5	7.91	6.60	5.85	5.37	5.05	4.82
5.5	8.17	6.88	6.14	5.68	5.37	5.16
6	8.44	7.16	6.44	6.00	5.70	5.50
6.5	8.71	7.46	6.75	6.32	6.04	5.85
7	8.99	7.75	7.07	6.65	6.39	6.21
7.5	9.27	8.06	7.39	6.99	6.74	6.58
8	9.56	8.36	7.72	7.34	7.10	6.95
8.5	9.85	8.68	8.05	7.69	7.47	7.33
9	10.14	9.00	8.39	8.05	7.84	7.71
9.5	10.44	9.32	8.74	8.41	8.22	8.10
10	10.75	9.65	9.09	8.78	8.60	8.49
10.5	11.05	9.98	9.44	9.15	8.98	8.89
11	11.37	10.32	9.80	9.52	9.37	9.28

Math Note

A Google search for the phrase "mortgage calculator" results in over 60 million hits! There are thousands of pages available that can be used to quickly calculate monthly payments on a mortgage.

But doing the calculations here will help you to become very familiar with the terms involved in mortgages.

In Example 4, we'll find the monthly payment on a mortgage using the table and the procedure that follows:

> **Procedure for Finding the Monthly Payment for a Fixed-Rate Mortgage**
>
> **Step 1** Find the down payment.
>
> **Step 2** Subtract the down payment from the cost of the home to find the principal of the mortgage.
>
> **Step 3** Divide the principal by 1,000.
>
> **Step 4** Find the number in the table that corresponds to the interest rate and the term of the mortgage.
>
> **Step 5** Multiply that number by the number obtained in Step 3 to get the monthly payment.

EXAMPLE 4   Finding Monthly Mortgage Payments

Math Note

You can reduce Steps 1 and 2 to a single calculation. In Example 4, a 20% down payment leaves 80% to be financed: 80% of $174,900 = $139,920.

The Petteys family plans to buy a home for $174,900, and has been offered a 30-year mortgage with a rate of 5.5% if they make a 20% down payment. What will the monthly payment be with this loan?

SOLUTION

Step 1 Find the down payment.

$$20\% \text{ of } \$174,900 = 0.20 \times \$174,900 = \$34,980$$

Step 2 Subtract the down payment from the cost of the home to get the principal.

$$\$174,900 - \$34,980 = \$139,920$$

Step 3 Divide by 1,000.

$$\frac{\$139,920}{1,000} = 139.92$$

Step 4 Find the value in Table 8-2 for a 30-year mortgage at 5.5%. It is $5.68.

Step 5 Multiply the value from Step 3, 139.92, by $5.68.

$$139.92 \times \$5.68 \approx \$794.75$$

The monthly payment is $794.75.

▼ **Try This One 4**

The Trissel family agreed on a price of $229,500 for a home. Their company credit union offers a 5.0% 20-year loan with 15% down. Calculate the monthly payment.

☑ 3. Find a monthly mortgage payment using a payment table.

It's an eye-opening experience to calculate the total interest on a mortgage. To do so, multiply the monthly payments by the total number of payments and then subtract the principal.

| EXAMPLE 5 | **Finding Total Interest on a Mortgage** |

Find the total amount of interest the Petteys family would pay if they take the loan in Example 4.

SOLUTION

On a 30-year mortgage, there are $30 \times 12 = 360$ payments. We found that the monthly payment would be $794.75.

$$794.75 \times 360 = \$286,110$$

This is the total of payments. We subtract the amount financed from Example 4:

$$\$286,110 - \$139,920 = \$146,190 \quad \textit{Interest on the loan.}$$

The interest paid exceeds the principal of the loan by over $6,000!

▼ Try This One 5

Find the total interest paid on the loan in Try This One 4.

Not surprisingly, the length of a loan has a profound effect on how much interest is paid. In the next example, we'll weigh the amount of extra monthly payment required versus the amount of interest saved.

Math Note

The long term of a home loan means you pay a LOT higher percentage of interest than on a shorter-term loan.

In January of 2012, the average loan on a new car in the United States was 4.73% for 5 years: with these terms, the interest on the loan amounts to about 12.5% of the amount borrowed.

For the 30-year mortgage in Example 5, the interest is 104.5% of the amount borrowed.

☑ 4. Find the total interest on a home loan.

| EXAMPLE 6 | **Comparing Mortgages with Different Terms** |

Suppose that the Petteys family from Examples 4 and 5 is also offered a 15-year mortgage with the same rate and down payment. Find the difference in monthly payment and interest paid between the 15- and 30-year mortgages.

SOLUTION

We essentially need to rework Examples 4 and 5 with a 15-year mortgage, then compare the results. Fortunately, some of the work we did carries over. We know that the principal is $139,920, and the principal divided by 1,000 is 139.92. This time we use the 15-year column and 5.5% row in Table 8-2 to get $8.17. Now we multiply that by 139.92:

$$139.92 \times \$8.17 \approx \$1,143.15 \quad \textit{Monthly payment with 15-year term.}$$

The difference in monthly payments is

$$\$1,143.15 - \$794.75 = \$348.40 \quad \textit{\$794.75 was payment for 30 years.}$$

With a monthly payment of $1,143.15 for 15 years (which is 180 months) the total payments are

$$\$1,143.15 \times 180 = \$205,767.00$$

and the interest paid is

$$\$205,767 - \$139,920 = \$65,847$$

Math Note

There is a series of costs associated with initiating a mortgage that add to the principal value of the loan. Known as **closing costs**, they averaged almost $2,800 nationally in 2012, but can vary dramatically from state to state.

These costs are added after the down payment is calculated as a percentage of selling price. When deciding on how much you can afford to pay for a house, it's important to find what the closing costs are.

Section 8-5   Student Loans and Home Buying   495

The interest paid on the 30-year mortgage was $146,190:

$$\$146{,}190 - \$65{,}847 = \$80{,}343$$

If the Petteys family can manage an extra $348.40 a month, they will save over $80,000 in interest!

▼ Try This One 6

If the Trissel family from Try This One 4 chooses a 15-year mortgage instead of 20, find the increase in monthly payment and total interest saved.

☑ 5. Compare two mortgages with different lengths.

There's a formula for computing monthly payments on a mortgage that can be used in place of Table 8-2. It can also be used for interest rates or terms not included in the table.

Formula for Computing Monthly Payments on a Mortgage

$$R = \frac{P\left(\dfrac{r}{n}\right)}{1 - \left(1 + \dfrac{r}{n}\right)^{-nt}}$$

R = regular monthly payment

P = amount financed, or principal

r = rate written as a decimal

n = number of payments per year

t = number of years

Math Note

The student loan payment formula on page 490 is a special case of this mortgage formula with $n = 12$ and $t = 10$.

Sidelight THE GREAT MORTGAGE CRISIS

Throughout much of the first decade of the 21st century, home-owners were very happy people. Housing prices were rising at an almost unprecedented rate, and people watched the value of their investment soar. New homes were being built everywhere you looked, and lending institutions were practically climbing over each other to hand out home loans.

Then a funny thing happened—the housing market got oversaturated and prices started to fall. At the same time, people who took adjustable-rate mortgages to buy larger houses had their rates go up and couldn't make their payments anymore. Foreclosures (when the lending institution takes back a home) started to rise, causing even more houses to go on the market. Soon, the whole house of cards came crashing down, taking the U.S. economy with it.

There is plenty of blame to go around, but put in its simplest terms, the blame is to be shared equally between home buyers and lenders. Millions of people bought homes they couldn't afford with adjustable-rate mortgages, and the lenders gave out loans to millions of people who couldn't afford

them. The result was an economic bust that cost 8.8 million American jobs before the job market bottomed out in February 2010. One lesson has been learned from this mess—lenders will be far less likely to put people in homes that they can't afford from now on.

| EXAMPLE 7 | **Finding a Monthly Payment Using the Formula** |

After one hit single, a young singer unwisely decides that she needs a $2.2 million dollar mansion. With some of the proceeds from her CD, she puts down $500,000, leaving $1,700,000 to finance at 6% for 30 years. Find her monthly payment.

SOLUTION

In the formula above, use $P = 1,700,000$, $r = 0.06$, $n = 12$, and $t = 30$.

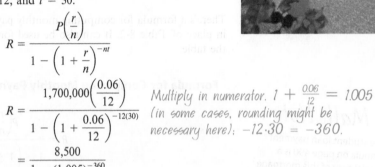

$$R = \frac{P\left(\dfrac{r}{n}\right)}{1 - \left(1 + \dfrac{r}{n}\right)^{-nt}}$$

$$R = \frac{1,700,000\left(\dfrac{0.06}{12}\right)}{1 - \left(1 + \dfrac{0.06}{12}\right)^{-12(30)}}$$ *Multiply in numerator.* $1 + \frac{0.06}{12} = 1.005$ *(in some cases, rounding might be necessary here);* $-12 \cdot 30 = -360$.

$$= \frac{8,500}{1 - (1.005)^{-360}}$$

$$\approx \$10,192.36$$

The monthly payment is $10,192.36, and the singer better hope her next CD does well, too.

▼ Try This One 7

☑ 6. Find a monthly mortgage payment using a formula.

Use the payment formula to find the monthly payment on the one-hit-wonder pop star's second house, a $120,000 mortgage at 5.2% for 15 years.

Computing an Amortization Schedule

After securing a mortgage, the lending institution will prepare an **amortization schedule**. This schedule shows what part of the monthly payment is paid on the principal and what part of the monthly payment is paid in interest.

In order to prepare an amortization schedule, the next procedure can be used.

Procedure for Computing an Amortization Schedule

Step 1   Find the interest for the first month. Use $I = Prt$, where $t = \frac{1}{12}$. Enter this value in a column labeled Interest.

Step 2   Subtract the interest from the monthly payment to get the amount paid on the principal. Enter this amount in a column labeled Payment on Principal.

Step 3   Subtract the amount of the payment on principal found in Step 2 from the principal to get the balance of the loan. Enter this in a column labeled Balance of Loan.

Step 4   Repeat the steps using the amount of the balance found in Step 3 for the new principal.

Math Note

Be sure to subtract any down payment from the cost of the home before beginning the amortization schedule.

| EXAMPLE 8 | Preparing an Amortization Schedule |

Compute the first two months of an amortization schedule for the loan in Example 4.

SOLUTION

> **Math Note**
>
> Preparing an amortization schedule makes it easy to see why more interest is paid earlier in a fixed installment loan, and more principal is paid later.

The value of the mortage is $139,920, the interest rate is 5.5%, and the monthly payment is $794.75.

Step 1 Find the interest for month 1.

$$I = Prt$$
$$= \$139{,}920 \times 0.055 \times \frac{1}{12}$$
$$= \$641.30$$

Enter this in a column labeled Interest.

Step 2 Subtract the interest from the monthly payment.

$$\$794.75 - \$641.30 = \$153.45$$

This goes into the Payment on Principal column.

Step 3 Subtract principal payment from principal.

$$\$139{,}920 - \$153.45 = \$139{,}766.55$$

This goes into the Balance of Loan column. Now we repeat Steps 1–3 using the balance of $139,766.55.

Step 4 $I = Prt$

$$= \$139{,}766.55 \times 0.055 \times \frac{1}{12}$$
$$= \$640.60$$

Step 5 $\$794.75 - \$640.60 = \$154.15$

Step 6 $\$139{,}766.55 - \$154.15 = \$139{,}612.40$

The first 2 months of the amortization schedule are:

Payment Number	Interest	Payment on Principal	Balance of Loan
1	$641.30	$153.45	$139,766.55
2	$640.60	$154.15	$139,612.40

☑ 7. Make an amortization schedule for a home loan.

▼ Try This One 8

Make an amortization schedule for the first 3 months for the loan in Try This One 4.

Answers to Try This One

1 (a) 30 day: $58.50; 31 day: $60.45
(b) $1,603.45

2 $146.79

3 (a) $1.95 times the number of days in the month
(b) $128.83 (c) $551.55

4 $1,287.50

5 $113,925

6 Increase in payment = $255.54;
interest saved = $31,252.80

7 $961.50

8

Payment Number	Interest	Payment on Principal	Balance of Loan
1	$812.81	$474.69	$194,600.31
2	$810.83	$476.67	$194,123.64
3	$808.85	$478.65	$193,644.99

EXERCISE SET 8-5

Writing Exercises

1. What's the difference between a subsidized and unsubsidized student loan?
2. What is the advantage of a federal student loan over private loans?
3. What does it mean to capitalize interest on a student loan?
4. What's the biggest difference between a student loan and a regular installment loan?
5. What specifically makes a loan a mortgage?
6. Explain how to find the total interest paid on a mortgage.
7. What are the advantages and disadvantages of getting a mortgage with a shorter term?
8. What is an amortization schedule?

Applications in Our World

For Problems 9–12, for the given student loan, find the interest that accrues in a 30-day month, then find the total amount of interest that will accrue before regular payments begin, again using 30-day months.

9. $7,200 at 6.8% interest; student graduates 3 years and 9 months after loan is acquired; payments deferred for 6 months after graduation
10. $11,500 at 6.8% interest; student graduates 2 years after loan is acquired; payments deferred for 3 months after graduation
11. $21,500 at 6.2% interest; student graduates 4 years after loan is acquired; payments deferred for 3 months after graduation
12. $16,500 at 6.2% interest; student graduates 1 year and 9 months after loan is acquired; payments deferred for 6 months after graduation

In Problems 13–16, find the monthly payment on the loans in Problems 9–12. Assume that the term of each loan is 10 years.

13. Monthly payment for Problem 9.
14. Monthly payment for Problem 10.
15. Monthly payment for Problem 11.
16. Monthly payment for Problem 12.
17. Mona takes out a $12,100 student loan to help pay for her first 2 years of college, then 2 years later needs another loan of $14,000 to get her through to graduation. She graduates 4 years and 9 months after acquiring the first loan, and payments are deferred until 6 months after graduation. The interest rate on both loans is 6.8%. Find the total amount of interest that will accrue until payments begin.
18. Huai takes out a $3,200 student loan at 6.8% to help him with 2 years of community college. After finishing

the 2 years, he transfers to a state university and borrows another $12,400 to defray expenses for the 5 semesters he needs to graduate. He graduates 4 years and 4 months after acquiring the first loan and payments are deferred for 3 months after graduation. The second loan was acquired 2 years after the first and had an interest rate of 7.2%. Find the total amount of interest that will accrue until payments begin.

19. Repeat Problem 17 if the first loan is subsidized and the second is not.

20. Repeat Problem 18 if the first loan is subsidized and the second is not.

21. Refer to Problem 17; find Mona's monthly payment when regular payments begin.

22. Refer to Problem 18; find Huai's monthly payment when regular payments begin.

23. Juanita takes out a federal unsubsidized loan for $13,100 with an interest rate of 6.8%, a term of 10 years, and payments deferred until 6 months after graduation. She decides not to capitalize the interest.
    (a) Find Juanita's monthly interest payment while in school. Assume a 30-day month.
    (b) What will her monthly payment be when payments begin? She graduates 5 years after acquiring the loan.
    (c) How much less will she pay over the life of the loan by not capitalizing the interest?

24. Ben takes out a federal unsubsidized loan for $9,275 with an interest rate of 6.2%, a term of 10 years, and payments deferred until 3 months after graduation. He decides not to capitalize the interest.
    (a) Find Ben's monthly interest payment while in school. Assume a 30-day month.
    (b) What will his monthly payment be when payments begin? He graduates 4 years after acquiring the loan.
    (c) How much less will he pay over the life of the loan by not capitalizing the interest?

In Problems 25 and 26, the interest is capitalized.

25. If you need to take out a $20,000 student loan 2 years before graduating, which loan option will result in the lowest overall cost to you: a subsidized loan with 6.8% interest for 10 years, a federal unsubsidized loan with 6.2% interest for 10 years, or a private loan with 6.0% interest and a term of 15 years? How much would you save over the other options? All payments are deferred for 6 months after graduation.

26. If you need to take out a $40,000 student loan 5 years before graduating, which loan option will result in the lowest overall cost to you: a subsidized loan with 7.0% interest for 10 years, a federal unsubsidized loan with 6.8% interest for 10 years, or a private loan with 6.5% interest and a term of 14 years? How much would you save over the other options? All payments are deferred for 6 months after graduation.

27. You receive a series of four annual federally subsidized loans to pay for 4 years of college, each for $7,100 at 6.8%. If you graduate 4 years and 6 months after acquiring the first loan, payments are deferred for 6 months after graduation, and the term is 10 years, find your monthly payment.

28. Pat receives a series of four annual federally subsidized student loans, each for $5,300 at 6.8%. To defray rising costs for her senior year, 3 years after acquiring the first loan she takes out a private student loan for $4,000 at 7.5% interest with a term of 10 years and capitalizes the interest for her last year of college. She graduates 9 months after getting the private loan. Payments on all loans are deferred until 6 months after graduation. Find her monthly payment.

Use Table 8-2 for Exercises 29–40.

29. A house sells for $145,000 and a 15% down payment is made. A mortgage was secured at 7% for 25 years.
    (a) Find the down payment.
    (b) Find the amount of the mortgage.
    (c) Find the monthly payment.
    (d) Find the total interest paid.

30. A house sells for $182,500 and a 5% down payment is made. A mortgage is secured at 7% for 15 years.
    (a) Find the down payment.
    (b) Find the amount of the mortgage.
    (c) Find the monthly payment.
    (d) Find the total interest paid.

31. A building sells for $200,000 and a 40% down payment is made. A 30-year mortgage at 6% is obtained.
    (a) Find the down payment.
    (b) Find the amount of the mortgage.
    (c) Find the monthly payment.
    (d) Find the total interest paid.

32. An ice cream store sells for $125,000 and a 12% down payment is made. A 25-year mortgage at 7.5% is obtained.
    (a) Find the down payment.
    (b) Find the amount of the mortgage.
    (c) Find the monthly payment.
    (d) Find the total interest paid.

33. An auto parts store sells for $325,000 and a 10% down payment is made. A 40-year mortgage at 7.5% is obtained, and closing costs are $3,200.
    (a) Find the down payment.
    (b) Find the amount of the mortgage.
    (c) Find the monthly payment.
    (d) Find the total interest paid.

34. A beauty shop sells for $175,000 and a 22% down payment is made. A 20-year mortgage at 6.5% is obtained, and closing costs are $2,700.
    (a) Find the down payment.
    (b) Find the amount of the mortgage.
    (c) Find the monthly payment.
    (d) Find the total interest paid.

500   **Chapter 8**   Consumer Math

35. A computer store sells for $1,200,000. The buyer made a 30% down payment and secured a 20-year mortgage on the balance at 5.5%.
    (a) Find the down payment.
    (b) Find the amount of the mortgage.
    (c) Find the monthly payment.
    (d) Find the total interest paid.

36. A grocery store sells for $550,000 and a 25% down payment is made. A 40-year mortgage at 6% is obtained.
    (a) Find the down payment.
    (b) Find the amount of the mortgage.
    (c) Find the monthly payment.
    (d) Find the total interest paid.

37. Find the monthly payment on the loan in Problem 29 if the term is reduced to 15 years. How much will be saved in total interest?

38. Find the monthly payment on the loan in Problem 30 if the term is increased to 30 years. How much extra interest will be paid?

39. The buyer of the store in Problem 33 is also offered a 30-year mortgage at 6.5%. How much would this option save him over the life of the loan?

40. The buyer of the beauty shop in Problem 34 is also offered a 15-year mortgage at 6.0%. How much would this save her over the life of the loan?

For Exercises 41–48, use the monthly payment formula on page 495.

41. A house is bought for $232,000 with a 15% down payment. A mortgage is secured at 6.75% for 20 years. Find the monthly payment.

42. A building sells for $330,000 with a down payment of 25%. Find the monthly payment on a 25-year mortgage at 5.3%.

43. A home is bought for $163,000 with a 12% down payment. Find the monthly payment if the mortgage is 6.75% for 18 years.

44. A house sells for $289,000. The buyer made a 20% down payment and financed the balance with a 5.75% loan for 15 years. Find the monthly payment.

45. A store was bought for $725,000 and the buyer made a 10% down payment. The balance was financed with a 6.35% loan for 27 years. Find the monthly payment.

46. A house was bought for $162,000.00 with a 5% down payment. The balance was financed at 5.6% for 18 years. Find the monthly payment.

47. A pizza parlor was bought for $327,000 with no down payment and a 6.7% loan for 10 years. Find the monthly payment.

48. A supermarket building was bought for $375,000. The down payment was 10%. The balance was financed at 7.2% for 15 years. Find the monthly payment.

49. Compute an amortization schedule for the first 3 months for the loan in Exercise 29 of this section.

50. Compute an amortization schedule for the first 3 months for the loan in Exercise 30 of this section.

51. Compute an amortization schedule for the first 3 months for the loan in Exercise 35 of this section.

52. Compute an amortization schedule for the first 3 months for the loan in Exercise 36 of this section.

A young couple has saved up $14,000 for a down payment on a home. They are currently paying $1,300 per month to rent a condo. Use this information in Exercises 53–56.

53. The couple is preapproved for a 30-year mortgage at 4.9%, and their realtor estimates that they will need to set aside $3,000 for closing costs at the time of sale. What is the price of the most expensive home they can buy without raising their monthly housing payment?

54. If the couple instead opts for a 15-year mortgage at 4.2%, how much is the most expensive home they can buy?

55. If the couple were to borrow the maximum amount you found in Exercises 53 and 54, how much more do you think they would pay in interest with the 30-year mortgage? Make a guess, then calculate the exact amount.

56. If the couple decides that they can afford to go up to $1,500 per month, how much more can they afford to spend on a home for each loan option?

Critical Thinking

57. You decide to buy a $180,000 home. If you make a 25% down payment, you can get a 20-year mortgage at 9%, but if you make a 10% down payment, you can get a 25-year mortgage at 7%. Which is the better option for you?

58. Which mortgage would cost you less, a 30-year mortgage at 6.5% or a 15-year mortgage at 10%?

59. Find the total amount of interest paid on the student loan in Problem 23(b), and the total amount of

interest paid on the mortgage in Problem 29. What percentage of the amount borrowed is the interest in each case?

60. Find the total amount of interest paid on the loan in Problem 37, then the percentage this represents of the amount borrowed. How does this compare to the percentages you found in Problem 59? What can you conclude?

Section 8-6   Investing in Stocks and Bonds

LEARNING OBJECTIVES

☐ 1. Find information from a stock listing.

☐ 2. Compute the P/E ratio for a stock.

☐ 3. Compute the total cost of a stock purchase.

☐ 4. Compute the profit or loss from a stock sale.

☐ 5. Compute profit from a bond sale.

We have seen that the magic of compound interest allows your money to grow considerably over long periods of time. However, interest rates on basic savings accounts are usually quite low, so if you rely on savings alone to build a nest egg, you better hope that you live a very, very long life indeed. Most successful investors grow their money much more quickly using the stock market. In this section, we'll learn about the basics of stocks and bonds, and how to get information about the performance of stocks that you might be interested in.

When a company files legal papers to become a corporation, it is able to issue **stock**. If an investor purchases shares of stock, he or she becomes a part owner of the company; for example, if a company issues 1,000 shares of stock and an investor buys 250 shares, then the investor owns one-quarter of the company. The investor is called a **shareholder**.

When a company makes money, it can choose to distribute part of the profit to its shareholders. This money is called a **dividend**. The stockholder receives a sum of money based on the number of shares of the stock that he or she owns. Sometimes if a company doesn't make a profit or its owners or managers decide to reinvest the money into the company, no dividends are paid.

Besides issuing stock, a company can also issue **bonds**. Usually bonds are issued to raise money for the company for start-up costs or special projects. A person who purchases a bond is really lending money to the company. The company, in turn, repays the owner of the bond its **face value** plus interest. As a general rule, bonds are a safer investment than stocks, but stocks have greater growth potential.

Stocks can be bought and sold on a **stock exchange**. The price of a stock varies from day to day (even from minute to minute) depending on the amount that investors are willing to pay for it. This can be affected by the profitability of the company, the economy, scandals, even global political concerns. Investors buy or sell stock through a **stockbroker**. Traditionally, this was an individual working for a brokerage firm, but it has become common for people to use online brokers, in which the investor initiates the buying and selling of stocks. In either case, the brokerage charges a fee, called a **commission**, for the service of having their representatives buy or sell the stock at an exchange. Bonds can also be bought and sold like stock.

Investors often own a combination of stocks and bonds. The set of all stocks and bonds owned is called an investor's **portfolio**. Sometimes a group of investors hire a manager to handle their investments. The manager invests in stocks and bonds, follows the activities of companies, and buys and sells in an attempt to achieve maximum profit for the group. This type of investment is called a **mutual fund**.

Stocks

In order to get information about a certain stock, you can refer to a stock table. These tables can be found in newspapers and online financial sites. The listings vary somewhat depending on the source. In this case, a stock listing for a company called Computer Programming and Systems, Inc. will be used as an example.

| 52 weeks | | | | | | | | |
HI	LO	STOCK	DIV	YLD%	P/E	VOL (1,000s)	CLOSE	NET CHG
31.00	17.07	CPSI	1.44	6.5%	16.8	1,244	22.25	+0.40

The first two columns give the highest and lowest selling prices for one share of stock in this company during the past 52 weeks. In this case, they are $31.00 and $17.07 respectively. The column labeled STOCK contains the letters CPSI. This is the symbol the company uses for trading. The column labeled DIV is the dividend per share that was paid to shareholders last year. In this case, it was $1.44 per share. The column labeled YLD% is the annual percentage yield: this is the dividend per share divided by the current price. In this case, it's 6.5%. This percent can be compared to other stocks as a measure of performance. The P/E column is the price-to-earnings ratio. It is the ratio of yesterday's closing price of the stock (found in the CLOSE column) to its annual earnings per share. In this case, the closing price of the stock, $22.25, is a bit less than 17 times the annual earnings per share. This concept will be explained in more detail after the first example.

The column labeled VOL (1,000s) means the number of shares in thousands that were traded yesterday. In this case, 1,244 × 1,000 = 1,244,000 shares were traded as of closing time. The column labeled NET CHG is the change in the price of the stock between the day before yesterday and yesterday at closing time. In this case, the value of the stock increased $0.40. This tells us that the value of the stock the day before yesterday was $22.25 − $0.40 = $21.85. Since the net change was positive, a + appears in the column. When . . . appears in this column, it means that there is no change.

EXAMPLE 1   Reading a Stock Listing

The following is a stock listing for the Terex Corporation. Use the listing to answer the questions.

| 52 weeks | | | | | | | | |
HI	LO	STOCK	DIV	YLD%	P/E	VOL (1,000s)	CLOSE	NET CHG
35	20.97	TEX	0.24	1.0	25	7,143	24.51	−0.06

(a) What was the highest price that the stock sold for during the past 52 weeks?
(b) What was the lowest price that the stock sold for during the past 52 weeks?
(c) What was the amount of the dividend per share that TEX paid last year?
(d) If you owned 250 shares of stock, how much did you make in dividends last year?
(e) How many shares were traded yesterday?
(f) What was the closing price per share the day before yesterday?

SOLUTION

(a) $35.00 *Found in the "HI" column.*
(b) $20.97 *Found in the "LO" column.*
(c) $0.24 *Found in the DIV column.*
(d) 250 × $0.24 = $60 *$0.24 dividend per share x 250 shares.*
(e) 7,143 × 1,000 = 7,143,000 *Number in VOL column x 1,000.*
(f) $24.51 + 0.06 = $24.57 *Closing price of $24.51 is 0.06 below previous day.*

☑ 1. Find information from a stock listing.

▼ Try This One 1

The following is a stock listing for Wabtec Corporation. Use the listing to answer the questions.

| 52 weeks | | | | | | | | |
HI	LO	STOCK	DIV	YLD%	P/E	VOL (1,000s)	CLOSE	NET CHG
82.90	49.38	WAB	0.04	0.2%	18	343	69.04	+0.38

(a) What was the highest price that the stock sold for during the past 52 weeks?

(b) What was the lowest price that the stock sold for during the past 52 weeks?

(c) What was the amount of the dividend per share that Wabtec paid last year?

(d) If you owned 432 shares of stock, how much did you make in dividends last year?

(e) How many shares were traded yesterday?

(f) What was the closing price per share the day before yesterday?

CAUTION

When finding the number of shares traded, don't forget to multiply by the units given for VOL in the table. In Example 1, it is thousands.

P/E Ratio

The P/E ratio of a stock is a comparison of the current selling price to the company's earnings per share.

Math Note

The abbreviation P/E is used to remind you that this is a ratio of Price to Earnings.

Formula for the P/E ratio

$$\text{P/E ratio} = \frac{\text{Yesterday's closing price}}{\text{Annual earnings per share}}$$

The annual earnings per share is found by dividing a company's total earnings by the number of shares that are owned by the stockholders for the last year. The annual earnings per share for a stock is found by subtracting expenses, taxes, losses, etc. from the gross revenues. These figures can be found in a company's annual reports.

EXAMPLE 2   **Computing a P/E Ratio**

If the annual earnings per share for Terex is $0.98, find the P/E ratio.

SOLUTION

$$\text{P/E ratio} = \frac{\text{Yesterday's closing price}}{\text{Annual earnings per share}} \quad \textit{Closing price from Example 1.}$$

$$= \frac{\$24.51}{\$0.98} = 25 \text{ (rounded)}$$

▼ **Try This One 2**

2. Compute the P/E ratio for a stock.

The most recent annual earnings per share for Wabtec, the company in Try This One 1, was $2.62. Find the updated P/E ratio for Wabtec.

Our answer to Example 2 means that the price of a share of stock is 25 times the company's annual earnings per share. If you divide $1.00 by the P/E ratio 25, you get 0.04, which means that for every dollar you invest in the company by purchasing its stock, the company makes 4¢. This however, does not mean that the company pays a dividend of 4¢. The dividends paid are determined by the board of directors of the company, and they may want to use some of the profits for other purposes, such as expansion.

Another way of looking at the P/E ratio is that you are paying the company $1.00 so it can earn 4¢. Now if the P/E ratio for another company's stock is 20, then $1.00 ÷ 20 = 5¢. This means that you are paying the company $1.00 so that it can earn 5¢. Based strictly on price and earnings, the investment in the second company is better. So in general, the lower the P/E ratio is, the better the investment, but there are many other factors to consider. Also remember that since the price of a company's stock is constantly changing, the P/E ratio also changes.

Knowing the price per share of stock and the P/E ratio, you can find the annual earnings per share for the last 12 months by using the following formula:

> ### *Math Note*
> This formula is obtained from solving the P/E ratio formula for earnings.

Formula for Annual Earnings per Share

$$\text{Annual earnings per share} = \frac{\text{Yesterday's closing price}}{\text{P/E ratio}}$$

EXAMPLE 3   Computing Annual Earnings per Share

> ### *Math Note*
> If you're a bargain shopper, you'll want to keep an eye on the P/E ratio when looking to buy stocks. A low P/E ratio typically indicates that a stock is currently selling at a bargain price.

If the closing price for Kellogg's stock was $44.23 and the P/E ratio is 15, find the annual earnings per share for last year.

SOLUTION

$$\begin{aligned}\text{Annual earnings per share} &= \frac{\text{Yesterday's closing price}}{\text{P/E ratio}} \\ &= \frac{\$44.23}{15} \approx \$2.95\end{aligned}$$

The annual earnings per share for Kellogg's was $2.95.

▼ Try This One 3

Find the annual earnings per share for Pepsico if yesterday's closing price was $62.43 and the P/E ratio is 8.6.

The current yield for a stock can be calculated by using the following formula:

Formula for Current Yield for a Stock

$$\text{Current stock yield} = \frac{\text{Annual dividend per share}}{\text{Closing price of stock}}$$

EXAMPLE 4   Computing Yield for a Stock

For the CPSI stock from page 501, the annual percent yield is 6.5%. Verify the current yield by using the preceding formula.

SOLUTION

The dividend per share is $1.44 and the closing price is $22.25:

$$\begin{aligned}\text{Current yield} &= \frac{\text{Annual dividend per share}}{\text{Closing price of stock}} \\ &= \frac{\$1.44}{\$22.25} = 0.065 \text{ (rounded)} = 6.5\%\end{aligned}$$

After rounding, the figure agrees with the 6.5% shown in the listing.

▼ Try This One 4

Find the current yield for a stock if the annual dividend per share is $1.51 and the closing price of the stock is $30.15.

There are two ways to make money from stocks: buy shares of a stock that pays dividends, or buy stock at a low price and sell it at a higher price. But of course, you can't just go buy stock at the corner store—you need to use a brokerage firm, placing an order which is then carried out by representatives at the stock exchange. In exchange for that service, the broker charges a commission, which varies among brokers. Brokers can also make recommendations concerning what stocks to buy and sell, which further justifies their commissions.

The amount that an investor receives from the sale of a stock is called the **proceeds**. The proceeds are equal to the amount of the sale minus the broker's commission. The next two examples illustrate the buying and selling of stocks.

EXAMPLE 5 Finding the Total Cost of Buying Stock

Shares of Apple Computer (AAPL) closed at $12.89 on April 1, 2004. Suppose that an investor bought 600 shares at that price using a broker that charged a 2% commission. Find the amount of commission and the total cost to the investor.

SOLUTION

Step 1 Find the purchase price.

$$600 \text{ shares} \times \$12.89 = \$7,734.00$$

Step 2 Find the broker's commission.

$$2\% \text{ of purchase price} = 0.02 \times \$7,734.00$$
$$= \$154.68$$

Step 3 Add the commission to the purchase price.

$$\$7,734.00 + \$154.68 = \$7,888.68$$

The investor paid a total of $7,888.68 for the transaction.

▼ Try This One 5

☑ 3. Compute the total cost of a stock purchase.

Apple closed at $38.45 on January 3, 2005. If 250 shares were bought at that price through a broker with a 1.6% commission, find the commission and total cost to the investor.

EXAMPLE 6 Finding the Amount Made from Selling Stock

On April 9, 2012, shares of Apple stock reached $530.38. If the investor in Example 5 sold all of his Apple stock at that point, and the broker also charges a 2% commission on sales, find the commission, proceeds, and the amount of profit made by the investor.

> *Math Note*
>
> Stockbrokers charge commission for both buying and selling your stock, so you end up paying on both ends when investing in stock.

SOLUTION

Step 1 Find the total amount of the sale.

$$600 \text{ shares} \times \$530.38 = \$318,228.00$$

Step 2 Find the commission.

$$2\% \text{ of } \$318,228.00 = 0.02 \times \$318,228.00 = \$6,364.56$$

Step 3 Subtract the commission amount from the total amount of the sale to get the proceeds.

$$\$318,228.00 - \$6,364.56 = \$311,863.44$$

Step 4 The profit is the proceeds minus the total cost from Example 5.

$$\$113,037.12 - \$7,888.68 = \$303,974.76$$

☑ 4. Compute the profit or loss from a stock sale.

▼ Try This One 6

When Apple founder Steve Jobs died in October 2011, the company's stock saw a temporary dip, falling to $369.80 on October 7. If the investor in Try This One 5 sold all of his Apple stock that day, and the broker charges 1.6% for sales, find the commission, proceeds, and profit made.

Bonds

When an investor buys bonds, the investor is actually loaning money to the company or government entity that issues the bonds. In exchange for lending that money, the investor will receive a fixed return on his or her investment for a given period of time. The ending value of the bond, is called the **face value**; this is typically $1,000, but can vary. Bonds also have a **maturity date**, which is the date that the interest is paid. In some cases, no interest is paid until the maturity date, at which time the full amount of interest is paid. **Coupon bonds**, on the other hand, pay an annual or semi-annual interest payment, known as a **coupon**.

You can think of it this way: if someone offers to sell you a $20 bill for $15, that's a pretty darn good deal. But the catch is that you don't get the $20 until some predetermined time later down the road. That's what a bond is; it's actually pretty simple.

But here's where it can get more interesting. Suppose that you get tired of waiting for the time when you get that $20 bill, and you sell the bond to your neighbor for $18. You've made $3 on your investment and you're done. Your neighbor now waits until the maturity date, cashes in the bond, and made the other $2 of the original $5 in profit. This is how bonds are bought and sold on the open market. Of course, your neighbor wouldn't pay more than $20 for a bond with a maturity value of $20. But if you were desperate for cash, you might be compelled to unload the bond for less than the $15 you originally paid. You've taken a loss, but at least you got some money out at the time you needed it.

Investors buy bonds for two main reasons. First, they're much safer investments than stocks, even though they have much less opportunity for a big profit. The interest is guaranteed, as long as the company that issued the bond stays in business and has the money to pay its debts. This makes bonds a safe, but not guaranteed, investment. Second, bonds are used to offset losses on stocks when the economy is in a down cycle, because the value of bonds tends to go up when the value of stocks go down.

Here's a short version of why that makes sense: in our earlier hypothetical example where you're making a $5 profit for waiting to cash in your bond, if the economy is booming in the meantime, prices in general will tend to go up, so the $5 you're getting at some point in the future has less buying power than the $5 you were expecting when you made the investment. This makes the bond in effect worth less. The opposite is also true: if the economy fizzles after you buy that bond, the $5 you eventually get will in effect be worth more than the $5 you thought you were getting, so the bond is worth more. Stocks tend to rise when the economy is doing well and fall when it's not, so the value of bonds usually goes in the opposite direction of the stock market. We'll study bond trading in Example 7.

EXAMPLE 7　Finding the Profit on a Bond Trade

Ellen buys a bond with face value $1,000 that was originally issued 30 months ago. The maturity date is 4 years from the time it was issued, and the interest rate is 4% simple interest per year. If she pays $820 for the bond and keeps it until the maturity date, what is her profit? What percent return does she get per year?

SOLUTION

With 4% simple interest, we can use the simple interest formula to find the value of the bond at maturity.

$$I = Prt = 1{,}000(0.04)(4) = \$160$$

After drawing $160 in interest, the value of the bond will be $1,160, so if Ellen paid $820, her profit is $1,160 − $820 = $340.

Her overall percent return is

$$\frac{\$340}{\$820} = 41.5\%$$

and she'll need to wait 18 months, or 1.5 years to cash in the bond, for a return of

$$\frac{41.5\%}{1.5} = 27.7\% \text{ per year.}$$

Ellen's pretty smart.

 5. Compute profit from a bond sale.

▼ Try This One 7

Rashard bought four bonds with face values of $1,000 each, simple interest rate of 5.8% per year, and a maturity date 10 years after they were issued. He paid $4,725 three years after the bonds were issued. If he keeps the bonds until maturity, find his total profit, and his percent return per year.

Mutual Funds

Many times investors purchase a group of stocks and bonds called a **mutual fund**. Mutual funds are managed by professional managers and include money from other investors. The manager follows the markets and makes the decisions of when to buy or sell the stocks and bonds. Mutual funds usually consist of a large number of relatively small investments in companies. This way, if a single stock doesn't perform well, only a small amount of money is lost. Sometimes mutual funds can be high return but also high risk.

Ratings for mutual funds can be found on most financial websites, and in business publications like the *Wall Street Journal*. They are rated either from A to F, or from 5 to 1, with 5 being the best. Often, two separate ratings are given. An overall rating compares the fund to all other stock funds. A category rating compares a fund to other funds that have similar holdings. For example, there are funds that invest strictly in smaller businesses, and it makes sense to compare those funds to others like them, as well as to the market as a whole.

Answers to Try This One

1 (a) $82.90
    (b) $49.38
    (c) $0.04
    (d) $17.28
    (e) 343,000
    (f) $68.66

2 26.4 (rounded)

3 $7.26

4 5.0%

5 Commission = $153.80, total cost = $9,766.30

6 Commission = $1,479.20, proceeds = $90,970.80, profit = $81,204.50

7 $1,595; 4.8% per year

EXERCISE SET 8-6

Writing Exercises

1. Explain in your own words what stock is.
2. What's the difference between stocks and bonds?
3. What is a mutual fund?
4. What is meant by the term P/E ratio?
5. What does a stockbroker do?
6. When selling stock, what's the difference between sale price, proceeds, and profit or loss?

7. Explain why the price of bonds tends to go up when the price of stocks goes down.
8. Why would an investor sell a bond for less than he paid for it?
9. If a bond is issued by a private company, is the investor guaranteed to make a profit? Why or why not?
10. If bonds are safer investments than stocks, why do more people invest in the stock market?

Applications in Our World

Use the following information about Sunoco stock for Exercises 11–20.

52 weeks								
HI	LO	STOCK	DIV	YLD%	P/E	VOL (1,000s)	CLOSE	NET CHG
97.25	57.50	SUN	1.23	1.6	7	4,626	62.06	+0.77

11. What is the highest price that the stock sold for during the last 52 weeks?
12. What was the lowest price that the stock sold for during the last 52 weeks?
13. What was the amount of the dividend per share that the company paid last year?
14. If you own 175 shares, how much in dividends did you make last lear?
15. How many shares were traded yesterday?
16. What was the closing price of the stock yesterday?

17. Find the annual earnings per share.
18. If you purchase 480 shares of Sunoco stock at $62.06 per share and the broker's commission is 1.5%, find the total cost of the purchase.
19. If an investor had 623 shares of Sunoco stock last year and the dividend per share was $1.23 last year, how much did the investor receive?
20. What was the closing price per share of stock the day before yesterday?

Use the following information about Wabtec stock for Exercises 21–30.

52 weeks								
							VOL	NET
HI	LO	STOCK	DIV	YLD%	P/E	(1,000s)	CLOSE	CHG
40.08	24.75	WAB	0.04	0.1	20	345	29.79	+0.39

21. What was the highest price that the stock sold for during the last 52 weeks?
22. What was the lowest price that the stock sold for during the last 52 weeks?
23. What was the amount of the dividend per share that the company paid last year?
24. If you own 357 shares, how much in dividends did you make last year?
25. How many shares were traded yesterday?
26. What was the closing price of the stock yesterday?

27. Find the annual earnings per share.
28. If you purchase 1,247 shares of stock at the closing price and the broker's commission is 2.6%, find the total cost of the purchase.
29. If an investor owned 1,562 shares of Wabtec and the dividend per share was $0.10, how much income did the investor receive?
30. What was the closing price of the stock the day before yesterday?

Use the following information about Wal-Mart stock for Exercises 31–40.

52 weeks								
							VOL	NET
HI	LO	STOCK	DIV	YLD%	P/E	(1,000s)	CLOSE	CHG
50.87	42.31	WMT	0.67	1.4	19	9,662	48.12	-0.10

31. What was the highest price that the stock sold for during the last 52 weeks?
32. What was the lowest price that the stock sold for during the last 52 weeks?
33. What was the amount of the dividend per share that the company paid last year?
34. If you own 682 shares, how much in dividends did you make last year?
35. How many shares were traded yesterday?
36. What was the closing price of the stock yesterday?
37. Find the annual earnings per share.
38. If you purchase 842 shares of Wal-Mart stock at $52.67 per share and the broker's commission is 2%, find the total cost of the purchase.
39. If an investor had 1,225 shares of Wal-Mart stock and the dividend per share was $0.67 last year, how much did the investor make?
40. What was the closing price of the stock the day before yesterday?
41. If the closing price of a stock is $21.92 and the annual earnings per share is $0.88, find the P/E ratio.
42. If the closing price of a stock is $6.65 and the annual earnings per share is $0.35, find the P/E ratio.
43. If the closing price of a stock is $24.19 and the annual earnings per share is $1.61, find the P/E ratio.
44. If the closing price of annual DirecTV stock is $20.18 and the annual earnings per share is $1.06, find the P/E ratio.
45. If the closing price of Gaither stock is $18.53 and the P/E ratio is 55, find the annual earnings per share.
46. If the closing price of Jacob Energy is $75.66 and the P/E ratio is 25, find the annual earnings per share.
47. If the closing price of Marine Max is $25.76 and the P/E ratio is 13, find the annual earnings per share.

48. If the closing price of Omnicare is $43.73 and the P/E ratio is 30, find the annual earnings per share.
49. An investor purchased 800 shares of stock for $63.25 per share and sold them later for $65.28 per share. The broker's commission was 2% of the purchase price and 2% of the selling price. Find the amount the investor made or lost on the stock.
50. An investor purchased 200 shares of a stock at $93.75 per share and sold it later at $89.50 per share. The broker's commission on the purchase and sale of the stock is 2.5%. Find the amount of money the investor made or lost on the sale.
51. An investor purchased 550 shares of stock at $51.60 per share. She later sold it at $49.70. The broker's commission on the purchase was 2% and 1.5% on the sale. Find the amount of money the investor made or lost on the stock.
52. An investor purchased 670 shares of a stock at $73.20 per share. Then he sold the stock at $82.35. If the broker's commission was 2.5% on the purchase and sale of the stocks, how much money did the investor make or lose on the transaction?
53. Some companies pay an annual dividend to stockholders, while others choose to instead invest that money back into the company. Suppose that you buy 500 shares of stock at $22 in a company that pays an annual dividend of $1.70 per share, then sell all of your shares at $38 three years later. Your best friend buys 500 shares of stock at $20 in a company that doesn't pay dividends, and sells it at $38 three years later. Which of you will make more money? By how much? (You can ignore commissions on the sales.)
54. Suppose that the investor in Examples 5 and 6 of Section 8-6 had used an online brokerage that charges a flat

fee of $39.95 for all trades, rather than a percentage of the sale. How much greater would her profit have been?

55. Shares of stock in the Ford Motor Company reached a low of $1.43 on November 10, 2008. One year later, the stock closed at $8.41. If you had invested $20,000 in Ford stock on 11/10/08, buying as many shares as possible while paying an online brokerage fee of $19.99 for the purchase, then sold the stock a year later with the same fee, how much profit would you have made? How much money would you have made per day for holding the stock for a year?

56. Refer to Exercise 55.
    (a) If you'd been wise and patient enough to wait until January 10, 2011, to sell the stock at $18.65, how much greater would your profit have been?
    (b) Using the Internet as a resource, investigate why Ford stock was so low in November 2008, and why it went up so much, then write a short essay summarizing your findings.

In Exercises 57–60, find the value at maturity for the bond described. All interest is simple interest.

57. Face value: $1,000; term: 5 years; rate: 4.9%
58. Face value: $5,000; term: 10 years; rate: 5.7%

59. Face value: $2,500; term: 90 months; rate: 6.19%
60. Face value: $3,750; term: 42 months; rate: 3.79%
61. If the bond in Exercise 57 is sold for $925 and is kept by the buyer until it matures, find the buyer's profit.
62. If the bond in Exercise 58 is sold for $4,000 and is kept by the buyer until it matures, find the buyer's profit.
63. If the bond in Exercise 59 is sold for $2,800 and is kept by the buyer until it matures, find the buyer's profit.
64. If the bond in Exercise 60 is sold for $4,190 and is kept by the buyer until it matures, find the buyer's profit.
65. Find the buyer's percent return per year for the bond purchase in Exercise 61 if it were bought 2 years after being issued.
66. Find the buyer's percent return per year for the bond purchase in Exercise 62 if it were bought $6\frac{1}{2}$ years after being issued.
67. Find the buyer's percent return per year for the bond purchase in Exercise 63 if it were bought 28 months after being issued.
68. Find the buyer's percent return per year for the bond purchase in Exercise 64 if it were bought 32 months after being issued.

Critical Thinking

69. Compare the two investments below and decide which would have been the better choice.

    Investment 1: $10,000 was invested in a 24-month CD that earned 5.1% annual interest compounded daily.
    Investment 2: 1,400 shares of stock in the Lybarger Aviation Company were bought at $7.11 per share using a brokerage with a 0.75% commission rate on both buying and selling stock. Over the 2 years the stock was held, it paid a dividend of $0.48 per share in the first year and $0.36 per share in the second year. The stock was sold through the same brokerage for $7.95 per share.

70. Compare the two investments and write a paragraph or two describing which you think is the better choice, and why.

    Investment 1: four 10-year bonds with face value $1,000 that draw 3.9% interest with 7 years remaining until maturity at a cost of $3,750 plus a 0.9% commission.
    Investment 2: putting $3,750 into a 4-year CD at 5.85% interest compounded monthly with no commissions or fees.

71. A bond with face value $10,000, simple interest 6.45%, and term 12 years is originally bought by Larry. After 33 months, he sells it to Curly for $11,400. Curly then holds on to it for 7 years, eventually selling it to Moe for $14,950. Moe keeps the bond until it matures and cashes it in.

    (a) Which investor made the greatest profit?
    (b) Which got the greatest percent return on his investment?
    (c) Which got the greatest percent return per year?

72. When workers invest for retirement, a general rule of thumb is to invest more in stocks when far from retirement, and convert more to bonds as retirement nears. Explain why this rule makes sense.

73. Using the Internet or a newspaper as a resource, look up a current stock quote for the Terex corporation (see Example 2).
    (a) If you had bought 400 shares of Terex at the price shown in Example 2 at an online brokerage with a $29.95 commission, then sold all shares at the current price (same commission), what would your profit/loss be? What percent is that of your original investment?
    (b) Based on the P/E ratio and the current closing price, find Terex's earnings per share for last year.

74. Repeat Problem 73 for Wal-Mart stock (see Problems 31–40).

75. Stock in Buckeye Brewers, Inc., is currently selling for $42.29 and earnings per share were $2.35 last year. One of their competitors, Nittany Beverage Distributors, is selling for $24.36 and earnings per share last year were $1.42. Which stock is the better buy? Why do you feel that way?

76. Some investors prefer stocks that pay a dividend, while others favor stocks that do not. Give some possible reasons for each perspective.

CHAPTER **8**   # Summary

Section	Important Terms	Important Ideas
8-1	Percent Percent increase Percent decrease	**Percent** means "per hundred," or "hundredths." So 45% means 45 per hundred. In order to do calculations with percents, they must be changed to fractions or decimals. The word "of" is important in calculations with percents: the phrase "40% of 80 is 32" translates to the equation $0.40 \times 80 = 32$. This allows us to set up many percent calculations.
8-2	Interest Simple interest Principal Rate Term Future value Banker's rule Discounted loan	**When you** borrow money, you pay a fee for its use. This fee is called interest. Likewise, when you put money into a savings account, the bank pays interest for the use of your money. Simple interest is interest computed only as a percentage of the principal. The formula $I = Prt$ is used to compute simple interest. Future value is the sum of the principal and any interest earned.
8-3	Compound interest Effective rate Annual yield Annuity Future value of an annuity	**Compound interest** is interest calculated on both the principal and any interest previously earned. Compound interest investments earn more interest than simple interest investments at the same rate. Compound interest can be calculated any number of times per year; typical compounding frequencies are annually (once per year), semiannually (twice per year), quarterly (four times per year), monthly, or daily. We can use the compound interest formula to find the future value of an account; using logarithms we can find the time needed to reach an investment goal. Since the actual rate is higher when interest is compounded more than once per year, the true rate is called the effective rate or annual yield. An annuity is a savings plan where an individual or business makes the same payment each period into a compound interest account where the rate remains the same for the term of the annuity.
8-4	Fixed installment loan Finance charge Down payment Total installment price Lease Annual percentage rate (APR) Payoff amount Actuarial method Rule of 78 Closed-ended credit Open-ended credit Unpaid balance method Average daily balance method	**A fixed** installment loan is a loan that is repaid in equal (usually monthly) payments. A down payment is a cash payment made on the purchase. Many times a finance charge is added to the amount financed. The total installment price is found by summing the monthly payments and adding the down payment. Because you pay back some of the principal each month, you do not have the full use of the money for the term of the loan. This means that the actual interest is higher than the stated interest rate. This actual interest rate is called the annual percentage rate and can be computed approximately using an APR table. When an installment loan is paid off early, the amount of interest saved can be determined by the rule of 78, or the actuarial method. Credit card companies also charge interest. There are two ways the companies compute interest. One method is computing interest on the unpaid balance. In this case you are charged interest only on last month's balance. The other method is called the average daily balance. Here the interest is computed on the average balance on all of the days of the month. This includes any purchases and payments made during the month.

8-5	Federal student loan Private student loan Subsidized Unsubsidized Capitalized Mortgage Fixed-rate mortgage Adjustable-rate mortgage Graduated payments Amortization schedule	**There are** three basic types of student loans available: federal loans made by the government, federal loans made by other lenders but guaranteed by the government , and private. In addition, a loan can be subsidized (no interest accrues while in school) or unsubsidized (interest accrues while in school). Interest on student loans is simple interest and can be paid while in school or capitalized (deferred until after graduation). Monthly payments can be calculated using a formula based on the principal at the time payments begin and the interest rate. When a loan is acquired to pay for the purchase of property, the loan is called a mortgage. The lender has the right to take ownership of the property if payments aren't made. Monthly payments can be calculated using a table, a formula, or an online calculator. A table listing the amount of each payment going to pay interest, the amount toward principal, and the remaining balance of the loan is called an amortization schedule.
8-6	Stock Dividend Bond Face value Maturity Date Stock exchange Stockbroker Commission Yield P/E ratio Proceeds Mutual fund	**Investors** can purchase stocks and bonds. A stock is a share of ownership in a company. A bond is actually a loan to a company. A mutual fund is a combination of stocks and bonds that is managed by a professional investor. Newspapers and websites show information about stocks and bonds by using tables. The tables show the 52-week high price and low price of the stocks and bonds. The table also shows the yield, the P/E ratio, the dividend, the volume of sales, the closing price, and the net change of a stock. P/E ratio is a comparison between the share price of a stock and the company's earnings per share. After being issued, but before their maturity date, bonds can be bought and sold like stocks. Bonds tend to be safer investments than stocks but have less growth potential. In addition, bonds tend to go up in value when stocks are declining, and vice versa.

MATH IN ▶ Student Loans REVISITED

1. Multiplying the yearly amount by 4, we get $85,788 needed for 4 years.
2. With 25% paid for, that leaves 75% we're responsible for, minus $5,000 a year we're contributing up front: 0.75 (21,447) − 5,000 = $11,085.25 per year. Multiply this by 4 and we get $44,341 we'll need to borrow.
3. If we pay interest while in school, the principal at the time payments start will remain $44,341. Using the student loan payment formula with $P = 44,341$, $r = 0.068$, and $n = 12$, we get monthly payments of $510.28. Multiplying this monthly payment by 120 (the number of payments in 10 years), we get a total payment of $61,233.60. The simple interest formula with $P = 44,341$, $r = 0.068$, and $t = 4$ will give us the interest that will be paid while in school: $I = 44,341 \cdot 0.068 \cdot 4 =$ 12,060.75. Adding these amounts, we'd make a total of

$73,294.35 in payments. Subtracting the amount borrowed, we find that total interest is $73,294.35 − $44,341 = $28,953.35.

4. If we capitalize the interest, upon graduation our principal will be $44,341 + $12,060.75 = $56,401.75. This time the monthly payment formula yields $649.07. Multiply this by 120 payments to get total payments of $77,888.40. Subtract the principal of $44,341 to get total interest of $35,547.40.

5. According to the table, the median salary with a bachelor's degree is $21,580 higher than with a high school diploma. In Question 4, we found that the total amount paid on loans is $77,888.40; add the $20,000 contributed while in school, and the total cost of the degree is $97,888.40. Finally, divide this amount spent by the extra $21,580 we'll make each year to find that it will take 4.54 years to make back the amount spent.

Review Exercises

Section 8-1

For Exercises 1–6, find the missing value.

	Fraction	Decimal	Percent
1.	$\frac{7}{8}$	_____	_____
2.		0.54	
3.			185%
4.	_____	0.06	
5.	$5\frac{3}{4}$		_____
6.	_____	_____	45.5%

7. Find 72% of 96.
8. 18 is what percent of 60?
9. 25% of what number is 275?
10. If the sales tax is 5% on a calculator, find the tax and the total cost if the calculator is $19.95.
11. If the sales tax on a coffee table is $3.60, find the cost of the table if the tax rate is 6%.
12. Marcia received a commission of $2,275 for selling a small home. If she receives a 7% commission, find the price of the home.
13. In 2000, households received 3.4 credit card offers per month on average. In 2005 the average was 5.9. Find the percent increase.
14. In 2001, there were 3,147 adolescents under 18 being held in state prisons. In 2005, the number was 2,226. Find the percent decrease.
15. A pair of jeans that usually sells for $71.50 is on sale at 30% off, and you also have a coupon for 10% off any purchase, including discounted merchandise.
    (a) Explain why you're not going to get 40% off.
    (b) Find the sale price including the coupon.
16. Annual in-state tuition for undergrads at Enormous State U. was $7,326 in 2012 and was projected to increase by 12% by 2014. If that happened, what was tuition in 2014?

Section 8-2

For Exercises 17–24, find the missing value.

	Principal	Rate	Time	Simple Interest
17.	$4,300	9%	6 years	_____
18.	$16,000	_____	3 years	$1,920
19.	$875	12%	_____	$262.50
20.	$50	6%	18 months	
21.	$230	_____	6.5 years	$104.65
22.	_____	3%	5 years	$63.75
23.	_____	14%	2 years	$385
24.	$785.00	12%	_____	$1,130.40

25. Ace Auto Parts borrowed $6,000 at 6% for 5 years to enlarge its display area. Find the simple interest and future value of the loan.
26. Sam's Sound Shack borrowed $13,450 at 8% for 15 years to remodel its existing store. Find the simple interest and future value of the loan.
27. Julie earned $60.48 in simple interest on a savings account balance of $4,320.00 over a 12-month period. Find the rate of interest.

28. John has an opportunity to buy a new boat. He has to borrow $5,300 at 11% simple interest for 36 months. Find the monthly payment.
29. Find the simple interest on a $2,300 loan at 5% for 80 days. Use the Banker's rule.
30. Find the simple interest on a $8,750 loan at 8.5% for 100 days. Use the Banker's rule.
31. David obtained a 3-year, $6,000 discounted loan at 6%. Find the discount and the amount of money David received.
32. Marla obtained a 4-year $9,250 discounted loan at 12%. Find the discount and the amount of money Marla received.

Section 8-3

For Exercises 33–36, find the compound interest and future value.

	Principal	Rate	Compounded	Time
33.	$1,775	5%	annually	6 years
34.	$200	4.2%	semiannually	10 years
35.	$45	3.04%	quarterly	42 months
36.	$21,000	5.19%	monthly	74 months

37. Find the effective rate when the stated rate is 12% and the interest is computed quarterly.
38. Which is the better investment: 4.3% compounded semiannually or 4.27% compounded daily?
39. How much money would you need to invest now in a 3-year certificate of deposit that pays 3.75% interest compounded monthly in order to have a future value of $10,000?
40. Charles inherits $12,500 from a favorite uncle and decides to invest it in an account that pays 4.6% compounded quarterly. His plan is to leave it in until it reaches $20,000. How long will he have to wait?
41. How many years does it take an investment to double if it draws 8.4% interest compounded semiannually? How much sooner will it double if interest is compounded daily?
42. The Evergreen Landscaping Company will need to purchase a new backhoe in 7 years. The owner purchases an annuity that pays 8.3% interest compounded semiannually. If the semiannual payment is $4,000, find the future value of the annuity in 7 years.
43. Mike and Marie plan to take an African vacation in 3 years. In order to save money for the trip, they purchase an annuity that pays 3% interest compounded quarterly. Find their monthly payment if they need $9,000 for the trip.

Section 8-4

In Exercises 44 and 45, for the automotive loan, find the amount financed, the total installment price, and the finance charge.

44. Purchase price including taxes and fees: $12,942.49; down payment: $4,300; payments: $261.34 for 36 months.
45. Purchase price: $22,400; sales tax 6.25%; license and title fees: $325; money credited for trade-in (subtracted from price of vehicle before taxes): $8,100; payments: $290.40 for 60 months.
46. Mary Cartworth purchased a four-piece luggage set for $750. She made a down payment of 15% and was

charged 6% interest. Find the total installment price and the monthly payment if she paid it off in 8 months.

47. Judy Harper purchased a Chevy Cobalt for $10,900. Her down payment was $1,000. She paid the balance with monthly payments of $310 for 3 years. Find the APR.

48. Max Dunbar bought a used BMW for $20,500 on www.Autotrader.com. His down payment was $6,000. He paid off the balance with monthly payments of $311 for 5 years. Find the APR.

49. Mike bought a mobile home for $149,500. He made a down payment of $8,000 and financed the remainder with an 8.5% simple interest loan for 25 years. Find his monthly payment.

50. In Exercise 47, Judy decided to pay off her loan at the end of 24 months. Use the actuarial method and find the unearned interest and the payoff amount.

51. In Exercise 48, Max was able to pay off his loan at the end of 3 years. Use the actuarial method and find the unearned interest and the payoff amount.

52. A loan for $1,500 is to be paid back in 30 monthly installments of $61.25. The borrower decides to pay off the balance after 24 payments have been made. Find the amount of interest saved. Use the rule of 78.

53. For the month of February, Pete had an unpaid balance on his credit card of $563.25 at the beginning of the month. He had purchases of $563.25 and made a payment of $350.00 during the month. Find the finance charge if the interest rate is 1.75% per month on the unpaid balance and find the new balance on March 1.

54. Sid's Used Cars had these transactions on its credit card statement:

April 1	Unpaid balance	$5,628.00
April 10	Purchases	$2,134.60
April 22	Payment	$ 900.00
April 28	Purchases	$ 437.80

Find the finance charge if the interest rate is 1.8% on the average daily balance and find the new balance on May 1.

55. If you have $845.32 on a credit card that charges 1.19% interest per month, and the minimum payment is interest due plus 2% of the principal balance, what will the balance be after 6 months of minimum payments?

Section 8-5

56. Latwan borrowed $4,700 to cover one-time college expenses in an unsubsidized federal student loan at 6.8% interest.
    (a) Find the amount of interest that accrues in a 30 and 31-day month.
    (b) The loan was acquired in August of 2011, and Latwan graduated in May of 2013. If payments began 6 months after graduation, how much interest will accrue while Latwan is in school?

57. Find the monthly payment on the loan in Exercise 56. The term is 10 years.

58. Find the monthly payment on the loan in Exercise 56 if it's a federally subsidized loan.

59. How much less interest would Latwan (Exercise 56) pay over the life of his student loan if he chooses not to capitalize interest on the loan?

60. A home was purchased for $145,000 with a 20% down payment. The mortgage rate was 8.5% and the term of the mortgage was 25 years.
    (a) Find the amount of the down payment.
    (b) Find the amount of the mortgage.
    (c) Find the monthly payment. Use Table 8-2.
    (d) Compute an amortization schedule for the first 2 months.

61. A business sold for $252,000. The down payment was 8%. The buyer financed the balance at 8.25% for 25 years. Find the monthly payment on the mortgage.

62. How much would the home buyers in Exercise 60 have saved over the life of the loan if they'd taken a 15-year mortgage? Use the payment formula for the 15-year loan.

Section 8-6

Use the table shown for Exercises 63–68.

52 weeks								
HI	LO	STOCK	DIV	YLD%	P/E	VOL (1,000s)	CLOSE	NET CHG
34.28	27.09	TRBCQ	0.72	2.2	30	5,528	32.79	−0.25

63. What was the high price and low price of the stock for the last 52 weeks?

64. If you own 475 shares of this stock, how much was the dividend you received?

65. How many shares of the stock were sold yesterday?

66. What was the closing price of the stock the day before yesterday?

67. Find the annual earnings per share of the stock.

68. An investor purchased 90 shares of stock for $86.43 per share and later sold it for $92.27 per share. How much did she make on the stock if the broker's fee was 2% on the purchase and the sale of the stock? Ignore the dividends.

69. Explain the difference between stocks and bonds.

70. Find the value at maturity for a bond with face value $10,000 with simple interest rate 4.2% and term 4 years.

71. A bond with face value $1,000, simple interest 5.3%, and term 6 years is bought by an investor for $1,145 with a commission of 1%. Who makes a greater profit on the bond, the original owner or the buyer?

72. If the buyer in Exercise 71 bought the bond with 40 months left until the maturity date and kept it until maturity, find her percent return on investment, and percent return per year.

Chapter Test

1. Change $\frac{5}{16}$ to a percent.
2. Write 0.63 as a percent.
3. Write 28% as a fraction in lowest terms.
4. Change 16.7% to a decimal.
5. Thirty-two of 40 people surveyed in a shopping mall said that they had used a credit card to make at least one purchase that day. What percent is that?
6. Of the 48 states in the continental United States, 89.6% have some form of state lottery. How many states is that?
7. Sixty-eight teams made the NCAA basketball tournament in 2012, which represented 19.6% of all Division 1 teams. How many Division 1 teams were there in 2012?
8. Find the sales tax and total price on a toaster oven that sells for $29.95. The tax rate is 8%.
9. If a salesperson receives a 15% commission on all merchandise sold, find the amount sold if his commission is $385.20.
10. On the first day of math class, 28 students were present. The next day, 7 more students enrolled in the class because the other section was canceled. Find the percent increase in enrollment.
11. Find the simple interest on $1,350 at 12% for 3 years.
12. Find the rate for a principal of $200 invested for 15 years if the simple interest earned is $150.
13. Ron's Detailing Service borrowed $435 at 3.75% for 6 months to purchase new equipment. Find the simple interest and future value of the loan, and the monthly payment.
14. Explain the difference between simple and compound interest.
15. Which account will draw more interest on a $6,000 investment: 7.2% simple interest for 4 years or 6.4% interest compounded monthly for 3 years?
16. Find the simple interest on a $5,000 loan at 4% for 60 days. Use the Banker's rule.
17. Latoya obtained a 6-year $12,650 discounted loan at 7.5%. Find the discount and the amount of money Latoya received.
18. Find the interest and future value for a principal of $500 invested at 6.5% compounded semiannually for 4 years.
19. Find the interest and future value on a principal of $9,750 invested at 10% compounded quarterly for 6 years.
20. In order to purchase a motorcycle, Jayden borrowed $12,000 at 9.5% for 4 years. Find his monthly payment.
21. Find the effective rate when the stated interest rate is 8% and the interest is compounded semiannually.
22. In order to open a new branch of her business in 3 years, the owner of Quick Fit Fitness Center purchases an annuity that pays 4.5% interest compounded semiannually. If her semiannual payment is $3,000, find the future value of the annuity in 3 years.

23. Sara bought furniture for her first apartment at a price of $935. She made a down payment of 30% and financed the rest for 6 months at 10% interest. Find the total installment charge and the monthly payment.
24. Bart Johnston purchased a Mazda for $15,000 and had a down payment of $2,000. He financed the balance at $305 per month for 48 months. Find the APR.
25. In Exercise 24, Bart was able to pay off his loan at the end of 24 months. Using the actuarial method, find the unearned interest and the payoff amount.
26. A loan for $2,200 is to be paid off in 24 monthly installments of $111.85. The borrower decides to pay off the loan after 20 payments have been made. Find the amount of interest saved, using the rule of 78.
27. For the month of November, Harry had an unpaid balance of $1,250 on his credit card. During the month, he made purchases of $560 and a payment of $800. Find the finance charge if the interest rate is 1.6% per month on the unpaid balance and find the new balance on December 1.
28. Rhonda's credit card statement for the month of May shows these transactions.

May 1	Unpaid balance	$474.00
May 11	Payment	$300.00
May 20	Purchases	$ 86.50
May 25	Purchases	$120.00

Find the finance charge if the interest rate is 2% on the average daily balance and find the new balance on June 1.
29. Yasmil took out an unsubsidized student loan when starting college. The amount was $11,200, the rate was 6.8%, and the term was 10 years.
   (a) Find the amount of interest that will accrue while Yasmil is in school during a 30-day month.
   (b) If interest is capitalized, how much will Yasmil owe when payments begin (54 months after acquiring the loan)?
   (c) Find Yasmil's monthly payment.
30. (a) How much less would payments be on the loan in Exercise 29 if interest had not been capitalized?
   (b) How much would not capitalizing the interest save over the life of the loan?
31. A home is purchased for $180,000 with a 5% down payment. The mortgage rate is 6% and the term is 30 years.
   (a) Find the amount of the down payment.
   (b) Find the amount of the mortgage.
   (c) Find the monthly payment. Use Table 8-2.
   (d) Compute an amortization schedule for the first 2 months.
32. How much more would the monthly payment be on the loan in Exercise 31 if the term were 15 years instead of 30? Use the payment formula. How much would be saved over the life of the loan?

Use the following table for Exercises 33–36.

52 weeks		STOCK	DIV	YLD%	P/E	VOL (1,000s)	CLOSE	NET CHG
HI	LO							
36.98	23.17	CAT	0.20	2.7	12	1,501	27.45	+0.80

33. What were the 52-week high and low prices of the stock?
34. If you own 300 shares of stock, how much money in dividends did you receive?
35. What was the closing price of the stock the day before yesterday?
36. Find the annual earnings per share of the stock.

37. A bond with face value $1,000, simple interest 5.5%, and term 8 years is sold for $1,250 with $5\frac{1}{2}$ years remaining until the maturity date. Find the amount of profit for the original owner and the buyer (assuming that the buyer keeps the bond until its maturity date). Who do you think made the better investment? Why?

Projects

1. Compare the investments below to decide which you think is the best. Consider such things as total profit, length of time, and amount of money needed up front.
   (a) $20,000 placed into a savings account at 3.8% compounded monthly for 10 years.
   (b) A 10-year annuity that pays 4.5% interest with monthly payments of $170.
   (c) Buying 700 shares of stock at $14.30 per share; selling 200 shares 4 years later at $25.10, and the rest 3 years after that at $28.05. The brokerage charges 1% commission on both buying and selling.
   (d) Buying a $150,000 house with $20,000 down and financing the rest with a 15-year mortgage at 5%. Then selling the house and paying off the balance of the loan in 8 years at a selling price, after commission, of $192,000. (*Hint:* You will need to calculate the monthly payment, then compute unearned interest and payoff amount.)

2. You have $1,000 to invest. Investigate the advantages and disadvantages of each type of investment.
   (a) Checking account
   (b) Money market account
   (c) Passbook savings account
   (d) Certificate of deposit
   Write a paper indicating which type of account you have chosen and why you chose that account.

3. Time to play fantasy stock market. Everyone in your group gets $10,000 to invest in whatever stocks you like. Here are the parameters:
   • You can invest as much or as little of that $10,000 as you choose.
   • Assume that you'd be trading through an online broker with a flat commission fee of $19.95 on all trades.
   • You can choose the time period for the game, but all remaining stocks have to be sold at the closing value on the last day of the time period you set.
   • If any companies you choose paid a dividend in the last year, divide that dividend by 365 and multiply by the number of days you owned the stock to prorate the dividend. (Don't forget to multiply by the number of shares!)
   • If you feel the market conditions are bad, you're perfectly welcome to not buy into the market. In that case, you'll need to compute your final amount by finding the best rate you could get locally on a savings account and compute the amount of interest you'd make during the chosen time period.

   • To find the final value of your account at the end of the time period, calculate the proceeds from any sales on the last day, add any dividends or cash value left in your account, and subtract the commission fees.
   • Ask your instructor to decide on what an appropriate reward would be for the winner.

4. In Section 8-4 we used simple interest on the amount borrowed to find the monthly payment on an auto loan, but in real life the amount you owe decreases as you pay down the loan, so calculating the monthly payment is more involved than that. Fortunately, there are a ton of online calculators out there to help.
   (a) Find an online calculator and use it to calculate payments for each car listed.

Car	Loan	Payments
Toyota Matrix	$12,000, 1.9%, 60 months	
Toyota Camry	$14,000, 4.75%, 36 months	
Toyota Sienna	$14,000, 1.9%, 2 years	
Mazda 929	$58,000, 3.9%, 6 years	
Mercedes S-class sedan	$92,000, 3.9%, 5 years	

   (b) Now let's explore a quick way to estimate a monthly payment for a situation where the Internet might not be available. At the beginning of your loan, you owe interest on the whole amount. At the end you owe nothing. So it's reasonable to guess that the average amount you owe interest on during the life of the loan is half of the principal balance. So we can estimate the payments with these steps:
      • Find the simple interest on half of the loan balance for the length of the loan.
      • Add that estimated interest to the principal balance.
      • Divide by the number of payments.
   Recalculate the payments for each loan using this estimation method.
   (c) Which loans did the method work best and worst for? What can you conclude?
   (d) Based on the work you've done, make a guess as to how accurately this estimation method would calculate the monthly payment for a 30-year home loan at 4.75% interest using a loan amount you choose. Explain how you made that guess. Then calculate the payment using one of our methods

from Section 8-5, and this estimation method. How well did you guess?

5. Obviously, new cars cost more than used ones. But how much more? That question isn't as easy as you might think because used cars are more likely to require expensive maintenance and repairs. Pick a brand new car model that you might be interested in buying. (Make sure that this model has been available for at least the last 4 years.) The website Edmunds.com is an excellent source of information on pricing and maintenance costs for new and used vehicles. Find what the price would be for the new model. Then do some research to find what the interest rate is in your area on a standard new car loan with term 5 years. Finally, use an online loan calculator to find the monthly payments for 60 months. Then repeat for the same model car, but one that's 4 years old and has average mileage for that age. (Note that the interest rates on used cars are almost always different than on new.) For both the new and used car purchase, use a 10% down payment. Finally, add in the maintenance and repair costs for each vehicle. Including the total amount paid over 5 years (based on the monthly payment), and total repair and maintenance costs, how do the prices compare?

Geometry

10-1   Points, Lines, Planes, and Angles
10-2   Triangles
10-3   Polygons and Perimeter
10-4   Area, Trapezoids, and Circles
10-5   Volume and Surface Area

10-6   Right Triangle Trigonometry
10-7   A Brief Survey of Non-Euclidean and Other
       Geometries
       Summary

CHAPTER **10**

Geometry

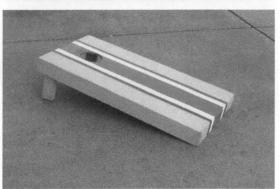

Outline

10-1   Points, Lines, Planes, and Angles

10-2   Triangles

10-3   Polygons and Perimeter

10-4   Areas of Polygons and Circles

10-5   Volume and Surface Area

10-6   Right Triangle Trigonometry

10-7   A Brief Survey of Non-Euclidean and Other
Geometries

Summary

MATH IN ⟩ Home Improvement

It probably won't surprise you to learn that one of the most common questions that math students ask is "How can I actually use this stuff?" Of course, how math is used in our world is the main theme of this book, and this chapter fits that framework especially well. The ideas presented in this chapter are commonly used in everyday things like working around the home, so we'll present some actual projects that geometry was used for in the home of one of the authors.

Geometry is one of those topics that most people recognize when they see it, but might have a hard time writing an actual definition for. If you look up a mathematical definition on the Web, it will refer to specific figures, like points, lines, triangles, and so forth. A more casual definition might say that geometry is the study of physical shapes and objects. Since we live in a physical world, in a very real sense, geometry is the study of the world around us.

If you really look for simple geometric figures, you can see them almost everywhere. The roads or sidewalks you took to get where you are right now are kind of like lines. The desk or table you're working at is probably rectangular, and the pen or pencil you're writing with is basically a cylinder. One way to think of the value of geometry in studying our world is that most of the things we encounter are in some way made up of basic geometric figures. This makes geometry one of the easiest areas of math to apply in our world.

In each of the projects described below, one or more of the techniques you will learn in this chapter was used to solve a problem. By the time you finish the chapter, you should be able to solve the problems yourself.

1. The diagram shows the measurements of all countertops in our kitchen. We originally decided on solid surface countertops at $56.62 per square foot including installation. We hated those countertops, and replaced them with granite 4 years later at $97.46 per square

foot installed. How much did we originally save by going with the cheaper material? How much more did we end up spending total than if we'd gone with granite in the first place?

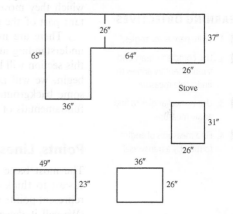

2. When finishing the basement, we needed trim along the new stairwell. From the landing at the top of the stairs in the top right photo on the facing page, the stairs extend 57 inches horizontally, and drop 42 inches. I wanted to cut the trim running along the stairs so that the bottom was parallel to the floor. At what angle did it need to be cut?

3. We built a bar out of 28 glass blocks arranged in four rows of seven each. Each block is $7\frac{3}{4}$ inches on a side, with $\frac{1}{4}$-inch mortar joints in between. We wanted to put a 3-inch trim around the outside of the blocks. How many square feet of wood did we need for the trim?

4. The boards for a cornbag toss game are 4 feet long. The bottom edge has a height of 4 inches, and the top edge has a height of 12 inches. The legs are attached so that they are perpendicular to the top. What angle did the bottom of the legs need to be cut at so that they sit flat on the ground?

For answers, see Math in Home Improvement Revisited on page 614

Section 10-1   Points, Lines, Planes, and Angles

LEARNING OBJECTIVES

☐ 1. Write names for angles.

☐ 2. Use complementary and supplementary angles to find angle measure.

☐ 3. Use vertical angles to find angle measure.

☐ 4. Find measures of angles formed by a transversal.

If you've ever watched really good billiards players, you probably noticed that they make bank shots look very easy. But if you try them yourself, you find they're not so easy at all. The secret to bank shots, and really to being a good pool player at all, is angles. Understanding the relationship between the angle at which two balls hit and the angles at which they move after impact is the most important part of the game.

There are many, many applications in which understanding angles is key, so our main focus in this section will be an understanding of angles. To begin, we will need to familiarize ourselves with some background information that will form the fundamentals of our entire study of geometry.

Points, Lines, and Planes

The most basic geometric figures we will study are points, lines, and planes. It's easiest to think of a **point** as a location, like a particular spot on this page. We represent points with dots, but in actuality a point has no length, width, or thickness. (We call it *dimensionless*.) A **line** is a set of connected points that has an infinite length, but no width. We draw representations of lines, but again, in actuality a line cannot be seen because it has no thickness. We will assume that lines are straight, meaning that they follow the shortest path between any two points on the line. This means that only two points are needed to describe an entire line. A **plane** is a two-dimensional flat surface that is infinite in length and width, but has no thickness. You might find it helpful to think of a plane as an infinitely thin piece of paper that extends infinitely far in each direction. Examples of the way we represent these basic figures are shown in Figure 10-1.

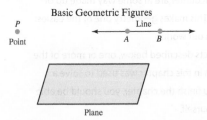

Basic Geometric Figures

Figure 10-1

We typically use capital letters to represent points, and symbolize them as dots. To name lines, we usually identify two points on the line, like A and B in Figure 10-1, and write $\overleftrightarrow{AB}$. We will sometimes assign a lowercase letter to represent a line, like l.

Points and lines can be used to make other geometric figures. A **line segment** is a finite portion of a line consisting of two distinct points, called **endpoints**, and all of the points on a line between them. The line segment connecting two points A and B is written as $\overline{AB}$.

Any point on a line separates the line into two halves, which we call **half lines**. A half-line beginning at point A and continuing through point B is written as $\overset{\circ}{\overrightarrow{AB}}$. The open circle over A indicates that the point A is not included. When the endpoint of a half line is included, we call the resulting figure a **ray**. A ray with endpoint A that continues through point B is written as $\overrightarrow{AB}$. The figures described in the last few paragraphs are summarized in Table 10-1.

Rays can be represented by rays of light starting at a source and continuing outward.

TABLE 10-1	**Lines and Portions of Lines**

Name	Figure	Symbol
Line	$\overset{\longleftrightarrow}{\underset{A \quad B}{\bullet \quad \bullet}}$	$\overset{\longleftrightarrow}{AB}$
Line segment	$\underset{A \qquad B}{\bullet \longrightarrow \bullet}$	$\overline{AB}$
Half line	$\underset{A \quad B}{\circ \longrightarrow \bullet}$	$\overset{\circ \longrightarrow}{AB}$
Ray	$\underset{A \quad B}{\bullet \longrightarrow}$	$\overset{\longrightarrow}{AB}$

Rays are used to define angles, which are the most important figures in this section.

> An **angle** is a figure formed by two rays with a common endpoint. The rays are called the **sides** of the angle, and the endpoint is called the **vertex**.

Math Note

When we use three letters to name an angle, the vertex of the angle is always represented by the letter in the middle. The order of the other two letters doesn't matter.

Some angles are represented in Figure 10-2. The symbol for angle is ∡, and there are a number of ways to name angles. The angle in Figure 10-2a could be called ∡*ABC*, ∡*CBA*, ∡*B*, or ∡1.

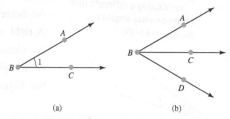

(a)   (b)

Figure 10-2

CAUTION	You should only use a single letter to denote an angle if there's no question as to the angle represented. In Figure 10-2b, ∡*B* is ambiguous, because there are three different angles with vertex at point *B*.

EXAMPLE 1	**Naming Angles**

Name the angle shown here in four different ways.

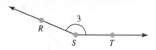

SOLUTION

∡*RST*, ∡*TSR*, ∡*S*, and ∡3.

☑ 1. Write names for angles.

> ▼ **Try This One 1**
>
> Write three different ways to represent the bottom angle in the diagram.
>
>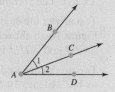

One way to measure an angle is in **degrees**, symbolized by °. One degree is defined to be $\frac{1}{360}$ of a complete rotation.

The instrument that is used to measure an angle is called a **protractor**. Figure 10-3 shows how to measure an angle using a protractor. The center of the base of the protractor is placed at the vertex of the angle, and the bottom of the protractor is placed on one side of the angle. The angle measure is marked where the other side falls on the scale. The angle shown in Figure 10-3 has a measure of 40°. The symbol for the measure of an angle is $m\angle$; so we would write $m\angle ABC = 40°$.

Angles can be classified by their measures.

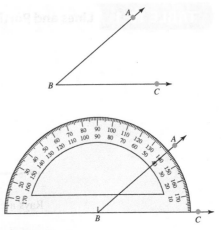

Figure 10-3

An **acute angle** has a measure between 0° and 90°.

A **right angle** has a measure of 90°.

An **obtuse angle** has a measure between 90° and 180°.

A **straight angle** has a measure of 180°.

See Figure 10-4.

(a) Adjacent angles

(b) Complementary angles
$m\angle 1 + m\angle 2 = 90°$

(c) Supplementary angles
$m\angle 1 + m\angle 2 = 180°$

Figure 10-5

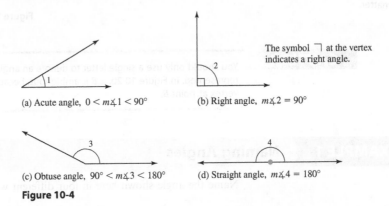

(a) Acute angle, $0 < m\angle 1 < 90°$ (b) Right angle, $m\angle 2 = 90°$

The symbol ⌐ at the vertex indicates a right angle.

(c) Obtuse angle, $90° < m\angle 3 < 180°$ (d) Straight angle, $m\angle 4 = 180°$

Figure 10-4

Pairs of Angles

Pairs of angles have various names depending on how they are related.

Two angles are called **adjacent angles** if they have a common vertex and a common side. Figure 10-5a shows a pair of adjacent angles, $\angle ABC$ and $\angle CBD$. The common vertex is B and the common side is $\overrightarrow{BC}$.

Two angles are said to be **complementary** if the sum of their measures is 90°. Figure 10-5b shows two complementary angles. The sum of the measures of $\angle GHI$ and $\angle IHJ$ is 90°.

Two angles are said to be **supplementary** if the sum of their measures is equal to 180°. Figure 10-5c shows two supplementary angles. The sum of the measures of $\angle WXY$ and $\angle YXZ$ is 180°.

| EXAMPLE 2 | Using Complementary Angles |

If $\angle FEG$ and $\angle GED$ are complementary and $m\angle FEG$ is 28°, find $m\angle GED$.

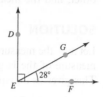

Math Note

It's not always *necessary* to draw a diagram for a geometry problem, but it is always *helpful*.

SOLUTION

Since the two angles are complementary, the sum of their measures is 90°, so $m\angle GED + m\angle FEG = 90°$, and solving we get:

$$m\angle GED = 90° - m\angle FEG$$
$$= 90° - 28°$$
$$= 62°$$

We say that the **complement** of an angle with measure 28° has measure 62°.

▼ **Try This One 2**

Find the measure of the complement of an angle with measure 41°.

| EXAMPLE 3 | Using Supplementary Angles |

If $\angle RQS$ and $\angle SQP$ are supplementary and $m\angle RQS = 135°$, find the measure of $\angle SQP$.

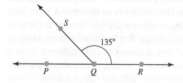

SOLUTION

Since $\angle RQS$ and $\angle SQP$ are supplementary, the sum of their measures is 180°, so $m\angle SQP + m\angle RQS = 180°$, and solving for the measure of $\angle SQP$ we get

$$m\angle SQP = 180° - m\angle RQS$$
$$= 180° - 135°$$
$$= 45°$$

We say that the **supplement** of an angle with measure 135° has measure 45°.

▼ **Try This One 3**

Find the measure of the supplement of an angle with measure 74°.

556   **Chapter 10**   Geometry

EXAMPLE 4   Using Supplementary Angles

If two adjacent angles are supplementary and one angle is 3 times as large as the other, find the measure of each.

SOLUTION

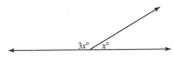

Let x = the measure of the smaller angle. The larger is three times as big, so $3x$ = the measure of the larger. The angles are supplementary, so their measures add to 180°. This gives us an equation:

$$x + 3x = 180° \qquad \textit{Smaller angle plus larger angle is 180°.}$$
$$4x = 180°$$
$$\frac{4x}{4} = \frac{180°}{4}$$
$$x = 45°$$

The smaller angle has measure 45°, and the larger has measure 3 × 45°, or 135°.

☑ 2. Use complementary and supplementary angles to find angle measure.

▼ Try This One 4

Two angles are complementary, and the smaller has measure 17° less than the larger. Find the measure of each.

Just as two intersecting streets have four corners at which you can cross, when two lines intersect, four angles are formed, as we see in Figure 10-6. The angles opposite

each other are called **vertical angles**. Angles 1 and 3 are vertical angles, as are angles 2 and 4.

If you study Figure 10-6 for a few seconds, a useful fact might occur to you: *two vertical angles have the same measure.* (You'll prove this in Problems 85–88.) Combining this fact with what we know about supplementary angles will allow us to find the measure of all four angles in a diagram like Figure 10-6 if we know just one of the angles. This is illustrated in Example 5.

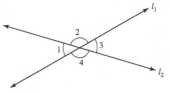

∢1 and ∢3 are vertical angles; $m\angle 1 = m\angle 3$
∢2 and ∢4 are vertical angles; $m\angle 2 = m\angle 4$

Figure 10-6

EXAMPLE 5   **Using Vertical Angles**

Math Note

When two angles are supplementary, you can always find the measure of one by subtracting the measure of the other from 180°.

Find $m\angle 2$, $m\angle 3$, and $m\angle 4$ when $m\angle 1 = 40°$.

SOLUTION

Since ∢1 and ∢3 are vertical angles and $m\angle 1 = 40°$, $m\angle 3 = 40°$. Since ∢1 and ∢2 form a straight angle (180°), $m\angle 1 + m\angle 2 = 180°$, and

$$m\angle 2 = 180° - m\angle 1$$
$$= 180° - 40°$$
$$= 140°$$

Finally, since ∢2 and ∢4 are vertical angles, $m\angle 4 = 140°$.

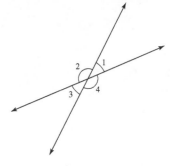

☑ 3. Use vertical angles to find angle measure.

▼ **Try This One 5**

Find $m\angle 1$, $m\angle 2$, and $m\angle 4$ when $m\angle 3 = 75°$.

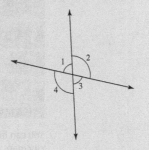

Two lines in the same plane are called **parallel** if they never intersect. You might find it helpful to think of them as lines that go in the exact same direction. If two lines l_1 and l_2 are parallel, we write $l_1 \parallel l_2$. When two parallel lines are intersected by a third line, we call the third line a **transversal**. As you can see in Figure 10-7, eight angles are formed. The angles between the parallel lines (angles 3–6) are called **interior angles**, and the ones outside the parallel lines (angles 1, 2, 7, and 8) are called **exterior angles**. The following box defines special relationships among these angles that allow us to find the measure of all of the angles if we know just one.

When two parallel lines are intersected by a transversal:

• **Alternate interior angles** are the angles formed between the parallel lines on opposite sides of the transversal. Alternate interior angles have equal measures.

558   **Chapter 10** Geometry

- **Alternate exterior angles** are the angles formed outside of the parallel lines on opposite sides of the transversal. Alternate exterior angles have equal measure.
- **Corresponding angles** consist of one exterior and one interior angle with no common vertex on the same side of the transversal. Corresponding angles have equal measures.

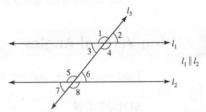

Pairs of alternate interior angles

∡3 and ∡6	$m∡3 = m∡6$
∡4 and ∡5	$m∡4 = m∡5$

Pairs of alternate exterior angles

∡1 and ∡8	$m∡1 = m∡8$
∡2 and ∡7	$m∡2 = m∡7$

Pairs of corresponding angles

∡1 and ∡5	$m∡1 = m∡5$
∡2 and ∡6	$m∡2 = m∡6$
∡3 and ∡7	$m∡3 = m∡7$
∡4 and ∡8	$m∡4 = m∡8$

Figure 10-7

You can find parallel roads and transversals on almost any city map.

EXAMPLE 6   Finding Angles Formed by a Transversal

Find the measures of all the angles shown when the measure of ∡2 is 50°.

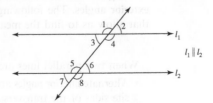

SOLUTION

First, let's identify the angles that have the same measure as $\angle 2$. They are $\angle 3$ (vertical angles), $\angle 6$ (corresponding angles), and $\angle 7$ (alternate exterior angles). Mark all of these as 50° on the diagram (Figure 10-8).

Since $\angle 1$ and $\angle 2$ are supplementary, $m\angle 1 = 180° - 50° = 130°$. This allows us to find the remaining angles: $\angle 4$ is a vertical angle with $\angle 1$, so it has measure 130° as well. Now $\angle 8$ is a corresponding angle with $\angle 4$, and $\angle 5$ is an alternate interior angle with $\angle 4$, which means they both have measure 130° as well.

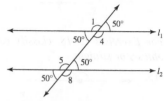

Figure 10-8

4. Find measures of angles formed by a transversal.

▼ **Try This One 6**

Find the measures of all the angles shown when the measure of $\angle 1$ is 165°.

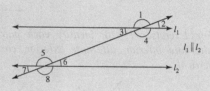

$l_1 \parallel l_2$

Answers to Try This One

1 $\angle 2, \angle CAD, \angle DAC$

2 49°

3 106°

4 $36\frac{1}{2}°$ and $53\frac{1}{2}°$

5 $m\angle 1 = 75°, m\angle 2 = 105°, m\angle 4 = 105°$

6 $m\angle 2, \angle 3, \angle 6, \angle 7 = 15°; m\angle 4, \angle 5, \angle 8 = 165°$

EXERCISE SET **10-1**

Writing Exercises

1. Explain why you can't actually draw a point or a line, just figures that represent them.
2. What is the difference between a half line and a ray?
3. Describe the four different ways that we name angles.
4. Explain why the two lines below are not parallel even though they don't meet in the diagram.

5. Describe how to find the complement and supplement of an angle.
6. When parallel lines are intersected by a transversal, there are four types of pairs of angles with equal measures formed. Describe each, using a diagram to illustrate.

Computational Exercises

For Exercises 7–12, identify and name each figure.

7. $\overset{\bullet}{A} \quad \overset{\bullet}{B}$

8. $\longleftarrow \overset{\bullet}{R} \quad \overset{\bullet}{S} \longrightarrow$

9. $\longleftarrow \longrightarrow l$

10. $\bullet P$

11. $\overset{\bullet}{T} \qquad \overset{\bullet}{U}$

12. $\overset{\circ}{E} \quad \overset{\bullet}{F} \longrightarrow$

560   **Chapter 10** Geometry

For Exercises 13 and 14, name each angle in four different ways.

13.

14.
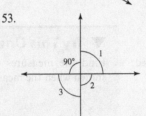

For Exercises 15–18, classify each angle as acute, right, obtuse, or straight.

15.

17.

16.

18.

For Exercises 19–26, identify each pair of angles as alternate interior, alternate exterior, corresponding, or vertical.

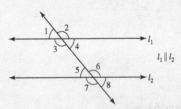

$l_1 \parallel l_2$

19. $\angle 1$ and $\angle 4$
20. $\angle 3$ and $\angle 6$
21. $\angle 2$ and $\angle 6$
22. $\angle 5$ and $\angle 8$

23. $\angle 1$ and $\angle 5$
24. $\angle 2$ and $\angle 7$
25. $\angle 1$ and $\angle 8$
26. $\angle 4$ and $\angle 8$

For Exercises 27–34, find the measure of the complement of each angle.

27. $8°$
28. $24°$
29. $32.4°$
30. $56.8°$

31. $18\frac{1}{4}°$
32. $81\frac{5}{8}°$
33. $(x + 10)°$
34. $(y - 5)°$

For Exercises 35–42, find the measure of the supplement for each angle.

35. $156°$
36. $90°$
37. $62.5°$
38. $143.1°$

39. $111\frac{5}{6}°$
40. $5\frac{3}{4}°$
41. $(y - 15)°$
42. $(x + 20)°$

In Problems 43–46, find the value of x if $\angle A$ and $\angle B$ are complementary angles.

43. $\angle A = (x + 5)°$ $\angle B = (2x - 15)°$
44. $\angle A = (x - 30)°$ $\angle B = (x + 45)°$
45. $\angle A = (x - 8)°$ $\angle B = (3x + 12)°$
46. $\angle A = (5x + 1)°$ $\angle B = (3x - 11)°$

In Problems 47–50, find the value of x if $\angle A$ and $\angle B$ are supplementary angles.

47. $\angle C = (x + 27)°$ $\angle D = (x + 18)°$
48. $\angle C = (3x - 44)°$ $\angle D = (5x - 20)°$
49. $\angle C = (2x + 10)°$ $\angle D = (4x - 28)°$
50. $\angle C = (10x + 20)°$ $\angle D = (20x + 10)°$

For Exercises 51–54, find the measures of $\angle 1$, $\angle 2$, and $\angle 3$.

51.
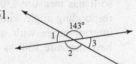

52.
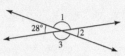

53.

54.
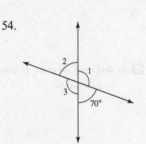

For Exercises 55–58, find the measure of $\angle 1$ through $\angle 7$.

55.
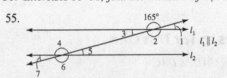

$l_1 \parallel l_2$

56.
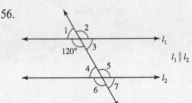

$l_1 \parallel l_2$

57.
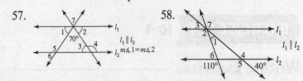

58.

In Problems 59–62, find the measure of each marked angle.

59.
$3x°$ $(2x - 10)°$

60.
$y°$ $3y°$

61.
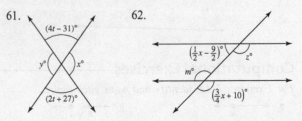
$(4t - 31)°$ $y°$ $x°$ $(2t + 27)°$

62.
$\left(\frac{1}{2}x - \frac{9}{2}\right)°$ $z°$ $m°$ $\left(\frac{3}{4}x + 10\right)°$

Applications in Our World

For Exercises 63–68, identify the measure of the angle made by the hands of a clock at these times:

63. 3 o'clock
64. 6 o'clock
65. 2 o'clock

66. 4 o'clock
67. 5:30
68. 9:15

Exercises 69–76 use the following description: Euclid Avenue and Prospect Avenue are parallel, both running west to east, with Euclid north of Prospect. East Ninth Street is a transversal running northwest to southeast. The angle made with Euclid on the northwest corner is 76°. Find the angle made by the path of the car for each of the following turns.

69. Driving west on Euclid and turning northwest on E. Ninth
70. Driving east on Prospect and turning northwest on E. Ninth
71. Driving southeast on E. Ninth and turning east on Euclid
72. Driving northwest on E. Ninth and turning east on Euclid
73. Driving east on Euclid and turning southeast on E. Ninth
74. Driving west on Prospect and turning northwest on E. Ninth
75. Driving northwest on E. Ninth and turning west on Prospect
76. Driving southeast on E. Ninth and turning west on Prospect

In Problems 77–80, think about both the interior and exterior of a house. Write all the examples you can of:

77. A pair of parallel lines
78. A pair of lines that meet in a right angle
79. A pair of parallel planes
80. A pair of planes that meet in a right angle

Critical Thinking

Degrees are a perfectly good way to measure angles, but they're made up: somebody decided that a full rotation is 360°, and that's that. Another measure used for angles, radian measure, is based on a physical size. We'll use radian measure in Problems 81–84.

81. Draw a circle with center (0, 0) and radius 1, then using a piece of string, mark off the exact length of the radius on that string. Next, attach one mark on the string to the circle at the point (1, 0), and align the string along the curve of the circle, going counterclockwise. Put a mark on the circle where the other mark on the string is, then draw a ray from the center of the circle to the point you just marked. Congratulations! You've drawn an angle that measures **one radian**.

82. The length all the way around a circle is called the **circumference**; it can be calculated using the formula Circumference = $2\pi r$, where r is the radius. Based on this formula, what is the radian measure of one complete rotation?

83. Use your answer to Question 82 to find a conversion factor between degree and radian measure. You'll need to remember the number of degrees in one full rotation.

84. Use your conversion factor from Question 83 to find the radian measure of an angle that measures:
(a) 90°   (b) 45°   (c) 120°   (d) 225°

In Problems 85–88, you'll prove one of the results from this section.

85. Write an equation describing the sum of the measures of angles 1 and 2 in the diagram below.

86. Repeat Question 85, but this time for angles 2 and 3.
87. Subtract the equation you wrote in Question 86 from the equation you wrote in Question 85.
88. Solve the result of Question 87 for the measure of angle 1. What result did you prove?

Section 10-2   Triangles

If you look for them, you can find familiar geometric shapes in a surprising number of places. Architects in particular are fascinated by creating complex designs out of basic shapes. The pyramid structure at the famous Louvre in Paris is one of the most well-known examples, blending an assortment of simple shapes into an architectural masterpiece.

562   **Chapter 10**   Geometry

LEARNING OBJECTIVES

☐ 1. Identify types of triangles.

☐ 2. Find one missing angle in a triangle.

☐ 3. Use the Pythagorean theorem to find side lengths.

☐ 4. Use similar triangles to find side lengths.

As we continue our study of geometry in our world, we use points, lines, rays, and angles to form more complex figures, beginning with the triangle. Although they are very simple figures, triangles have a surprising number of applications to applied situations.

A geometric figure is said to be **closed** when you can start at one point, trace the entire figure, and finish at the point you started without lifting your pen or pencil off the paper. One such figure is the triangle:

> A **triangle** is a closed geometric figure that has three sides and three angles. The three sides of the triangle are line segments, and the points where the sides intersect are called the **vertices** (plural of "vertex").

One way we can name a triangle is according to its vertices, using the symbol △. For example, we could call the triangle in Figure 10-9 △ABC. (In this case, the order of the vertices doesn't matter.)

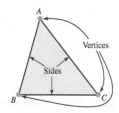

Figure 10-9

Types of Triangles

Special names are given to certain types of triangles based on either the lengths of their sides or the measures of their angles.

For sides:

> An **isosceles triangle** has two sides with the same length.
>
> An **equilateral triangle** has three sides with the same length.
>
> A **scalene triangle** has sides that are three different lengths.
>
> Examples are shown in Figure 10-10a.

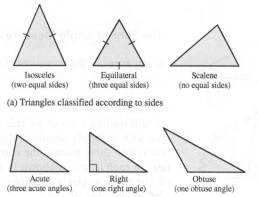

Isosceles
(two equal sides)

Equilateral
(three equal sides)

Scalene
(no equal sides)

(a) Triangles classified according to sides

Acute
(three acute angles)

Right
(one right angle)

Obtuse
(one obtuse angle)

(b) Triangles classified according to angles

Figure 10-10

For angles:

> An **acute triangle** has three acute angles (less than 90°).
>
> A **right triangle** has one right angle (90°).
>
> An **obtuse triangle** has one obtuse angle (greater than 90° and less than 180°).
>
> Examples are shown in Figure 10-10b.

| EXAMPLE 1 | **Identifying Types of Triangles** |

Identify the type of triangle.

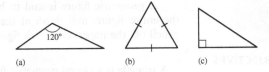

(a)   (b)   (c)

SOLUTION

(a) Obtuse triangle since one angle is greater than 90°.
(b) Equilateral triangle since all sides are equal, or acute triangle since all angles are acute.
(c) Right triangle since one angle is 90°.

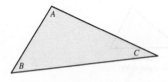

☑ 1. Identify types of triangles.

▼ **Try This One 1**

Identify the type of triangle.

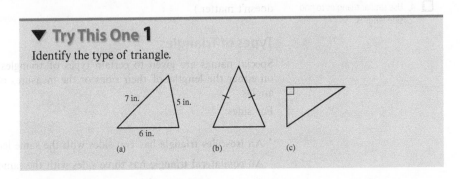

(a)   (b)   (c)

For a variety of reasons, it's very useful to know the following fact:

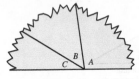

The Sum of Angle Measures in a Triangle

In any triangle, the measures of the three angles add to 180°.

We will outline a proof of this fact in Exercises 57–61, but you can see that it's true with a simple demonstration. Draw any triangle on a piece of paper, then tear it into three pieces, one containing each angle. Now arrange the three angles next to each other, as shown in Figure 10-11: you will find that when the vertices of the three angles are placed together, they always form a straight line (or a 180° angle). Try it!

Figure 10-11

| EXAMPLE 2 | **Finding an Angle in a Triangle** |

Find the measure of angle C in the triangle.

SOLUTION

Since the sum of the measures of the angles of a triangle is 180°,

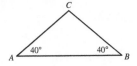

$$m\angle A + m\angle B + m\angle C = 180°$$ *m∠A and m∠B = 40°.*
$$40° + 40° + m\angle C = 180°$$ *Add on left side.*
$$80° + m\angle C = 180°$$ *Subtract 80° from both sides.*
$$m\angle C = 180° - 80°$$
$$= 100°$$

The measure of angle C is 100°.

☑ 2. Find one missing angle in a triangle.

▼ **Try This One 2**

Find the measure of angle B.

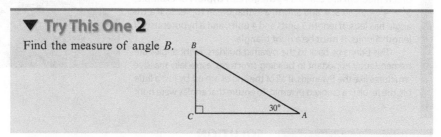

The Pythagorean Theorem

Right triangles are very special because there is a simple relationship among their sides. This is the famous Pythagorean theorem, which is attributed to the Greek mathematician Pythagoras around 500 BCE, although it was actually known much earlier in some form (see Sidelight on the next page). In any case, a **theorem** is a fact that has been proven true using deductive reasoning. This particular theorem allows us to find the third side of a right triangle if we know two sides. The side across from the right angle is called the **hypotenuse**, and the other two sides are called the **legs**.

The Pythagorean Theorem

The sum of the squares of the lengths of the two legs in a right triangle always equals the square of the length of the hypotenuse. If we use a and b to represent the lengths of the legs and c to represent the length of the hypotenuse, as in the figure, then

$$a^2 + b^2 = c^2$$

In addition, if the sides of any triangle satisfy this equation, the triangle is a right triangle.

CAUTION   Remember, the Pythagorean theorem only holds true if the triangle is a right triangle!

EXAMPLE 3   **Using the Pythagorean Theorem**

For the right triangle shown, find the length of side a.

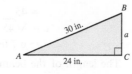

Sidelight PYTHAGORAS AND THE PYRAMIDS

The great pyramids in Egypt were completed about 2,000 years before Pythagoras was born, but the theorem that now bears his name played an important role in their construction. Three whole numbers that satisfy the equation in the Pythagorean theorem are called a **Pythagorean triple**. For example, $3^2 + 4^2 = 5^2$, so 3, 4, and 5 form a Pythagorean triple. So if a triangle has legs of length 3 units and 4 units, and a hypotenuse of length 5 units, it must be a right triangle.

This brings us back to the pyramid builders. Right angles are tremendously important in building structures, especially massive structures like the Pyramids. If all of the angles are off by just a little bit, the result is a crooked pyramid. To ensure that angles were right

angles, the Egyptians used a rope divided into even sections of 3, 4, and 5 units long with knots. If the rope wouldn't stretch into a taut triangle with sides of length 3 and 4 against an edge that was supposed to be a right angle, then they would know that the angle was off.

Calculator Guide

To find the length in Example 3:

Standard Scientific Calculator:

30 [x²] [−] 24 [x²] [=] [√]

Standard Graphing Calculator:

[2nd] [x²] 30 [x²] [−] 24 [x²] [)]
[ENTER]

Note: [2nd] [x²] is the square root operator: if your calculator does not automatically put in a (, you will need to do so manually.

SOLUTION

$$a^2 + b^2 = c^2 \qquad \text{Side } b \text{ is 24 in. and side } c \text{ is 30 in.}$$
$$a^2 + 24^2 = 30^2 \qquad \text{Subtract } 24^2 \text{ from both sides.}$$
$$a^2 = 30^2 - 24^2 = 324 \qquad \text{Apply square root to both sides.}$$
$$a = \sqrt{324} = 18 \qquad \text{Ignore the negative root: } a \text{ is a length.}$$

The missing side is 18 inches long.

▼ Try This One 3

If the hypotenuse of a right triangle is 13 feet long and one leg is 5 feet long, find the length of the other leg.

Notice that we ignored the negative root when solving for the length of side a in Example 3. Since we're finding a physical length when using the Pythagorean theorem, we'll keep doing that as we move forward.

EXAMPLE 4   Applying the Pythagorean Theorem

To build the frame for the roof of a shed, the carpenter must cut a 2 × 4 to fit on the diagonal. If the length of the horizontal beam is 12 feet and the height is 3 feet, find the length of the diagonal beam.

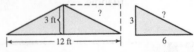

Triangles play a very important role in roof construction.

SOLUTION

The frame forms two right triangles with legs of 3 feet and 6 feet. The length of the diagonal beam can be found using the Pythagorean theorem.

$$c^2 = a^2 + b^2 \qquad \text{Use } a = 3, b = 6.$$
$$= 3^2 + 6^2 \qquad \text{Square each.}$$
$$= 9 + 36 \qquad \text{Add.}$$
$$= 45 \qquad \text{Apply square root to both sides.}$$
$$c = \sqrt{45}$$
$$\approx 6.7 \text{ feet}$$

The length of the beam should be about 6.7 feet, or about 6 feet $8\frac{1}{2}$ inches.

566   **Chapter 10** Geometry

☑ 3. Use the Pythagorean theorem to find side lengths.

▼ Try This One 4

The rectangular frame for a large sign is 10 feet long and 8 feet high. Find the length of a diagonal beam that will be used for bracing. (*Hint:* Draw a diagram.)

Similar Triangles

When two triangles have the same shape but not necessarily the same size, they are called **similar triangles**. Consider the triangles in Figure 10-12. Since the measure of angle A and the measure of angle A' are equal, they are called *corresponding angles*. Likewise, angle B and angle B' are corresponding angles since they have the same measure. Finally, angle C and angle C' are corresponding angles. When two triangles are similar, then their corresponding angles will have the same measure. Also, if all of the corresponding angles have equal measure, we know that two triangles are similar.

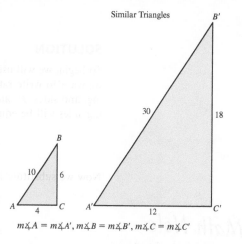

Similar Triangles

$m\angle A = m\angle A'$, $m\angle B = m\angle B'$, $m\angle C = m\angle C'$

$$\frac{\text{Length of side } AB}{\text{Length of side } A'B'} = \frac{\text{Length of side } BC}{\text{Length of side } B'C'} = \frac{\text{Length of side } AC}{\text{Length of side } A'C'}$$

Figure 10-12

The sides that are opposite the corresponding angles are called *corresponding sides*. When two triangles are similar, the ratios of the corresponding sides are equal. For the two triangles shown in Figure 10-12,

$$\frac{\text{Length of side } AB}{\text{Length of side } A'B'} = \frac{10}{30} = \frac{1}{3}$$

$$\frac{\text{Length of side } AC}{\text{Length of side } A'C'} = \frac{4}{12} = \frac{1}{3}$$

$$\frac{\text{Length of side } BC}{\text{Length of side } B'C'} = \frac{6}{18} = \frac{1}{3}$$

Since these three ratios are all equal, we can describe the situation by saying that the lengths of the corresponding sides are in proportion. In summary:

Math Note

Actually, since the sum of all three angle measures in a triangle is 180°, if two triangles have two pairs of corresponding angles equal, the third pair of angles must be equal as well, and they are similar triangles.

Math Note

The similar triangle relationships can be written more concisely as a single equation with two equal signs in it, but we chose to write it as three equations since, in practice, we choose two sets of corresponding sides and set up an equation with two sides.

Similar Triangle Relationships

If triangle ABC is similar to triangle $A'B'C'$ then

$$\frac{\text{Length of side } AB}{\text{Length of side } A'B'} = \frac{\text{Length of side } AC}{\text{Length of side } A'C'}$$

$$\frac{\text{Length of side } AB}{\text{Length of side } A'B'} = \frac{\text{Length of side } BC}{\text{Length of side } B'C'}$$

$$\frac{\text{Length of side } AC}{\text{Length of side } A'C'} = \frac{\text{Length of side } BC}{\text{Length of side } B'C'}$$

EXAMPLE 5 Using Similar Triangles

If the two triangles below are similar, find the length of side $B'C'$.

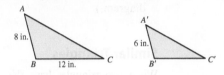

SOLUTION

To begin, we will use the variable x to represent the length we're asked to find. Now we want to write ratios of corresponding sides. Sides AB and $A'B'$ are corresponding, and sides BC and $B'C'$ are as well. So the ratios formed from these corresponding sides will be equal:

$$\frac{\text{Length of side } AB}{\text{Length of side } A'B'} = \frac{\text{Length of side } BC}{\text{Length of side } B'C'}$$

Now we substitute in the lengths and solve for x.

$$\frac{8}{6} = \frac{12}{x} \qquad \textit{Cross multiply.}$$
$$8x = 72 \qquad \textit{Divide both sides by 8.}$$
$$x = 9$$

The length of side $B'C'$ is 9 inches.

> ### Math Note
>
> In the proportion $\frac{8}{6} = \frac{12}{x}$, both numerators are sides from one triangle, and both denominators are sides from the other. Both lengths on the left side are left sides of the triangles, and both lengths on the right side are bottom sides. This can help assure you've set up the proportion correctly.

▼ Try This One 5

The two triangles shown are similar. Find the length of side AC.

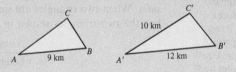

One clever use of similar triangles is to measure the height of objects that are difficult to measure directly. Example 6 shows how to use this form of indirect measurement.

EXAMPLE 6 Using Similar Triangles in Measurement

If a tree casts a shadow 12 feet long and at the same time a person who is 5 feet 10 inches tall casts a shadow of 5 feet, find the height of the tree.

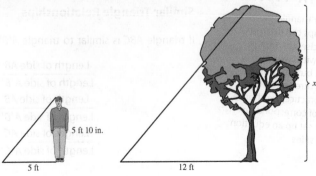

Math Note

In this solution, the situation allows us to conclude that two of the three corresponding angles are equal. Fortunately, that's enough: recall that since the three angles in each triangle have to add to 180°, we know the third angles have to be equal as well, so the triangles are definitely similar.

Also, note that we had to write the height of the person (5′10″) as the mixed number $5\frac{10}{12}$.

☑ 4. Use similar triangles to find side lengths.

SOLUTION

Both triangles in the diagram are right triangles, and since the sun makes the same angle with the ground in both diagrams, the triangles have two corresponding angles equal, and must be similar. That means we can set up and solve a proportion:

$$\frac{\text{Height of person}}{\text{Length of person's shadow}} = \frac{\text{Height of tree}}{\text{Length of tree's shadow}}$$

$$\frac{5\frac{10}{12}}{5} = \frac{x}{12} \qquad \text{Cross multiply.}$$

$$5x = 70 \qquad \text{Divide both sides by 5.}$$

$$x = 14 \text{ feet}$$

The height of the tree is 14 feet.

▼ Try This One 6

Find the length of a pole if it casts a 20-foot shadow at the same time that a 5′3″ woman casts a 15-foot shadow.

Answers to Try This One

1 (a) Scalene and acute
   (b) Isosceles and acute
   (c) Right

2 60°

3 12 feet

4 12.8 feet

5 7.5 km

6 7 feet

EXERCISE SET 10-2

Writing Exercises

1. Describe the three ways that triangles can be classified based on lengths of sides.
2. Describe the three ways that triangles can be classified based on measures of angles.
3. Explain why the following statement is incorrect: the sum of the squares of the lengths of two sides in a triangle is equal to the square of the length of the third side.
4. What does it mean for two triangles to be similar?
5. Explain how to find the measure of the third angle in a triangle if you know the measures of the other two.

6. Explain how to find the length of the third side of a right triangle when you know the lengths of the other two sides.
7. What does it mean for a geometric figure to be closed? Is a plane a closed figure?
8. Explain why two triangles have to be similar if they have two pairs of corresponding angles that are equal.
9. What did right triangles have to do with the construction of the great pyramids in Egypt?
10. Explain how you can use the length of a shadow to measure a tall object that you can't measure directly.

Computational Exercises

For Exercises 11–16, classify each triangle.

11.

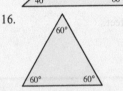
3 ft   3 ft
2 ft

12.

14.

7 ft   7 ft
7 ft

15.

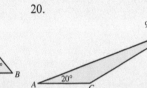
80°
40°   60°

13.

120°

16.

60°
60°   60°

For Exercises 17–22, find the measure of angle C.

17.

C
60°   50°
A   B

20.

$9\frac{3}{4}°$ B
20°
A   C

18.   B
25°
140°
A   C

21.

A
2x°
x+20°
x°   B
C

19.   B

$41\frac{1}{3}°$

A   C

22.   C
x°
3x°   2x°
A   B

In Exercises 23–30, *a* and *b* represent the lengths of the legs of a right triangle with hypotenuse length *c*. Find the length of the missing side.

23. $a = 16$ ft, $b = 30$ ft
24. $a = 272$ in., $b = 510$ in.
25. $a = 8.4$ yd, $b = 11$ yd
26. $a = 5$ cm, $b = 9.3$ cm
27. $b = 9$ mi, $c = 21$ mi
28. $b = 26$ ft, $c = 29$ ft

29. $a = 4\frac{1}{2}$ ft, $c = 12\frac{1}{8}$ yd
30. $b = 27\frac{3}{4}$ in., $c = 4\frac{1}{2}$ ft

For Exercises 31–34, the two triangles drawn are similar. Find the value of x.

31.

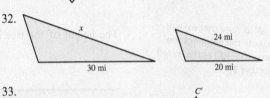
18 ft
x
12 ft
8 ft

32.

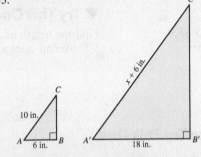
x
30 mi
24 mi
20 mi

33.

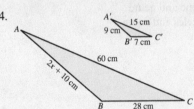
C
10 in.
A   6 in.   B
C'
x + 6 in.
A'   18 in.   B'

34.

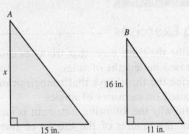
A'
9 cm   15 cm
B' 7 cm   C'
A
60 cm
2x + 10 cm
B   28 cm   C

For Exercises 35–40, explain why the two triangles are similar, then find the length x.

35. $m\angle A = 35°$; $m\angle B = 35°$

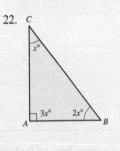
A
x
15 in.
B
16 in.
11 in.

36. $m\angle C = 49°$; $m\angle D = 41°$

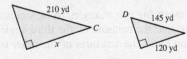
210 yd
C
x
D   145 yd
120 yd

570   **Chapter 10**   Geometry

37.

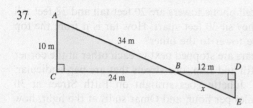

38.

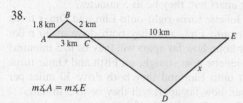

$m\angle A = m\angle E$

39.

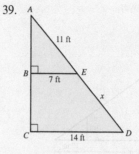

40.

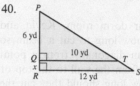

Applications in Our World

41. A baseball diamond is really a square with the bases at the corners. While playing intramural softball, Jane ran 60 feet from home plate to first base. The next batter hit the ball from home plate directly to second base. What distance did he hit the ball?

42. Television screens are sized according to the length of a diagonal across the screen, from one corner to another. The screen of a 52 in. widescreen TV is 24.5 in. high. How wide is it?

43. Kendall needs to fix a loose screen in her second-story bedroom. The bad spot is 17′4″ off the ground. The manufacturer of her 14-foot ladder recommends for safety reasons that the base be placed at least 5 feet from a wall it's leaning against, and Kendall can reach 4′3″ above the spot where the ladder hits the wall. Will she be able to safely reach the screen?

44. My swimming pool is an 18 × 36 foot rectangle. The vacuum hose has to be long enough to reach from one corner to the one diagonally opposite. What's the length of the shortest hose that will work?

45. A carpenter needs to build a stairway down to a basement in a house under construction. The vertical drop is 8′9″, and in order to keep the staircase from being too steep it will extend 14 feet horizontally. The main supports will go diagonally from the top of the stairs to the basement floor. How long do they need to be?

46. What's the tallest piece of plywood sheeting that you can take through a door that's 6′8″ tall and 32″ wide? (You can disregard the thickness of the plywood.)

47. For a triathlon, the athletes start at point *A*, swim directly across Siegel Lake to point *B*, then cycle to point *C*, a distance of 7 miles. They then discard their bikes and run 2 miles to point *D*, then turn to run 4 miles to point *E*, then go under the tunnel another 2 miles back to point *C*. They then finish the race back on their bicycles for 7 miles to the finish line at point *A*. What is the distance they swam across Siegel Lake if the measure of angle *A* is the same as the measure of angle *E*?

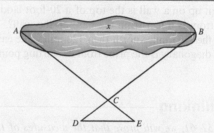

48. At the local mall, Suzette and her friends ate lunch at the food court, located at point *A*. Afterward, they walked 60 yd to Best Buy at point *C* to check out the latest CDs. From there, they went 25 yd to Macy's at point *B* to sample some perfume. After, they continued walking 150 yd to point *D*, where they saw the latest Batman movie. After the show, they found Suzette's car at point *E*. How far away from the movie theater was Suzette's car?

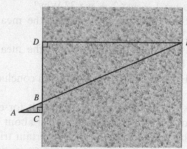

49. Find the height of the tree.

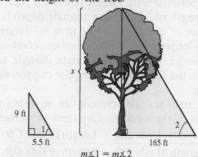

$m\angle 1 = m\angle 2$

50. Find the height of the tower.

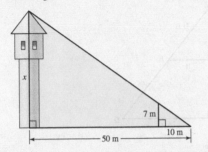

51. To build a loft in their dorm room, Kevin and Neil had to figure out how long to cut a beam so that the beam would run diagonally from a point on the floor 6 feet away from the wall to the top of the 8-foot-high wall. How long should they cut the beam?

52. How high up on a wall is the top of a 20-foot ladder if its bottom is 6 feet from the base of the wall?

53. A plane flies 175 miles north then 120 miles due east. How far diagonally is the plane from its starting point?

54. Two cell phone towers are 20 feet tall and 38 feet tall and they sit 30 feet apart. How far is it from the top of one tower to the other?

55. Two cars are stopped next to each other at the corner of Fifth and Elm, two streets that are perpendicular.
    (a) If Juliette goes straight on Fifth Street at 30 miles per hour, and Omar stalls at the light, how far apart will they be in 5 minutes?
    (b) If Juliette turns right onto Elm and Omar turns left onto Elm, and they both drive at 30 miles per hour, how far apart will they be in 5 minutes?
    (c) If Juliette goes straight on Fifth and Omar turns left onto Elm and they both drive 30 miles per hour, how far apart will they be in 5 minutes?

56. (a) Refer to Exercise 55. If Juliette turns right onto Elm and Omar makes a U-turn, heading back down Fifth, and they're 1.7 miles apart after 2 minutes, how fast were they going (in miles per hour) if their average speeds were the same?
    (b) Under the same circumstances, what was the average speed for each (in miles per hour) if Juliette was driving twice as fast as Omar?

Critical Thinking

In Exercises 57–61, we will prove that the measures of the angles in a triangle sum to 180°, using the diagram below.

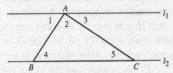

Lines l_1 and l_2 are parallel.

57. What is $m\angle 1 + m\angle 2 + m\angle 3$? Why?
58. What is the relationship between the measures of angles 3 and 5? Why?
59. What is the relationship between the measures of angles 1 and 4? Why?
60. Using Exercises 47–49, what can you conclude about $m\angle 2 + m\angle 4 + m\angle 5$?
61. Discuss whether this proves the result for every triangle, or if there is anything special about this diagram that makes it apply only to certain triangles.
62. Explain how the Pythagorean theorem guarantees that the hypotenuse is the longest side in any right triangle.
63. The length of a side in a triangle depends on the measure of the angle across from it—larger angles means longer sides. This observation, combined with Exercise 62, shows that in a right triangle, the right angle is the largest angle. How else can you show this is true?
64. In the right triangle below, it can be shown that the lengths of the segments have these properties:

$$\frac{\text{Length of side } AD}{\text{Length of side } CD} = \frac{\text{Length of side } CD}{\text{Length of side } DB}$$

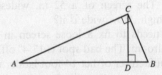

Show the proportion is true by using similar triangles.

65. Michelle and Brad hire a local contractor to build a stone retaining wall in their yard. When he's finished, Michelle thinks the left edge of the wall looks like it's not quite perpendicular to the ground. The wall is 12'7" long and 2'8" tall at the left edge. Describe how Michelle and Brad could use just a tape measure and their knowledge of triangles to see if the left side is in fact perpendicular to the ground. Then find what the measurement your method describes will be if the contractor did a good job.

66. Mika hires a landscaper to build three triangular flower beds in her back yard. She insists that all three have the exact same shape but differ in size depending on the type of flowers that will be planted (kind of a picky request, but the customer's always right). When the work was done, Mika measured the sides of all three beds and got the following measurements:

$$\text{Bed 1: } 10'3'' \times 7'9'' \times 14'$$
$$\text{Bed 2: } 17'5'' \times 13'2'' \times 23'9\tfrac{1}{2}''$$
$$\text{Bed 3: } 7'8\tfrac{1}{4}'' \times 5'9\tfrac{3}{4}'' \times 10'6''$$

Did Mika ask for her money back? How did you decide?

Section 10-3 Polygons and Perimeter

LEARNING OBJECTIVES

☐ 1. Find the sum of angle measures of a polygon.

☐ 2. Find the angle measures of a regular polygon.

☐ 3. Find the perimeter of a polygon.

High-rise buildings capture our imagination and get most of the attention, but did you know that as recently as 2008, the largest building in the United States had only five floors? The Pentagon in suburban Washington, D.C., has a floor area of over $6\frac{1}{2}$ million square feet, and is one of the world's finest examples of the importance of geometry in architecture.

Triangles, as we've seen, are very useful in many settings. But of course they are limited to three sides. In this section, we will study closed figures with more than three sides, including the five-sided figure known as the pentagon.

Polygons

Closed geometric figures whose sides are line segments are classified according to the number of sides. These figures are called *polygons*. Table 10-2 shows the number of sides and some of the shapes of these polygons: **triangle**, **quadrilateral**, **pentagon**, **hexagon**, **heptagon**, **octagon**, **nonagon**, **decagon**, **dodecagon**, and **icosagon**.

In Section 10-2, we saw that the sum of the measures of the angles of a triangle is equal to 180°. The sum of the measures of the angles of any polygon can be found using the next formula.

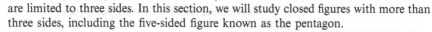

The Sum of Angle Measures of a Polygon

The sum of the measures of the interior angles of a polygon with n sides is $(n - 2)180°$.

TABLE 10-2 | **Basic Polygons**

Math Note

The word "polygon" comes from the Greek word "polygonos," meaning "many-angled."

Name	Number of sides	
Triangle	3	
Quadrilateral	4	
Pentagon	5	
Hexagon	6	
Heptagon	7	
Octagon	8	
Nonagon	9	
Decagon	10	
Dodecagon	12	
Icosagon	20	

In Problem 54, we'll see why the formula for the sum of angle measures in a polygon makes perfect sense. The technique you learn will also help you to remember the formula in a pinch.

Many shapes found in nature are polygons.

EXAMPLE 1   Finding the Sum of Angle Measures of a Polygon

Find the sum of the measures of the angles of a heptagon.

SOLUTION

According to Table 10-2, a heptagon has seven sides, so the sum of the measures of the angles of the heptagon is

$$(n - 2)180° = (7 - 2)180° \qquad \textit{Use } n = 7.$$
$$= 5 \cdot 180°$$
$$= 900°$$

The sum of the measures of the angles of a heptagon is 900°.

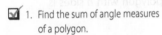

1. Find the sum of angle measures of a polygon.

▼ Try This One 1

Find the sum of the measures of the angles of an icosagon.

Quadrilaterals

Just as there are special names for certain types of triangles, there are names for certain types of quadrilaterals as well. (Recall that a quadrilateral is a polygon with four sides.)

A **trapezoid** is a quadrilateral that has exactly two parallel sides. See Figure 10-13a.

A **parallelogram** is a quadrilateral in which opposite sides are parallel and equal in measure. See Figure 10-13b.

A **rectangle** is a parallelogram with four right angles. See Figure 10-13c.

A **rhombus** is a parallelogram in which all sides are equal in length. See Figure 10-13d.

A **square** is a rhombus with four right angles. See Figure 10-13e.

Types of Quadrilaterals

(a) Trapezoid

(b) Parallelogram

(c) Rectangle

(d) Rhombus

(e) Square

Figure 10-13

The next diagram explains the relationships of the quadrilaterals. Looking at the relationships, you can see that a square is also a rectangle and a rhombus. A rhombus and a rectangle are also parallelograms.

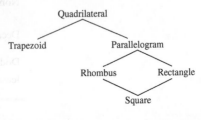

Most of the polygons drawn in Table10-2 are actually special polygons: all of the sides have the same length, and all of the angles are equal in measure. We call such a figure a **regular polygon**. The most common examples of regular polygons are squares and equilateral triangles.

EXAMPLE 2   Finding Angle Measure for a Regular Polygon

☑ 2. Find the angle measures of a regular polygon.

Find the measure of each angle of a regular hexagon.

SOLUTION

First, find the sum of the measures of the angles for a hexagon. The formula is $(n - 2) \cdot 180°$, where n is the number of sides. Since a hexagon has six sides, the sum of the measures of the angles is $(6 - 2) \cdot 180° = 720°$. Next, divide the sum by 6 since a hexagon has six angles: $720 \div 6 = 120°$.

Each angle of a regular hexagon has a measure of $120°$.

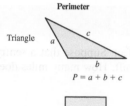

Triangle

$P = a + b + c$

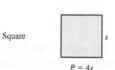

Square

$P = 4s$

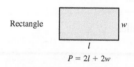

Rectangle

$P = 2l + 2w$

Figure 10-14

▼ **Try This One 2**

Find the measure of each angle of a regular pentagon.

Perimeter

The **perimeter** of a polygon is the sum of the lengths of its sides. The perimeter of a triangle with sides of length a, b, and c is simply $P = a + b + c$. For a square with side length s, the perimeter is $P = s + s + s + s$, or $P = 4s$. For a rectangle with length l and width w, there are two sides that are l units long, and two that are w units long, so the perimeter is $P = l + l + w + w$, or $P = 2l + 2w$. See Figure 10-14.

EXAMPLE 3   Finding the Perimeter of a Rectangle

The Houser family finds their dream home perfect in every way except one: the backyard is not fenced in, and their dog Bunch needs room to roam. The rectangular portion they plan to enclose is 95 feet wide and 70 feet long. How much fence will they need to enclose the yard on all four sides?

SOLUTION

The amount of fence needed is the perimeter of the rectangle.

$$P = 2l + 2w$$
$$= 2(70) + 2(95)$$
$$= 140 + 190 = 330$$

The Housers need 330 feet of fence.

▼ **Try This One 3**

The intramural field at Fiesta University is a large square measuring 600 yards on a side. Find the perimeter.

Sidelight A TRIUMPH OF GEOMETRY

Completed in 1943, the Pentagon is a marvel of architectural design, packing an incredible amount of floor space into a five-story building. Although it covers an area of just 29 acres, the total floor space is more than 152 acres. Over 25,000 people work there on an average day; this would make it the fourth-largest city in Alaska. There are 17.5 *miles* of corridors in the building; at an average walking pace, it would take almost 6 hours to walk all of them. And yet because of the geometric design, it takes at most 7 minutes to walk from any point in the building to any other.

EXAMPLE 4 Finding the Perimeter of a Polygon

The length of each outside wall of the Pentagon is 921 feet. Suppose that a sentry must walk the outside wall six times during his 4-hour shift. How many miles does he walk in one shift?

SOLUTION

A pentagon has five sides, and each has length 921 feet, so the sum of the lengths of the sides is 5 × 921 = 4,605 feet. In walking the perimeter six times, the sentry covers 6 × 4,605 = 27,630 feet. Now we convert to miles:

$$\frac{27,630 \text{ feet}}{1} \times \frac{1 \text{ mi}}{5,280 \text{ feet}} \approx 5.23 \text{ miles}$$

▼ **Try This One 4**

3. Find the perimeter of a polygon.

The running path at a state park is a right triangle with legs 0.7 mile and 1.3 miles. What's the total length around the path?

Answers to Try This One

1 3,240°

2 108°

3 2,400 yards

4 About 3.5 miles

EXERCISE SET 10-3

Writing Exercises

1. Is a circle a polygon? Why or why not?
2. How can you find the sum of the angle measures for a polygon?
3. What makes a polygon regular?
4. How can you find the measure of the angles for a regular polygon?
5. What is the perimeter of a polygon?
6. Is the perimeter of a pentagon five times the length of one side? Why or why not?

576   **Chapter 10**   Geometry

Computational Exercises

For Exercises 7–12, identify each polygon and find the sum of the measures of the angles.

7.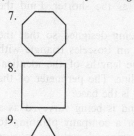

8.

9.

10.

11.

12.

For Exercises 13–16, identify each quadrilateral.

13.

15.

14.

16.

For Exercises 17–32, find the perimeter of the pictured or described polygon. Dotted lines are for measurement reference only and don't affect the perimeter. If a polygon appears to be regular, you can assume that it is.

17. 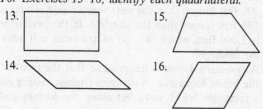 22 yd, 16 yd

19. 3 ft, 7 ft, 8 ft, 10 ft

18. 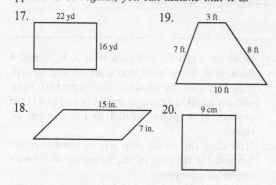 15 in., 7 in.

20. 9 cm

21. 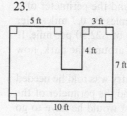 6 in., 6 in., 10 in., 10 in., 6 in., 6 in.

22. 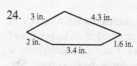 8 yd, 10 yd, 5 yd, 20 yd

23. 5 ft, 3 ft, 4 ft, 7 ft, 10 ft

24. 3 in., 4.3 in., 2 in., 3.4 in., 1.6 in.

25. 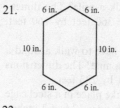 7 mi

26. 14 km

27. 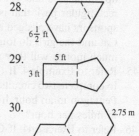 14 in., 11.5 in.

28. $6\frac{1}{2}$ ft

29. 5 ft, 3 ft

30. 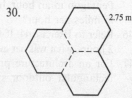 2.75 m

31. A regular icosagon with sides of length 11.2 cm
32. A regular dodecagon with sides of length 4′3″
33. A heptagon has perimeter 110 feet. Four of the sides are the same length, and the remaining sides are half as long. How long are the shorter sides?
34. The four sides of an octagon that are vertical or horizontal are all one length, while the four slanted sides are 4 inches less. If the perimeter is 124 inches, how long are the shorter sides?

Applications in Our World

35. At least how far does a major league player run when he hits a home run? The baseball diamond is a square with sides 90 feet.
36. A rectangular plot of land where outdoor concerts are held is about to be enclosed by a fence. How many feet of fence will be needed if the plot is 110 yards on one side and 270 feet on the other, and requires a 4-foot opening for entrances on two of the four sides?
37. How many feet of hedges will be needed to enclose a triangular display at an amusement park if the sides measure 62 feet, 85 feet, and 94 feet?
38. Jim and Joe have built a rectangular stage for their band that measures 40 feet by 56 feet. They want to put fiber optic lighting around the border that comes

in 8-foot sections for $24.00 each. Find the cost of the lighting for their stage.
39. How much molding in length will be needed to frame an 11 × 14-inch picture if there is to be a 2-inch mat around the picture?
40. A carpenter needs to put baseboard around the room shown. How many feet are needed? Each door is 30 inches wide.

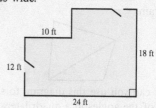
10 ft, 18 ft, 12 ft, 24 ft

41. How many times would you have to walk around a football field in order to walk a mile? The dimensions of a football field are 360 feet by 160 feet. One mile is 5,280 feet.

42. How many times would you have to walk around a soccer field in order to walk a mile? The dimensions of a soccer field are 345 feet by 223 feet.

43. Ultimate Fighting matches take place in a steel cage that is a regular octagon with sides 12 feet 3 inches. Jed and Bubba decide to build an Ultimate Fighting cage in Jed's backyard, using fence they can buy at Home Depot for $4 per foot. How much will it cost to build the cage?

44. For a LiveStrong walkathon, Cat is walking her dogs Macleod and Tessa around the perimeter of a rectangular park that is 0.4 miles by 0.7 miles. Her sponsors have pledged a total of $22.50 per mile. If Cat and the girls do four laps around the park, how much money will they raise?

45. Refer to Example 4. If the sentry was told he needed to complete two circuits around the perimeter of the Pentagon in an hour, how fast would he have to go in miles per hour?

46. Refer to Exercise 44. If Cat completed her four laps in 2 hours, what was her average speed in miles per hour?

47. For an architecture project, Lauren is designing a rectangular outdoor space for a town center. She wants a perimeter of 620 yards, and because she's a fan of the golden ratio (see Sidelight on page 250 if you're interested), she wants the longer sides to be 1.618 times as long as the shorter. Find the lengths of each side.

48. An A-frame cabin is being designed so that the front of the building is an isosceles triangle with base 6 feet less than the lengths of the identical sides forming the roof line. The perimeter of the front is 67′6″. How long is the base?

49. A triangular plot of land is being surveyed as a possible building site for a company planning to relocate its factory. The company's architect believes that the site will need at least 1,000 feet of frontage to fit the company's needs. The longest side is 400 feet longer than the next shorter side, which is 175 feet longer than the shortest. If the perimeter is 3,000 feet, which (if any) of the sides will work for frontage?

50. A two-story house is designed so that the front of the house looks like an isosceles triangle resting on a rectangle, which is 46 feet along the bottom and 19 feet high. The top vertex of the triangle is 12 feet directly above the halfway mark of the rectangle's top. The owner wants to string Christmas lights around the entire perimeter of the front. How many feet of lights will he need?

Critical Thinking

51. For the triangle shown, ∡BCD is called an exterior angle. If you know the measures of ∡A and ∡B, explain how the measure of ∡BCD can be found.

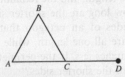

52. What is the measure of each exterior angle of a regular pentagon? (See Problem 51.)

53. Make a table with the number of sides in a regular polygon in one column and the measure of each angle in the other (see Example 2). Start with 8 sides and increment by 2 until you reach 20 sides. Do you see any pattern? Where do you think that pattern is headed as the number of sides gets larger and larger?

54. Notice that you can divide a quadrilateral into two triangles by drawing a line segment from any vertex to another vertex that's not adjacent to it, as seen in the diagram:

(a) How can you use this diagram to show that the sum of the angles in a quadrilateral is 360°?

(b) Draw examples of polygons with 5, 6, 7, and 8 sides, then divide each into a set of nonoverlapping triangles by drawing line segments from vertices to other nonadjacent vertices. How is the number of triangles related to the number of sides?

(c) How does this result help you to remember the formula for the sum of the measures of interior angles in a polygon?

55. A city park is being planned with a rectangular walking path around the outside. The original plans called for the path to be 2,400 feet on one side and 1,300 on the other. Due to a dispute with local landowners, the plans need to be altered so that the path is moved 50 feet inward on all sides.

(a) Find the length of the original path in miles.

(b) How many feet less is the new path?

(c) What percentage of the length was lost by moving the sides in by 50 feet?

56. Each of the following figures is a regular polygon. Measure the side length for each, then the distance d from any angle to the one directly across from it (making sure to go through the center of the figure), and use that information to fill in the table. What do you notice? (It would be a BIG help to make a copy of the figures and enlarge them with a copier or scanner. Big, I tell you.)

578   **Chapter 10**   Geometry

# sides	
Perimeter	
Distance	
Perimeter Distance	

Section 10-4   Areas of Polygons and Circles

LEARNING OBJECTIVES

☐ 1. Find areas of rectangles and parallelograms.

☐ 2. Find areas of triangles and trapezoids.

☐ 3. Find circumferences and areas of circles.

In the 21st century, more and more people are taking on home improvement projects that would have been done only by professionals 20 years ago. Stores like Lowe's and Home Depot have become regular stops for homeowners looking to personalize their little corner of the world.

Suppose that you plan to install ceramic tile in your kitchen to cover up that ridiculous yellow linoleum—what were the previous owners thinking? Tiles come in many different sizes, and while planning the job, you want to make sure you buy enough tile. But you also don't want to buy TOO much. A calculation of area is just the ticket to make sure the job is well planned and ultimately successful. In this section we will learn how to find the area of various geometric figures.

Areas of Polygons

We already know that the area of a geometric figure is a measure of the region bounded by its sides. We also know that area is measured in square units, like square feet or square meters. Let's say that your kitchen is a rectangle measuring 8 feet by 10 feet, and that the tiles you've picked out are 12 inches on a side. Then each tile covers exactly one square foot of space. Figure 10-15 is a diagram of the kitchen.

Notice that the floor is divided into a grid by marking off 1-foot units along each side. This shows that it would take 80 tiles to cover the entire floor, so the area is 80 square feet. It's no coincidence that this number is the product of the length and width—this gives us our first area formula:

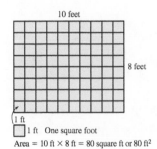

1 ft   One square foot
Area = 10 ft × 8 ft = 80 square ft or 80 ft²

Figure 10-15

Area Formulas for Rectangles and Squares

The area of a rectangle is the product of the length and width. If *l* is the length and *w* is the width, then

$$A = lw$$

In a square, the length and width are equal, so if *s* is the length of the sides,

$$A = s^2$$

EXAMPLE 1　　Finding the Cost of Installing Carpet

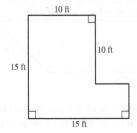

A couple plans to carpet an L-shaped living room, as shown to the left. Find the total cost of the carpet if it is priced at $25.00 per square yard.

SOLUTION

With a little bit of ingenuity, we can divide the room into two figures we know the area of: a rectangle and a square.

$$A = lw \qquad\qquad A = s^2$$
$$= 15 \cdot 10 \qquad\qquad = 5^2$$
$$= 150 \text{ square feet} \qquad = 25 \text{ square feet}$$

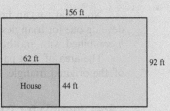

The total area is 150 square feet + 25 square feet = 175 square feet.

Now we can use dimensional analysis to finish the calculation:

$$175 \text{ ft}^2 \times \frac{1 \text{ yd}^2}{9 \text{ ft}^2} \times \frac{\$25}{1 \text{ yd}^2} = \$486.11$$

It will cost $486.11 to carpet the room.

▼ Try This One 1

A homeowner plans to install sod around his new house, as shown.

| 156 ft |
| 62 ft　　　　　92 ft |
| House　　44 ft |

If sod costs $3.98 per square yard, find the total cost.

Once we know the formula for the area of a rectangle, we can use it to develop formulas for other polygons. We'll start with the parallelogram, shown in Figure 10-16.

The key dimensions here are the base (length of the bottom side) and height (vertical distance from the bottom side to the top side). The trick is to "cut" the bottom left corner piece off and attach it to the right side. This turns the parallelogram into a rectangle, and we can find the area using length times width.

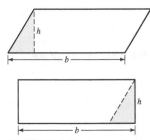

Figure 10-16

Area Formula for Parallelograms

The area of a parallelogram is the product of the base and the height. If *b* is the length of the base and *h* is the height,

$$A = bh$$

CAUTION

Be careful when working with parallelograms! The base is the length of the bottom (or top) side, but the height is *not* the length of the left or right side. It is the vertical distance from the bottom side to the top side.

| EXAMPLE 2 | **Finding the Area of a Parallelogram** |

Find the area of the parallelogram:

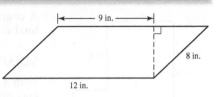

SOLUTION

We're given the base but not the height, so we'll need to find that first. The dashed line forms a right triangle with hypotenuse 8 inches and one leg 3 inches (we know the top side of the parallelogram is also 12 inches by the definition of parallelogram). So we can use the Pythagorean theorem to find the height:

$$h^2 + 3^2 = 8^2 \implies h^2 = 55 \implies h = \sqrt{55}$$

Now we use the formula for the area of a parallelogram.

$$A = bh = 12 \text{ in.} \times \sqrt{55} \text{ in.} = 12\sqrt{55} \text{ in.}^2 \approx 89 \text{ in.}^2$$

☑ 1. Find areas of rectangles and parallelograms.

▼ **Try This One** 2

Find the area of the parallelogram:

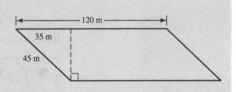

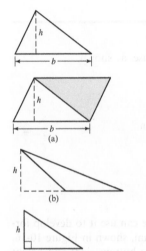

Now that we can find the area of a parallelogram, we can use that formula to develop one for triangles. In Figure 10-17(a), we see a triangle with base b and height h combined with another identical triangle to form a parallelogram.

The area of that parallelogram is $A = bh$, and since it is built from two copies of the original triangle, the area of the triangle is half as much.

Area Formula for Triangles

The area of a triangle is half the base times the height. If b is the length of the base and h is the height, then

$$A = \frac{1}{2}bh$$

Figure 10-17

| CAUTION |

Again, be careful! The height of a triangle is not usually the length of one of the sides. Note that the height could be outside the triangle, as shown in Figure 10-17(b). The height is one of the sides only if the triangle is right [Figure 10-17(c)].

| EXAMPLE 3 | **Finding the Area of a Triangle** |

Find the area of the triangle shown.

SOLUTION

The base is 15 ft and the height is 10 ft:

$$A = \frac{1}{2}bh = \frac{1}{2}(15)(10) = 75 \text{ square feet}$$

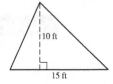

▼ Try This One 3

Find the area of the triangle:

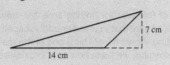

We can also use parallelograms to find the area of a trapezoid. In the first drawing in Figure 10-18, we see the relevant dimensions. It's important to recall that the top and bottom sides are parallel. In the second figure, we have an identical copy of the original trapezoid flipped both horizontally and vertically: it fits together with the original to form a parallelogram with area $h(a + b)$. Since this parallelogram consists of two copies of the trapezoid, the area of the trapezoid is half as much.

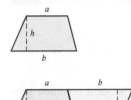

Figure 10-18

How would you find the area of the front of this house to estimate the amount of paint needed to paint it?

Math Note

When finding the area of a trapezoid, make sure that a and b are the lengths of the parallel sides.

Area Formula for Trapezoids

The area of a trapezoid with parallel sides a and b and height h is

$$A = \frac{1}{2}h(a + b)$$

EXAMPLE 4   Find the Area of a Trapezoid

Find the area of the trapezoid:

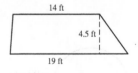

SOLUTION

The two parallel sides have length 14 and 19 feet, and the height is 4.5 feet:

$$A = \frac{1}{2}h(a + b) = \frac{1}{2}(4.5)(14 + 19) = 74.25 \text{ square feet.}$$

▼ Try This One 4

Find the area of the trapezoid shown.

☑ 2. Find areas of triangles and trapezoids.

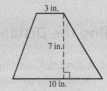

Sidelight CALCULUS AND AREA

We now have a variety of formulas for finding area, but how would you find the area of a figure that's curved or oddly shaped, like the front of the building shown here? This is one of the major topics of calculus. In calculus, we learn how to approximate areas, and in many cases find exact areas of figures when we don't have basic formulas for them.

It's all based on a really simple idea: we're good at computing areas of rectangles, so to approximate areas of other shapes, we'll fit little rectangles inside the shape, and sum the areas of the rectangles. This is not terribly different than the way we started with the simple rectangle formula in this section and used it to build other area formulas.

> **Math Note**
>
> The center of a circle is inside the circle, but is not actually part of the circle.

> **Math Note**
>
> An interesting fact: manhole covers are circular because there are just a small handful of shapes that make it completely impossible for the lid to fall into the hole, and the circle is by far the simplest of them.

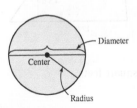

Figure 10-19

Circles

By definition, polygons have sides that are line segments. The most common geometric figure that doesn't fit that criterion is the circle—no part of a circle is straight.

> A **circle** is the set of all points in a plane that are the same distance from a fixed point, which we call the **center** of the circle.

Based on the definition of circle, a line segment from any point on a circle to the center is always the same length. We call this length the **radius** of the circle. A line segment starting at a point on a circle, going through the center, and ending at a point on the opposite side is called a **diameter** of the circle, and its length is twice the radius. If we use r to represent radius and d to represent diameter,

$$d = 2r \quad \text{and} \quad r = \frac{d}{2}$$

The distance around the outside of a circle is called the **circumference** (C) of the circle. (This is analogous to the perimeter of a polygon.) The key parts of a circle are illustrated in Figure 10-19.

Thousands of years ago, people started to realize that if you divide the circumference of any circle by its diameter, the result is always the same number. Eventually, this number was given a special name, the Greek letter π (pronounced **pi**). We can't write an exact value of pi, because it's irrational, so its decimal expansion is infinitely long. But 3.14 is commonly used as an approximation. (See the Sidelight on page 248 for a discussion of pi.)

The fact that circumference divided by diameter always equals pi gives us a formula for the circumference of a circle.

> **Circumference Formula for Circles**
>
> The circumference of a circle is π times the diameter, or 2π times the radius:
>
> $$C = \pi d \quad \text{or} \quad C = 2\pi r$$

EXAMPLE 5   Finding the Distance Around a Track

A dirt track is set up for amateur auto racing. It consists of a rectangle with half-circles on the ends, as shown in Figure 10-20. The track is 300 yards wide, and 700 yards from end to end. What is the distance around the track?

SOLUTION

From the diagram, we can see that the diameter of the circular ends is 300 yards, so the circumference is $C = \pi d = \pi(300) \approx 942$ yards. (This is the total length of the curved portion, since the two half-circles make one full circle.) The length of each straightaway is the total length of the track (700 yards) minus twice the radius of the circular ends, which is 150 yards (see Figure 10-21). So each straightaway is $700 - 2(150) = 400$ yards. Now we can find the total length:

$$L = 942 + 400 + 400 = 1{,}742 \text{ yards}$$

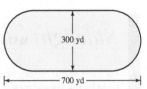

Figure 10-20

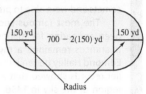

Figure 10-21

Calculator Guide

As a substitute for using the approximation $\pi \approx 3.14$, most calculators have π built in. To find $\pi \cdot 300$ in Example 4:

Standard Scientific Calculator

Standard Graphing Calculator

▼ Try This One 5

The entrance to Joe's living room is an arch consisting of a rectangle that is 7 feet high and 4 feet wide with a half-circle on top. How many feet of trim would be needed to go around the outside of the arch, not including the bottom?

Through exhaustive experiments involving comparing areas of circles to other known figures, the Greeks found that the ratio of a circle's area to the square of its radius is π. This provides our next area formula:

Area Formula for Circles

The area of a circle is pi times the square of the radius: $A = \pi r^2$

EXAMPLE 6   Finding the Area Enclosed by a Track

Find the area enclosed by the track in Example 5.

SOLUTION

The area is the sum of the area of a rectangle and the area of a circle (again because the two half-circles form one full circle).

Rectangle	Circle
$A = lw$	$A = \pi r^2$
$= 400 \cdot 300$	$= \pi \cdot 150^2$
$= 120{,}000$	$\approx 70{,}650$

The combined area is about $120{,}000 + 70{,}650 = 190{,}650$ square yards.

▼ Try This One 6

Find the area of the doorway in Try This One 5.

3. Find circumferences and areas of circles.

584   **Chapter 10**   Geometry

Sidelight MATH AND THE ORBITS OF COMETS

For most of our history, humans have been fascinated and mystified by the appearance of comets. But starting in the 16th century, astronomers were able to use math to unlock the secrets of comets and were able to predict their appearances.

The most famous such comet is Halley's Comet. It has been appearing for millions of years, but its occasional appearances remained a mystery until British astronomer Sir Edmond Halley began studying it in 1704. He noticed that earlier records showed that a comet had appeared in the same region of the sky in 1456, 1531, 1607, and 1682. He was the first person to suggest that it was the same comet appearing every 75 or 76 years, and correctly predicted that it would

reappear in 1758. (Sadly, he didn't live to see his prediction come true.)

When a circle is stretched in one direction, the resulting figure is called an ellipse. Scientists have determined that the paths comets take through the solar system are elliptical in shape. Armed with this knowledge and some data, they can use math to calculate the path, speed, and appearance dates of some comets.

Answers to Try This One

1 $5,140.39

2 ≈ 3,394 square meters

3 49 square centimeters

4 45.5 square inches

5 20.3 feet

6 34.3 square feet

EXERCISE SET 10-4

Writing Exercises

1. How can we use the formula for the area of a rectangle to find the area of a parallelogram?
2. How can we use the formula for the area of a parallelogram to find the area of a triangle?
3. Explain the difference between perimeter and circumference.
4. What is the connection between the number π and the dimensions of a circle?

5. Explain the difference between area and perimeter.
6. Which polygon measure is of interest to you in each situation? Explain.
   (a) The amount of tile needed to refloor a room
   (b) Installing a fence around the outside of your back yard

Computational Exercises

For Exercises 7–26, find the area of each figure.

7.   17 in.

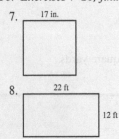

8.   22 ft
      12 ft

9.   15 yd
      30 yd

10.   105 cm
      150 cm

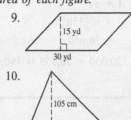

11.   20 m
      20 m

12.   10 ft
      14 ft

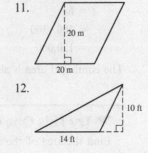

13.   26 mi
      24 mi

14.   11 in.
      9 in.

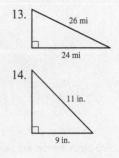

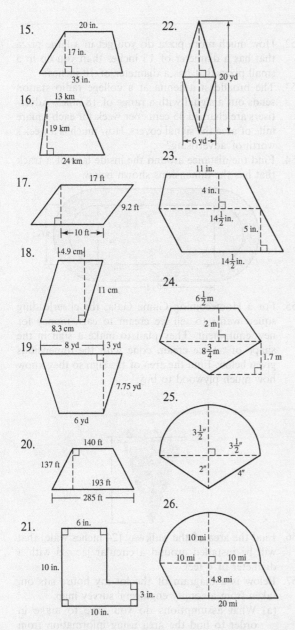

15.
16.
17.
18.
19.
20.
21.
22.
23.
24.
25.
26.

For all calculations involving π, answers may vary slightly depending on whether you use π = 3.14 or the π key on a calculator.

For Exercises 27–32, find the circumference and the area of each circle.

27.
28.

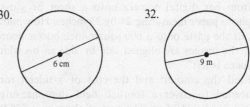

29.
31.
30.
32.

In Problems 33–38, find the area of the shaded region.

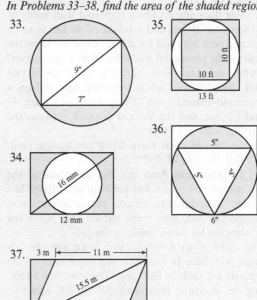

33.
35.
34.
36.

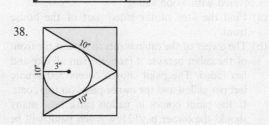

37.
38.

39. A circle has area 32 square feet. Find the radius.
40. A circle has area 9 square inches. Find the diameter.
41. A parallelogram has area 100 square miles and two of the parallel sides have length 12 miles. How far apart are those parallel sides?
42. A trapezoid has bases 9.2 feet and 11.3 feet and an area of 48 square feet. How far apart are the bases?

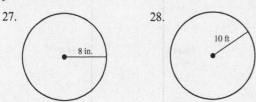

Applications in Our World

43. How many square yards of carpeting are needed to cover a square dorm room that measures 10 feet on a side?

44. Find the cost of coating a rectangular driveway that measures 11 feet by 21 feet, at $2.50 per square foot.

45. Dawn printed off several 3-inch by 5-inch pictures from her digital camera onto a sheet of glossy photo paper measuring 24 by 25 inches. How many can she paste onto a 600-square-inch poster board if the images are aligned side by side so no white space is left?

46. Find the amount and the cost of artificial turf needed to cover a football field that measures 360 feet by 160 feet. The cost of the turf is $20.00 per square foot.

47. A stage floor shaped like a trapezoid with bases of 60 feet and 75 feet and a height of 40 feet is to be covered with plywood for a play. What would be the cost for the plywood if it sells for $0.60 a square foot?

48. Derek and Amir have started a lawn care service and their first big job is installing new sod on a trapezoid-shaped lawn. The parallel sides are 41 and 62 feet, and the vertical distance between the parallel sides is 80 feet.
    (a) If the sod costs them $7.00 per square yard, find the cost of sod.
    (b) If Derek and Amir can put down sod at the rate of 900 square feet per hour and charge $65 per hour for their services plus a 20% markup on the sod, how much should they write the invoice for when finishing the job?

49. The front of an A-frame cabin is an isosceles triangle with base 16 feet. The two other sides of the triangle are each 18 feet long. The front has a rectangular doorway measuring 88″ by 34″ and two windows that are 3-foot by 3-foot squares. The rest is covered with wood siding.
    (a) Find the area of the sided part of the house front.
    (b) The owner of the cabin wants to repaint the front of the cabin because it faces the sun all day and has faded. The paint chosen covers 350 square feet per gallon and the owner plans on two coats. If the paint comes in gallon cans, how many should the owner buy? How much paint will be left over?

50. The fabric for a triangular team banner with base 6 feet and height twice as much costs $6.98 per square yard. How much will the fabric cost if 10% extra is bought to allow for waste?

51. Janelle and Sandra are planting various colors of flowers in a circular shape on the front lawn of their university to display the school's new logo. The circle has a diameter of 12 feet and the flowers cost $15.00 per square yard. Find the cost of the flowers.

52. How much more pizza do you get in a large pizza that has a diameter of 15 inches than you do in a small pizza that has a diameter of 10 inches?

53. The broadcast antenna at a college radio station sends out a signal with a range of 18 miles. Advertisers are charged 45 cents per week for each square mile of area the signal covers. How much is a week's worth of advertising?

54. Find the distance around the inside lane of a track that has the dimensions shown below.

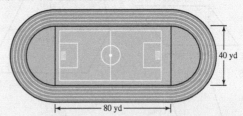

55. For a Homecoming Game Gala, the cheerleading squad wants to sell ice cream to earn money for new equipment. They plan to make a sign in the shape of an ice cream cone with the dimensions given below. Find the area of the sign so they know how much plywood to buy.

56. Find the area of the walkway (24 inches wide) that will be installed around a circular jacuzzi with a diameter of 6 feet.

57. Below is a diagram of the lot my house sits on, taken from a county engineers' survey map.
    (a) What assumptions do you have to make in order to find the area using information from this section?
    (b) Using your assumptions from part (a), find the area in square feet and acres. (One acre is 43,560 square feet.)

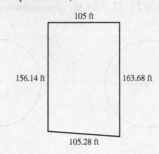

58. The next diagram is the lot owned by our friends across the street, the Pettys.
    (a) What assumptions do you have to make in order to find the area using information from this section?
    (b) Using your assumptions from part (a): Is their lot bigger or smaller than ours? By how many square feet? How many acres?

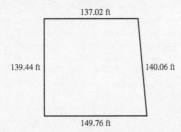

137.02 ft

139.44 ft

140.06 ft

149.76 ft

59. A rectangular billboard to advertise a new medical center opening is designed by a graphic artist to have length 12 feet more than height. The budget allows for an area of 240 square feet of space. How tall should the billboard be?

60. An engineer is designing a water ski jump with sides in the shape of right triangles. To get the slope she wants, the length of the base should be 3.4 times the height of the triangles, and in order to fit in the allotted space at the ski park, the area of each triangle should be no more than 30 square feet. Find the dimensions of the largest triangle she can design.

Critical Thinking

61. Under what conditions will the area of a circle be the same as its circumference?

62. We used the formula for the area of a parallelogram to develop a formula for the area of a trapezoid, but it can also be done by dividing a generic trapezoid into two triangles. Give it a try!

63. Review the definition of a circle on page 582. How can you use that definition to draw a perfect circle using things you can find lying around the house? (Tracing a circular object doesn't count!)

64. The area of a triangle can be found if the measures of the three sides are known. This formula was discovered about 100 BCE by a Greek mathematician known as Heron. Heron's formula is

$$A = \sqrt{s(s - a)(s - b)(s - c)}$$

where $s = \frac{1}{2}(a + b + c)$ and a, b, and c are the measures of the lengths of the sides of the triangle. Using the formula, find the area of a triangle if the sides are 5 in., 12 in., and 13 in.

65. The triangle in Problem 64 is also a right triangle. Find the area using the formula $A = \frac{1}{2}bh$ and see if you get the same answer.

66. What is the minimum number of measurements you need to find the area of a nonregular pentagon, like the one in the diagram? Explain how you came up with your answer.

67. Suppose that you want to fence in a rectangular plot of land, and you buy 80 feet of fence.
    (a) How much area will you enclose if you make one side 5 feet long?
    (b) Find the area enclosed if you make one side 10 feet, 15 feet, and 20 feet.
    (c) What do you think is the largest area you can enclose? What is the smallest?

68. Suppose that you plan to enclose 400 square feet of space in the shape of a rectangle with a fence.
    (a) Find the amount of fence you will need if you make one side 40 feet.
    (b) Find the amount of fence you will need if you make one side 35 feet, 30 feet, 25 feet, and 20 feet.
    (c) What do you think is the least amount of fence you can use? What about the most?

69. Suppose that the track in Exercise 54 has 8 lanes, each of which is 48 inches wide.
    (a) How much longer is one lap around the outside lane than the inside lane? (Assume that a runner has the sense to run as far inside his or her lane as possible.)
    (b) If two runners both run 10 laps at a pace of 6 minutes per mile, one in the inside lane and one in the outside lane, how much sooner would the inside runner finish?

70. A regular hexagon can be divided into six equilateral triangles. Use this fact to find the area of a regular hexagon that has 2-foot-long sides.

Section 10-5　Volume and Surface Area

Owning a swimming pool sounds pretty great, especially during those hot summer weekends. But a lot of work goes into maintaining a pool, and it takes a while to learn everything you need to know. A surprising amount of math goes into it, too. Once you

588   **Chapter 10**   Geometry

LEARNING OBJECTIVES

☐ 1. Find the volumes of three-dimensional figures.

☐ 2. Find the surface areas of three-dimensional figures.

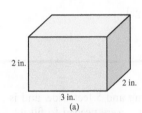

2 in.

3 in.
(a)

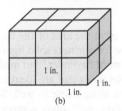

1 in.

1 in.   1 in.
(b)

Figure 10-22

fill up your pool with sparkling clear water, it won't stay that way very long if you don't add chemicals. But how much should you add? The amount of chemicals you need depends on the capacity of the pool, and that's where the math comes in.

In Section 9-2, we learned that capacity is a measure of volume, which is the amount of space enclosed by a three-dimensional object. We know that volume is measured in cubic units, like cubic inches or cubic meters, and we also have conversions to write volume in terms of familiar capacity units like gallons or liters.

A **polyhedron** is a three-dimensional figure bounded on all sides by polygons. The simplest polyhedra are rectangular solids and cubes, which are bounded on all sides by rectangles or squares. A rectangular solid is shown in Figure 10-22a. It has three dimensions: length (3 in.), width (2 in.), and height (2 in.). In Figure 10-22b, we see that you could build the solid out of 12 cubes that are 1 inch on all sides. That tells us that the volume of the rectangular solid is 12 cubic inches.

This volume can be obtained by multiplying the length, width, and height, giving us our first volume formula.

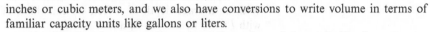

Volume Formulas for Rectangular Solids and Cubes

The volume of a rectangular solid is the product of the length, width, and height. For a cube, all three dimensions are equal, so the volume is the length of a side raised to the third power (cubed).

Rectangular Solid

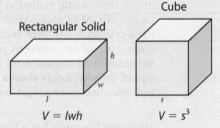

Cube

$V = lwh$ $V = s^3$

EXAMPLE 1   **Finding the Volume of a Rectangular Solid**

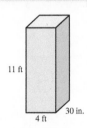

11 ft

4 ft   30 in.

Figure 10-23

Find the volume of the rectangular solid pictured in Figure 10-23.

SOLUTION

The length is 4 feet, the width is 30 inches, and the height is 11 feet. First, we need to rewrite 30 inches in terms of feet:

$$30 \text{ in.} \times \frac{1 \text{ ft}}{12 \text{ in.}} = \frac{30}{12} \text{ ft} = 2.5 \text{ ft}$$

Now we use the volume formula with $l = 4$, $w = 2.5$, and $h = 11$:

$$V = lwh = 4 \times 2.5 \times 11 = 110 \text{ ft}^3$$

▼ Try This One 1

Find the volume of a rectangular solid with length 10 meters, width 12 meters, and height 50 centimeters.

EXAMPLE 2

EXAMPLE 2   **Finding the Volume of a Swimming Pool**

In order to figure out how much chlorine to use, Judi needs to know the capacity of her pool. The pool is a rectangle 18 feet wide and 36 feet long, and has an average depth of 4 feet. How many gallons does it hold? (There are 7.48 gallons in 1 cubic foot.)

SOLUTION

With an average depth of 4 feet, we can think of the pool as a rectangular solid with $l = 36$ ft, $w = 18$ ft, and $h = 4$ ft.

$$V = lwh = 36 \times 18 \times 4 = 2{,}592 \text{ ft}^3$$

Now we use dimensional analysis to convert to gallons:

$$2{,}592 \text{ ft}^3 \times \frac{7.48 \text{ gal}}{1 \text{ ft}^3} \approx 19{,}388 \text{ gal}$$

The capacity of the pool is about 19,388 gallons.

▼ **Try This One 2**

A rectangular dunking tank at a carnival is 4 feet long and 5 feet wide, and is filled to a depth of 4 feet. How many gallons of water were needed to fill it?

Notice that the volume of a rectangular solid can be thought of as the area of the base (length times width) multiplied by the height. The same is true for our next solid figure, the cylinder. Most people think "round" when they hear the word "cylinder," but actually a cylinder is any three-dimensional figure with two parallel bases that are identical shapes, and all cross-sections parallel to those bases are that same shape as well. So technically a rectangular solid is also a cylinder. In this section, we'll study a special type of cylinder: a **right circular cylinder** is a figure with a circular top and bottom, and with sides that make a right angle with the top and bottom. (Think of a soda can.)

Volume Formula for a Right Circular Cylinder

The volume of a right circular cylinder is given by the formula

$$V = \pi r^2 h$$

where r is the radius of the circular ends and h is the height.

Cylinder

$$V = \pi r^2 h$$

Math Note

Since the area of a circle with radius r is πr^2, the volume of a right circular cylinder is the area of the base times the height, just like a rectangular solid.

EXAMPLE 3   **Finding the Volume of a Cylinder**

How many cubic inches does a soup can hold if it is a right circular cylinder with height 4 inches and radius 1.5 inches? How many ounces? (One ounce is about 1.8 cubic inches.)

SOLUTION

Using $r = 1.5$ in. and $h = 4$ in., we get

$$V = \pi r^2 h = \pi \cdot 1.5^2 \cdot 4 = 9\pi \approx 28.3 \text{ in.}^3$$

Back to our old friend dimensional analysis to convert to ounces:

$$28.3 \text{ in.}^3 \times \frac{1 \text{ oz}}{1.8 \text{ in.}^3} = 15.7 \text{ oz}$$

▼ Try This One 3

Find the volume of an oil storage tank that is a right circular cylinder with height 40 feet and radius 15 feet. How many quarts of oil will it hold? (One cubic foot is about 29.9 quarts.)

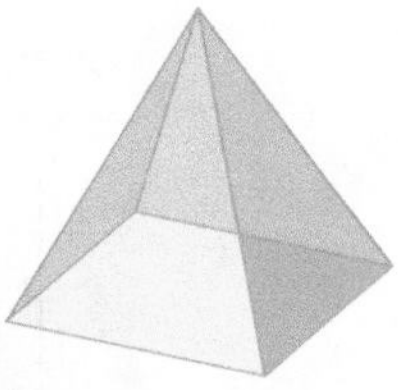

A right circular cylinder is not a polyhedron because the edges aren't polygons, but our next figure is. A **pyramid** is a polyhedron whose base is a polygon and whose sides are triangles. An example with a square base is shown in Figure 10-24.

Figure 10-24

Volume Formula for a Pyramid

The volume of a pyramid is given by the formula

$$V = \frac{1}{3}Bh$$

where B is the area of the base and h is the height.

$V = \frac{1}{3}Bh$, where B is the area of the base

Math Note

Notice that the formula for the volume of a pyramid also multiplies the area of the base by the height. But the factor of $\frac{1}{3}$ is needed because with the pyramid tapering to a point, the volume has to be a lot less than a cylinder with the same base.

EXAMPLE 4   Finding the Volume of a Pyramid

Math Note

For some perspective, the volume of the Great Pyramid found in Example 4 is almost two and a half times the volume of the Empire State Building, which was the tallest building in New York City until the new World Trade Center surpassed it in 2012.

The Great Pyramid at Giza was built by the Egyptians roughly 4,570 years ago. It has a square base measuring 230.6 meters on a side and is 138.8 meters high. Find its volume.

SOLUTION

Since the base is a square that is 230.6 meters on a side, its area is 230.6^2, or 53,176.36 square meters. Using the volume formula with $B = 53,176.36$ and $h = 138.8$, we get

$$V = \frac{1}{3} \cdot 53,176.36 \cdot 138.8 \approx 2,460,293 \text{ m}^3$$

▼ Try This One 4

The smallest of the three great pyramids is the Pyramid of Menkaure. Its base measures 339 feet on each side, and it is 215 feet high. Find the volume.

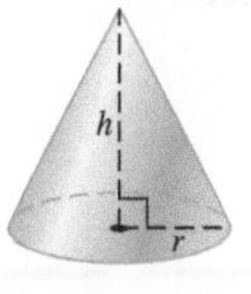

Figure 10-25

The next figure we will discuss is the **right circular cone**. This is similar to a pyramid with a circular base, as shown in Figure 10-25.

Not surprisingly, the volume formula matches the pyramid formula: one-third times the area of the base times the height. But the base is a circle with area πr^2, so we get the following:

Volume Formula for a Right Circular Cone

The volume of a right circular cone is given by

$$V = \frac{1}{3}\pi r^2 h$$

where r is the radius of the circular bottom and h is the height.

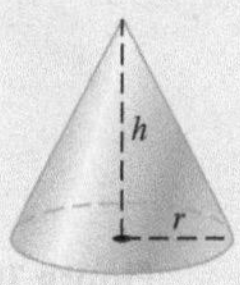

$V = \frac{1}{3}\pi r^2 h$

EXAMPLE 5   Finding the Volume of a Cone

Math Note

Like the formula for the volume of a pyramid, the volume formula for a right circular cone is area of the base times height with a factor of $\frac{1}{3}$ multiplied in to account for the figure tapering to a point.

The cups attached to a water cooler on a golf course are right circular cones with radius 1.5 inches and height 3 inches. How many ounces of water do they hold? (One ounce is about 1.8 cubic inches.)

SOLUTION

Using $r = 1.5$ and $h = 3$, we get

$$V = \frac{1}{3}\pi r^2 h = \frac{1}{3}\pi (1.5 \text{ in.})^2 (3 \text{ in.}) \approx 7.1 \text{ in.}^3$$

Now we convert to ounces:

$$7.1 \text{ in.}^3 \times \frac{1 \text{ oz}}{1.8 \text{ in.}^3} \approx 3.9 \text{ oz}$$

The cups hold about 3.9 ounces of water.

▼ Try This One 5

How many ounces of melted ice cream does an ice cream cone hold if it has a radius of 1.1 inches and a height of 5 inches?

Many of the games we play use solid objects that are circular in three dimensions—basketballs, baseballs, golf balls, pool balls, etc. The geometric name for such an object is a **sphere**. Just as a circle is the set of all points in a plane that are the same distance from a fixed point, a sphere is the set of all points in space that are the same distance away from a fixed point. And we use the same terminology: the fixed point is called the **center** of the sphere, and the distance is called the **radius**. (Twice the radius is called the **diameter**.)

592   **Chapter 10**   Geometry

Math Note

The formula for the volume of a sphere was originally developed experimentally, and its original proof is considered to be one of the greatest works of ancient Greek mathematics. But calculus turned the proof into a very simple exercise.

Volume Formula for a Sphere

The volume of a sphere is given by the formula

$$V = \frac{4}{3}\pi r^3$$

where r is the radius of the sphere.

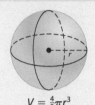

$V = \frac{4}{3}\pi r^3$

EXAMPLE 6   **Finding the Volume of a Sphere**

The famous ball at Epcot center in Orlando has a diameter of 164 feet. Find its volume.

SOLUTION

To find the volume, we need the radius. The diameter is twice the radius, so the radius in this case is half of 164 feet, or 82 feet.

$$V = \frac{4}{3}\pi r^3 = \frac{4}{3}\pi(82)^3 \approx 2{,}309{,}565 \text{ ft}^3$$

The volume of the ball is about 2,309,565 cubic feet.

▼ **Try This One 6**

An official NBA basketball is a sphere with diameter 9.4 inches. What is the volume?

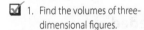 1. Find the volumes of three-dimensional figures.

Surface Area

The area of the outer surface of a three-dimensional figure is called the **surface area**. For example, consider a cube. A cube has six faces (think of a standard die, numbered 1 through 6). Each of them is a square with area s^2, where s is the length of a side. So the surface area is $6s^2$.

The surface areas of some of the figures we've studied are listed in Table 10-3.

TABLE 10-3   **Surface Area Formulas for Three-Dimensional Figures**

Math Note

In the case of the polyhedra (cube and rectangular solid) the surface area is obtained by simply adding the areas of the polygons that make up its sides.

All variables represent the same dimensions as in the volume formulas. SA represents surface area.

Cube	$SA = 6s^2$
Rectangular	$SA = 2lw + 2lh + 2wh$
Right circular cylinder	$SA = 2\pi r^2 + 2\pi rh$
Sphere	$SA = 4\pi r^2$
Pyramid (Square base)	$SA = l^2 + 2l\sqrt{\dfrac{l^2}{4} + h^2}$ (l = length of base)
Right circular cone	$SA = \pi r^2 + \pi r\sqrt{r^2 + h^2}$

The relation between surface area and volume is important when determining how something will absorb or lose heat. Ice absorbs heat through its surface. When you break up a large piece of ice, the volume stays the same, but the surface area is greatly increased. So small ice cubes melt quickly, and large blocks of ice last much longer.

| **EXAMPLE 7** | **Finding the Surface Area of a Cylinder** |

How many square inches of sheet metal are needed to form the soup can in Example 3?

SOLUTION

The radius of the can is 1.5 inches, and the height is 4 inches. Using the formula from Table 10-3:

$$
\begin{aligned}
SA &= 2\pi r^2 + 2\pi rh \\
&= 2\pi(1.5)^2 + 2\pi(1.5)(4) \\
&= 4.5\pi + 12\pi \\
&= 16.5\pi \approx 51.8 \text{ in.}^2
\end{aligned}
$$

▼ Try This One 7

☑ 2. Find the surface areas of three-dimensional figures.

How many square inches of leather are needed to cover an NBA basketball? (See Try This One 6 for dimensions, and ignore the seams on the ball.)

| **EXAMPLE 8** | **Finding the Amount of Building Material Needed** |

4 ft

14 ft

5.5 ft

Figure 10-26

An aluminum silo is being made from a right circular cylinder with a right circular cone on top. The radius of the cylinder is $5\frac{1}{2}$ feet and the height is 14 feet; the cone has height 4 feet. How many square feet of aluminum will be needed for construction?

SOLUTION

The most important thing to note is that the amount of material in square feet makes this a surface area problem. A diagram will be helpful: see Figure 10-26.

We'll have to be careful with the cylinder part: we'll want a bottom but not a top, so instead of $2\pi r^2$ in the formula, we use just πr^2.

Cylinder with no top: $\begin{aligned} SA &= \pi r^2 + 2\pi rh \\ &= \pi(5.5)^2 + 2\pi(5.5)(14) \\ &\approx 578.8 \text{ ft}^3 \end{aligned}$

For the cone, we'll also need to remove the bottom, which is the πr^2 part of the formula.

Cone with no bottom: $\begin{aligned} SA &= \pi r\sqrt{r^2 + h^2} \\ &= \pi(5.5)\sqrt{(5.5)^2 + 4^2} \\ &\approx 117.5 \text{ ft}^3 \end{aligned}$

Total surface area: $578.8 + 117.5 = 696.3 \text{ ft}^3$.

594   **Chapter 10**   Geometry

▼ Try This One 8

A sheet metal storage shed will be a rectangular solid with square base (8 feet on a side) and height 7 feet. The roof will be a pyramid with base matching the rectangular solid and height 2 feet. Find the number of square feet of sheet metal needed.

Answers to Try This One

1   60 cubic meters

2   598.4 gallons

3   About 28,274 cubic feet; about 845,392.6 quarts

4   8,236,005 cubic feet

5   About 3.5 ounces

6   About 435 cubic inches

7   About 277.6 square inches

8   About 295.6 square feet

EXERCISE SET 10-5

Writing Exercises

1. Explain why the volume of a rectangular solid is the product of length, width, and height.
2. Explain why the volume of a cube is the length of a side raised to the third power.
3. What is the difference between volume and surface area?
4. Describe the connection between the volume formulas $V = lwh$ and $V = \pi r^2 h$.
5. Explain why the surface area of a cube is $6s^2$, where s is the length of a side.
6. Is the height of a pyramid the length of one of the sides? Why or why not?

Computational Exercises

For Exercises 7–18, find the volume of each figure.

7.

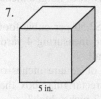

5 in.

8.

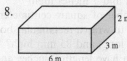

2 m
3 m
6 m

9.

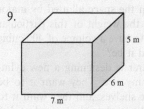

5 m
6 m
7 m

10.

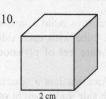

2 cm

11.

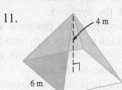

4 m
6 m
6 m

12.

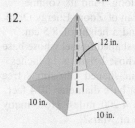

12 in.
10 in.
10 in.

13.

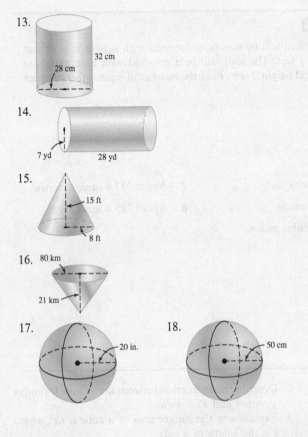

14.

15.

16.

17.   18.

For Exercises 19 and 20, find the volume of the solid figure not including the hole cutout.

19.

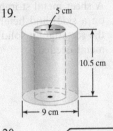

20.

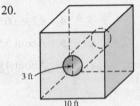

In Exercises 21–32, find the surface area of the figure from the given exercise.

21. Exercise 7	27. Exercise 13
22. Exercise 8	28. Exercise 14
23. Exercise 9	29. Exercise 15
24. Exercise 10	30. Exercise 16
25. Exercise 11	31. Exercise 17
26. Exercise 12	32. Exercise 18

Applications in Our World

33. How many cubic feet of dirt will be removed to build an inground swimming pool whose dimensions are 18 feet in length, 12 feet in width, and 3 feet in depth?

34. At a college tech expo, Jamal wants to build a simple display table in the shape of a cube with each side measuring 6 feet. How many square feet of plywood will be needed?

35. A pyramid found in Central America has a square base measuring 932 feet on each side and a height of 657 feet. Find the volume of the pyramid.

36. For her class in entrepreneurship, Jenny designed a pop-up tent made for dogs in the shape of a pyramid with a square base measuring 6 feet on a side with a height of 4 feet. Find the volume of the tent.

37. A cylindrical-shaped gasoline tank has a 22-inch diameter and is 36 inches long. Find its volume.

38. Find the surface area of a can of Zoom Energy Drink with a diameter of 8 cm and a height of 8.5 cm.

39. Find the volume of a cone-shaped funnel whose base diameter is 7 inches and whose height is 11 inches.

40. Find the volume of a cone-shaped Christmas tree that is 6 feet tall and has a base diameter of 4 feet.

41. The diameter of Mars is 4,200 miles. How many square miles is the surface of Mars?

42. The diameter of the moon is 3,474 kilometers. If the moon were made of green cheese, how many cubic kilometers of cheese would there be?

43. How many cubic inches of packing peanuts can be held by a rectangular box that is 1 foot long, 8 inches wide, and 2 feet tall?

44. A storage shed maker charges $2.50 per cubic foot. Find the price of a custom shed measuring 4 yards long, 5 yards wide, and 8 feet tall.

45. What is the minimum number of square inches of cardboard required to make a rectangular box that is 1 foot long, 2 feet wide, and 7 inches high?

46. What is the minimum number of square centimeters of wrapping paper needed to wrap a rectangular box that is 40 cm wide, 60 cm long, and 85 mm high?

47. A cereal box is required to have length 9 inches and height 13 inches to fit in the space allotted by major grocery chains. To hold the weight of this particular cereal required, it needs to have a volume of 400 cubic inches. How wide should it be?

48. A motor oil manufacturer is designing a new cylindrical can for its economy size. They want it to be 23 cm tall so it fits store shelves, and they want it to hold 2 liters of oil. What should the radius be? (Recall that 1 cubic centimeter = 1 milliliter.)

596   **Chapter 10**   Geometry

For Exercises 49–52, suppose that a particular brand of paint claims that under normal conditions, each gallon will cover 350 square feet. The paint is sold in 5-gallon and 1-gallon cans, with the 5-gallon costing the same as 4 1-gallon cans. Find how many cans of each should be bought for each situation to keep the cost as low as possible.

49. To paint the walls and flat roof of a rectangular building that is 40 feet long, 30 feet wide, and 12 feet high.

50. To paint forty 55-gallon drums that are being reconditioned for sale, including the top and bottom. Each drum has a height of 35 inches and a diameter of 24 inches.

51. To paint the outside walls of a round above-ground swimming pool with a diameter of 25 feet and a height of 4 feet.

52. To paint a giant papier-mâché model of the moon, which is a sphere with a diameter of 26 feet.

53. Sarah and Jack got an air purifier as a wedding gift. The maker of this particular model claims that it processes 10,000 cubic feet per hour and that all air in a room is processed five times every hour.
    (a) Find the volume of a room for which those two claims match.
    (b) If Sarah and Jack's master bedroom measures 22 feet by 18 feet and has 10-foot ceilings, how many times per hour can the purifier process the air in the room?

54. Now that they have a shiny new air purifier, Sarah and Jack (Problem 53) decide to repaint and recarpet the master bedroom as well, so it's off to Home Depot. Paint for the walls is $27 per gallon and each gallon covers 350 square feet. The ceiling paint is $16 per gallon with the same coverage, and the carpet is $26 per square yard installed. How much will they spend? (Don't forget that they have to buy paint by the full gallon. And you can ignore doors and windows.)

Critical Thinking

55. Twelve rubber balls with 3-inch diameters are placed in a box with dimensions 12 inches × 9 inches × 3 inches. Find the volume of the space that is left over.

56. A rain gutter (cross section shown) is 24 feet long. How much water will it hold when it's full? One cubic foot of water is equal to 7.48 gallons.

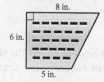

57. Find the surface area of the pyramid in Exercise 11 without using the formula provided in Table 10-3 by finding areas of the sides first. (*Hint:* You'll need the Pythagorean theorem.)

58. Use the technique from Question 57 to prove the formula for the surface area of a pyramid provided in Table 10-3.

59. By finding the area of the top, bottom, and sides separately, prove the formula for the surface area of a cylinder provided in Table 10-3. (*Hint:* What would the sides look like if you unrolled the cylinder?)

60. Find the surface area of a silo that is a cylinder with radius 9 feet and height 22 feet, with a dome-shaped top that is half of a sphere.

61. A bowling ball is a sphere (duh) with diameter $8\frac{1}{2}$ inches.
    (a) How many bowling balls can you fit into a rectangular room with a square base ($8\frac{1}{2}$ feet on a side) that is 10 feet tall if the balls are stacked directly on top of each other?
    (b) How much empty space will there be in the room in cubic feet?
    (c) What percentage of the space in the room is filled?

(d) The bowling balls as stacked in part (a) don't quite reach the ceiling. Suppose that the ceiling is lowered so that the number of bowling balls found in (a) exactly touches all the walls and the ceiling. What percentage of the space in the room is filled now?

62. A golf ball is a sphere (again, duh) with radius 2.13 cm.
    (a) How many golf balls can you fit inside the room in Exercise 61 if the balls are stacked directly on top of each other?
    (b) How much empty space will there be in the room in cubic feet?
    (c) What percentage of the space in the room is filled?
    (d) If the walls and ceiling were moved in a bit so that the number of golf balls from part (a) fit exactly inside [as in 61(d)], what percentage of the space in the room would be filled?

63. A pyramid is placed flat side down into a rectangular box with a square base. The dimensions of the base of the pyramid are the same as those for the base of the box, and the pyramid reaches just to the top of the box. What percentage of the box is filled by the pyramid?

64. (a) A right circular cone is placed inside a right circular cylinder with the same radius as the base of the cone. The cone just reaches to the top of the cylinder. What percentage of the cylinder is filled by the cone?
    (b) Another cone is sitting on a flat surface covered by a dome that is made from half of a sphere. The base of the cone is the same size as the bottom of the dome, and the cone just reaches the top of the dome. What percentage of the dome is filled by the cone?

Section 10-6   Right Triangle Trigonometry

We have seen that triangles can be used to solve many practical problems, but there are still many problems involving triangles that we can't solve using what we've learned so far. Here's a simple example. Like pretty much everything you buy today, ladders come with a variety of safety warnings designed to keep the manufacturer from getting sued. Suppose you buy a 12-foot ladder to do some work around the house, and the safety warning tells you it should not be placed at an angle steeper than 65° with the ground. Assuming that you don't have a protractor handy, how can you decide if it's safe to place the bottom 4 feet from the wall?

In this section we will study the basics of **trigonometry**, a very old subject whose name literally means "angle measurement." In trigonometry, we use relationships among the sides and angles of triangles to solve problems. This is in some ways like the work we did earlier with similar triangles, but is more widely applicable.

The big restriction we work with when studying the basics of trigonometry is that all triangles have to be right triangles. In this section, we'll use capital letters A, B, and C to represent the angles, and lower-case letters a, b, and c to represent the lengths of the sides. **We will always use C to represent the right angle**. In each case, the letter of an angle matches the letter of the side across from it. So, for example, a will represent the length of the side across from angle A. (See Figure 10-27.)

Figure 10-27

Math Note

Remember, in a right triangle, the side across from the right angle is called the hypotenuse. It's always the longest side.

The Trigonometric Ratios

There are three basic trigonometric ratios. They are called the **sine** (abbreviated sin), the **cosine** (abbreviated cos), and the **tangent** (abbreviated tan). The trigonometric ratios are defined as follows:

The Trigonometric Ratios

$$\sin A = \frac{\text{Length of side opposite angle } A}{\text{Length of hypotenuse}} = \frac{a}{c}$$

$$\cos A = \frac{\text{Length of side adjacent to angle } A}{\text{Length of hypotenuse}} = \frac{b}{c}$$

$$\tan A = \frac{\text{Length of side opposite angle } A}{\text{Length of side adjacent to angle } A} = \frac{a}{b}$$

Math Note

Generations of students have remembered the trigonometric ratios using this simple mnemonic device: SOHCAHTOA (which most students pronounce "sow-cah-tow-ah").

This stands for Sine is Opposite over Hypotenuse, Cosine is Adjacent over Hypotenuse, Tangent is Opposite over Adjacent.

EXAMPLE 1   Finding Basic Trigonometric Ratios

For the triangle shown, find sin B, cos B, and tan B.

SOLUTION

Since two of the three ratios involve the length of the hypotenuse, we need to find that first, using the Pythagorean theorem. (The hypotenuse is across from angle C, so we label its length c.)

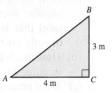

598   **Chapter 10** Geometry

Math Note

Notice that the units divide out when you compute the trigonometric ratios, so the units of length are unimportant in defining the ratios.

But the units have to be consistent! If the hypotenuse is given in feet and one of the legs in inches, you have to convert one or the other to make the units match before finding the trig ratios.

☑ 1. Find basic trigonometric ratios.

$$c^2 = a^2 + b^2$$
$$= 4^2 + 3^2 = 16 + 9 = 25 \quad \textit{Apply the square root to both sides.}$$
$$c = \sqrt{25} = 5 \text{ m} \qquad \textit{Discard the negative answer: c is a length.}$$

Now we can use the trigonometric ratios from the definitions above; the hypotenuse is 5 m, the side opposite B is 4 m, and the side adjacent to B is 3 m.

$$\sin B = \frac{\text{Opposite}}{\text{Hypotenuse}} = \frac{4 \text{ m}}{5 \text{ m}} = \frac{4}{5}$$

$$\cos B = \frac{\text{Adjacent}}{\text{Hypotenuse}} = \frac{3 \text{ m}}{5 \text{ m}} = \frac{3}{5}$$

$$\tan B = \frac{\text{Opposite}}{\text{Adjacent}} = \frac{4 \text{ m}}{3 \text{ m}} = \frac{4}{3}$$

▼ **Try This One 1**

Find sin A, cos A, and tan A for the triangle below.

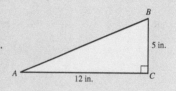

CAUTION

The symbols "sin," "cos," and "tan" are instructions to do something to the angle that comes after them, much like the symbol $\sqrt{\ }$ is an instruction to do something to the number underneath. So you should NEVER write one of those symbols with nothing after it: cos is just as meaningless as a square root symbol with nothing under it.

Calculator Guide

To use a calculator in solving problems involving trigonometric ratios, you will have to make sure your calculator is set to degree mode:

Standard Scientific Calculator

Press MODE, DRG, or RAD until you see "Deg" in the display window.

Standard Graphing Calculator

Press MODE, use arrow keys to select "DEGREE," then exit by pressing 2nd MODE

The trigonometric ratios wouldn't be very useful if they gave different values for the same angle measure in different triangles—certainly we want sin 30° to be the same regardless of the size of the triangle the 30° angle came from. Fortunately, this is the case, because of what we learned about similar triangles. In Figure 10-28, we see two different right triangles with a 30° angle. Because the triangles are similar, the ratios of corresponding sides are equal, so sin 30° is $\frac{1}{2}$ in both triangles.

One situation that trigonometry is often used for is to find the lengths of sides of a triangle. If we know one side and one of the acute angles, we can find either of the remaining sides, as in Example 2.

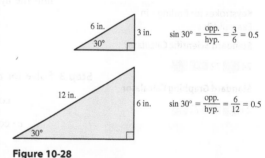

Figure 10-28

EXAMPLE 2   Finding a Side of a Triangle Using Tangent

In the right triangle ABC, find the length of side a when $m\angle A = 30°$ and $b = 200$ feet.

SOLUTION

Step 1 Draw and label the figure.

Step 2 Choose an appropriate trigonometric ratio and substitute values into it. In this case, we know the

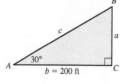

Math Note

There's usually more than one way to find the length of a side using the trigonometric ratios. In Example 2, we could have noticed that $m\angle B = 60°$ and used the tangent of B to set up an equation.

side adjacent to angle A, and are asked to find the side opposite, so tangent is a good choice.

$$\tan A = \frac{\text{Opposite}}{\text{Adjacent}} = \frac{a}{b}$$

$$\tan 30° = \frac{a}{200}$$

Step 3 Solve the resulting equation for a.

$$\tan 30° = \frac{a}{200} \qquad \textit{Multiply both sides by 200.}$$

$$a = 200 \tan 30°$$

To evaluate this answer, we use a calculator in degree mode (see Calculator Guide on previous page) and press 200 ⊠ 30 ⟨TAN⟩ ⟨=⟩ (standard scientific calculator), or 200 ⟨TAN⟩ 30 ⟨ENTER⟩ (standard graphing calculator). The result in either case, rounded to two decimal places, is 115.47, so the length of side a is 115.47 feet.

▼ Try This One 2

In the right triangle ABC, find the length of side b if $m\angle B = 58°$ and $a = 12$ inches.

EXAMPLE 3   Finding a Side of a Triangle Using Cosine

In the right triangle ABC, find the measure of side c when $m\angle B = 72°$ and the length of side a is 24 feet.

SOLUTION

Step 1 Draw and label the figure.

Step 2 We know the side adjacent to B and want to find the hypotenuse, so cosine is a good choice.

$$\cos B = \frac{a}{c}$$

$$\cos 72° = \frac{24}{c}$$

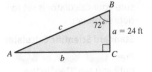

Step 3 Solve for c.

$$\cos 72° = \frac{24}{c} \qquad \textit{Multiply both sides by } c.$$

$$c \cdot \cos 72° = 24 \qquad \textit{Divide both sides by } \cos 72°.$$

$$c = \frac{24}{\cos 72°} \approx 77.67 \text{ ft (to two decimal places)}$$

Calculator Guide

Keystrokes for finding c in Example 3:

Standard Scientific Calculator

24 ⟨÷⟩ 72 ⟨COS⟩ ⟨=⟩

Standard Graphing Calculator

24 ⟨÷⟩ ⟨COS⟩ 72 ⟨ENTER⟩

☑ 2. Use trigonometric ratios to find sides of a right triangle.

▼ Try This One 3

In the right triangle ABC, find the measure of side b when $m\angle A = 53°$ and the hypotenuse (side c) is 18 cm.

Trigonometric ratios can be used to find angles as well, provided that we know at least two sides of a right triangle. To accomplish this, we'll need to use special routines programmed into a calculator known as **inverse trigonometric functions**. They are accessed using the ⟨2nd⟩ key on most calculators, as illustrated in Example 4.

EXAMPLE 4   **Finding an Angle Using Trigonometric Ratios**

In the right triangle ABC, side c (the hypotenuse) measures 25 inches and side b measures 24 inches. Find the measure of angle B.

SOLUTION

Step 1 Draw and label the figure.

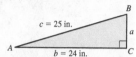

Step 2 We know the hypotenuse and the side opposite angle B, so sine is a good choice.

$$\sin B = \frac{\text{Opposite}}{\text{Hypotenuse}} = \frac{24}{25} = 0.96$$

Step 3 Solve for B. To accomplish this, we will need to access the inverse sine feature on a calculator: .96 [2nd] [SIN] (standard scientific calculator), or [2nd] [SIN] .96 [ENTER] (standard graphing calculator). The result, rounded to two decimal places, is 73.74, so $m\angle B \approx 73.74°$.

▼ Try This One 4

Find the measure of angle A for the right triangle ABC if the measure of side a is 42 inches and the measure of side b is 18 inches.

In the remainder of the section, we will demonstrate just a few of the many, many problems in our world that can be solved using trigonometry. To begin, we return to the ladder question that began the section.

EXAMPLE 5   **An Application of Trigonometry to Home Improvement**

The safety label on a 12-foot ladder says that the ladder should not be placed at an angle steeper than 65° with the ground. What is the closest safe distance between the base of the ladder and the wall?

SOLUTION

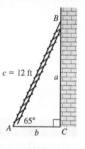

Step 1 Draw and label the figure.

Step 2 Choose the appropriate formula and substitute the values for the variables. Since we need to find the length of side b and we are given the measures of angle A and side c, cosine is a good choice.

$$\cos A = \frac{\text{Adjacent}}{\text{Hypotenuse}} = \frac{b}{c}$$

$$\cos 65° = \frac{b}{12}$$

Step 3 Solve for b. $\cos 65° = \dfrac{b}{12}$

$$b = 12 \cos 65° \approx 5.07 \text{ feet}$$

The bottom of the ladder can't be any closer than 5.07 feet from the wall.

▼ Try This One 5

Being afraid of heights, a homeowner determines that he's unwilling to place the ladder in Example 5 any steeper than a 50° angle with the ground. How far up the wall will the ladder reach at that angle?

Math Note

The symbol $\sin^{-1}$ is used to represent the inverse of sine. Likewise, $\cos^{-1}$ and $\tan^{-1}$ represent the inverses of cosine and tangent, respectively. When working with right triangles, you can think of these symbols as instructions that "undo" sine, cosine, or tangent, leaving the angle behind.

☑ 3. Use trigonometric ratios to find angles of a right triangle.

Calculator Guide

Keystrokes for finding b:

Standard Scientific Calculator

12 [×] 65 [COS] [=]

Standard Graphing Calculator

12 [×] [COS] 65 [ENTER]

Angle of Elevation and Angle of Depression

A lot of applications of right angle trigonometry in our world use what we call the *angle of elevation* or the *angle of depression*.

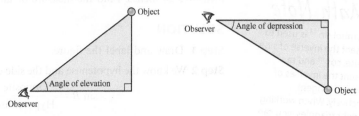

Figure 10-29

Trigonometry is used extensively in surveying.

The **angle of elevation** of an object is the measure of the angle from a horizontal line at the point of an observer upward to the line of sight to the object. The angle of **depression** is the measure of an angle from a horizontal line at the point of an observer downward to the line of sight to the object. See Figure 10-29.

EXAMPLE 6   Finding the Height of a Tall Object Using Trigonometry

In order to find the height of a building, an observer who is 6 feet tall measures the angle of elevation from his head to the top of the building to be 32° when he is standing at a point 200 feet from the building. How tall is the building?

SOLUTION

Step 1 Draw and label the figure.

Step 2 Choose the appropriate formula and substitute the values for the variables. Since we are given the measure of angle A and the measure of side b, we can use tangent.

$$\tan A = \frac{\text{Opposite}}{\text{Adjacent}} = \frac{a}{b}$$

$$\tan 32° = \frac{a}{200}$$

Step 3 Solve for a.

$$\tan 32° = \frac{a}{200} \quad \textit{Multiply both sides by 200.}$$

$$a = 200 \tan 32° \approx 125 \text{ feet (to the nearest foot)}$$

Looking back at the diagram, we see that the height of the building is side a (125 feet) plus 6 feet, so the building is 131 feet tall.

Calculator Guide

Keystrokes for finding a:

Standard Scientific Calculator

200 [×] 32 [TAN] [=]

Standard Graphing Calculator

200 [×] [TAN] 32 [ENTER]

▼ **Try This One 6**

A hiker standing on top of a 150-foot cliff sights a boat at an angle of depression of 24°. How far is the boat from the base of the cliff? (The hiker's eye level is 5.6 feet above the top of the cliff.)

602   **Chapter 10**   Geometry

EXAMPLE 7   **Finding an Angle of Depression**

A local photographer gets a hot tip that a famous starlet is sunbathing on a boat cruising down a river in a state of undress that her father would not be proud of. He sets up his camera on a bridge that is 22 feet above the water hoping to get a shot as the boat rounds a nearby bend in the river (the photographer, not the starlet's father). A laser range finder tells him that his eye level is 72 feet from the point where the boat will come into view. At what angle of depression should he aim the camera's tripod?

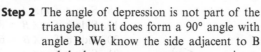

SOLUTION

Step 1 Draw and label the figure (in the margin).

Step 2 The angle of depression is not part of the triangle, but it does form a 90° angle with angle B. We know the side adjacent to B and the hypotenuse, so we can use cosine to find angle B, then subtract from 90° to get the angle of depression.

$$\cos B = \frac{\text{Adjacent}}{\text{Hypotenuse}} = \frac{22}{72}$$

Step 3 Solve for B using the inverse cosine feature on a calculator (see Calculator Guide).

$$B \approx 72.2°$$

Step 4 Subtract angle B from 90°: 90° − 72.2° = 17.8°. The angle of depression should be a bit less than 18°.

Calculator Guide

Keystrokes for finding angle B:

Standard Scientific Calculator

22 ÷ 72 = 2nd COS

Standard Graphing Calculator

2nd COS 22 ÷ 72 ENTER

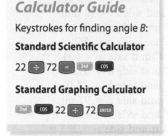

☑ 4. Solve problems using trigonometric ratios.

▼ **Try This One 7**

Marie hopes to photograph the rising sun as it just peeks over the top of a 20-foot-tall house across the street, 120 feet from where she is sitting on the ground. At what angle of elevation should she aim the camera?

CAUTION

If you're planning to use trig ratios to solve an applied problem, the most important step is to make sure that there's actually a right triangle in the diagram. If not, the trig ratios simply don't apply.

Answers to Try This One

1   $\sin A = \frac{5}{13}$; $\cos A = \frac{12}{13}$; $\tan A = \frac{5}{12}$

2   19.20 inches

3   10.83 cm

4   66.80°

5   9.19 feet

6   349.48 feet

7   9.46°

Math for Liberal Arts Majors

EXERCISE SET 10-6

Writing Exercises

1. Describe each of the trigonometric ratios in terms of sides of a right triangle.
2. Given a right triangle ABC with right angle C, explain how we would label the lengths of the sides using the letters we used in this section.
3. Why can we be sure that $\sin 30°$ always has the same value regardless of the size of the right triangle containing the 30° angle?
4. Describe what is meant by an angle of elevation and an angle of depression.
5. Explain why the question "Find tan" is silly and meaningless.
6. What feature of a calculator is needed to solve for one of the angles in a right triangle? Describe how to use it.

Computational Exercises

For Exercises 7–14, use the given right triangle to find cos A, sin A, and tan A.

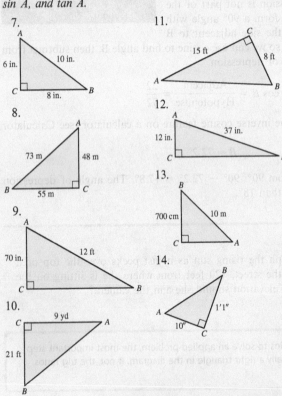

7.

8.

9.

10.

11.

12.

13.

14.

17. Side c if $m\angle A = 76°$ and side $b = 18.6$ in.
18. Side a if $m\angle A = 30°$ and side $c = 40$ km
19. Side b if $m\angle B = 8°$ and side $c = 10$ mm
20. Side c if $m\angle B = 62°$ and side $a = 313$ mi
21. Side a if $m\angle A = 32°$ and side $b = 86\frac{1}{8}$ in.
22. Side b if $m\angle B = 82.4°$ and side $a = 634.8$ ft
23. Side c if $m\angle A = 28°$ and side $a = 872$ ft
24. Side a if $m\angle A = 22°$ and side $b = 27$ ft
25. Side b if $m\angle B = 53°$ and side $c = 97$ mi
26. Side c if $m\angle A = 15°$ and side $b = 1,250$ ft
27. $m\angle A$ if side $b = 183$ ft and side $c = 275$ ft
28. $m\angle B$ if side $b = 104$ yd and side $c = 132$ yd
29. $m\angle A$ if side $b = 18$ mi and side $c = 36$ mi
30. $m\angle B$ if side $a = 529$ mi and side $c = 1,000$ mi
31. $m\angle A$ if side $a = 306$ in. and side $b = 560$ in.
32. $m\angle B$ if side $a = 1,428$ ft and side $c = 1,800$ ft
33. $m\angle B$ if side $a = 62\frac{1}{2}$ ft and side $b = 18$ yd
34. $m\angle A$ if side $a = 192.6$ yd and side $c = 701$ ft

Every triangle has three sides and three angles. "Solving" a triangle means finding the lengths of all three sides and the measures of all three angles. Solve each triangle in Exercises 35–38.

35.

36.

37.

38.

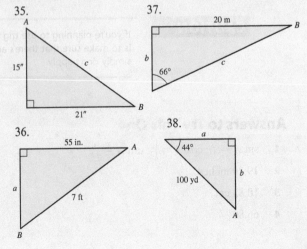

Exercises 15–34 refer to right triangles labeled like the one below. Use trigonometric ratios to find each measure.

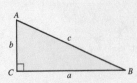

15. Side a if $m\angle B = 72°$ and side $c = 300$ cm
16. Side b if $m\angle A = 41°$ and side $c = 200$ yd

604   **Chapter 10** Geometry

Applications in Our World

39. An airplane is flying at an altitude of 6,780 feet and sights the angle of depression to a control tower at the next airport to be 16°. Find the horizontal distance the plane is from the control tower. (Disregard the height of the tower.)

40. If the angle of elevation from ground level to the top of a building is 38° and the observer is 500 feet from the building, find the height of the building.

41. How high is a satellite radio tower if the angle of elevation from the ground is 82 degrees and the observation point is 700 meters from the base of the tower?

42. Trey locked his keys in his house again and desperately needs to get his term paper from his desk on the second floor of his house. He grabs a 25-foot ladder and leans it 63 degrees against the house to the bottom of the second floor window. How high is the window from the ground?

43. One common use of trigonometry is to measure inaccessible objects. Based on the measurements in the diagram, how wide is the lake?

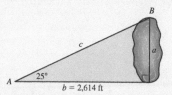

44. During a recent intramural game of Capture the Flag, Pete noticed the flag was hidden atop a light pole. Pete was standing 105 feet from the pole and he estimated that the angle of elevation from his feet to the top of the 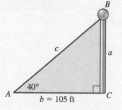 pole was 40 degrees. How far will he have to climb up the pole to capture the flag?

45. A treadmill that's 6 feet long has an adjustable back leg so that the back edge can be anywhere from 0 to 8 inches lower than the front. Find the range of angles at which this model can be inclined.

46. A two-story building that's 20 feet tall casts an 8-foot shadow, and 2 hours later the shadow is $12\frac{1}{2}$ feet long. How much did the sun's angle of elevation change in those 2 hours?

47. In a moment of frustration, Kelly tosses her math book out the window of her dorm room. (Legal

disclaimer: don't try this at home.) The window is 138 feet from the ground, and the book was thrown at a 21 degree angle of depression. Find the horizontal distance from where the book landed to Kelly's dorm. (Assume that the book traveled a straight-line path.)

48. Archaeologists find a lost city with a map room leading them to the treasure of a long-dead civilization. When the instructions carved into a stone tablet are translated, they find that that location of the treasure room is found by following the shadow of a 10-foot staff to a location on the map at 2 P.M. on the day of the winter solstice. They check with meteorologists at a nearby university and find that the angle of elevation of the sun at that location on that day and time is 44°. How far away from the staff is the location of the treasure on the map?

49. Patty sits on a bench with her laptop 2,456 feet from the base of the WiFi antenna and the angle of elevation from her laptop, which is 2.5 feet from the ground, to the top of the antenna is 58 degrees. How tall is the antenna?

50. A hotel security camera is installed at a point 9 feet above the ground. According to the manufacturer, the widest field of view will result if the camera is aimed at a spot 22 feet down the hall from the point where it's mounted. At what angle of depression should the camera be aimed?

51. On a military training exercise, a group of artillerymen are instructed to train their weapon on a target that is $\frac{3}{4}$ mile away and 80 feet high. At what angle of elevation should they set the weapon?

52. While finishing his basement, Dave finds that the stairs have a horizontal span of 12 feet while going down 8.5 feet. At what angle should the hand railing be placed to match the incline of the stairs?

53. A business jet is instructed to make a straight-line approach and landing, starting at an altitude of 4,500 feet and a distance of 7 miles from the runway. At what angle of depression should the pilot fly?

54. A sniper sets up on a roof across the street from a hostage situation. The roof is 36 feet high, and the laser distance finder on his rifle indicates that his straight-line distance from the target is 90 yards. At what angle of depression should he aim his rifle to train in on the target?

Critical Thinking

55. Look at the instructions in the Calculator Guide on page 598 for putting your calculator in degree mode. You can use a similar approach to put your calculator in radian mode, which measures angles in radians rather than degrees. Rework Example 5 with your calculator

in radian mode. How can you tell that you get the wrong answer without actually looking at the correct answer?

56. Refer to Question 55. Rework Example 6 in radian mode. Can you tell that the answer is wrong without checking the correct answer? What can you conclude

from the last two questions about the danger of having your calculator in the wrong mode?

57. Based on the way we've defined sine and cosine in terms of right triangles, explain why the values of these trig ratios always have to be between zero and one.

58. Refer to Question 57. Can we make any analogous statements about the value of tangent? Why or why not?

59. From the top of a building 300 feet high, the angle of elevation to a plane is 33° and the angle of depression to an automobile directly below the plane is 24°. Find the height of the plane and the distance the automobile is from the base of the building.

60. The angle of elevation to the top of a tree sighted from ground level is 18°. If the observer moves 80 feet closer, the angle of elevation from ground level to the top of the tree is 38°. Find the height of the tree.

61. Suppose that there is no trigonometric ratio known as tangent. Can you solve the problem in Example 2 without it? Describe the procedure you would use.

62. How can you solve the problem in Example 3 without using the cosine ratio?

63. When you're asked to solve a right triangle and you're given two of the sides, you've really been given all three. When you're given one of the nonright angles, you've actually been given both of them. Explain these statements.

64. In Exercises 35 through 38, you were given two pieces of information about the triangle in addition to the fact that it's a right triangle. Explain why being given only the other two angles will not allow you to solve a triangle.

Section 10-7   A Brief Survey of Non-Euclidean and Other Geometries

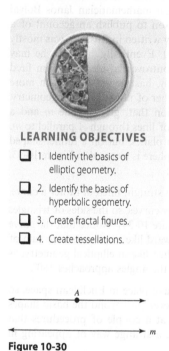

LEARNING OBJECTIVES

☐ 1. Identify the basics of elliptic geometry.

☐ 2. Identify the basics of hyperbolic geometry.

☐ 3. Create fractal figures.

☐ 4. Create tessellations.

The Euclidean geometry that we have studied so far in this chapter helps us to solve many problems in our world, and because of this, many people would say that Euclidean geometry is the geometry that describes our physical world. But does it really? Suppose you hop in your car and drive 500 miles due south. In your perception, you have driven a straight-line path. But in fact, you were driving along a curved path, matching the surface of the earth. This is why when you look out over the ocean, you can't see the other side—the water literally curves out of your sight at some point, which we call the horizon.

After thousands of years of accepting Euclid's geometry as the only one, in the 1800s mathematicians and scientists started to question whether the principles of Euclidean geometry really were universal, or if maybe there were other systems in which Euclid's principles didn't apply. And so the field of non-Euclidean geometry was born. There are entire courses taught on non-Euclidean geometries, so in this section we will simply take a quick look at some of them.

A **postulate** is a fundamental assumption underlying an area of study that cannot be proved, but rather is assumed to be true. It turns out that Euclidean geometry has at its foundation the **parallel postulate**, which says that given any line m and a point A not on that line, there is exactly one line parallel to m through A. See Figure 10-30.

Figure 10-30

Mathematicians spent about 2,000 years trying to prove the parallel postulate without success. Many of these attempts tried proof by contradiction: it was assumed that the parallel postulate didn't always hold, and an attempt was made to find something that contradicted the known theorems of geometry. Along the way, though, an interesting thing happened: new geometries were discovered that didn't follow the rules set out by Euclid. One such system is elliptic geometry.

Elliptic Geometry

Elliptic geometry was developed by the German mathematician Bernhard Riemann (1826–1866). While Euclidean geometry is based on planes, elliptic geometry is based on spheres. In elliptic geometry, the lines are finite in length, and are defined to be *great circles* of a sphere. A **great circle** is a circle on the sphere that has the same center as the sphere. See Figure 10-31.

Figure 10-31 Great circles on a sphere.

Figure 10-32 A triangle in elliptic geometry.

☑ 1. Identify the basics of elliptic geometry.

This explains why elliptic geometry doesn't satisfy the parallel postulate: since all lines are great circles, there ARE no parallel lines. Think first of lines of longitude on a globe: all of them meet at the poles. Any other great circle that doesn't meet those at the poles (think of the equator) have to intersect them in two other points. In any case, if there are no parallel lines period, given a line and a point not on it, you certainly can't find a unique line through that point parallel to the line.

Another interesting feature of elliptic geometry is that the sum of the angles in a triangle is more than 180° (see Figure 10-32). Not only that, but the sum of the angles isn't fixed—it depends on the area of the triangle. As the area gets smaller, the sum approaches but never reaches 180°. The Pythagorean theorem also fails in elliptic geometry: it's actually possible to draw a triangle with three 90° angles, in which case all the sides have the same length. But it still qualifies as a right triangle, and $a^2 + b^2 = c^2$ can only hold if side c is longer than the other two sides.

If you find it hard to imagine an elliptic geometry, consider the fact that you live on one! That's why that 500-mile path you drove felt like a line to you even though it was curved—when you live on a sphere, lines follow the contour of the sphere.

Hyperbolic Geometry

Hyperbolic geometry was developed independently by the Russian mathematician Nikolay Lobachevsky (1792–1856) and the Hungarian mathematician János Bolyai (1802–1860). Lobachevsky was actually the first person to publish an account of a non-Euclidean geometry, in 1829. His work, originally written in Russian, was mostly ignored until it was translated into German in 1840. Eventually, however, he may have longed for the days of being ignored, as his controversial ideas got him fired from his university post in 1846. History, fortunately, has viewed him much more favorably, and he is generally considered to be the father of non-Euclidean geometry.

Hyperbolic geometry is based on the assumption that, given a line m and a point A not on the line, there are an infinite number of lines through A parallel to m. The shapes in hyperbolic geometry are drawn not on planes, but on a funnel-shaped surface known as a **pseudosphere**. A line on a pseudosphere is pictured in Figure 10-33. Here are some facts about hyperbolic geometry:

- The shortest distance between two points is not a straight line but rather a curve.
- Like elliptic geometry, the role of lines is played by curves, so the sides of triangles are arcs along the pseudosphere (as shown in Figure 10-34). Notice that the curve of the pseudosphere arcs inward rather than outward like a sphere, so the sum of the angles in a triangle is always *less* than 180°. Just like in elliptical geometry, as the area of the triangle gets smaller, the sum of the angles approaches 180°.

The remaining types of geometries we look at take place in Euclidean space, so they're not non-Euclidean geometries. They do, however, go beyond the basic shapes and formulas we've used so far. We'll have a look at a couple of procedures that lead to fascinating patterns, and in some cases have a strange way of appearing in nature as well, starting with fractals.

☑ 2. Identify the basics of hyperbolic geometry.

Figure 10-33 A line in hyperbolic geometry.

Figure 10-34 A triangle in hyperbolic geometry.

Fractal Geometry

It's pretty unusual when an entire area in math can be traced to a single paper, but such is the case with fractal geometry. In 1965, the French mathematician Benoit Mandelbrot (1924–2010) published a fascinating paper conjecturing that Great Britain has an infinitely long coastline. The idea is that the measured length depends very much on the scale of the device used to measure. Think of it this way: if you measure around the outside rails of a round swimming pool with a yardstick, you will be missing a lot of the curve and conclude the circumference is quite a bit smaller than it actually is. If you switch to a foot-long ruler, you'll get a larger (and more accurate) measurement but still too small because you'll still be "cutting corners."

If you continue this process, you'll conclude that no matter how short your ruler is the same thing will happen, just on a much smaller scale. Looking at it this way, the only way to get a true measurement of a detailed object like a coastline would be to use a ruler with length zero, which of course is impossible to measure anything with! And so was born fractal geometry (although Mandelbrot didn't coin that term until 1975).

The cornerstone of fractal geometry is making new geometric figures from simpler shapes using a repeated process. Figure 10-35 shows a famous example, the Sierpinski triangle. Starting with an equilateral triangle, an equilateral triangle-shaped portion is removed from the middle, leaving behind three smaller triangles. This process is then continued indefinitely, and the resulting figure is called a **fractal**. The repeating process that leads to a fractal is called **iteration**. If there's anything computers are good at, it's repeating iterations of a process, so computers are awesome at drawing fractals—one cool example is shown in Figure 10-36. Oddly enough for something discovered in the late 1960s, fractals appear in nature as well, as we will see shortly.

So iteration is one feature that makes a geometric figure a fractal. A second is **self-similarity**. Look back at the fourth picture in Figure 10-35. If you look carefully at the portion that was the lower right triangle in the picture directly above it, you'll see that this portion of the fractal looks just like a miniature version of the entire thing. That's self-similarity. Which brings us back to nature. An amazing variety of things in nature exhibit either exact or approximate self-similarity. One striking example is a particular variety of broccoli known as Romanesco broccoli, pictured in Figure 10-37. As you look more and more closely, you see that the individual portions look amazingly like the entire head no matter how far you zoom in.

Other examples of self-similarity in nature include mountain ranges, coastlines, snowflakes, fern leafs, clouds, DNA strands, galaxies . . . should I go on?

The third feature defining a fractal figure is called the **fractal dimension**. This is a ratio that describes how much the measurement of an object changes based on the scale at which it is measured. A straight line has fractal dimension one because you'll get the same length no matter how small your measuring device is. Almost all fractals have dimension that is not an integer, unlike regular Euclidean figures, which have dimension zero (points), one (lines), two (planes), etc. As you can picture from the "coast of Britain" example, the more complex a fractal is, the more error you're likely to have measuring with a large scale, and the higher the fractal dimension.

Let's have a look at a method for creating a different fractal figure.

Step 1   Start with an equilateral triangle.
Step 2   Replace each – side with .
Step 3   Repeat Step 2 in the new figure.
Step 4   Continue the process as long as you like. See Figure 10-38 for several iterations of the process. The figure is called the Koch snowflake.

Figure 10-38 exhibits the three classic characteristics of a fractal: it comes from iterations of a process; it exhibits perfect self similarity (look carefully at the "arms" of the snowflake, and if you're really interested there's a very cool animation on Wikipedia illustrating this); and it turns out to have fractal dimension about 1.26.

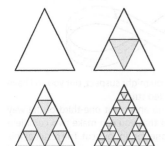

Figure 10-35

Figure 10-36

Figure 10-37

Sidelight THE MOBIUS STRIP

An unusual mathematical shape can be created from a flat strip of paper. After cutting a strip, give it a half twist and tape the ends together to make a closed ring as shown.

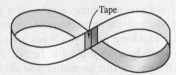

The shape you have made is called a Mobius strip, named for the German mathematician Augustus Ferdinand Mobius (1790–1868) who created it. What is unusual about the Mobius strip is that it has only one side. You can draw a line through the center of the strip, starting anywhere and ending where you started without crossing over an edge. You can color the entire strip with one color by starting anywhere and ending where you started without crossing over an edge.

The Mobius strip has more unusual properties. Take a scissors and cut through the center of the strip following the line you drew as shown.

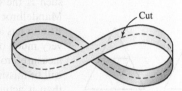

You won't get two strips as you might suspect, but you will have one long continuous two-sided strip.

Finally, make a new strip and cut it one-third of the way from the edge. You will find that you can make two complete trips around the strip using one continuous cut. The result of this cut will be two distinct strips: one will be a two-sided strip, and the other will be another one-sided Mobius strip.

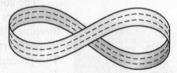

The Mobius strip is a shape that belongs to a recently developed branch of mathematics called *topology*. Topology is a kind of geometry in which solid shapes are bent or stretched into different shapes. The properties of the shape that remain unchanged in the new shape are then studied.

Math Note

Fun facts about some of the fractals we looked at:

1. The total area of the Sierpinski triangle is zero.

2. The area of the Koch snowflake is 8/5 times the area of the triangle you start with, but the perimeter is infinite.

☑ 3. Create fractal figures.

Math Note

Not every regular polygon can be used to create a tessellation. For example, it can be shown that regular pentagons alone cannot create a tessellation.

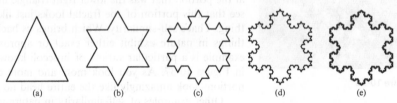

Figure 10-38 The Koch snowflake.

One final note about fractals: because of them, your cell phone works much better than cell phones did 15 or 20 years ago. The effectiveness of an antenna is largely determined by how much perimeter it has compared to area. With a fractal figure like the Koch snowflake, with each iteration, the ratio of the perimeter to the area increases, so most modern cell phone antennas have a fractal design.

Tessellations

Yet another method for designing interesting geometric shapes is known as *tessellation*. The formal mathematical study of tessellations dates to the 1600s, but the concept itself is almost surely one of the oldest in all of math. For thousands and thousands of years, civilizations have used tessellations in art and architecture.

A **tessellation**, also called a **tiling**, is a pattern that uses the same geometric shape to cover a plane without any gaps.

Figure 10-39 shows several tessellations. These figures are made by using regular polygons. (Recall that a regular polygon is a polygon in which all sides have the same length and all interior angles have the same measure.) The tessellation shown in

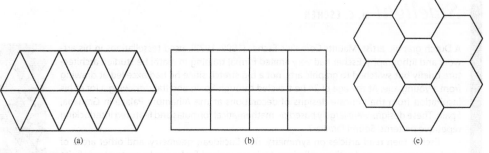

Figure 10-39

Figure 10-39a is made from equilateral triangles. The one shown in Figure 10-39b is made from squares, and the one shown in Figure 10-39c is made from regular hexagons.

Tessellations can also be formed using more than one regular polygon. Figure 10-40 shows a tessellation created by a square and a regular octagon.

You may have noticed that there's not a single formula in this section so far: let's fix that. Recall that the endpoints of the segments that make up a polygon are called its vertices.

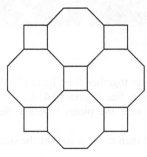

Figure 10-40

Polygons That Can Form Tessellations

A tessellation can be formed by polygons exactly when the sum of the angles around the vertices is 360°.

Notice that this is the case for all of the tessellations shown in Figures 10-39 and 10-40: the first has six equilateral triangles meeting at any vertex ($6 \times 60° = 360°$); the second has four squares ($4 \times 90° = 360°$); the third has three hexagons ($3 \times 120° = 360°$); the last has a square and two octagons ($90° + 2 \times 135° = 360°$).

If you're not into repeated copies of regular polygons, you can make your own tessellation using these steps:

Step 1 Draw a regular geometric polygon. In this case, we'll use a square.
Step 2 Cut the square from top to bottom using any design. See Figure 10-41a.

> ### Math Note
>
> The angle measures for regular polygons we use here come from the formula for the sum of the measures of the angles in a regular polygon back in Section 10-3.

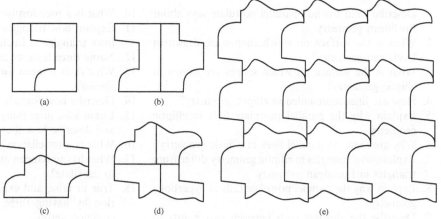

Figure 10-41

Sidelight M. C. ESCHER

A Dutch graphic artist, Maurits Cornelius Escher (1898–1972), used tessellations in his art-work and lithography. Escher had very limited formal training in math; he studied architec-ture briefly but switched to graphic arts, not a big stretch since he had excelled at drawing from a young age. At the age of 24 he traveled through Spain and Italy, drawing a lot of his inspiration from the intricate designs of decorations at the Alhambra Palace in Granada, Spain. These designs were largely based on mathematical formulas and featured interlocking repetitive patterns. Sound familiar?

Escher then read articles on symmetry, non-Euclidean geometry, and other areas of mathematics associated with tessellations. He is recognized for his works containing infinite repeating geometric patterns and created paintings of objects that could be drawn in two dimensions but were impossible to create in three dimensions.

Step 3 Move the left piece to the right side. Tape the pieces together. See Figure 10-41b.

Step 4 Cut the piece from left to right using any design. See Figure 10-41c.

Step 5 Move the top piece to the bottom piece and tape the pieces together. See Figure 10-41d.

Step 6 Trace the figure on another sheet of paper and then move it so that the sides line up like puzzle pieces.

Step 7 Continue the process as many times as you like until a tessellation figure is complete. See Figure 10-41e.

Tessellations are very common in architectural design, but are most commonly used in mosaic designs of floors, walls, and windows. (There's at least a 70% chance that the next restroom you use will have a tessellation in it somewhere.) The most famous user of tessellations is without question the Dutch artist M. C. Escher, profiled in the sidelight.

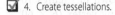 4. Create tessellations.

EXERCISE SET 10-7

Writing Exercises

1. Describe what Euclid's parallel postulate says about Euclidean geometry.

2. What is the surface on which shapes are drawn in Euclidean geometry?

3. What is the surface on which shapes are drawn in elliptic geometry?

4. How are lines represented in elliptic geometry?

5. Explain why the parallel postulate fails in elliptic geometry.

6. Why are there no parallel lines in elliptic geometry?

7. Explain how triangles in elliptic geometry differ from triangles in Euclidean geometry.

8. Explain why the parallel postulate fails in hyperbolic geometry.

9. Describe the shortest path between two points in hyperbolic geometry.

10. What is a pseudosphere?

11. Explain how triangles in hyperbolic geometry differ from triangles in Euclidean geometry.

12. Name three features common to all fractal figures.

13. What does it mean for a geometric figure to be self-similar?

14. Describe how fractals are drawn using iterations.

15. List at least three things in nature that are self-similar and describe how they exhibit that feature.

16. What is a tessellation? How are tessellations used?

17. What has to happen at vertices in order for polygons to tessellate?

18. True or false, and explain: you can make a tessellation by having three regular hexagons meet at a common vertex.

Computational Exercises

19. Using the letter H and putting an H at each corner, create a fractal-like figure.
20. Develop a fractal by replacing each _____ side in a square with ⌐⌐⌐.
21. Do you think that you can build a Sierpinski triangle with a nonequilateral triangle? Try it with a triangle that is isosceles but not equilateral.
22. Try to build a Sierpinski triangle starting with a right triangle with legs that are the same length.
23. Try to build a Sierpinski triangle starting with a triangle that has three different side lengths.
24. What can you conclude from the results of Exercises 21–23?

Tessellations are also called "tilings" for a reason: the most common application for literally thousands of years has been designing decorative tile for floors, walls, etc.

25. Design a tile pattern using a tessellation where the basic shape is a square and an equilateral triangle with side length the same as the square.

26. Design a tile pattern using a tessellation where the basic shape is a square and two equilateral triangles with side lengths the same as the square. How does your pattern compare to the one in Exercise 25?
27. In Figure 10-39, we saw how to tessellate equilateral triangles. Can the same be done with isosceles triangles that are not equilateral? See if you can design a pattern.
28. What is the result of tessellating any right triangle? What is the result of tessellating any scalene triangle that is not a right triangle?
29. Use a square and the procedure described on pages 609–610 to create a tessellation.
30. Use a regular hexagon and the procedure described on pages 609–610 to create a tessellation.

Critical Thinking

31. Try to form a tessellation using only regular pentagons, then explain why it's not possible.
32. Repeat Exercise 31 using regular octagons.
33. Use the rule for tessellating polygons to develop a rule for when a regular polygon can be tessellated with itself *based on the number of sides it has*.
34. Many of the sports we commonly play use spheres (or as we call them, balls). Make a list of as many sports you can think of that use a ball, and using the Internet as a resource where necessary, decide if the pattern on the ball for each does or does not represent a tessellation.
35. Use Google maps or another Internet site that shows satellite images of land masses and look at a satellite view of the coast of California. Use the zoom button

to zoom in one level at a time, then describe how the changing view applies to self-similarity.
36. Use the Internet to find and download a high-resolution image of a fern leaf, then zoom in repeatedly on the leaf. Describe how close you think the image is to exact self-similarity.
37. When building the tessellation shown in Figure 10-40, I decided to start with a square and find a regular polygon that I could use two copies of to tessellate with the square. I used the formula $(n - 2)180°$ for finding the sum of angles in an n-sided regular polygon. How did I come up with octagon? (You can do this numerically, but your instructor should give you extra credit if you do it algebraically, which is both trickier and nearly 70% cooler.)

CHAPTER **10**

Summary

Section	Important Terms	Important Ideas
10-1	Point Line Plane Line segment Half line Ray Angle Vertex Degree Acute angle Right angle Obtuse angle Straight angle Complementary angles Supplementary angles Vertical angles Parallel lines Transversal Alternate interior angles Alternate exterior angles Corresponding angles	**The principles** of geometry have long been useful in helping people understand the physical world. The basic geometric figures are the point, the line, and the plane. From these figures, other figures such as segments, rays, and half lines can be made. When two rays have a common endpoint, they form an angle. Angles can be measured in degrees using a protractor. When lines intersect, several different types of angles are formed; vertical, corresponding, alternate interior, and alternate exterior. Two angles are called complementary if the sum of their measures is equal to 90°. Two angles are called supplementary if the sum of their measures is equal to 180°. Pairs of corresponding angles have the same measure, as do pairs of alternate interior angles, and pairs of alternate exterior angles.
10-2	Triangle Sides Vertices Isosceles triangle Equilateral triangle Scalene triangle Acute triangle Obtuse triangle Right triangle Hypotenuse Legs Pythagorean theorem Similar triangles	**A closed** geometric figure with three sides is called a triangle. A triangle can be classified according to the lengths of its sides or according to the measures of its angles. For a right triangle, the Pythagorean theorem states that $c^2 = a^2 + b^2$, where c is the length of the hypotenuse and a and b are the lengths of the legs. Two triangles with the same shape are called similar triangles. Corresponding sides of similar triangles are in proportion. This allows us to solve problems involving finding the lengths of sides.
10-3	Polygon Quadrilateral Pentagon Hexagon Heptagon Octagon Nonagon Decagon Dodecagon Icosagon Trapezoid Parallelogram	**A polygon** is classified according to the number of sides. A quadrilateral has four sides; a pentagon has five sides, etc. The sum of the measures of the angles of a polygon with n sides is $(n-2)180°$. Special quadrilaterals such as the trapezoid, parallelogram, rhombus, and square are used in this chapter. A regular polygon is a polygon in which all sides are the same length and all angles have the same measure. The distance around the outside of a polygon is called the perimeter.

	Rectangle Rhombus Square Regular polygon Perimeter	
10-4	Area Circle Center Radius Diameter Circumference π (pi)	**The measure** of the portion of the plane enclosed by a geometric figure is called the area of the geometric figure. Area is measured in square units: if lengths are measured in inches, area is measured in square inches. One square inch is the area of a square that measures 1 inch on each side. Area formulas can be developed for many familiar geometric figures. A circle is a closed geometric figure in which all the points are the same distance from a fixed point called the center. A segment connecting the center with any point on the circle is called a radius. A segment connecting two points on the circle and passing through the center of the circle is called a diameter. The circumference of a circle is the distance around the outside of the circle.
10-5	Volume Rectangular solid Cube Right circular cylinder Pyramid Cone Sphere Surface area	**In geometry,** we also study three-dimensional figures. Some of the familiar three-dimensional figures are the cube, the rectangular solid, the pyramid, the cone, the cylinder, and the sphere. The volume of a three-dimensional geometric figure is the amount of space that is enclosed by the surfaces of the figure. Volume is measured in cubic units: if lengths are measured in inches, volume is measured in cubic inches. One cubic inch is the volume of a cube that measures 1 inch on each side. The surface area of a three-dimensional figure is the area of the faces or surfaces of the figure.
10-6	Trigonometry Sine Cosine Tangent Inverse trigonometric functions Angle of elevation Angle of depression	**Trigonometry** is the study of the relationship between the angles and the sides of a triangle. The trigonometric ratios of sine, cosine, and tangent are defined with a right triangle. Using the trig ratios, we can find side lengths and angle measures in a right triangle when we are given some of those measurements. The concepts of right triangle trigonometry can be used to solve many problems in navigation measurement, engineering, physics, and many other areas.
10-7	Parallel postulate Elliptic geometry Great circle Hyperbolic geometry Pseudosphere Fractal Iteration Self-similarity Fractal dimension Tessellation	**Euclidean geometry** is based on the parallel postulate, which says that given any line m and a point not on it, there is exactly one line parallel to m through that point. In elliptic geometry, there are no parallel lines, and shapes are drawn on a sphere. In hyperbolic geometry, there are infinitely many lines parallel to any given line through a point, and shapes are drawn on a pseudosphere. Fractal figures are formed by starting with a basic shape and repeating the shape indefinitely in a series of steps called iterations. Fractal figures exhibit self-similarity and typically have a non-integer fractal dimension. Tessellations are formed when the same geometric shapes are used repeatedly to cover a plane without any gaps.

614   **Chapter 10**   Geometry

MATH IN ▸ Home Improvement REVISITED

1. The U-shaped section can be divided into three rectangles, giving a total of six rectangles we can find the area of using length times width. The combined area is 7,835 square inches, which is about 54.4 square feet. The cost of the solid surface countertops was 54.4 × $56.62 = $3,080.13. The cost of the granite was 54.4 × $97.46 = $5,301.82. So we initially saved the difference, which is $2,221.69, but in the long run spent $3,080.13 more than we needed to. Sigh.

2. Draw a right triangle diagram with the given measurements:

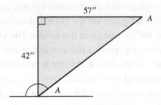

Angle A of the triangle is found using the equation $\tan A = \frac{42}{57}$ Solving for A, we get 36.4°. The angle marked A along the bottom is also 36.4° because of alternate interior angles, and the angle marked with the arc, which the trim should be cut at, is the supplement of 36.4°, or 143.6°.

3. The width of the glass block part is $55\frac{3}{4}$" (7 blocks at $7\frac{3}{4}$" each, and 6 mortar joints at $\frac{1}{4}$" each). The height is $31\frac{3}{4}$" (4 blocks and 3 mortar joints). The diagram shows the trim:

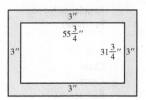

The area of the trim can be found either by subtracting the area of the small rectangle from the area of the large rectangle, or by breaking the trim into four rectangles. In either case, the result is 561 square inches of trim needed, which is about 3.9 square feet.

4. This is another triangle diagram:

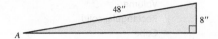

The 8″ side comes from the difference between the front edge and back edge heights. Solving the equation $\sin A = \frac{8}{48}$, we find that angle A measures 9.6°. If the legs were perpendicular to the hypotenuse and cut at a 90° angle, the bottom would make the same 9.6° angle with the ground (see below, left drawing). So to make it sit flat, it needs to be cut 9.6° short of 90°, or 80.4°.

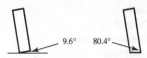

None of these were made up—they are the actual calculations done by the author while doing the projects.

Review Exercises

Mixed Review

For Exercises 1–10, identify each figure.

1.
    A   B

2.
    R   S

3.
    C   D

4.
    5

5.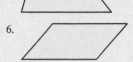

6.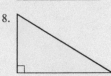

7.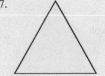

8.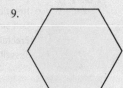

9. (hexagon figure)

10.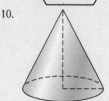

Section 10-1

For Exercises 11–16, identify each type of angle or pairs of angles.

11.

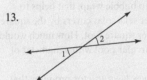

12.

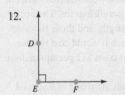

13.

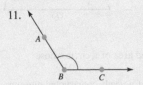

∡1 and ∡2

14.

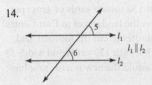

$l_1 \parallel l_2$

∡5 and ∡6

15.

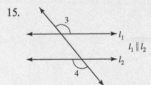

$l_1 \parallel l_2$

∡3 and ∡4

16.

∡7 and ∡8

17. Find the complement of each angle.
    (a) 27°   (b) 88°
18. Find the supplement of each angle.
    (a) 172°   (b) 13°
19. Find the measures of ∡1, ∡2, and ∡3.

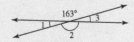

20. Find the measures of ∡1 through ∡7.

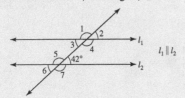

Section 10-2

21. Find the measure of the third angle of a triangle if the measures of the other two angles are 95° and 42°.
22. Find the measure of the hypotenuse of a right triangle if the lengths of the two legs are 8 inches and 15 inches.
23. Find the height of a water tower if its shadow is 24 feet when a 6-foot fence pole casts a shadow of 2 feet.

In Exercises 24–27, classify each triangle by angles (acute, obtuse, or right) and by sides (equilateral, isosceles, or scalene).

24.   26.

25.   27.

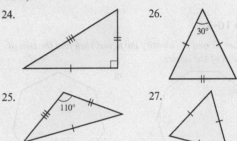

In Exercises 28–29, use the Pythagorean theorem to find the length of the missing side.

28.

29.

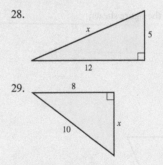

In Exercises 30–31, use the proportional property of similar triangles to find the missing sides (assume the two triangles in each exercise are similar).

30.

31.

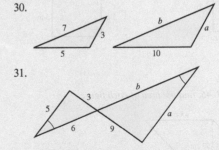

32. If a 6-foot-tall man casts a 10-foot-long shadow, find the height of a building that casts a 150-foot-long shadow at the same time.
33. If a 12-foot ladder reaches 9 feet, 6 inches up a wall, how far up would a 20-foot ladder reach when placed at the same angle?

34. If the 20-foot ladder from Question 33 is placed with its base 9 feet from the wall, how high up does it reach?

35. A series of guy wires hold a radio antenna tower in place. If the tower is 140 feet high and the wires are attached to a point on the ground 90 feet from the base of the tower, how long are the wires?

36. While doing conditioning drills for spring training, a baseball player is supposed to run the length and width of a rectangular field that is 500 yards long and 800 feet wide. If he cheats and runs straight across on a diagonal, how much less distance does he run?

Section 10-3

In Exercises 37 and 38, identify the figure, then find the sum of the measures of the angles.

37. 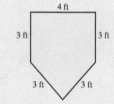   38.

In Exercises 39–42, find the perimeter.

39. Find the perimeter of the figure shown.

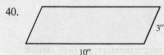

40.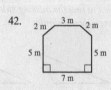

41.   42.

Section 10-4

For Exercises 43–46, find the area of each figure.

43.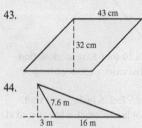

44.

45. 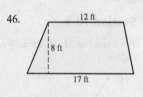   46.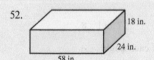

47. Find the circumference and area of a circle whose diameter is 16.5 yards.

48. The main gathering area of a newly constructed museum of modern art is shaped like a parallelogram. The north and south sides are 40 feet in length, and those two sides are 65 feet apart. Find how much it would cost to have the room tiled with marble that costs $12 per square foot installed.

49. Solar covers for swimming pools are made of a special plastic material, similar to bubble wrap, that helps to hold in heat. One supplier sells solar covers by the square foot, charging 22 cents per square foot. How much would a solar cover cost for a circular pool with a diameter of 17 feet?

50. The manufacturer of a new lawn tractor promises that in average use, it can cut 130 square yards of grass per minute. It currently takes the landscaper at East Central State an hour and 20 minutes to cut the football field, which is a rectangle with length 120 yards and width 53 yards. How much time would the new tractor save him?

Section 10-5

For Exercises 51–54, find the volume.

51.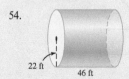

52.

53.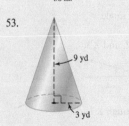

54.

55. Find the surface area of the figure in Exercise 52.
56. Find the surface area of the figure in Exercise 54.
57. If the diameter of a bicycle wheel is 26 inches, how many revolutions will the wheel make if the rider rides 1 mile (1 mile = 5,280 feet)?
58. Find how many square inches of fabric are needed to make the kite shown.

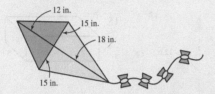

59. Find the volume of a ball if the diameter is 4.2 cm.
60. Find the surface area for the walls of the building shown. The door is a 3-foot by 6-foot rectangle with a half-circle on top of it, and there are two windows that measure 4 feet wide and 3 feet high.

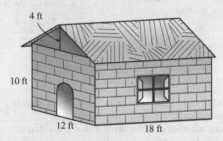

Section 10-6

61. For the triangle shown, find sin B, cos B, and tan B.

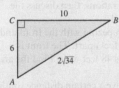

In Exercises 62–65, find the measure of the requested side or angle in triangle ABC. Note that C is the right angle.

62. Find b if $c = 27$ inches and $m\angle B = 49°$.
63. Find a if $b = 12$ yards and $m\angle A = 11°$.

64. Find $m\angle A$ if $c = 11$ meters and $b = 7.5$ meters.
65. Find $m\angle B$ if $a = 100$ miles and $b = 127$ miles.
66. If a tree 32 feet tall casts a shadow of 40 feet, find the angle of elevation of the sun.
67. A pole is leaning against a wall. The base is 15 feet from the wall, and from that point the angle of elevation to the top of the pole is 63°. How long is the pole?
68. The ramp for a motorcycle jump is a straight, flat surface 130 feet long. The beginning is at ground level, and the end is 27 feet high. What angle does the ramp make with the ground?
69. A plane takes off in a straight line and flies for a half-hour at 160 miles per hour. At that point, the pilots are informed by air traffic control that they have flown 17° off course. They are instructed to change direction and fly at the same speed along a perpendicular path back to the line they should have flown on, then turn and continue to the destination. How long will it take them to get back on course?

Section 10-7

70. Starting with an equilateral triangle, create a tessellation using the procedure described in Section 10-7.
71. Make a fractal figure by starting with a square piece of paper 8 inches on a side, then drawing a square that is 3 inches on a side in each corner. Continue the process for at least four iterations, each time drawing squares in each corner that are $\frac{3}{8}$ the length of the square they are inside.
72. Describe lines in elliptic geometry in terms of a globe.
73. The figure shows the first iteration of a fractal starting with a square. Draw the next two iterations.

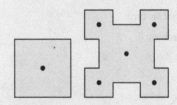

74. Discuss the self-similarity of the fractal in Exercise 73.

Chapter Test

1. Find the complement and supplement of an angle whose measure is 73°.
2. Find the measures of $\angle 1$, $\angle 2$, and $\angle 3$.

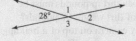

3. Find the measures of $\angle 1$ through $\angle 7$.

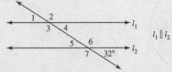

4. If two angles of a triangle have a measure of 85° and 47°, respectively, find the measure of the third angle.

5. Find the measure of side x. The two triangles are similar.

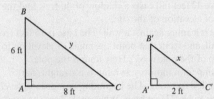

6. One way to measure the height of a tree is to cut it down and use a tape measure. But that's pretty drastic . . . another is to measure the length of its shadow, then measure the length of your shadow at the same time. Suppose the shadow of the tree is 13′11″ long at a time when a person who is 5′10″ tall casts a shadow 2′8″ long. How tall is the tree?

7. Find the sum of the angles of an octagon.

8. Maureen is building a flowerbed in her backyard in the shape below. She wants to put three layers of landscape timbers along the border. If the timbers come in 8-foot lengths, how many will she need to buy?

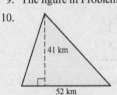

For Exercises 9–12, find the area.

9. The figure in Problem 8.

10.

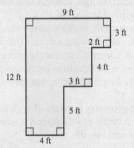

11.

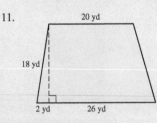

12.

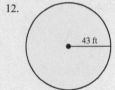

For Exercises 13–17, find the volume and surface area of each.

13.

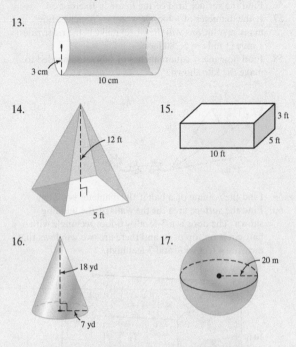

14.

15.

16.

17.

18. Are lines of latitude on a globe examples of lines in elliptic geometry? Explain why or why not.

19. Discuss whether or not a brick wall is a tessellation.

20. Design a fractal by starting with a square then drawing a smaller square whose vertices are the midpoints of the sides of the original square. For the next iteration, draw a square inside the second one using the same technique. Continue for at least five iterations, then discuss the self-similarity of your fractal.

21. A city lot is shaped like a trapezoid with the front and back sides parallel and 157 feet apart. The front is 32 feet wide, and the back is 48 feet wide. Find the area of the lot.

22. Starting from home, you drive a certain distance south to Best Buy to get a new monitor for your computer. You then drive 5 miles west to return that awful shirt your mother bought you for your birthday. You then drive 25 miles home. How far is it from your house to Best Buy?

23. You create a masterpiece in your art studio and it is selected for the student art exhibition. Your painting is 70 inches by 100 inches, and you choose framing that costs $4.35 per yard. Find the cost of the framing.

24. During your chemistry lab, you fill a cone-shaped beaker that has a 1-inch diameter and a 2-inch height with lead, which weighs 0.41 pounds per cubic inch. Find the weight of the lead in the beaker.

25. To install a satellite television transmitter, the technician digs a cylindrical hole that is 3 feet in diameter with a depth of 5 feet. How much dirt in pounds must be removed if 1 cubic foot of dirt weighs 98 pounds?

26. A bank sets up a security camera on top of a building across the street from their entrance. The camera is

controlled by a computer, and the head of security needs to input an angle of depression for proper aim. If the camera is at a height of 46 feet and the base of the building across the street is 70 feet from the bank entrance, what angle should the manager input?

Projects

1. In a Sidelight feature back in Section 5-3, we referred to a website (http://www.angio.net/pi/piquery.html) where you can search for strings of numbers within the first 200 million digits of pi. Go to the site and search for the following:

   (a) Your birthday, in the form MMDDYYYY
   (b) Your phone number, without area code
   (c) Your phone number with the area code
   (d) The first 8 natural numbers consecutively
   (e) The first 9 natural numbers consecutively
   (f) The first 6 even natural numbers consecutively
   (g) The first 7 odd natural numbers consecutively

   Based on these results, what can you say about the likelihood of finding a given string based on the number of digits in that string? Try to make some general conjectures about how likely you are to find a given string based on the number of digits, and try several numbers to test out your conjectures.

2. The numbers 3, 4, and 5 are called a Pythagorean triple, because a right triangle with sides 3, 4, and 5 units satisfies the Pythagorean theorem. That is, $3^2 + 4^2 = 5^2$. The numbers 5, 12, and 13 form another Pythagorean triple.

   (a) Do 6, 8, and 10 form a Pythagorean triple?
   (b) Do 9, 12, and 15 form a Pythagorean triple?
   (c) Do 10, 24, and 26 form a Pythagorean triple?
   (d) Based on your answers for parts a through c, can you make any definite statements about how many Pythagorean triples there are?
   (e) Based on parts (a) through (c), write a general formula or formulas for finding Pythagorean triples.
   (f) Can you find a Pythagorean triple where the numbers are not multiples of either 3, 4, 5 or 5, 12, 13?
   (g) Search the Internet for the string "Pythagorean triple" and find how many Pythagorean triples there are where all three numbers are less than 100.

   (h) Research the question "are Pythagorean triples more common, or more rare, among three-digit numbers than among two-digit numbers?" In general, are they harder or easier to find as the lengths get larger?

3. Gather a variety of objects that you could pour a liquid into: glasses, buckets, pitchers, coolers, aquariums, sinks, or anything else that you could calculate (or estimate) the volume of, using the volume formulas we learned in Section 10-5.

   (a) Calculate the volume of each in both cubic inches and cubic centimeters by taking measurements and using volume formulas. If the containers are not exactly regular, like a bucket that is wider at the top than the bottom, make your best estimate of the volume.
   (b) Convert the measurements in cubic inches to gallons using the conversions from Chapter 9. Convert the measurements in cubic centimeters to liters also.
   (c) Calculate the volume of each container in gallons and liters by pouring measured amounts of water into it using a measuring cup, pitcher, or beaker.
   (d) Compare the measurements done with water to your calculations. How well did you do?

4. Math class . . . photography class . . . whatever. In this project, your job is to search the world around you for as many examples as you can find of tessellations and fractals, then photograph them and submit a report on each. For tessellations, discuss the basic shape or shapes that are tessellated. If they happen to be polygons, show that the sum of the measures of the angles around the vertices is 360°. If not, discuss how the shapes fit together and how you think they may have been designed. For fractals, describe why you think your picture shows a fractal and discuss the self-similarity.

Probability and Counting Techniques

Outline

11–1 The Fundamentals of Counting Principles and Permutation

11–2 Combinations

11–3 Basic Concept of Probability

11–4 Tree Diagrams, Tables, and Sample Spaces

11–5 Probability Using Permutations and Combinations

11–6 Odds and Expectation

11–7 The Addition Rules for Probability

11–8 The Multiplication Rules of Conditional Probability

11–9 The Binomial Distribution

Summary

CHAPTER **11**

Probability and Counting Techniques

Outline

11-1   The Fundamental Counting Principle and Permutations

11-2   Combinations

11-3   Basic Concepts of Probability

11-4   Tree Diagrams, Tables, and Sample Spaces

11-5   Probability Using Permutations and Combinations

11-6   Odds and Expectation

11-7   The Addition Rules for Probability

11-8   The Multiplication Rules and Conditional Probability

11-9   The Binomial Distribution

Summary

MATH IN ▶ Gambling

The fact that you're reading this sentence means that you're probably taking a math class right now. But maybe not . . . you could be an instructor evaluating the book, or maybe an editor looking for mistakes (unsuccessfully, we hope). Still, I would be willing to bet that you're taking a math class. The word "probably" indicates a certain likelihood of something happening, and that basic idea is the topic of this chapter. We call the study of the likelihood of events occurring *probability*.

Probability is one of the most useful concepts in math because being able to anticipate the likelihood of events can be useful in so many different areas. Games of chance, business and investing, sports, and weather forecasting are just a few samples from a seemingly limitless list of applications. What are the chances of your team winning the championship? Should you take an umbrella to the golf course today? Will stock in a company you're keeping an eye on go up or down? Is that new job offer a good opportunity, or a disaster waiting to happen? Every day you make decisions regarding possible events that are governed at least in part by chance. The more you know about the likelihood of events, the more informed your decisions are likely to be.

One of the more common applications of probability is gambling, or "gaming" as the casinos call it. The amount of money paid out for pretty much any bet you might make isn't based on random guesses or the whims of the casino: it's based on probability.

In order to compute probabilities of events occurring, we're going to need to know all of the possible outcomes for an event. For example, in deciding whether or not to bring an umbrella, there are only two outcomes: it will either rain, or it won't. But in considering whether or not to take a job, there are a wide variety of possible outcomes, some good, some not so good. Since counting up the number of possible outcomes is important in probability, we will begin our study with a look at methods for counting. (Don't worry—that's not quite as elementary as it sounds!) Then we'll be ready to tackle the basic concepts of probability. Along the way, we'll learn about odds and the expected value of a probability experiment, and this is where gambling really comes into play.

A handful of gambling scenarios is provided below. In each case, find the expected value (that is, the average amount a person would win or lose) if placing the bet 100 times. Then rank the scenarios from best to worst in terms of your likelihood of winning or losing money.

1. At a church fair, you bet $1 and roll two dice. If the sum is 2, 3, 11, or 12, you get back your dollar plus four more. On any other roll, you lose.

2. In a casino, you bet $1 on 33 at a roulette table. There are 38 possible numbers that can come up. If you win, you get your dollar back, plus 35 more.

3. You buy a $1 ticket to a multistate lottery. If you match all six numbers, including the Mega Ball, you win the $20 million jackpot. If not, you lose. There are 175,711,536 possible combinations, and only one of them will be a winner.

4. You bet $1 on flipping a coin with your roommate. Heads, you win, tails, your roommate wins.

For answers, see Math in Gambling Revisited on page 693

Section 11-1   The Fundamental Counting Principle and Permutations

Many problems in probability and statistics require knowing the total number of ways a sequence of events can occur. Suppose that as part of an exciting new job, you're responsible for designing a new license plate for your state. You want it to look cool, of course. But if you want to keep your job, you better make sure that the sequence of letters and numbers you choose guarantees that there are enough different combinations so that every registered vehicle has a different plate number.

In this chapter, we'll study three basic rules for counting the number of outcomes for a sequence of events. The first is the *fundamental counting principle*.

LEARNING OBJECTIVES

☐ 1. Use the fundamental counting principle.

☐ 2. Calculate the value of factorial expressions.

☐ 3. Find the number of permutations of *n* objects.

☐ 4. Find the number of permutations of *n* objects taken *r* at a time.

☐ 5. Find the number of permutations when some objects are alike.

The Fundamental Counting Principle

After getting that new job, you naturally want a new apartment, and furniture to go along with it. The hip furniture boutique around the corner has the couch you want in either leather or microsuede, and each comes in your choice of four colors. How many different couches do you have to choose from?

We'll illustrate the situation with a *tree diagram,* which displays all the possible combinations.

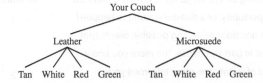

Each of the colors at the bottom of the diagram actually represents a different couch. For example, if you follow the left branch at each stage, you get a tan leather couch. The eight branches at the bottom shows that there are eight possible couches. Notice that this is the same number you'll get if you multiply the number of choices at each stage.

Now what if each couch can also come with or without an end recliner? Each of the eight choices in our diagram would have two more possibilities beneath it.

This would give us a total of 16 couches, which is $2 \cdot 4 \cdot 2$, which is again the product of the number of choices at each stage. This illustrates our first key counting principle.

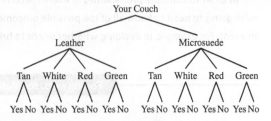

> **Math Note**
>
> The occurrence of the first event in no way affects the occurrence of the second event, which in turn does not affect the occurrence of the third event, etc.

The Fundamental Counting Principle

In a sequence of *n* procedures, if the first can occur in k_1 ways, the second in k_2 ways, the third in k_3 ways, and so on, the total number of ways the sequence of procedures can occur is

$$k_1 \cdot k_2 \cdot k_3 \cdot \cdots \cdot k_n$$

EXAMPLE 1   Using the Fundamental Counting Principle

There are four basic blood types, represented by letters: A, B, AB, and O. There is also an Rh factor represented by either + or −. If a local blood bank labels donations according to type, Rh factor, and gender of the donor, how many different ways can a blood sample be labeled?

SOLUTION

There are four possibilities for blood type, two for Rh factor, and two for gender of the donor. Using the fundamental counting principle, there are

$$4 \cdot 2 \cdot 2 = 16$$

different ways that blood could be labeled.

▼ Try This One 1

A discount paint manufacturer plans to make several different paints. The categories include

Color	Red, blue, white, black, green, brown, yellow
Type	Latex, oil
Texture	Flat, semigloss, high gloss
Use	Outdoor, indoor

How many different kinds of paint can be made?

When determining the number of different ways a sequence of procedures can occur, we'll need to know whether or not repetitions are permitted. The next example shows the difference between the two situations.

EXAMPLE 2   Using the Fundamental Counting Principle with Repetition

(a) The letters A, B, C, D, and E are to be used in a four-letter ID card. How many different cards are possible if letters are allowed to be repeated?
(b) How many cards are possible if each letter can only be used once?

SOLUTION

(a) There are four spaces to fill and five choices for each. The fundamental counting principle gives us

$$5 \cdot 5 \cdot 5 \cdot 5 = 5^4 = 625$$

(b) The first letter can still be chosen in five ways. But with no repetition allowed, there are only four choices for the second letter, three for the third, and two for the last. The number of potential cards is

$$5 \cdot 4 \cdot 3 \cdot 2 = 120$$

Hopefully, this ID card is for a pretty small organization.

How many three-digit codes are possible if repetition is not permitted?

1. Use the fundamental counting principle.

▼ Try This One 2

The lock on a storage facility is controlled by a keypad containing digits 1 through 5.

(a) How many three-digit codes are possible if digits can be repeated?
(b) How many three-digit codes are possible if digits cannot be repeated?

Factorial Notation

The next couple of counting techniques we'll learn use **factorial notation**. The symbol for a factorial is the exclamation mark (!). In general, $n!$ means to multiply the whole numbers from n down to 1. For example,

$$1! = 1 = 1$$
$$2! = 2 \cdot 1 = 2$$
$$3! = 3 \cdot 2 \cdot 1 = 6$$
$$4! = 4 \cdot 3 \cdot 2 \cdot 1 = 24$$
$$5! = 5 \cdot 4 \cdot 3 \cdot 2 \cdot 1 = 120$$

The formal definition of factorial notation is given next.

Calculator Guide

Most graphing calculators, and many scientific calculators have factorials programmed into them. To quickly compute 5!:

Standard Scientific Calculator

5 [x!] or 5 [SHIFT] [x!]

Standard Graphing Calculator

5 [MATH]; use right arrow to choose PRB, then press [4] [ENTER].

For any natural number n

$$n! = n(n-1)(n-2)(n-3) \cdots 3 \cdot 2 \cdot 1$$

$n!$ is read as "**n factorial**."
0! is defined as 1. (This might seem strange, but will be explained later.)

Some of the formulas we'll be working with require division of factorials. This will be simple if we make two key observations:

- $\dfrac{n!}{n!}$ is always 1. For example, $\dfrac{3!}{3!} = \dfrac{3 \cdot 2 \cdot 1}{3 \cdot 2 \cdot 1} = \dfrac{6}{6} = 1$
- You can write factorials without writing all of the factors down to 1. For example, $5! = 5 \cdot 4 \cdot 3 \cdot 2 \cdot 1$, but we can also write this as $5 \cdot 4!$, or $5 \cdot 4 \cdot 3!$, etc.

In Example 3, we'll use these ideas to simplify our calculations.

EXAMPLE 3   Evaluating Factorial Expressions

Evaluate each expression:

(a) 8!   (b) $\dfrac{12!}{10!}$

SOLUTION

(a) $8! = 8 \cdot 7 \cdot 6 \cdot 5 \cdot 4 \cdot 3 \cdot 2 \cdot 1 = 40,320$
(b) First, write 12! as $12 \cdot 11 \cdot 10!$, then note that $\dfrac{10!}{10!} = 1$.

$$\frac{12!}{10!} = \frac{12 \cdot 11 \cdot 10!}{10!} = 12 \cdot 11 = 132$$

▼ **Try This One 3**

Evaluate each expression:

(a) 6!   (b) $\dfrac{9!}{4!}$

☑ 2. Calculate the value of factorial expressions.

CAUTION   You cannot divide factorial expressions by reducing fractions. In Example 3(b), $\frac{12!}{10!}$ is *not* equal to $\frac{6}{5!}$.

Permutations

The second rule that we can use to find the total number of outcomes for a sequence of events is the *permutation rule*.

> An arrangement of *n* distinct objects in a specific order is called a **permutation** of the objects.

For example, suppose that a photographer wants to arrange three people, Carmen, Juan, and Christina, in a specific order for a portrait. There are six ways he could arrange them:

Carmen	Juan	Christina		Carmen	Christina	Juan
Juan	Carmen	Christina		Juan	Christina	Carmen
Christina	Juan	Carmen		Christina	Carmen	Juan

We could use the fundamental counting principle to see that there are six possible permutations as well:

$$3 \quad \cdot \quad 2 \quad \cdot \quad 1 \quad = \quad 3!$$

Choices for 1st position   Choices for 2nd position   Choices for 3rd position

In general,

> ### Permutations of *n* Objects
>
> The number of permutations of *n* distinct objects using all of the objects is *n*!.

Example 4 illustrates this formula.

EXAMPLE 4   Calculating the Number of Permutations

There are seven horses in a race and a large jackpot for anyone who can pick the finishing order of all seven exactly right. How difficult is that? Find the number of possible orders they can finish in.

SOLUTION

This is a permutation problem because we're interested in the number of ways to order seven objects (not that I consider race horses to be merely objects). There are

$$7! = 5,040$$

possible finishing orders.

▼ Try This One 4

 3. Find the number of permutations of *n* objects.

In how many different orders can the 12 basketball teams in the Big Ten conference finish? (Seriously, there are 12 teams in the Big Ten, at least as of 2012.)

So far, in calculating permutations, we've used all of the available objects. But what if only some of them are selected?

Solving a Permutation Problem

How many different ways can a pledge class with 20 members choose a president, vice president, and Greek Council representative? (No pledge can hold two offices.)

SOLUTION

There are 20 choices for president, 19 remaining candidates for vice president, and 18 members left to choose from for Greek Council rep. So there are $20 \cdot 19 \cdot 18 = 6,840$ different ways to assign these three offices.

> *Math Note*
>
> Notice that the calculation in Example 5 can also be written as $\frac{20 \cdot 19 \cdot 18 \cdot 17!}{17!} = \frac{20!}{17!}$. The factorial in the numerator is the number of people we're choosing from; the one in the denominator is the difference between the total number of people and the number being chosen.

▼ **Try This One 5**

How many ways can a manager and assistant manager be selected from a department consisting of 10 employees?

In Example 5, a certain number of objects (people in this case) have been chosen from a larger pool. The order of selection is important, and no repetition is allowed. (No pledge can be both president and vice president—power trip!) We call such an arrangement of objects a **permutation of n objects taken r at a time**. In the pledge problem, n is 20 and r is 3. We will use the symbol $_nP_r$ to represent this type of permutation.

We solved Example 5 using the fundamental counting principle, but the result suggests the formula below:

> **Permutation of n Objects Taken r at a Time**
>
> The arrangement of n objects in a specific order using r of those objects without replacement is called a **permutation of n objects taken r at a time**. It is written as $_nP_r$ and is calculated using the formula
> $$_nP_r = \frac{n!}{(n-r)!}$$

Solving a Permutation Problem

In a lottery game, 40 numbered Ping-Pong balls are put in a bin, and 4 are chosen at random, 1 at a time. To win the game, players need to match all 4 in the order in which they were drawn. How many different winning orders are there?

SOLUTION

This is a permutation problem because 4 balls are picked from 40 with no repetition, and the order is important. So we use the permutation formula with $n = 40$ and $r = 4$.

$$_{40}P_4 = \frac{40!}{(40-4)!} = \frac{40!}{36!} = \frac{40 \cdot 39 \cdot 38 \cdot 37 \cdot 36!}{36!} = 40 \cdot 39 \cdot 38 \cdot 37 = 2,193,360$$

This is why playing lotteries is not the best idea I've ever heard.

> *Calculator Guide*
>
> Most graphing calculators have the permutation formula built in. To find $_{10}P_5$ on a standard graphing calculator: 10 [MATH], then use right arrow to select PRB, and press [2] to select $_nP_r$ and finally 5 [ENTER].

 4. Find the number of permutations of n objects taken r at a time.

▼ **Try This One 6**

How many six-letter passwords are there that use only lowercase letters with no letter repeated?

Math Note

There's a bit of a shortcut that can sometimes be helpful in calculating permutations. In Example 6, after using the permutation formula and simplifying, we were left with $40 \cdot 39 \cdot 38 \cdot 37$.

Notice that this is a product starting with the number of choices (40) that looks like a factorial, but has four factors, which is the number of objects being chosen.

We now have two permutation formulas: there are $n!$ permutations of n objects using all of them, and $\frac{n!}{(n-r)!}$ using only r of the objects. We should probably make sure that these formulas are consistent with each other. To check, we'll use the second formula to calculate the number of permutations when n objects are taken n at a time. The result should be $n!$ (to match the first formula). Let's see.

If we arrange five people in order for a group picture, we can think of it as a permutation of the five people chosen five at a time; that is,

$$_5P_5 = \frac{5!}{(5-5)!} = \frac{5!}{0!}$$

This will agree with the first formula if we agree to define 0! as 1. This is one of the reasons that 0! is defined to be 1: so we know that our two permutation formulas are consistent. This is good news, because it means we only need to remember the second permutation rule.

Problems involving permutation without duplicate objects can be solved using the fundamental counting rule; however, not all problems that can be solved with the fundamental counting rule can be solved using permutations.

When some of the objects are the same, a different permutation rule is used. Suppose that to solve a word puzzle, you need to find the number of permutations of the letters in the word *moon*. First label the letters as M, O_1, O_2, and N. This would be 4!, or 24, permutations. But since the O's without the subscripts are the same, the permutation M, O_1, O_2, N would be the same as M, O_2, O_1, N. The duplicates are eliminated by dividing 4! by the number of ways to arrange the O's (2!) to get 12. This leads to the next rule.

Permutation Rule When Objects Are Alike

The number of permutations of n objects in which k_1 objects are alike, k_2 objects are alike, etc. is

$$\frac{n!}{k_1!k_2!\ldots k_p!}$$

where $k_1 + k_2 + \cdots + k_p = n$

EXAMPLE 7   Solving a Permutation Problem with Like Objects

How many different passwords can be made using all of the letters in the word *Mississippi*?

SOLUTION

The letters can be rearranged as M IIII SSSS PP. Then $n = 11$, $k_1 = 1$, $k_2 = 4$, $k_3 = 4$, and $k_4 = 2$.

Using our newest formula, there are

$$\frac{11!}{1!4!4!2!} = 34,650$$

different passwords.

▼ Try This One 7

Find the number of different passwords using all of the letters in the word *Massachusetts*.

5. Find the number of permutations when some objects are alike.

In summary, the formulas for permutations are used when we're looking for the number of ways to arrange objects when the order matters, and once an object is used, it can't be used again.

Sidelight   WIN A MILLION OR BE STRUCK BY LIGHTNING?

Do you think you would be more likely to win a large lottery and become a millionaire or more likely to be struck by lightning? Of course, this depends on how often you play lotteries and how much time you spend outside, but on average you would be quite a bit more likely to be struck by lightning.

An article in the Associated Press noted that researchers have found that the chance of winning $1 million or more is about 1 in 1.9 million. The chances of winning $1 million in a recent Pennsylvania lottery were 1 in 9.6 million. The chances of winning a $10 million prize in Publisher's Clearinghouse Sweepstakes were 1 in 200 million. In contrast, the chances of being struck by lightning are about 1 in 600,000. In other words, a person is at least 3 times more likely to be struck by lightning than to win $1 million.

One way to guarantee winning a lottery is to buy all possible combinations of the winning numbers. In 1992, an Australian investment group purchased 5 million of the 7 million

possible combinations of the lottery numbers in a Virginia State Lottery. Because of the time, they could not purchase the other two million tickets. However, they were able to purchase the winning number and won $27 million. Their profit was about $22 million. Not bad!

States have written laws to prevent this from happening today, and they are devising lottery games with many more possibilities so that it would be impossible to purchase all the possible tickets to win.

The consequence is that your odds of winning are now even lower! There's an old joke among statisticians: lotteries are a tax on people who are bad at math.

Answers to Try This One

1	84		**5**	90
2	(a) 125	(b) 60	**6**	165,765,600
3	(a) 720	(b) 15,120	**7**	64,864,800
4	479,001,600			

EXERCISE SET   11-1

Writing Exercises

1. Explain the fundamental counting principle in your own words.
2. What do we mean by the phrase "a permutation of n distinct objects"?
3. How does a permutation of n objects differ from a permutation of n objects taken r at a time?
4. Explain what the symbols $n!$ and $_nP_r$ represent, and explain how to compute each for given values of n and r.

5. Describe the difference between finding the number of ways to choose five objects if each can only be chosen once and the number of ways if the objects can be chosen more than once.
6. We developed two permutation formulas in this section, but you really only need to know one of them. Which one and why?

Computational Exercises

Evaluate each.

7. 10!
8. 5!
9. 1!
10. 0!

11. $\frac{8!}{5!}$
12. $\frac{9!}{7!}$
13. $\frac{11!}{(11-3)!}$
14. $\frac{14!}{(14-6)!}$

15. $\frac{6!9!}{4!3!}$
16. $\frac{8!5!}{3!6!}$
17. $\frac{7!}{2!3!}$
18. $\frac{10!}{2!5!}$

19. $\frac{150!}{148!}$
20. $\frac{200!}{197!}$
21. $_8P_2$
22. $_7P_5$

23. $_{12}P_{12}$
24. $_5P_3$
25. $_6P_6$
26. $_6P_0$

27. $_{11}P_3$
28. $_6P_2$
29. $\frac{_4P_2}{_{14}P_3}$
30. $\frac{_9P_6}{_{20}P_2}$

Applications in Our World

31. How many four-letter passwords can be formed from the letters in the word *panicky* if each letter has to be distinct? What if letters are allowed to be repeated?

32. Out of a group of eight students serving on the Student Government Association, how many different ways can a president, a vice president, and a treasurer be selected?

33. How many different ID cards can be made if there are six digits on a card and no digit can be used more than once? What if digits can be repeated?

34. How many different ways can seven types of laser printer be displayed on a shelf in a computer store?

35. How many different ways can four Super Bowl raffle tickets be selected from 50 tickets if each ticket wins a different prize?

36. How many different ways can a psychology student select five subjects from a pool of 20 subjects and assign each one to a different experiment?

37. How many website graphics can be created by using at least three of five different bitmap images?

38. A chemistry lab group has seven experiments to choose from and five members in the group. How many different ways can the experiments be assigned if only one experiment is assigned to each group member?

39. A radio DJ has a choice of seven songs in the queue. He must select three different songs to play in a certain order after the commercial break. How many ways can he select the three different songs?

40. A professor has five different tasks to assign, one to each of her five teaching assistants. In how many different ways could she make the assignments?

41. A nursing student can be assigned to one of six different floors each day depending on staffing needs. How many different ways can she be assigned during a 5-day work week?

42. A hotel manager has 12 different promotional events she can choose from, and plans to run a promotion during each of the 4 weeks in February. She doesn't have a problem with repeating a promotion if it's successful. How many different ways can she choose the promotions?

43. Out of 17 contacts in her cell phone, how many different ways can Shana set the first four speed-dial contacts?

44. In how many different ways can you visit the seven stores you like at an outlet mall?

45. How many different code words can be made from the symbols *, *, *, @, @, $, #, #, #, # if each word has 10 symbols?

46. How many different passwords can be made from the letters in the word *Alabama*?

47. A radio DJ is contractually obligated to run a commercial for Pepsi three times, a commercial for a local law firm once, and a new promo for the station twice per hour. In how many different ways can he do this?

48. A graphic designer is choosing from three red squares, two blue squares, and four white squares to design a backdrop pattern for a tech expo. How many different orders can she choose?

49. The panel for a political forum consists of four Democrats, five Republicans, and three independents. In how many orders can they be seated if all that matters is party, not individual?

50. There are 16 teams in each conference in professional football, and 6 make the playoffs each year. In how many different ways can that happen? (The teams are seeded from 1 to 6.)

51. In how many ways can the panelists in Problem 49 be chosen to answer five questions posed by the moderator with no regard for party? Panelists can answer more than one question.

52. In how many ways can a team from one of the conferences be chosen (see Problem 50) to be featured on the NFL pregame show for the first 6 weeks of the season? Teams can be featured more than once.

53. A major league baseball team has 25 players on the active roster. How many choices does a manager have for batting order, listing the nine starters from 1 through 9?

54. A college basketball team has 14 women on the roster. In how many ways can the coach choose a lineup featuring five different positions?

55. For the new fall season, a network president has 11 shows in development, and six openings in the prime time schedule. In how many ways can she arrange new shows to fit into the schedule?

56. For the 2012 Orion Music and More Festival, there were eight bands scheduled on the main stage over 2 days. In how many different orders could they be scheduled? What if Metallica is scheduled to close the show both days, but every other band is scheduled only once?

While making up his schedule for spring semester, Tom complains that he doesn't have very many choices of schedule because of the general education requirements he has to meet. His advisor tells Tom that he has to take one course from each of English (three choices), history (five choices), math/stats (five choices), computer science (four choices), and general science (six choices). Does Tom have a legitimate gripe? Let's examine this in Problems 57–60.

57. If every possible course is available at the time he's registering, how many possible schedules can he choose from (disregarding when the classes meet)?

58. If Tom hasn't met the prerequisites for two of the math/stat courses and three of the general science

courses, by how much does this reduce his number of possible schedules?

59. When trying to schedule, Tom finds that all but one of the English courses is closed, as are two history courses and one general science course. How many schedules does he have to choose from now?

60. In an unprecedented effort to make the general education requirements more accessible, the dean of Tom's college decides to double the number of acceptable courses in each of those five areas. What effect does this have on the number of possible schedules?

Critical Thinking

61. A campus pizzeria offers regular crust, thin crust, or pan pizzas. You can get either white or red sauce. The owner is kind of eccentric, and only sells pizzas with one topping, chosen from pepperoni, sausage, ham, onions, and ground beef. First, use a tree diagram like the one on page 622 to diagram out all possible choices of pizza. Then show that using the fundamental counting principle yields the same answer.

62. (a) Suppose that a chef is choosing from 20 toppings to make a gourmet pizza, and he plans to choose 6 of them. How many different ways can he do

so if you're keeping track of the order in which he adds them?

(b) Let's be honest, though . . . when you're putting toppings on a pizza, it doesn't really matter what order you choose. So how many different pizzas can the chef make? (*Hint*: How can you get rid of all of the different possible orders in your count?)

63. Show that
$$\frac{n!}{(n-r)!} = n!(n-1)!(n-2)! \cdots (n-r+1)$$

64. Explain why a combination lock should actually be called a permutation lock.

Section 11-2 Combinations

LEARNING OBJECTIVES

☐ 1. Distinguish between a combination and a permutation.

☐ 2. Find the number of combinations of *n* objects taken *r* at a time.

☐ 3. Use the combination rule in conjunction with the fundamental counting principle.

Suppose that after waiting in line overnight, you manage to snag the last three tickets to a big concert. Sweet! The bad news is that you can only take two of your four housemates. How many different ways can you choose the two friends that get to go?

This sounds a little bit like a permutation problem, but there's a key difference: the order in which you choose two friends doesn't make any difference. They either get to go or they don't. So choosing Ruth and

Ama is exactly the same as choosing Ama and Ruth. When order matters in a selection, we call it a permutation, but when order is not important we call it a *combination*.

A selection of objects without regard to order is called a **combination**.

In Example 1, we'll examine the difference between permutations and combinations.

EXAMPLE 1   Comparing Permutations and Combinations

Given four housemates, Ruth, Elaine, Ama, and Jasmine, list the permutations and combinations when you are selecting two of them.

SOLUTION

We'll start with permutations, then eliminate those that have the same two people listed.

Permutations

Ruth Elaine	Elaine Ruth	Ruth Ama
Ama Ruth	Ruth Jasmine	Jasmine Ruth
Elaine Ama	Ama Elaine	Elaine Jasmine
Jasmine Elaine	Ama Jasmine	Jasmine Ama

Combinations

| Ruth   Elaine | Ruth   Ama | Ruth   Jasmine |
| Elaine   Ama | Elaine   Jasmine | Ama   Jasmine |

There are 12 permutations, but only 6 combinations.

▼ Try This One 1

If you are choosing two business classes from three choices, list all the permutations and combinations.

It will be very valuable in our study of counting and probability to be able to decide if a given selection is a permutation or a combination.

EXAMPLE 2   Identifying Permutations and Combinations

Decide if each selection is a permutation or a combination.

(a) From a class of 25 students, a group of 5 is chosen to give a presentation.
(b) A starting pitcher and catcher are picked from a 12-person intramural softball team.

SOLUTION

(a) This is a combination because there are no distinct roles for the 5 group members, so order is not important.
(b) This is a permutation because each selected person has a distinct position, so order matters.

▼ Try This One 2

Decide if each selection is a permutation or a combination.

(a) A 5-digit passcode is chosen from the numbers 0 through 9.
(b) A gardener picks 4 vegetable plants for his garden from 10 choices.

1. Distinguish between a combination and a permutation

Recall that the number of combinations in Example 1 was half as great as the number of permutations. This is because once two people are picked, there are two ways to arrange them. So the number of combinations of n objects chosen r at a time should be the number of permutations divided by the number of ways to arrange r objects. But we know that is $r!$. This gives us a formula for combinations.

Math Note

Notice that the combination formula is the permutation formula from Section 11-1 with an extra factor of $r!$ in the denominator; that makes it $\frac{_nP_r}{r!}$.

The Combination Rule

The number of combinations of n objects taken r at a time without replacement is denoted by $_nC_r$ and is given by the formula

$$_nC_r = \frac{n!}{(n-r)!r!}$$

632   **Chapter 11**   Probability and Counting Techniques

| EXAMPLE 3 | **Using the Combination Rule** |

How many combinations of four objects are there taken two at a time?

Calculator Guide

Most graphing calculators have the combination formula built in. To find $_4C_2$ on a standard graphing calculator:

4 **MATH**, then use right arrow to select PRB, and press **3** to select $_nC_r$, and finally 2 **ENTER**.

SOLUTION

Since this is a combination problem, the answer is

$$_4C_2 = \frac{4!}{(4-2)!\,2!} = \frac{4!}{2!2!} = \frac{4 \cdot 3 \cdot 2!}{2 \cdot 1 \cdot 2!} = 6$$

This matches our result from Example 1.

> ▼ **Try This One 3**
>
> How many combinations of eight objects are there taken five at a time?

| EXAMPLE 4 | **An Application of Combinations** |

Math Note

Some people use the terminology "10 choose 3" to describe the combination $_{10}C_3$, and it is sometimes represented using the notation $\binom{10}{3}$.

While studying abroad one semester, Tran is required to visit 10 different cities. He plans to visit 3 of the 10 over a long weekend. How many different ways can he choose the 3 to visit? Assume that distance is not a factor.

SOLUTION

The problem doesn't say anything about the order in which they'll be visited, so this is a combination problem.

$$_{10}C_3 = \frac{10!}{(10-3)!\,3!} = \frac{10!}{7!3!} = 120$$

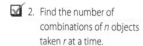 2. Find the number of combinations of n objects taken r at a time.

> ▼ **Try This One 4**
>
> An instructor posts a list of eight group projects to her website. Every group is required to do four projects at some point during the semester. How many different ways can a group choose the four projects they want to do?

In some cases, the combination rule is used in conjunction with the fundamental counting principle. Examples 5 and 6 illustrate some specific situations.

| EXAMPLE 5 | **Choosing a Committee** |

At one school, the student government consists of seven women and five men. How many different committees can be chosen with three women and two men?

SOLUTION

You can think of this problem as having two distinct stages: first choosing the three women, then choosing the two men. So it's a fundamental counting principle problem. At each stage, though, we have a combination. We can choose three women from the seven candidates in $_7C_3 = 35$ ways. We can choose two men from the five candidates in $_5C_2 = 10$ ways. Now we use the fundamental counting principal to multiply: there are $35 \cdot 10 = 350$ different committees.

▼ Try This One 5

On an exam, a student has to pick 2 essay questions from 6 essay questions and 10 multiple choice questions from 20 multiple choice questions to answer. How many different ways can the student pick questions to answer?

EXAMPLE 6   **Designing a Calendar**

To raise money for a charity event, a sorority plans to sell a calendar featuring tasteful pictures of some of the more attractive professors on campus. They will need to choose six models from a pool of finalists that includes nine women and six men. How many possible choices are there if they want to feature at least four women?

SOLUTION

Since we need to include at least four women, there are three possible compositions: four women and two men, five women and one man, or six women and no men.

Four women and two men:

$$_9C_4 \cdot {}_6C_2 = \frac{9!}{(9-4)!4!} \cdot \frac{6!}{(6-2)!2!} = 126 \cdot 15 = 1{,}890$$

Five women and one man:

$$_9C_5 \cdot {}_6C_1 = \frac{9!}{(9-5)!5!} \cdot \frac{6!}{(6-1)!1!} = 126 \cdot 6 = 756$$

Six women and no men:

$$_9C_6 \cdot {}_6C_0 = \frac{9!}{(9-6)!6!} \cdot \frac{6!}{(6-0)!0!} = 84 \cdot 1 = 84$$

The total number of possibilities is $1{,}890 + 756 + 84 = 2{,}730$.

▼ Try This One 6

A four-person crew for the international space station is to be chosen from a candidate pool of 10 Americans and 12 Russians. How many different crews are possible if there must be at least two Russians?

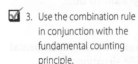

3. Use the combination rule in conjunction with the fundamental counting principle.

This is a good time to talk about the significance of the words *and* and *or* when applying counting techniques. In Example 5, we needed a committee with three women AND two men; this led us to conclude that we could think of it as a two-stage process and *multiply* using the fundamental counting principle. In Example 6, we end up choosing between three possible options: four women OR five women OR six women. In this case, we found the number of possibilities for each and *added* them.

Table 11-1 summarizes all of the counting rules from sections 11-1 and 11-2. It's important to know the formulas, but it's far more important to understand the situations that each formula is needed for.

TABLE 11-1	Summary of Counting Rules	
Rule	**Description**	**Formula**
Fundamental counting principle	The number of ways a sequence of n events can occur if the first event can occur in k_1 ways, the second event can occur in k_2 ways, etc. (Events are unaffected by the others.)	$k_1 \cdot k_2 \cdot k_3 \cdots k_n$
Permutation rule	The number of permutations of n objects taking r objects at a time. (Order is important.)	$\dfrac{n!}{(n-r)!}$
Permutation rule for duplicate objects	The number of permutations in which k_1 objects are alike, k_2 objects are alike, etc.	$\dfrac{n!}{k_1! k_2! \cdots k_p!}$
Combination rule	The number of combinations of r objects taken from n objects. (Order is not important.)	$\dfrac{n!}{(n-r)!r!}$

Answers to Try This One

1 Call the classes A, B, and C:

Permutations
A B B A A C
C A B C C B

Combinations
A B A C B C

2 (a) Permutation

(b) Combination

3 56

4 70

5 2,771,340

6 5,665

EXERCISE SET 11-2

Writing Exercises

1. What is meant by the term combination?
2. What is the difference between a permutation and a combination?
3. Describe a real-life situation in which it would be appropriate to use combinations to count possibilities.
4. Describe a situation related to the one in Exercise 3 in which it would be appropriate to use permutations to count possibilities.
5. Describe a situation where counting would require both the combination formula and the fundamental counting principle.

6. Explain why it makes sense that $_nC_r = \frac{_nP_r}{r!}$.
7. In counting problems that use the word *and* between two different possibilities, what operation will we use? Explain.
8. In counting problems that use the word *or* between two different possibilities, what operation will we use? Explain.

Computational Exercises

For Exercises 9–22, evaluate each expression.

9. $_5C_2$
10. $_8C_3$
11. $_7C_4$
12. $_6C_2$

13. $_6C_4$
14. $_3C_0$
15. $_3C_3$
16. $_9C_7$

17. $_{12}C_2$
18. $_4C_3$
19. $_{10}C_7 \cdot {_5C_4}$

20. $_8C_5 \cdot {_6C_2} \cdot {_3C_1}$
21. $\dfrac{_{10}C_3 \cdot {_6C_2}}{_6C_3 \cdot {_5C_2}}$
22. $\dfrac{_{12}C_8 \cdot {_7C_3}}{_5C_2}$

For Exercises 23–30, find both the number of combinations and the number of permutations for the given number of objects.

23. 8 objects taken 5 at a time
24. 5 objects taken 3 at a time
25. 6 objects taken 2 at a time
26. 10 objects taken 6 at a time
27. 9 objects taken 9 at a time
28. 12 objects taken 1 at a time
29. 12 objects taken 4 at a time
30. 15 objects taken 7 at a time

For Exercises 31–40, decide whether the selection described is a combination or a permutation.

31. Ten fans at a concert are chosen to go backstage after the show.
32. From a list of 20 dishes he knows how to cook, Maurice chooses different dishes for breakfast, lunch, and dinner on his girlfriend's birthday.

33. A state elects a governor and lieutenant governor from a pool of eight candidates.
34. A state elects two senators from a pool of 12 candidates.
35. Lupe chooses an eight-letter password from the letters of the alphabet.
36. Of the six optional community service projects in a service learning course, Haylee picks three of them.
37. When looking for a new car, you read about ten different models and choose four that you would like to test drive.
38. Mark looks over the novels on his bookshelf and lists his five favorites ranked 1 through 5.
39. In planning a salad for a banquet, a chef chooses one of two types of greens, one of three types of croutons, and two of five types of vegetables.
40. Morton schedules his classes for next semester from 12 different course choices, scheduling times that fit into his work schedule.

Applications in Our World

41. In 5-card poker, each player is dealt 5 cards (go figure) from a standard deck of 52 cards. How many different hands can be dealt?
42. How many ways are there to select three math help websites from a list that contains six different websites?
43. How many ways can a student pick five questions from an exam containing nine questions? How many ways are there if he is required to answer the first question and the last question?
44. How many ways can four finalists for a job be selected from ten interviewees?
45. A sheriff is choosing three shift commanders from 10 candidates who have expressed interest in the promotion. In how many ways can he do this?
46. How many different possible tests can be made from a test bank of 20 questions if the test consists of 5 questions? (Ignore the order of questions.)
47. The general manager of a fast-food restaurant chain must select 6 restaurants from 11 for a promotional program. How many different possible ways can this selection be done?
48. How many ways can 3 cars and 4 trucks be selected from 8 cars and 11 trucks to be tested for a safety inspection?
49. During the tryouts for a university pep band, there were 4 trumpet players, 12 drummers, and 7 saxophonists. How many ways can the jazz band be chosen so there are 2 trumpet players, 5 drummers, and 3 saxophonists?
50. There are seven men and five women in line at a Salsa dance club. The bouncer can only admit two more men and two more women. How many ways can he choose from those in line? How many ways can he choose if instead he is told he can admit four people and at least two have to be women?

51. Coca-Cola comes in two low-calorie varieties: Diet Coke and Coke Zero. If a promoter has 10 cans of each, how many ways can she select 3 cans of each for a taste test at the local mall?
52. At the movies, Shana wants to get snacks for her friends. How many ways can she select three types of candy and two types of soda from the eight types of candy and five types of soda available?
53. Steve wants to download new music into his iPod from iTunes. How many ways can Steve select two rock songs, three alternative songs, and three rap songs from a list of eight rock songs, six alternative songs, and ten rap songs?
54. How many ways can 2 men and 2 women be selected for a debate tournament if there are 10 male finalists and 12 female finalists?
55. A resort manager is choosing a committee of four people to discuss employment issues. He'll choose from eight housekeepers, three desk clerks, and five maintenance workers. How many possible committees are there if there have to be at least two housekeepers?
56. The California Bureau of Investigation is putting together an elite serial crimes task force with seven members. The candidates are five members of the CBI, eight members of local law enforcement agencies, and nine state patrol members. Find the number of possible task forces if there has to be at least one representative from each agency, and no more than one state patrol member.
57. An inspector with the Nuclear Regulatory Commission is tasked to visit five nuclear plants this month, randomly chosen from three in Ohio, four in New York, and five in Pennsylvania. How many different ways can he choose the plants to visit if at least three will be in Pennsylvania?

58. Eleven patients with Type 2 diabetes are being chosen for a clinical trial of an experimental medication. Twenty patients that developed the disease after age 40 have been identified as good candidates for the study, as well as 14 that developed it as children. The plan is to divide the number of patients as equally as possible among those that developed the disease early and late. Find the number of ways that patients can be chosen for the study.

Critical Thinking

59. In a class of 30 people, the professor decides that everyone should get to know each other, so she insists that everyone have at least a 2-minute conversation with everyone else in the class. What's the least amount of total time that will be spent on these conversations?

60. (a) Refer to Exercise 59. Find the least amount of time needed if the class has 10 students, 20 students, and 40 students.
    (b) Based on the amount of time calculated for 10, 20, 30, and 40 students, try to make a conjecture as to the time needed if there are 50 students, then check your answer.

61. (a) The 2011 baseball team at the Ohio State University consisted of 10 freshmen, 9 sophomores, 7 juniors, and 7 seniors. The coaches want to choose two players from each class to represent the team at a booster club banquet. How many different ways can they choose?

    (b) The coaches also need to choose four players overall to visit elementary schools in the community, with each player going to a different school. How many different ways can they make this choice?

62. A state lottery offers two games in which you choose 6 numbers. In the first, there are 25 numbers to choose from and you need to match the numbers in the order in which they are drawn. In the second, there are 50 numbers to choose from and you need to match all 6 regardless of the order. Which one is easier to win?

63. Show that for any natural numbers n and r, $_nC_r = {_nC_{n-r}}$.

64. Using the definitions of what $_nP_r$ and $_nC_r$ mean (not the formulas for computing them), explain why both are zero if $r > n$. Then try to compute them using the formulas. What goes wrong?

Section 11-3 Basic Concepts of Probability

LEARNING OBJECTIVES

☐ 1. Compute classical probabilities.

☐ 2. Compute empirical probabilities.

Walking into a casino without knowing anything about probability is kind of like going to a stick fight without a stick—you're likely to take a beating. Casinos aren't in the business of losing money, and the games are designed so that most people lose more than they win. But an understanding of what is likely to happen in a given situation can give you an advantage over other players, giving you a better chance of walking out the door with  some cash in your pockets. (Although if you learn enough about probability, you might decide that staying away from casinos is your best approach.)

The study of probability originated in an effort to understand games of chance, like those that use coins, dice, and playing cards. Generally speaking, probability is simply a number that describes how likely an event is to occur. We will use games of chance to illustrate the ideas, but will eventually see that probability has many applications beyond simple games. In this section, we'll examine the basic concepts involved in studying probability. In short, the probability of something occurring is a number that represents how likely it is to occur.

Sample Spaces

Processes such as flipping a coin, rolling a die, or drawing a card from a deck are called *probability experiments*.

> A **probability experiment** is a process that leads to well-defined results called outcomes. An **outcome** is the result of a single trial of a probability experiment.

Some examples of a trial are flipping a coin once, rolling a single die, and drawing one card from a deck. When a coin is tossed, there are two possible outcomes: heads or tails. When rolling a single die, there are six possible outcomes: 1, 2, 3, 4, 5, or 6.

In a probability experiment, we can predict what outcomes are possible, but we can't predict with certainty which one will occur. We say that the outcomes occur at random. In any experiment, the set of all possible outcomes is called the *sample space*.

A **sample space** is the set of all possible outcomes of a probability experiment.

Some sample spaces for various probability experiments are shown here.

Experiment	Sample Space
Flip one coin	{head, tail}
Roll a die	{1, 2, 3, 4, 5, 6}
Answer a true-false question	{true, false}
Flip two coins	{head/head, tail/tail, head/tail, tail/head}

It's important to realize that when two coins are flipped, there are *four* possible outcomes. Consider flipping a quarter and a dime at the same time. Both coins could fall heads up; both coins could fall tails up; the quarter could fall heads up and the dime could fall tails up and, finally, the quarter could fall tails up and the dime could fall heads up. The situation is the same even if the coins are indistinguishable.

In finding probabilities, it's sometimes necessary to consider several outcomes of a probability experiment. For example, when a die is rolled, we may want to consider obtaining an odd number, i.e., 1, 3, or 5. Getting an odd number when rolling a die is an example of an event.

Experiment: draw a card. Sample space: 52 cards. Event: drawing an ace.

An **event** is any subset of the sample space of a probability experiment.

There's a subtle distinction between an outcome and an event: an outcome is a single occurrence, while an event can contain a number of outcomes. So rolling 2 with a single die is an outcome, but can also be considered an event. Rolling an odd number, on the other hand, is an event made up of three outcomes, but is not itself an outcome.

Classical Probability

Now we're ready to specifically define what is meant by probability. The first type we will study is called *classical probability*, because it was the first type of probability to be studied in the 17th and 18th centuries. In classical probability, we study all of the possible outcomes in a sample space and determine the probability, or likelihood, of an event occurring without actually performing experiments.

There is one key assumption we make in classical probability: that every outcome in a sample space is equally likely. For example, when a single die is rolled, we assume that each number is equally likely to come up. When a card is chosen from a deck of 52 cards, we assume that each card has the same probability of being drawn.

> **Math Note**
>
> Because classical probabilities are based on theory, not experiments, they are also called theoretical probabilities.

Formula for Classical Probability

Let E be an event in the sample space S, $n(E)$ be the number of outcomes in E, and $n(S)$ the number of outcomes in S. The probability of E is

$$P(E) = \frac{n(E)}{n(S)} = \frac{\text{Number of outcomes in } E}{\text{Number of outcomes in } S}$$

In Example 1, we'll compute some simple probabilities using the formula above.

EXAMPLE 1   **Computing Classical Probabilities**

A single die is rolled. Find the probability of getting

(a) A 2.
(b) A number less than 5.
(c) An odd number.

SOLUTION

In this case, since the sample space is 1, 2, 3, 4, 5, and 6, there are six outcomes: $n(S) = 6$.

(a) There is one possible outcome that gives a 2, so $P(2) = \frac{1}{6}$.

(b) There are four possible outcomes for the event of getting a number less than 5: 1, 2, 3, or 4. So $n(E) = 4$, and

$$P(\text{a number less than 5}) = \frac{n(E)}{n(S)} = \frac{4}{6} = \frac{2}{3}$$

(c) There are three possible outcomes for the event of getting an odd number: 1, 3, or 5. So $n(E) = 3$, and

$$P(\text{odd number}) = \frac{n(E)}{n(S)} = \frac{3}{6} = \frac{1}{2}$$

A die roll has six outcomes. If $E =$ roll a 2, then $P(E) = \frac{1}{6}$.
If $E =$ roll an even number, then $P(E) = \frac{3}{6} = \frac{1}{2}$.

> ▼ **Try This One 1**
>
> Each number from one to twelve is written on a card and the twelve cards are placed in a box. If a card is selected at random, find the probability that the number on the card is
>
> (a) A 7.
> (b) An odd number.
> (c) A number less than four.
> (d) A number greater than seven.

EXAMPLE 2   **Computing Classical Probabilities**

Two coins are flipped. Find the probability of getting

(a) Two heads.
(b) At least one head.
(c) At most one head.

SOLUTION

The sample space is {HH, HT, TH, TT}; so $n(S) = 4$.

(a) There's only one way to get two heads: HH. So

$$P(\text{two heads}) = \frac{n(E)}{n(S)} = \frac{1}{4}$$

(b) "At least one head" means one or more heads; i.e., one head or two heads. There are three ways to get at least one head: HT, TH, and HH. So $n(E) = 3$, and

$$P(\text{at least one heads}) = \frac{n(E)}{n(S)} = \frac{3}{4}$$

(c) "At most one head" means no heads or one head: TT, TH, HT. So $n(E) = 3$, and

$$P(\text{at most one head}) = \frac{n(E)}{n(S)} = \frac{3}{4}$$

> ### ▼ Try This One 2
>
> Suppose that in a certain game, it's equally likely that you will win, lose, or tie. Find the probability of
>
> (a) Losing twice in a row.
> (b) Winning at least once in two tries.
> (c) Having the same outcome twice in a row.

> **Math Note**
>
> A good problem-solving strategy to use is to make a list of all possible outcomes in the sample space before computing the probabilities of events.

☑ 1. Compute classical probabilities.

Now that we know a little bit about probability, we can make a series of simple but important observations.

1. **Probability is never negative.** Both $n(E)$ and $n(S)$ have to be zero or positive, so we can't get a negative number by dividing them.

2. **Probability is never greater than one.** An event is a subset of the sample space, so there can't be more outcomes in any event than in the entire sample space; that means the numerator is less than or equal to the denominator in the probability formula.

3. **When an event can't possibly occur, its probability is zero. When an event is certain to occur, the probability is one.** If an event can't occur, then none of the outcomes in the sample space satisfy it and $n(E) = 0$. If an event has to occur, then every outcome in the sample space satisfies it and $n(E) = n(S)$.

4. **If you add the probabilities for every outcome in the sample space, the result is always one.** For example, when a die is rolled, each of the six outcomes has probability $\frac{1}{6}$ so the sum of the probabilities for those six outcomes is one.

Probabilities are usually expressed as fractions or decimals between (and including) zero and one. But occasionally we'll express probabilities as percents. For example, when the probability of an event is $\frac{1}{2}$, there's a 50% chance that it'll occur. If an event has probability close to zero, it's very unlikely to occur, and if the probability is close to one, it's very likely to occur. See Figure 11-1.

WEEKEND FORECAST

A 10% chance of rain doesn't mean it won't rain. You would expect it to rain on roughly 1 in 10 days when a 10% chance of rain was forecast.

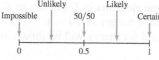

Figure 11-1

In addition to finding the probability that an event will occur, it can be useful to find the probability that the event will not occur. For example, when rolling a die, if E is the event of rolling 2, then the complement of E, written E', is the event of not rolling 2. We know that $P(E) = \frac{1}{6}$; there are five ways for E not to occur: 1, 3, 4, 5, and 6, so $P(E') = \frac{5}{6}$. Notice that these probabilities add to 1, which is no coincidence.

The Probability of a Complement

For any event E, if E' is the event "E does not occur," then

$$P(E') = 1 - P(E)$$

EXAMPLE 3   **Finding a Probability Using Complements**

Of the next 32 trials on the docket in a county court, 5 are homicides, 12 are drug offenses, 6 are assaults, and 9 are property crimes. If jurors are assigned to trials randomly, what's the probability that a given juror won't get a homicide case?

SOLUTION

The simplest way to solve this problem is using complements. There are 32 trials and 5 are homicides, so the probability of getting a homicide is $\frac{5}{32}$. The probability of not getting a homicide is then

$$1 - \frac{5}{32} = \frac{27}{32}$$

▼ **Try This One 3**

For the docket in Example 3, what's the probability that a juror gets assigned to a case that isn't a drug offense?

Probability and Sets

The theory of probability is related to the theory of sets discussed in Chapter 2. For a given probability experiment, the sample space can be considered the universal set, and an event E can be considered as a subset of the universal set.

For example, when rolling a die, the sample space is {1, 2, 3, 4, 5, 6}; so the universal set is $U = \{1, 2, 3, 4, 5, 6\}$. Let the event E be getting an odd number; i.e., 1, 3, or 5. In sets, $E = \{1, 3, 5\}$. A Venn diagram can now be drawn illustrating this example. See Figure 11-2.

Notice that set E contains 1, 3, and 5 while the numbers 2, 4, and 6 are in the universal set but not in E. So $E' = \{2, 4, 6\}$. Now recall from set theory that $E \cup E' = U$. As stated previously, the sum of the probabilities of the outcomes in the sample space is one, so $P(U) = 1$. E' represents the elements in U but not in E, so $P(E) + P(E') = 1$. Subtracting $P(E)$ from both sides, we get $P(E') = 1 - P(E)$. Additional relationships between probability theory and set theory will be shown in other sections of this chapter.

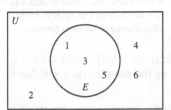

$E \cup E' = U$
$P(E) + P(E') = 1$

Figure 11-2

Sidelight YOU BET YOUR LIFE!

You probably think of gambling as betting money at a casino or on a sporting event, but people gamble all the time in many ways. In fact, people bet their lives every day by engaging in unhealthy activities like smoking, using drugs, eating a high-fat diet, and texting while driving. Maybe people don't care about the risks involved in these activities because they don't understand the concept of probability. On the other hand, people tend to fear things that are far less likely to harm them, like flying, because the occasional negative consequence is sensationalized in the press.

In his book *Probabilities in Everyday Life* (Ivy Books, 1986), author John D. McGrevey states:

> When people have been asked to estimate the frequency of death from various causes, the most overestimated causes are those involving pregnancy, tornados, floods, fire, and homicide. The most underestimated categories include death from diseases such as diabetes,

stroke, tuberculosis, asthma, and stomach cancer (although cancer in general is overestimated).

Which do you think is safer: flying across the United States on a commercial airline, or driving cross country? According to our friend McGrevey, the probability of being killed on any given airline flight is about 1/1,000,000, while the probability of being killed on a transcontinental automobile trip is just 1/8,000. That means that driving across the country is 125 times more dangerous than flying!

Empirical Probability

The second approach to probability we will study is computed using experimental data, rather than counting equally likely outcomes. For example, suppose 100 games into the season, your favorite baseball team has won 60 games and lost 40. You might reasonably guess that since they've won 60 of their 100 games so far, the probability of them winning any given game is about 60/100, or 0.6. This type of probability is called **empirical probability**, and is based on *observed frequencies*—that is, the number of times a particular event has occurred out of a certain number of trials. In this case, the observed frequency of wins is 60, the observed frequency of losses is 40, and the total number of trials is 60 + 40 = 100.

> **Math Note**
>
> The total number of trials is the sum of all observed frequencies.

Formula for Empirical Probability

$$P(E) = \frac{\text{Observed frequency of the specific event } (f)}{\text{Total number of trials } (n)} = \frac{f}{n}$$

In this coin toss, the empirical probability of heads was $\frac{6}{10}$, or $\frac{3}{5}$. With more tosses, you would expect P (heads) to approach $\frac{1}{2}$.

The information in the baseball problem can be written in the form of a **frequency distribution** that consists of classes and frequencies for the classes, as shown below:

Result (Class)	Observed Frequency
Win	60
Lose	40
Total	100

This technique is often helpful in working out empirical probabilities.

EXAMPLE 4   Computing an Empirical Probability

In a random sample of 500 people, 210 had type O blood, 223 had type A, 51 had type B, and 16 had type AB. Set up a frequency distribution and find the probability that a randomly selected person from the general population has

(a) Type O blood.
(b) Type A or B blood.
(c) Neither type A nor type O blood.
(d) A blood type other than AB.

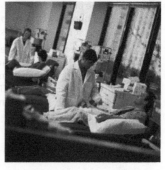

Type O negative blood is the least likely to react badly with a patient's blood, so if it's not possible to test the patient's blood before a transfusion, O negative is used.

SOLUTION

Type (class)	Observed Frequency
A	223
B	51
AB	16
O	210
Total	500

(a) $P(O) = \frac{f}{n} = \frac{210}{500} = 0.42$

(b) The frequency for A or B is $223 + 51 = 274$. $P(A \text{ or } B) = \frac{274}{500} = 0.548$

(c) Neither A nor O is the same as B or AB, which has frequency $51 + 16 = 67$.
$P(\text{neither A nor O}) = \frac{67}{500} = 0.134$

(d) We can find the probability of not AB by subtracting the probability of AB from 1.

$$P(\text{not AB}) = 1 - \frac{16}{500} = \frac{484}{500} = 0.968$$

Math Note

We could also find the probability in part c using complements: $P(\text{neither A nor O}) = 1 - P(A \text{ or } O)$.

☑ 2. Compute empirical probabilities.

▼ Try This One 4

A 2-lb bag of Hershey's miniatures contains 33 milk chocolate bars, 27 Krackel bars, 26 Mr. Goodbars, and 19 Special Dark bars. Set up a frequency distribution and find the probability that a bar chosen from a randomly selected bag is

(a) A Mr. Goodbar.
(b) A Krackel or Special Dark.
(c) Not a milk chocolate bar.

It's important to understand the relationship between classical probability and empirical probability in certain situations. In classical probability, the probability of rolling a 3 when a die is thrown is found by looking at the sample space, and is $\frac{1}{6}$. To find the probability of getting a 3 when a die is thrown using empirical probability, you would actually roll a die a certain number of times and count the number of times a 3 was obtained; then divide that number by the number of times the die was

Sidelight PROBABILITY AND YOUR FEARS

All of us at one time or another have thought about dying. Some people have fears of dying in a plane crash or dying from a heart attack. In the Sidelight on page 641, we saw that it's safer to fly across the United States than to drive. Statisticians who work for insurance companies (called actuaries) also calculate probabilities for dying from other causes. For example, based on deaths in the United States, the risks of dying from various other causes are shown.

Motor vehicle accident	1 in 7,000
Shot by a gun	1 in 10,000
Accident while walking across the street	1 in 60,000
Lightning strike	1 in 3 million
Shark attack	1 in 100 million

The death risk for various diseases is much higher:

Heart attack	1 in 400
Cancer	1 in 600
Stroke	1 in 2,000

As you can see, the chances of dying from diseases are much higher than dying from accidents. (For the record, this is intended to ease some of your fears, not encourage you to act recklessly. Your chances of dying in a motor vehicle accident go up by an awful lot if you're sending texts and speeding while you drive.)

rolled. For example, suppose a die was rolled 60 times, and a 3 occurred 12 times. Then the empirical probability of getting a 3 would be $\frac{12}{60} = \frac{1}{5}$. Most of the time, the probability obtained from empirical methods will differ from that obtained using classical probability. The question is, then, "How many times should I roll the die when using empirical probability?" There is no specific answer except to say that the more times the die is tossed, the closer the results obtained from empirical probability will be to those of classical probability.

In summary, then, classical probability uses sample spaces and assumes the outcomes are equally likely. Empirical probability uses observed frequencies and the total number of trials.

Answers to Try This One

1   (a) 1/12   (b) 1/2   (c) 1/4   (d) 5/12

2   (a) 1/9   (b) 5/9   (c) 1/3

3   5/8

4   (a) 0.248   (b) 0.438   (c) 0.686

EXERCISE SET 11-3

Writing Exercises

1. Define in your own words what the probability of an event means.
2. What is a sample space?
3. What's the difference between an outcome and an event?
4. What is the range of numbers that can represent probabilities? Why?
5. What is the probability of an event that can't occur? Explain why.
6. What is the probability of an event that is certain to occur? Explain why.
7. Explain the difference between classical and empirical probability.
8. Describe how to find the empirical probability of an event after conducting an experiment.
9. How does probability apply to percentages?
10. If you know the probability of an event occurring, how can you find the probability that it doesn't occur?

Computational Exercises

For Exercises 11–18, decide whether or not the given number could represent a probability.

11. $\frac{3}{4}$

12. 0.75

13. $-\frac{1}{2}$

14. 0

15. $\frac{41}{40}$

16. $\frac{40}{41}$

17. 72%

18. 111%

For Exercises 19–22, decide whether the probability described is classical or empirical.

19. At one school, 59% of the students having lunch in the union are women, so the probability of a randomly selected student from the campus phone directory being male is 0.41.

20. A pool table has 15 balls labeled 1 through 15. The probability of a ball made on the break having a number less than 6 is $\frac{1}{3}$.

21. The probability of a randomly selected state beginning with the letter A is $\frac{2}{25}$.

22. While at a casino, Catalina won 10 of the first 15 hands of blackjack she played, so she has a $\frac{2}{3}$ chance of winning the next hand.

Applications in Our World

23. If a die is rolled one time, find the probability of
    (a) Getting a 4.
    (b) Getting an even number.
    (c) Getting a number greater than 4.
    (d) Getting a number less than 7.
    (e) Getting a number greater than 0.
    (f) Getting a number greater than 3 or an odd number.
    (g) Getting a number greater than 3 and an odd number.

24. A couple has two children. Find the probability that
    (a) Both children are girls.
    (b) At least one child is a girl.
    (c) Both children are of the same gender.

25. On the *Price Is Right* game show, a contestant spins a wheel with numbers 1 through 7, with equally sized regions for each of these numbers. If the contestant spins once, find the probability that the number is
    (a) A 6.
    (b) An even number.
    (c) A number greater than 4.
    (d) A number less than 8.
    (e) A number greater than 7.

26. A list contains the names of five anthropology students, two sociology students, and three psychology students. If one name is selected at random to assist in the professor's new study, find the probability that the chosen student is
    (a) An anthropology student.
    (b) A psychology student.
    (c) An anthropology student or a sociology student.
    (d) Not a psychology student.
    (e) Not an anthropology student.

27. On a shelf at a gaming store, there are five Sony Playstations and four Nintendo Wii consoles left. If one gaming system is selected at random, find the probability that the system is a Wii console.

28. If there are only 50 lottery tickets for the Big Game, one of which is a winning ticket, and you buy 7 of those tickets at random, what is the probability that you'll win the super jackpot?

29. In a math class of seven women and nine men, if one person is selected at random to come to the board to show the solution to a problem, what is the probability that the student is a man?

30. A recent survey reported that 67% of Americans approve of human embryonic stem cell research. If an American is selected at random, find the probability that he or she will disapprove or have no opinion on the issue.

31. The Federal Bureau of Investigation reported that in 2010 there were 3,725 single-bias hate crimes that were racially motivated. Of those, 2,600 were motivated by antiblack bias, 678 by antiwhite bias, 212 by bias against a multiracial person, 190 by anti-Asian bias, and 45 by anti-Native American bias. Make a frequency distribution and use it to find the probability that a racially motivated hate crime picked at random was
    (a) Motivated by bias against Asians.
    (b) Motivated by bias against blacks or Native Americans.
    (c) Not motivated by bias against whites.

32. Of 7,690 single-bias hate crime offenses reported in 2010, 3,725 were based on racial bias, 1,409 on religious bias, 1,470 on sexual orientation bias, 1,040 on ethnic bias, and 46 on bias against those with disabilities. Make a frequency distribution and use it to find the probability that a randomly selected hate crime was
    (a) Motivated by sexual orientation bias.
    (b) Motivated by bias against race or ethnicity.
    (c) Not motivated by bias against religion or those with disabilities.

33. In a survey, 16% of male college students said they lie sometimes to get a woman to go out on a date with them. If a male college student is chosen at random, find the probability that he does not lie to get a date with a woman.

34. While conducting a survey on smartphone use in a shopping mall, a marketing consultant found that

24 people she talked to had an iPhone, 16 had an Android, 8 had a BlackBerry, and 4 didn't have a smartphone. Find the probability that a randomly selected person in the mall has

(a) An iPhone.

(b) A smartphone.

(c) An Android or BlackBerry.

Exercises 35–38 refer to a standard deck of playing cards. If you are unfamiliar with playing cards, see the description on page 650.

35. During a game of Texas Hold'em poker, each of four players is dealt two cards, then the dealer "burns" a card (puts it face down), then deals the "flop" (three cards face up). He then burns another card, then flips over the "turn" card (one card face up). One player needs a spade on the "turn" to make a flush. No one else has a spade, and he has two in his hand and there are two on the flop. If neither of the burn cards are spades, what's the probability the turn card will be a spade?

36. During a game of Gin Rummy, Sven needs the eight of diamonds to make a straight in his hand. He and the other player have been dealt 10 cards each, the other player does not have the card he wants, and all other cards are in the deck. What is the probability that the next card picked from the deck is the eight of diamonds?

37. During a game of Blackjack, three players are dealt two cards each, and the dealer has two cards. No one has a card that is worth 10 or 11, which would be a 10, a face card, or an ace. What is the probability that the next player dealt a card would get a card worth 10 or 11?

38. (a) Before the cards are dealt for a game of poker, what's the probability that the 31st card in the deck is a spade?

    (b) After 5 cards have been dealt to each of six players, with eight spades among those dealt, what's the probability that the 31st card in the deck is a spade?

39. A survey on campus revealed that 68% of the students felt that a new attendance policy was unfair. If a student is randomly asked to give an opinion of the new attendance policy, find the probability that the student will either think it's fair or have no opinion.

40. A survey of 25 students in line during registration revealed that 3 were math majors, 10 were history majors, 2 were psychology majors, 7 were biology majors, and the rest were undecided. If the clerk calls a name from the same line of students at random, find the probability the student would be either a history or biology major.

41. On one college campus with 5,300 students, 31% are freshman, 28% are sophomores, 26% are juniors, and the rest are seniors. If a student is randomly chosen from the campus phone book to win a $500 gift card to the bookstore, find the probability that

(a) The student isn't a freshman.

(b) The student is a senior.

(c) The student is a sophomore or junior.

42. There are 248 students in a large-lecture history course. On the first exam, 12% got an A, 28% a B, 41% a C, 11% a D, and the rest failed. Based on these results, what's the probability that a randomly selected student will

(a) Get better than a C on the second test?

(b) Fail the second test?

(c) Not get an A on the second test?

43. On a 10-question true/false test, there are seven false questions and the rest are true. If Marcus answered the first eight questions correctly, and five of them were false, find the probability that when he answers true for the next question, his answer will be correct.

44. According to www.namestatistics.com, the five most common male names and their percentages are as follows:

Name	Percentage
James	3.318%
John	3.271%
Robert	3.143%
Michael	2.629%
William	2.451%

(a) If Mary meets a man at a party, find the probability his name is one of the most popular five male names in the country.

(b) If Jane goes to the grocery store and the clerk is a man, find the probability his name would be John or Robert.

(c) If Bob and Sue rent a new apartment and the landlord is a man, find the probability his name would be in the top three most popular male names.

45. Many people blame Wall Street greed for causing the economic crisis that gripped the nation in late 2008. In February 2009, the Harris Poll surveyed 1,010 Americans, using the statement that people on Wall Street are "as honest and moral as other people." The number giving each response is summarized in the table below:

Agree	707
Disagree	263
Not sure	40

Based on these results, if you ask a randomly selected American this question,

(a) What is the probability that a randomly selected American thinks that people on Wall Street are less honest than other people?

(b) What is the probability that he or she either agrees or disagrees?

46. In December 2008, 500 men and 500 women were surveyed by Omnitel about their opinion on whether federal government bailout money should be used to help homeowners in default. The number giving each response is shown below.

Response	Men	Women
Yes	195	235
No	290	220
Not sure	15	45

(a) If a person who participated in the survey is selected at random, what is the probability that he or she answered no?

(b) What is the probability that the person is a man who answered either yes or no?

(c) Based on the data from the survey, if you had stopped a random woman on the street in December 2008 and asked her opinion, what is the probability that she would have said that bailout money should not be used to help homeowners in default?

47. In a survey conducted by Bank of America, college graduates were asked how much money they typically donate to their alma mater each year. The responses are summarized below:

Nothing	58%
Something, but less than $500	32%
$500 or more	10%

Based on these results:

(a) What is the probability that a randomly selected college graduate gives at least something in a typical year?

(b) What is the probability that a randomly selected college graduate gives less than $500 in a typical year?

48. Jockey International surveyed men to find out how old their oldest pair of underwear is. The results are summarized below:

Less than 1 year	17%
1–4 years	59%
5–9 years	15%
10–19 years	7%
20 or more years	2%

Based on these results:

(a) What is the probability that a randomly selected man has a pair of underwear that is older then 4 years? 9 years?

(b) What is the probability that a randomly selected man has no pair of underwear more than a year old?

(c) What is the probability that a randomly selected man has no underwear more than 9 years old?

49. The students at a university are classified by a 0 for freshman, a 1 for sophomores, a 2 for juniors, a 3 for seniors, and a 4 for graduate students. There are two extra scholarships to assign, so an administrator randomly selects from a box with only the numbers 0, 1, 2, 3, and 4 to choose the class of the first recipient. She then puts the number back into the box and randomly selects a number for the class of the second recipient. Find the sample space, and then find the probability of the following events:

(a) An odd number is chosen first and an even number is chosen second. (*Note:* 0 is considered an even number.)

(b) The sum of the two numbers selected is greater than 4.

(c) For both selections, an even number is drawn.

(d) The sum of the two numbers selected is odd.

(e) The same number is drawn twice.

50. Only six students attended a school charity event, so each of their names was placed into three boxes for the three raffles for the event. What is the probability that the same student's name will be drawn from each box?

Critical Thinking

51. (a) Compute the empirical probability of a randomly selected person in your math class being left-handed. (You'll need to find out which hand everyone writes with.)

(b) Do some research on the Internet to compare that probability to the probability that a person in the general population is left-handed. How do they compare?

(c) The website mlb.com lists rosters for all 30 Major League Baseball teams, along with which hand each player throws with. Look up your favorite team (or the one closest to your campus if you don't have one) and see how the empirical probability of a player being

left-handed compares to your class and the general population. Try to explain any apparent discrepancies.

52. (a) Compute the empirical probability of a randomly selected person in your math class having brown eyes.

(b) Do some research on the Internet to compare that probability to the analogous probability for the general public in the United States. If the results for (a) and (b) are significantly different, do some more research to make up a list of possible reasons.

53. (a) Find the classical probability of rolling a number less than three with one roll of a single die.

(b) Roll a die each of the number of times in the following table, record the results, and fill in the empirical probabilities. Describe any trends or anomalies that you observe, with possible explanations. (If you don't have any dice, do a Google search for "roll dice online.")

Number of rolls	10	20	30	40	50
Probability of rolling less than 3					

54. (a) Find the classical probability of rolling either 6, 7, or 8 with two dice.
    (b) Roll two dice each of the number of times in the next table, record the results, and fill in the empirical probabilities. Describe any trends or anomalies that you observe, with possible explanations. (If you don't have any dice, do a Google search for "roll dice online.")

Number of rolls	10	20	30	40	50
Probability of rolling 6, 7, or 8					

55. Mike and Jose flip the same coin every day at work to decide who pays for the morning coffee. After looking over credit card receipts, Jose realizes that he's paid 73 of the last 100 days. Can Jose conclude that there's something funny about the coin they're flipping? Discuss.

56. When entering a chemistry class one semester, a student decided that he had a 50% chance of passing the class. He justified this by saying "Only two things can happen: I'll either pass or I won't." Critique the student's reasoning.

Section 11-4   Tree Diagrams, Tables, and Sample Spaces

LEARNING OBJECTIVES

☐ 1. Use tree diagrams to find sample spaces and compute probabilities.

☐ 2. Use tables to find sample spaces and compute probabilities.

For centuries, people have tried a wide variety of techniques, some of them pretty bizarre, to try and influence the gender of their children. The truth is, without the aid of cutting-edge science, you don't get to choose. But that doesn't stop many young couples from planning the type of family they hope to have. Suppose that one couple would like to have three children, but they definitely want to have at least one boy and one girl. What is the probability that they'll get their wish without having to go beyond three kids?

When working with classical probabilities, we know that we need to decide on the sample space for an event, and then find how many individual outcomes are in that event. When situations start to get complicated, it might not always be apparent how to do so. That's where tree diagrams and tables can help.

Tree Diagrams

A **tree diagram** is a diagram consisting of branches corresponding to the outcomes of two or more probability experiments that are done in sequence.

Math Note

Recall that we used tree diagrams to illustrate the fundamental counting principle back in Section 11-1.

When constructing a tree diagram, use branches emanating from a single point to show the outcomes for the first experiment, and then show the outcomes for the second experiment using branches emanating from each branch that was used for the first experiment, and so on.

In Example 1, we'll use a tree diagram to find the sample space for our hopeful young couple.

648   **Chapter 11**   Probability and Counting Techniques

| EXAMPLE 1 | **Using a Tree Diagram to Find a Sample Space** |

Use a tree diagram to find the sample space for the genders of three children in a family.

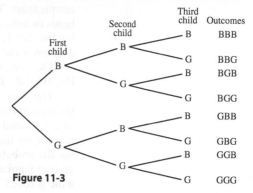

Figure 11-3

SOLUTION

There are two possibilities for the first child, boy or girl, two for the second, boy or girl, and two for the third, boy or girl. So the tree diagram can be drawn as shown in Figure 11-3.

> **Math Note**
>
> The genders of the children are listed in their birth order. For example, the outcome GGB means the firstborn was a girl, the second a girl, and the third a boy.

After a tree diagram is drawn, the outcomes can be found by tracing through all of the branches. In this case, the sample space would be {BBB, BBG, BGB, BGG, GBB, GBG, GGB, GGG}.

> ▼ **Try This One 1**
>
> A soda machine dispenses both Coke and Pepsi products, in both 12-ounce cans and 20-ounce bottles. For each brand, it has a regular cola, diet cola, and lemon-lime drink. Use a tree diagram to find the sample space for the experiment of choosing one drink at random from this machine.

Once a tree diagram is drawn and the sample space is found, you can compute the probabilities for various events.

| EXAMPLE 2 | **Computing a Probability** |

If a family has three children, find the probability that they have at least one boy and one girl. (Assume that each child is equally likely to be a boy or girl.)

SOLUTION

The sample space we found in Example 1 has eight outcomes, and only two of them have three kids with the same gender. So six of the eight outcomes have at least one boy and one girl, making the probability $\frac{6}{8}$ or $\frac{3}{4}$.

> ▼ **Try This One 2**
>
> Suppose the soda machine from Try This One 1 goes berserk and starts dispensing drinks randomly. If you want a diet cola, what is the probability that you'll get one?

| EXAMPLE 3 | **Using a Tree Diagram to Compute Probabilities** |

A coin is flipped, and then a die is rolled. Use a tree diagram to find the probability of getting heads on the coin and an even number on the die.

SOLUTION

First, we'll use a tree diagram to find the sample space. The coin will land on either heads or tails, and there are six outcomes for the die: 1, 2, 3, 4, 5, or 6. The tree diagram is shown in Figure 11-4.

The sample space is {H1, H2, H3, H4, H5, H6, T1, T2, T3, T4, T5, T6}.

The total number of outcomes for the experiment is 12. The number of ways to get a head on the coin and an even number on the die is 3: H2, H4, or H6. So, the probability of getting a head and an even number when a coin is tossed and a die is rolled is $\frac{3}{12}$, or $\frac{1}{4}$.

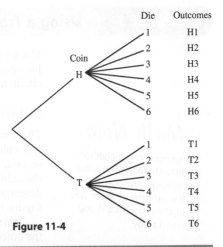

Figure 11-4

☑ 1. Use tree diagrams to find sample spaces and compute probabilities.

▼ Try This One 3

In order to collect information for a student survey, a researcher classifies students according to eye color (blue, brown, green), gender (male, female), and class rank (freshman, sophomore). A folder for each classification is then made up (e.g., freshman/female/green eyes). Find the sample space for the folders using a tree diagram. If a folder is selected at random, find the probability that

(a) It includes students with blue eyes.
(b) It includes students who are female.
(c) It includes students who are male freshmen.

In constructing tree diagrams, not all branches have to be the same length. For example, suppose two players, Alice and Diego, play chess, and the first one to win two games wins the tournament. The tree diagram would be like the one shown in Figure 11-5. For any game, A means that Alice wins, and D means that Diego wins.

Notice that if Alice wins the first two games, the tournament is over. So the first branch is shorter than the second one. But if Alice wins the first game and Diego wins the second game, they need to play a third game in order to decide who wins the tournament. Similar reasoning can be applied to the rest of the branches.

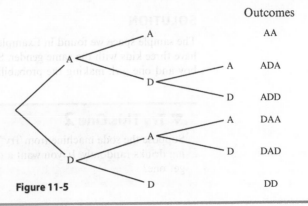

Figure 11-5

> **CAUTION** When the branches of a tree diagram are not equal in length, the outcomes are not equally likely even if the probability of every individual trial is $\frac{1}{2}$. In the tournament example above, if each player is equally likely to win any given game, the outcomes AA and DD both have probability $\frac{1}{4}$, while the outcomes ADA, ADD, DAA, and DAD all have probability $\frac{1}{8}$.

Sidelight MATH AND THE DRAFT LOTTERY

If you're like most people, winning the lottery sounds pretty good to you. But if you were an 18-year-old male in 1970, you would have felt a lot differently. During the Vietnam War, men were drafted for service based on their age and birthday, with older candidates chosen first. This allowed those born in the last months of the year to avoid military service, which didn't sound particularly fair to those born in January.

So in 1970, the government decided to change the system and instituted a lottery to decide who would be drafted. The days of the year were numbered 1 through 366 (for leap years) and mixed in a barrel. The numbers corresponding to birth dates were drawn one at a time and men were drafted based on these numbers.

Sounds perfectly random, right? Everyone thought so, until mathematicians noticed that a disproportionate number of draft-

ees were born later in the year, far more than would be expected with random chance. There's no evidence that anything nefarious was going on, however. It's most likely that the numbers later in the year were put into the barrel last, leaving them on top, and the barrel wasn't mixed well enough.

Tables

Another way of determining a sample space is by making a **table**. Consider the sample space of selecting a card from a standard deck of 52 cards. (The cards are assumed to be shuffled to make sure that the selection occurs at random.) There are four suits—hearts, diamonds, spades, and clubs, and 13 cards of each suit consisting of the denominations ace (A), 2, 3, 4, 5, 6, 7, 8, 9, 10, and 3 picture or face cards— jack (J), queen (Q), and king (K). The sample space is shown in Figure 11-6.

	A	2	3	4	5	6	7	8	9	10	J	Q	K
♥	A♥	2♥	3♥	4♥	5♥	6♥	7♥	8♥	9♥	10♥	J♥	Q♥	K♥
♦	A♦	2♦	3♦	4♦	5♦	6♦	7♦	8♦	9♦	10♦	J♦	Q♦	K♦
♠	A♠	2♠	3♠	4♠	5♠	6♠	7♠	8♠	9♠	10♠	J♠	Q♠	K♠
♣	A♣	2♣	3♣	4♣	5♣	6♣	7♣	8♣	9♣	10♣	J♣	Q♣	K♣

Figure 11-6

EXAMPLE 4　　Using a Table to Compute Probabilities

A card is drawn from an ordinary deck. Use the sample space shown in Figure 11-6 to find the probabilities of getting

(a) A jack.　　　　(b) The 6 of clubs.　　　　(c) A 3 or a diamond.

SOLUTION

(a) There are four jacks and 52 possible outcomes, so

$$P(\text{jack}) = \frac{4}{52} = \frac{1}{13}$$

(b) Since there is only one 6 of clubs, the probability of getting a 6 of clubs is

$$P(6 \text{ of clubs}) = \frac{1}{52}$$

(c) There are four 3s and 13 diamonds, but the 3 of diamonds is counted twice in this listing. So, there are 16 possibilities of drawing a 3 or a diamond, and

$$P(3 \text{ or diamond}) = \frac{16}{52} = \frac{4}{13}$$

▼ Try This One 4

A single card is drawn at random from a well-shuffled deck. Using the sample space shown in Figure 11-6, find the probability that the card is

(a) An ace. (c) A club. (e) The 6 or 8 of spades.
(b) A face card. (d) A 4 or a heart.

> **Math Note**
>
> The sample space for rolling two dice is the same regardless of the color of the dice. We just used color to help distinguish between (2, 4) and (4, 2).

When two dice are rolled, how many outcomes are in the sample space? Suppose for the purpose of illustration that one die is red and the other is blue. The sample space for the red die is {1, 2, 3, 4, 5, 6}, and the sample space for the blue die is also {1, 2, 3, 4, 5, 6}. Now if the outcomes for each die are combined, the sample space will consist of 36 outcomes, as shown in Figure 11-7. Note that the color indicates which die the number comes from.

The outcome (3, 6) means the 3 was obtained on the red die and a 6 was obtained on the blue die. The sum of the spots on the faces then would be $3 + 6 = 9$.

	Blue die					
	1	**2**	**3**	**4**	**5**	**6**
1	(1, 1)	(1, 2)	(1, 3)	(1, 4)	(1, 5)	(1, 6)
2	(2, 1)	(2, 2)	(2, 3)	(2, 4)	(2, 5)	(2, 6)
3	(3, 1)	(3, 2)	(3, 3)	(3, 4)	(3, 5)	(3, 6)
4	(4, 1)	(4, 2)	(4, 3)	(4, 4)	(4, 5)	(4, 6)
5	(5, 1)	(5, 2)	(5, 3)	(5, 4)	(5, 5)	(5, 6)
6	(6, 1)	(6, 2)	(6, 3)	(6, 4)	(6, 5)	(6, 6)

(Red die is labeled vertically on the left)

Figure 11-7

EXAMPLE 5   Using a Table to Compute Probabilities

When two dice are rolled, find the probability of getting

(a) A sum of 8.
(b) Doubles (the same number on each die).
(c) A sum less than 5.

SOLUTION

Using the sample space shown in Figure 11-7, there are 36 possible outcomes.

(a) There are five ways to get a sum of 8: (2, 6), (3, 5), (4, 4), (5, 3), and (6, 2). So $n(E) = 5$, $n(S) = 36$, and

$$P(\text{sum of 8}) = \frac{n(E)}{n(S)} = \frac{5}{36}$$

(b) There are six ways to get doubles: (1, 1), (2, 2), (3, 3), (4, 4), (5, 5), and (6, 6). So $n(E) = 6$, $n(S) = 36$, and

$$P(\text{doubles}) = \frac{n(E)}{n(S)} = \frac{6}{36} = \frac{1}{6}$$

(c) A sum less than 5 means a sum of 4, 3, or 2. The number of ways this can occur is 6, as shown.

Sum of 4: (1, 3), (2, 2), (3, 1)
Sum of 3: (1, 2), (2, 1)
Sum of 2: (1, 1)
$n(E) = 6$, $n(S) = 36$, and so

$$P(\text{sum less than 5}) = \frac{6}{36} = \frac{1}{6}$$

☑ 2. Use tables to find sample spaces and compute probabilities.

▼ Try This One 5

Two dice are rolled. Use the sample space shown in Figure 11-7 to find the probability of

(a) Getting a sum of 9.
(b) Getting a sum that is an even number.
(c) Getting a sum greater than 6.

Answers to Try This One

1 Sample space: {Coke, can, cola; Coke, can, diet cola; Coke, can, lemon-lime; Coke, bottle, cola; Coke, bottle, diet cola; Coke, bottle, lemon-lime; Pepsi, can, cola; Pepsi, can, diet cola; Pepsi, can, lemon-lime; Pepsi, bottle, cola; Pepsi, bottle, diet cola; Pepsi, bottle, lemon-lime}.

2 $\dfrac{1}{3}$

3 Sample space: {blue, male, freshman; blue, male, sophomore; blue, female, freshman; blue, female, sophomore; brown, male, freshman; brown, male, sophomore; brown, female, freshman; brown, female, sophomore; green, male, freshman; green, male, sophomore; green, female, freshman; green, female, sophomore}.

4 (a) $\dfrac{1}{13}$ (b) $\dfrac{3}{13}$ (c) $\dfrac{1}{4}$
   (d) $\dfrac{4}{13}$ (e) $\dfrac{1}{26}$

5 (a) $\dfrac{1}{9}$ (b) $\dfrac{1}{2}$ (c) $\dfrac{7}{12}$

EXERCISE SET 11-4

Writing Exercises

1. Explain how to draw a tree diagram, and how tree diagrams help to find sample spaces.

2. Think of an example, other than the one provided in the section, where a tree diagram would have branches of different lengths.

Applications in Our World

3. Three computers are chosen at random from an inventory of Dell and Acer computers for a bookstore display. Find the probability that
   (a) All three will be Acers.
   (b) Exactly two will be Dells.
   (c) At least two will be Acers.

4. While walking into his stats class, Klutzy Kramer bumped into a table and knocked off a coin and a die the instructor was planning to use in demonstrating probability. Using a sample space similar to Example 3, find the probability that as each landed on the floor,
   (a) There was a head on the coin and an odd number on the die.
   (b) There was a head on the coin and a prime number on the die.
   (c) There was a tail on the coin and a number less than 5 on the die.

5. After the incident in Exercise 4, the professor got smart and dropped the die and the quarter in a box to prevent Klutzy Kramer from knocking them onto the floor again. Using a sample space similar to Example 3, find the probability that as each landed in the box,
   (a) There was a tail on the coin and a number greater than 1 on the die.
   (b) There was a head on the coin and an even number on the die.
   (c) There was a tail on the coin and a number divisible by 3 on the die.

6. Sara came across a new website that featured a "live" fortune-teller. She typed in three questions and found (shockingly) that the fortune-teller could only answer yes or no to her questions. Draw a tree diagram for all possible answers for her three questions. Assuming that this spooky fortune-teller is actually just choosing the responses at random, find the probability that

(a) All answers will be yes or all answers will be no.

(b) The answers will alternate (i.e., Yes–No–Yes or No–Yes–No).

(c) Exactly two answers will be yes.

7. After a late night studying, Ebony decides to grab a latte before class so she can stay awake through her morning lecture. She has only a one-dollar bill, a five-dollar bill, and a ten-dollar bill in her wallet. She pulls one out and looks at it, but then she puts it back. Distracted by a flyer for a new campus organization, she randomly hands a bill from her wallet to the clerk. Draw a tree diagram to determine the sample space and find the probability that

(a) Both bills have the same value.

(b) The second bill is larger than the first bill.

(c) The value of each of the two bills is even.

(d) The value of exactly one of the bills is odd.

(e) The sum of the values of both bills is less than $10.

8. A coin flip determines who gets the ball first at the beginning of a football game, with the visiting team calling heads or tails. The captain of one particular team always calls heads. In the first four games as visitor of a season, find the probability that his team

(a) Wins the toss three times.

(b) Loses the toss all four times.

(c) Wins the toss more than once.

(d) Loses the toss no more than twice.

(e) Loses the toss at least once.

9. Mark and Raul play three games of pool. They are equal in ability. Draw a tree diagram to determine the sample space and find the probability that

(a) Either Mark or Raul win all three games.

(b) Either Mark or Raul win two out of three games.

(c) Mark wins only two games in a row.

(d) Raul wins the first game, loses the second game, and wins the third game.

10. Frank, Sofia, Eldridge, and Jake are the four qualifiers for a charity raffle with two $500 prizes. One of their names will be drawn for the first prize then replaced, at which point the second prize winner will be drawn. Draw a tree diagram to determine the sample space and find the probability that

(a) One person wins both prizes.

(b) There are two different winners.

(c) Sofia wins at least one prize.

(d) Frank wins both prizes.

(e) The two winners are Jake and Eldridge.

11. The pool table in the student lounge is broken, and when Carrie puts her quarter into the slot, only the balls numbered 1 through 5 come down the chute. She selects one without looking and puts it on the table. She then selects another without looking. Draw a tree diagram to determine the sample space and find the probability that

(a) The sum of the numbers of the balls is odd.

(b) The number on the second ball is larger than the number on the first ball.

(c) The sum of the numbers on the balls is greater than 4.

12. Akira wants to purchase his first new car and can select one option from each category:

Model	Engine Type	Color
Ford Focus	Hybrid	Burnt copper
Honda Civic	E-85	Cobalt blue
Toyota Corolla		Metallic green

Draw a tree diagram and find the sample space for all possible choices. Find the probability that the car, if chosen at random,

(a) Has an E-85 engine.

(b) Is a burnt copper Ford Focus.

(c) Is a metallic green hybrid Honda Civic.

(d) Is cobalt blue.

(e) Is either a metallic green or cobalt blue Toyota Corolla.

13. Kimberly goes onto Dell's website to order a custom-made Tablet PC. She can select one option from each category:

Operating System	Processor	Wireless Options
Windows Vista Ultimate	Intel Core 2 Duo	Dell Wireless Mini Card
Windows Vista Home Premium	Intel Celeron 540	Bluetooth 2.0
Windows Vista Home Basic		

Draw a tree diagram to determine the sample space and find the probability that her Tablet PC, if chosen at random, will have

(a) An Intel Celeron 540 Processor.

(b) A Windows Vista Home Premium operating system and an Intel Core 2 Duo Processor.

(c) An Intel Core 2 Duo Processor with a Bluetooth 2.0 wireless option.

14. To choose the order of bands for the finals of the campus Battle of the Bands competition, Freddy puts a penny, a nickel, a dime, a quarter, and a half-dollar into five separate envelopes and has one band choose an envelope. Another band then chooses from the envelopes remaining. Draw a tree diagram to determine the sample space and find the probability that

(a) The amount of the first coin is less than the amount of the second coin.

(b) Neither coin is a quarter.

(c) One coin is a penny and the other coin is a nickel or a dime.

(d) The sum of the amounts of both coins is even.

(e) The sum of the amounts of both coins is less than $0.40.

15. At the beginning of a magic trick, The Great Mancini shuffles an ordinary deck of 52 cards as shown in Figure 11-6, and has the nearest person in the

audience draw a single card. Using the sample space for drawing a single card from this deck, find the probability that the contestant got
(a) A 10.
(b) A club.
(c) The ace of hearts.
(d) A 3 or a 5.
(e) A 6 or a spade.
(f) A queen or a club.
(g) A diamond or a club.
(h) A red king.
(i) A black card or an 8.
(j) A red 10.

16. At a town fair, for one of the game booths contestants pick a single card from a standard deck and payouts are based on the card chosen. Find the probability that your card is
(a) The 6 of clubs.
(b) A black card.
(c) A queen.
(d) A black 10.
(e) A red card or a 3.
(f) A club and a 6.
(g) A 2 or an ace.
(h) A club, diamond, or spade.

(i) A diamond face card.
(j) A red ace.

17. In between classes, Jade plays a game of online Monopoly on her laptop. Using the sample space for rolling two dice shown in Figure 11-7, find the probability that when Jade rolls the two dice, she gets a
(a) Sum of 5.
(b) Sum of 7 or 11.
(c) Sum greater than 9.
(d) Sum less than or equal to 5.
(e) Three on one die or on both dice.
(f) Sum that is odd.
(g) Prime number on one or both dice.
(h) Sum greater than 1.

18. During a charity Las Vegas Casino Night, Rosie plays craps and gets to roll the dice. Using the sample space for rolling two dice as shown in Figure 11-7, find the probability she rolled a
(a) Sum of 8.
(b) Sum that is prime.
(c) Five on one or both dice.
(d) Sum greater than or equal to 7.
(e) Sum that is less than 3.
(f) Sum greater than 12.
(g) Six on one die and 3 on the other die.

Critical Thinking

19. An online math quiz made up of true-false questions starts every student out with two questions. If they get both wrong, they're done. If they get at least one right, they get a third question. Suppose that a student guesses on all questions. Draw a tree diagram and find the sample space for all possible results. Then explain why every outcome is not equally likely.

20. To get past security at a club, potential patrons must answer a series of four questions. If they get any of the first three wrong, they get no more questions and don't get in. Draw a tree diagram and find the sample space for all possible results. Then explain why all of the outcomes are not equally likely.

21. Consider the sample space when three dice are rolled. How many different outcomes would there be?

22. When three dice are rolled, how many ways can a sum of 6 be obtained?

23. When three dice are rolled, find the probability of getting a sum of 6.

24. Find the probability of rolling 10 with two eight-sided dice, with the sides numbered 1 through 8.

25. (a) We know that when flipping a coin, the probability of getting tails is 1/2. Use a tree diagram to find the probability of getting tails twice in a row.
(b) We also know that the probability of rolling a 5 with one die is 1/6. Use tree diagrams to find the probability of getting tails and then rolling a 5 when you flip a coin and then roll a single die.

(c) Based on the results of parts (a) and (b), how do you think you find the probability of two unconnected events occurring consecutively when you know the probability of each occurring individually? (Answer successfully, and you've discovered an important rule we'll study in Section 11-8.)

26. In the finals of an Angry Birds tournament, Bob is the number one seed, and he'll win the championship if he wins one game in the finals. The other two finalists are Fran and Julio, and they each need to win two games to claim the title.
(a) Draw a tree diagram and find the sample space for each possible result of the finals.
(b) Assuming that all three players have an equal likelihood of winning any individual game, find the probability of each outcome in the sample space. (*Hint:* Use the rule you discovered in 25[c].) Make sure that all of your probabilities add to 1!
(c) Use the results of (b) to find the probability of each contestant winning the championship.

27. Disappointed in her failure to gain the top seed for the tournament in Exercise 26, Fran resorts to using a banned substance that improves her reflexes and makes her twice as likely to win any individual game as Bob or Julio. Find the probability of each winning the championship.

28. If Fran's cheating (see Exercise 27) had made her three times as likely to win any individual match as Bob or Julio, would this have been enough to make her the most likely winner?

Section 11-5   Probability Using Permutations and Combinations

LEARNING OBJECTIVES

☐ 1. Compute probabilities using combinations.

☐ 2. Compute probabilities using permutations.

Sometimes a friendly game of poker can become less friendly when someone seems just a bit too lucky. Suppose one player in such a game gets dealt all four aces in one hand. Would you suspect that something fishy was going on? What is the probability of that happening?

In Section 11-4, we used tree diagrams and tables to find sample spaces and the number of outcomes in certain events. This was a pretty good strategy, but when the number of possibilities gets larger, diagrams can get out of hand. Fortunately, we know about counting techniques that are tailor-made for answering questions about probability. If our job is to find how many ways something can happen, the combination and permutation rules from Section 11-2 will be our best friends.

Our general game plan will be to use these rules to find the number of outcomes that satisfy a certain event, as well as the total number of outcomes in the sample space. Then we can divide the first number by the second to obtain the probability of the event occurring.

EXAMPLE 1   Using Counting Techniques to Compute Probability

Stacy has the option of selecting three books to read for a humanities course. The suggested book list consists of 10 biographies and five current events books. She decides to pick the three books at random. Find the probability that all three books will be current events books.

SOLUTION

All we're interested in is whether or not the three books are on current events; so the order doesn't matter, making this a combination. Specifically, we want to know how many ways we can choose three books from five current events books: this is $_5C_3$.

$$_5C_3 = \frac{5!}{(5-3)!3!} = \frac{5 \cdot 4 \cdot 3!}{2 \cdot 1 \cdot 3!} = 10 \quad \textit{10 ways to choose 3 current events books.}$$

The total number of outcomes in the sample space is $_{15}C_3$ since she has to pick three books from 15 books.

$$_{15}C_3 = \frac{15!}{(15-3)!3!} = \frac{15!}{12!3!} = \frac{15 \cdot 14 \cdot 13 \cdot 12!}{12! \cdot 3 \cdot 2 \cdot 1} = 455 \quad \textit{455 total choices.}$$

The probability of selecting three current events books is

$$\frac{10}{455} = \frac{2}{91} \approx 0.022$$

▼ Try This One 1

There are 12 women and 8 men in a seminar course. If the professor chooses five-person groups at random, what is the probability that the first group chosen will consist of all women?

Now back to that poker game . . .

EXAMPLE 2	**Using Counting Techniques to Compute Probability**

What is the probability of getting 4 aces when drawing 5 cards from a standard deck of 52 cards?

> ## Math Note
>
> The probability in Example 2 means that you would expect to draw four aces on average once every 54,145 tries.

SOLUTION

First, we'll figure out how many five-card hands have four aces. The key observation is that we need to get all four aces in the deck, and there's only one way to do that. After we have our four aces, we still have to choose a fifth card, and there are 48 other cards left in the deck. Using the fundamental counting principle, there are $1 \cdot 48$ possible hands that have four aces.

Order doesn't matter again, so the total number of five-card hands is a combination of 52 objects taken 5 at a time, or $_{52}C_5$.

$$_{52}C_5 = \frac{52!}{(52-5)!\,5!} = \frac{52!}{47!\,5!} = \frac{52 \cdot 51 \cdot 50 \cdot 49 \cdot 48 \cdot \cancel{47!}}{\cancel{47!} \cdot 5 \cdot 4 \cdot 3 \cdot 2 \cdot 1} = 2{,}598{,}960$$

The probability of getting four aces is

$$\frac{48}{2{,}598{,}960} = \frac{1}{54{,}145} \approx 0.0000185$$

It's certainly possible to get dealt four aces, and we would hate to accuse your friend of cheating, but to say the least that's an extremely unlikely occurrence.

▼ Try This One 2

☑ 1. Compute probabilities using combinations.

Suppose the deck of cards in Example 2 has all 32 cards with numbers less than 10 removed, so that only 10s, jacks, queens, kings, and aces remain. Now what is the probability of getting 4 aces when drawing 5 cards?

In Example 3, order matters.

EXAMPLE 3	**Using Permutations to Compute Probability**

Permutations determine the number of combinations that can open a combination lock.

A combination lock has 40 numbers on it, from zero to 39. Find the probability that if the combination to unlock it consists of three numbers, it will contain the numbers 1, 2, and 3 in some order. Assume that numbers cannot be repeated in the combination. (It's interesting to note that a combination lock should really be called a permutation lock since the order of the numbers is important when you are unlocking the lock.)

SOLUTION

The statement of the question was kind enough to point out that order matters when opening a combination lock, so we're dealing with permutations in this problem. The number of combinations for the lock containing 1, 2, and 3 is $_3P_3$.

$$_3P_3 = \frac{3!}{(3-3)!} = \frac{3!}{0!} = \frac{3 \cdot 2 \cdot 1}{1} = 6$$

The total number of combinations is a permutation of the 40 numbers taken 3 at a time, or $_{40}P_3$.

$$_{40}P_3 = \frac{40!}{(40-3)!} = \frac{40!}{37!} = \frac{40 \cdot 39 \cdot 38 \cdot 37!}{37!} = 59{,}280$$

The probability of the combination containing 1, 2, and 3 is $\frac{6}{59{,}280} \approx 0.000101$

▼ **Try This One 3**

2. Compute probabilities using permutations.

A different "permutation" lock has letters from A through L on it, and the combination consists of four letters with no repeats. What is the probability that the combination is I, J, K, and L in some order?

In Example 4, we will again need to use the fundamental counting principle.

EXAMPLE 4   **Using Counting Techniques to Compute Probability**

A store has six different fitness magazines and three different news magazines. If a customer buys three magazines at random, find the probability that the he'll pick two fitness magazines and one news magazine.

SOLUTION

We want to know how many of each magazine the customer buys, not the order in which he buys them, so we're dealing with combinations. There are $_6C_2$ or 15 ways to choose two fitness magazines from six fitness magazines, as shown:

$$_6C_2 = \frac{6!}{(6-2)!2!} = \frac{6!}{4!2!} = \frac{6 \cdot 5 \cdot 4!}{4! \cdot 2 \cdot 1} = 15$$

There are $_3C_1$ or three ways to choose one magazine from three news magazines:

$$_3C_1 = \frac{3!}{(3-1)!1!} = \frac{3!}{2! \cdot 1!} = \frac{3 \cdot 2!}{2! \cdot 1} = 3$$

Note the use of "and"; the event in question is picking two fitness magazines AND one news magazine, so we can think of this as a two-step process and use the fundamental counting principle to multiply, giving us $15 \cdot 3 = 45$ ways to pick two fitness and one news magazine.

Next, there are $_9C_3$ or 84 ways to pick three magazines from nine magazines:

$$_9C_3 = \frac{9!}{(9-3)!3!} = \frac{9!}{6!3!} = \frac{9 \cdot 8 \cdot 7 \cdot 6!}{6! \cdot 3 \cdot 2 \cdot 1} = 84$$

The probability of picking two fitness magazines and one news magazine is

$$\frac{45}{84} \approx 0.536$$

▼ **Try This One 4**

Find the probability that the customer in Example 4 picks at least two fitness magazines.

Now we see why Chapter 11 began with a study of permutations, combinations, and the fundamental counting principle: a large variety of probability problems can be solved using these counting techniques in conjunction with the probability rules.

Sidelight THE CLASSICAL BIRTHDAY PROBLEM

You're in a room with 29 other people and someone says "I'll bet you fifty bucks that two people in this room have the same birthday." Would you take the bet? Most people would; since there's 365 days in year, you'd think that the probability of 2 out of 30 having the same birthday should be pretty low. Believe it or not, the probability is actually greater than 0.7, meaning you'd have at least a 70% chance of losing that bet. With 50 people in the room, the probability is over 0.97! If you're skeptical, read on.

We can find the probability using permutation rules and the probability rule for complements: the strategy is to find the probability that everyone in the room has a different birthday, then subtract from one. We'll need to assume that every day of the year is equally likely as a birthday, which is certainly reasonable.

Let's start with three people in the room. There are 365 possible days for the first person, then 364 for the second and 363 for the third. So the number of ways to get three different birthdays is $365 \cdot 364 \cdot 363$, which happens to be $_{365}P_3$. The total number of possible birthdays for three people is 365^3, so the probability of all three having different birthdays is

$$\frac{_{365}P_3}{365^3} \approx 0.992$$

and the probability of two having the same birthday is about $1 - 0.992 = 0.008$. That sounds totally reasonable. But here's

where things get weird. The general formula we can take from this is that the probability of k people in a room all having different birthdays is

$$\frac{_{365}P_k}{365^k}$$

which makes the probability that at least two people have the same birthday

$$1 - \frac{_{365}P_k}{365^k}$$

With 30 people, the probability is

$$1 - \frac{_{365}P_{30}}{365^{30}} \approx 0.7063$$

and with 50, it's

$$1 - \frac{_{365}P_{50}}{365^{50}} \approx 0.9704$$

It turns out that the breakeven point is 23 people: for groups of 23 or more, there's a better than 50-50 chance that two have the same birthday.

It's interesting to note that two presidents, James K. Polk and Warren G. Harding, were both born on November 2. Also, John Adams and Thomas Jefferson both died on July 4, which is ironic to begin with—but it was the SAME July 4, in 1826.

Answers to Try This One

1. $33/646 \approx 0.051$

2. $1/969 \approx 0.00103$

3. $1/495 \approx 0.002$

4. $\dfrac{65}{84}$

EXERCISE SET 11-5

Writing Exercises

1. Explain how combinations and permutations are useful in computing probabilities.

2. What is the biggest advantage of combinations and permutations over tree diagrams when computing probability?

Applications in Our World

3. A student-faculty government committee of 4 people is to be formed from 20 student volunteers and 5 faculty volunteers. Find the probability that the committee will consist of the following, assuming the selection is made at random:
    (a) All faculty members.
    (b) Two students and two faculty members.
    (c) All students.
    (d) One faculty member and three students.

4. In a company there are seven executives: four women and three men. Three are chosen at random to attend a management seminar. Find these probabilities.
    (a) All three will be women.
    (b) All three will be men.

(c) Two men and one woman will be chosen.

(d) One man and two women will be chosen.

5. A city council consists of 10 members. Four are Republicans, three are Democrats, and three are independents. If a committee of three is to be selected, find the probability of selecting
   (a) All Republicans. (b) All Democrats.
   (c) One of each party.
   (d) Two Democrats and one independent.
   (e) One independent and two Republicans.

6. In a class of 18 students, there are 11 men and seven women. Four students are picked to present a demonstration on the use of graphing calculators. Find the probability that the group consists of
   (a) All men.
   (b) All women.
   (c) Three men and one woman.
   (d) One man and three women.
   (e) Two men and two women.

7. A chef is choosing from 12 different entrees for an important banquet, 3 of which contain spinach. The guests will have a choice of 4 entrees. If the chef chooses those 4 at random, find the probability that
   (a) None contain spinach.
   (b) At least one has spinach.
   (c) Three have spinach.
   (d) All 4 have spinach.

8. There are 50 tickets sold for a raffle for the Student Art Auction, and there are two prizes to be awarded. If Dionte buys two tickets, find the probability that he'll win both prizes.

9. An engineering company has four openings and the applicant pool consists of six database administrators and eight network engineers. If the hiring is done without regard for the specific qualifications of the applicants, find the probability that the four hired will be
   (a) All network engineers.
   (b) Two database administrators and two network engineers.
   (c) All database administrators.
   (d) Three database administrators and one network engineer.
   (e) One database administrator and three network engineers.

10. The list of potential parolees at a monthly parole hearing consists of eight drug offenders, five violent offenders, and two convicted of property crimes. I'd surely like to think that parolees aren't chosen at random, but if this particular board chooses three parolees randomly, find the probability that
    (a) All three are drug offenders.
    (b) Two of the three are property offenders.
    (c) All three are violent offenders.
    (d) One of each type of offender is paroled.
    (e) Two are drug offenders and one is a violent offender.

11. Find the probability of getting any triple-digit number where all the digits are the same in a lottery game that consists of selecting a three-digit number.

12. Binh is choosing from eight YouTube videos and nine online role-playing games to link to his Facebook page. If he randomly picks seven links total, find the probability that Binh chooses three YouTube videos and four online role-playing games.

13. A physical therapist is scheduling appointments for the day. She has eight worker's comp cases and four Medicare patients awaiting care. If she chooses five at random for her morning schedule, find the probability that she'll pick three worker's comp cases and two Medicare patients.

14. A five-digit identification card is made. Find the probability that the card will contain the digits 0, 1, 2, 3, and 4 in any order.

15. The combination lock in Example 3 has 40 numbers from zero to 39, and a combination consists of 3 numbers in a specific order with no repeats. Find the probability that the combination consists only of even numbers.

16. Is it more or less likely that the combination for the lock in Problem 15 consists of all even numbers if it consists of four numbers in a specific order with no repeats? Explain why this answer makes sense.

In one lottery game, contestants pick five numbers from 1 through 40 and have to match all five for the big prize (in any order). Exercises 17–22 refer to this game.

17. What's the probability you'll win if you buy one ticket? (*Hint:* Your chances are NOT good.)

18. You'll get second prize in the lottery game in Problem 17 if you match four of the five numbers. Find the probability of winning second prize if you buy five tickets.

19. You'll get twice your money back if you match three of the five numbers. If you buy two tickets, what's the probability of matching three out of five numbers?

20. What's the probability of utter failure in this game, defined by yours truly to mean matching none of the numbers?

21. Find the probability that you win some money when buying one ticket. (Refer to Exercises 17–20.)

22. To celebrate Fourth of July week, the lottery commission is offering a $1 million bonus if a winner of the big prize matches the numbers in the order in which they were drawn. What's the probability of this happening if you buy one ticket?

Exercises 23–28 refer to poker hands consisting of 5 cards dealt at random from a standard deck of 52 cards. Find the probability of getting each hand.

23. A full house (three of one denomination and two of another)

24. A flush (five cards of the same suit)

25. Three of a kind (exactly three of one denomination, remaining cards are two different denominations)
26. Four of a kind (four of the same denomination)
27. A royal flush (ten, jack, queen, king, and ace of the same suit)
28. A straight flush (five cards of the same suit that are consecutive in denomination)

Critical Thinking

29. At a carnival game, the player pays a dollar, then flips a quarter, rolls two dice, and draws two cards from a standard deck. If the result is tails, 7, and a pair of spades, he gets back $100. What is the probability of this happening?
30. (a) If you play the game in Problem 29 1,000 times, how many would you expect to win? (*Hint:* Remember that you can think of probability as a percent chance of something happening.)
    (b) Use your answer to part (a) to calculate how much you would expect to win or lose if you played the game 1,000 times. (Don't forget that it costs a dollar to play!)
31. Many lottery games are based on choosing some numbers from a larger group. Devise a lottery game with at least three different ways of winning, compute the probability of winning for each way, and assign payouts for each winning combination that you think are fair.

32. (a) Suppose that we choose 3 letters at random from the first 10 letters of the alphabet without repeats. Find the probability of choosing ABC in that order, then find the probability of choosing ABC in any order.
    (b) If we change the scenario in part (a) to include repeats, recompute the probabilities.
33. (a) What is the arithmetic relationship between the two probabilities in Exercise 32(a)?
    (b) Suppose the scenario in Exercise 32 is repeated, this time choosing four letters rather than three. Without actually computing either probability, what do you think the relationship between the two probabilities will be? Explain how you got your answer. (*Hint:* Think about part [a] and the effect of order mattering.)
34. Think of a real-life scenario for which it would be reasonable to compute probabilities using combinations, and one in which it would be reasonable to use permutations. (No stealing any of the scenarios from the section!)

Section 11-6   Odds and Expectation

The New York Giants won the Super Bowl on February 5, 2012, and by the time the ink dried on newspapers reporting the victory, oddsmakers in Las Vegas had listed the odds against the Giants winning it again in 2013 as 18 to 1. But what exactly does that mean? The term "odds" is used all the time in describing the likelihood of something happening, but a lot of people don't understand exactly what a given set of odds means.

Odds are used by casinos, racetracks, and other gambling establishments to determine the payoffs when bets are made or lottery tickets are purchased. They're also used by insurance companies in determining the amount to charge for premiums. The formulas for computing odds are similar to the formula we've been using for classical probability, and shortly we will see a strong connection between the two concepts.

LEARNING OBJECTIVES

☐ 1. Compute the odds in favor of and against an event.

☐ 2. Compute odds from probability.

☐ 3. Compute probability from odds.

☐ 4. Compute expected value.

If an event E has a favorable outcomes and b unfavorable outcomes, then

1. The **odds in favor** of event E occurring $= \frac{a}{b}$ (also written as $a{:}b$)
2. The **odds against** event E occurring $= \frac{b}{a}$ (also written as $b{:}a$)

CAUTION

Be careful not to confuse the formula for odds in favor of an event with the formula for classical probability. The probability formula is the number of favorable outcomes over the *total* number of outcomes, while the one for odds is the number of favorable outcomes over the number of *unfavorable* outcomes.

Odds can be expressed as a fraction or a ratio. For example, the odds against New York repeating as Super Bowl champion could be listed as $\frac{18}{1}$, 18:1, or 18 to 1. In common usage, the phrase "the odds of" really means "the odds against"; if we are told that the odds of rolling a 12 with two dice are 35 to 1, it means that the odds against rolling 12 are 35 to 1. So by setting New York's odds at 18:1, the oddsmakers are predicting that if the season were played 19 times, New York would win the Super Bowl 1 time, and not win it 18 times.

EXAMPLE 1   Computing Odds

A card is drawn from a standard deck of 52 cards.

(a) Find the odds in favor of getting an ace.
(b) Find the odds against getting an ace.

SOLUTION

(a) In a deck of cards there are 52 cards and there are 4 aces, so $a = 4$ and $b = 52 - 4 = 48$. (In other words, there are 48 cards that are not aces.)
The odds in favor of an ace $= \frac{4}{48} = \frac{1}{12}$.

(b) The odds against an ace $= \frac{48}{4} = \frac{12}{1}$.
The odds in favor of an ace are 1:12 and the odds against an ace are 12:1.

> **Math Note**
>
> Notice that if the odds in favor of an event occurring are $a{:}b$, the odds against it occurring are $b{:}a$.

☑ 1. Compute the odds in favor of and against an event.

▼ Try This One 1

What are the odds in favor of rolling a prime number sum with a roll of two dice? What are the odds against? (Figure 11-7 on page 651 will help.)

When an event E has a favorable and b unfavorable outcomes, there are $a + b$ total outcomes, and the probability of E is

$$P(E) = \frac{a}{a + b}$$

The probability of E not occurring is

$$1 - P(E), \text{ or } \frac{b}{a + b}$$

If we divide these two probabilities, we get

$$\frac{P(E)}{1 - P(E)} = \frac{\dfrac{a}{a + b}}{\dfrac{b}{a + b}} = \frac{a}{a + b} \cdot \frac{a + b}{b} = \frac{a}{b}$$

The result is the odds in favor of event E. This gives us a strong connection between probability and odds.

Formulas for Odds in Terms of Probability
Odds in favor $= \dfrac{P(E)}{1 - P(E)}$
Odds against $= \dfrac{1 - P(E)}{P(E)}$

where $P(E)$ is the probability that event E occurs.

EXAMPLE 2   Finding Odds from Probability

The probability of getting exactly one pair in a five-card poker hand is 0.423. Find the odds in favor of getting exactly one pair, and the odds against.

SOLUTION

This is a direct application of the formula relating probability and odds. The odds in favor of getting exactly one pair are

$$\frac{P(\text{getting exactly one pair})}{1 - P(\text{getting exactly one pair})} = \frac{0.423}{1 - 0.423} = \frac{0.423}{0.577}$$

We can convert this into fraction form by multiplying both the numerator and denominator by 100.

$$\frac{0.423}{0.577} \cdot \frac{100}{100} = \frac{423}{577}$$

So the odds in favor of getting exactly one pair are 423:577, and the odds against are 577:423.

> *Math Note*
>
> The probability 0.423 in Example 2 comes from dividing the number of hands with exactly one pair by the total number of five-card hands. This uses the fundamental counting principle and the combination formula.

☑ 2. Compute odds from probability.

> ▼ **Try This One 2**
>
> According to the American Cancer Society, the probability of an American female developing some type of cancer at some point in her life is about $\frac{1}{3}$. Find the odds in favor of and against an American woman developing cancer.

In Example 2, the odds for an event were found when the probabilities were known. As we saw on page 661, when the odds of an event are given, the probability of an event can be found.

> *Math Note*
>
> When the odds are 1:1, a game is said to be fair. That is, both parties have an equal chance of winning or losing.

> **Formula for Probability in Terms of Odds**
>
> If the odds in favor of an event E are $a:b$, then the probability that the event will occur is
> $$P(E) = \frac{a}{a + b}$$

EXAMPLE 3   Finding Probability from Odds

According to the National Safety Council, the odds of dying due to injury at some point in your life are about 10:237. Find the probability of dying from injury.

SOLUTION

In the formula for converting to probability, the odds in favor are $a:b$. In this case, those odds are 10:237, so $a = 10$ and $b = 237$.

$$P(\text{dying from injury}) = \frac{10}{10 + 237} = \frac{10}{247} \approx 0.040$$

☑ 3. Compute probability from odds.

> ▼ **Try This One 3**
>
> When two dice are rolled, the odds in favor of getting a sum of 9 are 1:8. Find the probability of not getting a sum of 9 when two dice are rolled.

Sidelight ODDS AND BETTING

In almost any gambling enterprise, from Vegas to a church raffle, odds are used to determine what the payouts will be. Let's use the game of roulette as an example. There are 38 partitions on a roulette wheel, with a small ball that is equally likely to land in any of them. Players make various bets on where the ball will land. If you simply bet on a particular number, the odds against you are 37:1. If you win, the casino will pay 35 times what you bet. So if you bet a dollar on each spin, on average, in 38 spins, you would lose 37 times and win once, meaning you'd be two dollars in the hole. That doesn't sound like the recipe for the casino making a lot of money, but when you consider the large number of people in a typical casino, and the fact that they're placing multiple bets at frequent intervals, it starts to make more sense.

This is where it becomes clear that state lotteries are an awful bet. In the Ohio lottery's "Classic Lotto" game, for example, the odds in favor of matching 5 of 6 numbers are 1:54,021. So to make the game completely fair, the payout should be in the neighborhood of $54,000 on a $1 ticket. The actual payout? Just $1,500! Any gambler or statistician will tell you that lotteries offer the worst odds of just about any game of chance.

So why do so many people play lotteries? For one, a complete lack of understanding of probability. But the biggest reason is probably that the massive payouts grab people's attention and make it seem like it's worth the risk of losing money. In almost every case though, no matter how huge the payout is in a lottery, it's still many, many times smaller than the odds of winning would dictate.

Expected Value

Another concept related to probability is **expectation**, or **expected value**. Expected value is used to determine the result that would be expected over the long term in some sort of gamble. It is used not only for games of chance, but in areas like insurance, management, engineering, and others. Here's the key thing to remember as we study expected value: *it only makes sense for events that have numerical outcomes.*

For example, rolling a die has a numerical outcome (1 through 6), and expected value can be used to determine what the average long-run result is likely to be. (We'll find out in Example 5.) But it doesn't make sense to ask what the long-term average of flipping a coin is.

Example 4 will illustrate a procedure for computing the expected value of a game, and then we'll summarize that procedure for future reference.

EXAMPLE 4   Finding the Expected Value of a Dice Game

You pay a dollar to roll two dice. If you roll 5 or 6, you get your dollar back plus two more just like it. If not, you get nothing and like it. Find the expected value of playing this game 100 times.

SOLUTION

First, we'll find the probability of winning and losing. We know that there are 36 possible rolls of two dice. Four of them result in 5: (1, 4), (2, 3), (3, 2), and (4, 1). Five result in 6: (1, 5), (2, 4), (3, 3), (4, 2), and (5, 1). So the probability of winning the game is $\frac{9}{36}$, or $\frac{1}{4}$, and the probability of losing is $\frac{3}{4}$. This means that, on average, you can expect to win 25% of the time.

So if you play the game 100 times, on average you'd expect to win 25 times and lose 75. With each win, you make $2, and with each loss, you lose $1. So after 100 tries:

$$\$2 \times 25 + (-\$1) \times 75 = \$50 - \$75 = -\$25$$

If you play the game 100 times, on average you'll lose $25.

▼ Try This One 4

On a roulette wheel, there are 38 slots, 18 of which are colored red. If you bet $5 on red and win, you get $10 back. If red doesn't come up, you lose your $5. Find the expected value of playing the game 100 times.

In Example 4, we saw that playing a dice game 100 times would result in a loss of $25 on average. That means that every time we play the game once, we can expect to lose 25 cents. That might not make sense to you at first, since you can't possibly lose 25 cents playing the game once: you either win $2 or lose $1. But that's really the point of expected value: it's about what the result of a probability experiment would be on average. It doesn't tell us what will happen on any given trial.

In any case, to mimic what we did in Example 4 for one trial, we would simply multiply each numerical outcome of the game by the probability of it occurring, then add the results. This is our method for finding expected value.

Expected Value

The expected value for the outcomes of a probability experiment is

$$E = X_1 \cdot P(X_1) + X_2 \cdot P(X_2) + \cdots + X_n \cdot P(X_n)$$

where the X's correspond to the numerical outcomes and the $P(X)$'s are the corresponding probabilities of the outcomes.

EXAMPLE 5   Computing Expected Value

When a single die is rolled, find the expected value of the outcome.

SOLUTION

Since each numerical outcome, 1 through 6, has a probability of $\frac{1}{6}$, the expected value is

$$E = 1 \cdot \frac{1}{6} + 2 \cdot \frac{1}{6} + 3 \cdot \frac{1}{6} + 4 \cdot \frac{1}{6} + 5 \cdot \frac{1}{6} + 6 \cdot \frac{1}{6} = \frac{21}{6} = 3.5$$

▼ Try This One 5

If seven cards are numbered with integers from -2 to 4, then placed into a box and picked out at random, find the expected value.

In gambling games, the expected value is found by multiplying the amount won, or net gain, and the amount lost by the corresponding probabilities and then finding the sum.

EXAMPLE 6   Computing Expected Value

The prize in a raffle is a flat-screen TV valued at $350, and 1,000 tickets are sold. What's the expected value if you buy 1 ticket?

SOLUTION

We begin with two notes. First, for a win, the net gain is $349, since you don't get the cost of the ticket ($1) back. Second, for a loss, the gain is represented by a negative number, in this case, $-\$1$.

The problem can then be set up as follows:

	Win	Lose
Gain, X	$349	$-\$1$
Probability, $P(X)$	$\dfrac{1}{1,000}$	$\dfrac{999}{1,000}$

The expected value is

$$E(X) = \$349 \cdot \frac{1}{1,000} + (-\$1) \cdot \frac{999}{1,000} = -\$0.65$$

Sidelight **MATH IN SLOT MACHINES**

Today, most slot machines are electronic—really, they're video games. But early slot machines were mechanical. The first slot machines were invented by the Fey Manufacturing Company of San Francisco in 1895. There were three large wheels with different symbols on them that spun when a control handle on the side was pulled. Each of the wheels contained 20 symbols, and payouts were based on matching symbols facing forward when the wheels came to a stop. The manufacturer controlled the payouts by cleverly arranging the symbols, using probability. For example, there might be three cherries on the first wheel and six on the second, but none on the third. So if you get cherries on the first two wheels, it feels like you almost won. But since there were no cherries on the

third wheel, the probability of your getting three cherries was actually zero.

Using probability theory, slot machine makers set the payouts for each winning combination. Expected value calculations will then let the owner know what long-term profits should be. The key is to let people win enough that they feel like it's worthwhile to play but not so much that the owner of the machine has to get a real job.

▼ Try This One **6**

With his house in foreclosure, a homeowner comes up with a plan to salvage the situation: he sells 10,000 raffle tickets at $50 each for the home, which is valued at $200,000. Find the expected value from buying one ticket.

In Example 6, we got an expected value of $-\$0.65$. Again, this doesn't mean that you'd lose 65 cents from buying a ticket, because you can only lose a dollar or win a $350 prize. It means that if you were to buy tickets to a similar raffle repeatedly, in the long run you'd average a 65 cent loss for each ticket bought.

EXAMPLE 7   **Computing Expected Value**

A stock you bought two years ago with high hopes is now selling for less than you paid, and things look grim for the company. Do you sell, or hold on and hope it will come back to the original price before you sell?

A model economists use for such situations is a game no one wants to play: suppose you have a choice: lose $100, or take a 50-50 chance between losing nothing, and losing $300. Which do you choose? Find the expected value for each strategy over 10 trials. (See Exercise 24.)

☑ 4. Compute expected value.

One thousand tickets are sold at $1 each for four prizes of $100, $50, $25, and $10. What is the expected value if you buy two tickets?

SOLUTION

First, let's find the expected value of buying one ticket.

Gain, x	$99	$49	$24	$9	$-\$1$
Probability, $P(x)$	$\dfrac{1}{1,000}$	$\dfrac{1}{1,000}$	$\dfrac{1}{1,000}$	$\dfrac{1}{1,000}$	$\dfrac{996}{1,000}$

$$E(x) = \$99 \cdot \frac{1}{1,000} + \$49 \cdot \frac{1}{1,000} + \$24 \cdot \frac{1}{1,000} + \$9 \cdot \frac{1}{1,000} - \$1 \cdot \frac{996}{1,000} = -\$0.815$$

Now multiply by 2 since two tickets were bought.

$$-\$0.815(2) = -\$1.63$$

▼ Try This One **7**

The profit made by a small ski resort, not surprisingly, depends largely on the seasonal weather. In a season with more than 75 inches of snow, it makes an average of $250,000. If snowfall is between 40 and 75 inches, the average profit is $160,000, and if snowfall is less than 40 inches, it loses $70,000. The resort gets over 75 inches of snow 40% of years, between 40 and 75 inches 45% of years, and less than 40 inches 15% of years. Find the resort's expected yearly profit.

Math Note

In American roulette, there are 22 different types of bets you can place, but it's interesting to note that all but one of them have the exact same expected value: −$0.053 on a $1 bet. (Betting on 0, 00, 1, 2, and 3, called a five-number bet, is worse, at −$0.079.)

In gambling games, if the expected value of the gain is 0, the game is said to be fair. If the expected value of the gain of a game is positive, then the game is in favor of the player. That is, the player has a better-than-even chance of winning. If the expected value of the gain is negative, then the game is said to be in favor of the house. That is, in the long run, the players will lose money. Can you guess what the sign of the expected value is for every game in a casino?

Answers to Try This One

1	In favor: 5:7; against: 7:5	**4**	−$26.32	**6**	−$30
2	In favor: 1:2; against: 2:1	**5**	1	**7**	$161,500
3	$\frac{8}{9}$				

EXERCISE SET 11-6

Writing Exercises

1. Explain the difference between the odds in favor of an event and the odds against an event.
2. Explain the numerical relationship between the odds in favor of an event and the odds against an event.
3. Explain the meaning of odds in a gambling game.

4. Explain how to find the probability of an event occurring when given the odds in favor of an event.
5. Explain what is meant by the expected value of a probability experiment.
6. Why does every game in a casino have a negative expected value for the player?

Computational Exercises

In Exercises 7–12, find the odds in favor of and odds against each event given the probability.

7. $P(A) = \frac{7}{8}$ 10. $P(D) = \frac{7}{10}$
8. $P(B) = \frac{1}{9}$ 11. $P(E) = \frac{9}{13}$
9. $P(C) = \frac{5}{11}$ 12. $P(F) = \frac{9}{14}$

In Exercises 13–18, find the probability of each event given the odds.

13. 5:8 in favor   16. 12:7 against
14. 9:13 in favor   17. 3:7 in favor
15. 6:5 against   18. 15:6 against

In Exercises 19–22, find the expected value of the probability experiment with outcomes $X_1, X_2, \ldots$

19. $X_1 = 6, X_2 = 2, X_3 = 4; P(X_1) = \frac{1}{5}, P(X_2) = \frac{2}{5}, P(X_3) = \frac{2}{5}$
20. $X_1 = \$10, X_2 = \$5, X_3 = \$1, X_4 = \$20; P(X_1) = \frac{3}{10}, P(X_2) = \frac{2}{10}, P(X_3) = \frac{1}{10}, P(X_4) = \frac{4}{10}$
21. $X_1 = \$1, X_2 = \$2, X_3 = \$3; P(X_1) = \frac{2}{7}, P(X_2) = \frac{1}{7}, P(X_3) = \frac{4}{7}$
22. $X_1 = 15, X_2 = 20, X_3 = 25, X_4 = 30, X_5 = 35; P(X_1) = \frac{2}{5}, P(X_2) = \frac{1}{15}, P(X_3) = \frac{4}{15}, P(X_4) = \frac{1}{5}, P(X_5) = \frac{1}{15}$

Applications in Our Word

23. In planning a gambling booth for a charity festival, Antoine needs to know the odds of various combinations in order to decide on payouts that will be high enough that people want to play, but low enough that the charity will make money. If the player rolls two dice, find the odds
    (a) In favor of getting a sum of 10.
    (b) In favor of getting a sum of 12.
    (c) Against getting a sum of 7.
    (d) Against getting a sum of 3.
    (e) In favor of getting doubles.

24. If the game in Exercise 23 has players who roll only one die, find the odds
    (a) In favor of getting a 3.
    (b) In favor of getting a 6.
    (c) Against getting an odd number.
    (d) Against getting an even number.
    (e) In favor of getting a prime number.
25. Steve shuffled a deck of 52 cards and asked Sally to draw one card to start a magic trick. Find the odds
    (a) In favor of getting a queen.
    (b) In favor of getting a face card.

(c) Against getting a club.

(d) In favor of getting an ace.

(e) In favor of getting a black card.

26. Monica is trying to design a coin-flipping game for a charity fair. The plan is for contestants to flip three coins. Find the odds

(a) In favor of getting exactly three heads.

(b) In favor of getting exactly three tails.

(c) Against getting exactly two heads.

(d) Against getting exactly one tail.

(e) In favor of getting at least one tail.

27. Your friends have taken bets on whether you will pass this class. (Sounds like maybe you need new friends.) Find the probability that you will pass given these odds:

(a) 7:4 in favor of you passing

(b) 2:5 against you passing

(c) 3:1 in favor of you passing

(d) 1:4 against you passing

28. Find the probability that you will win a Wii bowling tournament given these odds:

(a) 3:4 in favor of you winning

(b) 1:7 against you winning

(c) 5:4 in favor of you winning

(d) 6:5 in favor of you winning

29. If the odds against a horse winning a race are 9:5, find the probability that the horse will win the race.

30. A game show contestant rolls two dice and wins if he or she throws doubles. What are the odds in favor of the event? What are the odds against the event?

A roulette wheel has 38 numbers: 1 through 36, 0, and 00. A ball is rolled, and it falls into one of the 38 slots, giving a winning number. Each bet in Problems 31–36 lists the payout for winning on a $1 bet, including the dollar that was bet. Find the odds in favor of each bet, and the expected value.

31. Betting on an individual number: $36

32. Row zero bet (0 and 00): $18

33. First dozen (1 through 12): $3

34. Even numbers from 2 through 36: $2

35. Corner (any four adjoining numbers on the betting grid): $9

36. Top line (0, 00, 1, 2, 3): $7

When 150 people were surveyed by phone about their favorite cola, the results were tabulated in the given table. Use the table to find the odds in favor of each response in Exercises 37–42.

Favorite cola	Number of responses
Coke	29
Pepsi	21
Diet Coke	37
Diet Pepsi	28
Coke Zero	19
Other	16

37. Coke

38. Diet Pepsi

39. A Pepsi product

40. A Coke product

41. Neither a Coke nor a Pepsi product

42. A low-calorie product (one of the diets or Coke Zero)

In sports betting, odds are often given in terms of the profit on a $100 bet if your team wins. For example, if a team is listed as +130, that means if you bet $100 and win, you'll get back $230: your original $100 plus a profit of $130. If the odds against a team winning are 5:1, it means that a $1 bet would return a total of $6, making a profit of $5. Use these facts in Exercises 43 and 44.

43. At the beginning of the 2011 NBA playoffs, the four Las Vegas favorites to win were the L.A. Lakers at +160, the Miami Heat and Chicago Bulls, both at +300, and the Boston Celtics at +550. According to the oddsmakers, what was the probability of each team winning the title?

44. At the beginning of the 2011 Major League Baseball season, the four Las Vegas favorites to win the World Series were Philadelphia (3:1 odds against), Boston (9:2 odds against), New York Yankees (5:1 odds against), and San Francisco (15:1 odds against). According to the oddsmakers, (a) what was the probability of each team winning the World Series, and (b) how would the odds have been listed in terms of profit on a $100 bet?

The University of Kentucky won the 2012 men's NCAA basketball tournament. The table lists the heights and weights of all players on the team's roster. Use this information for Problems 45–50.

Ht.	Wt.	Ht.	Wt.	Ht.	Wt.
6'7"	235	6'7"	232	6'11"	244
6'9"	252	6'2"	189	6'5"	205
6'4"	210	6'7"	215	6'2"	175
6'9"	239	6'4"	200	5'11"	190
6'10"	220	6'2"	185	5'9"	150

45. Find the odds in favor of a randomly selected player being over 6 feet tall.

46. Find the odds in favor of a randomly selected player being under 230 pounds.

47. Find the odds against a randomly selected player being 6'7" tall.

48. Find the odds against a randomly selected player weighing between 199 and 221 pounds.

49. Find the expected value for height if one player is chosen at random.

50. What numeric quantity does your answer from Problem 49 match?

51. A cash prize of $5,000 is to be awarded at a fundraiser. If 2,500 tickets are sold at $5 each, find the expected value.

52. You start your shift as a cashier with your drawer containing ten $1 bills, five $2 bills, three $5 bills, one $10 bill, and one $100 bill. Find the expectation if one bill is chosen at random.

53. In a scratch-off game, if you scratch the two dice on the ticket and get doubles, you win $5. For the game to be fair, how much should you pay to play the game?

54. At this year's State Fair, there was a dice rolling game. If you rolled two dice and got a sum of 2 or 12, you won $20. If you rolled a 7, you won $5. Any other roll was a loss. It cost $3 to play one game with one roll of the dice. What is the expectation of the game?

55. Melinda buys one raffle ticket at the Spring Fling since there is one $1,000 prize, one $500 prize, and five $100 prizes. There were a total of 1,000 tickets sold at $3 each. What is Melinda's expectation?

56. If Melinda buys two tickets to the raffle in Exercise 55, what is her expectation?

57. For a daily lottery, players pick any three-digit number from 000 to 999. If a player pays $1, he or she can win $500. Find the expectation. In the same daily lottery, if a player boxes a number, he or she can win $80. Find the expectation if the number 123 is played for $1 and boxed. (When a number is "boxed," it wins when the digits occur in any order.)

58. If a 60-year-old buys a $1,000 life insurance policy at a cost of $60 and has a probability of 0.972 of living to age 61, find the expectation of the policy until the buyer reaches 61.

59. A new flat-screen TV comes with a 1-year warranty which completely covers any parts and repairs. At the end of the warranty period, the buyer is offered an extended warranty for 3 more years at a cost of $90. Industry records indicate that during that 3-year period, there's an 8% chance that a minor repair averaging $85 will be needed, and a 3.5% chance that a major repair averaging $370 will be needed. Find the expected value of buying the extended warranty.

60. A company that makes wireless routers has found that, on average, 1.6% of the units are defective. It makes a $38 profit from selling nondefective units but ends up losing $24 when selling a defective unit due to repair and shipping costs. Find the expected profit from selling 10,000 units.

Critical Thinking

61. You stop on the street between errands to engage in a shell game with a street vendor. The vendor shows you a two-headed penny under one shell, a two-tailed penny under the second shell and a fair penny (one head and one tail) under the third shell. He shuffles the shells around and then you choose a shell. He shows you that under the shell is a penny with the head side up. He is willing to bet you $5 that it is the two-headed penny. He says it cannot be the two-tailed penny because a head is showing. Therefore, he says there is a 50-50 chance of it being the two-headed coin. Should you take the bet?

62. Stuck in a bad situation, you're given a choice: lose $100, or take a 50-50 chance between losing nothing and losing $300. Choose the option that sounds better to you, then find the expected value of each option over 10 trials.

63. Since expected value only applies to numerical outcomes, it takes some ingenuity to use it for flipping a coin.
    (a) Choose any two numbers at random, assigning one to heads and another to tails. Then find the expected value of flipping the coin.
    (b) Repeat part (a) for two different numbers. What can you conclude?

64. Chevalier de Mere, a famous gambler, won money when he bet unsuspecting patrons that in four rolls of a die, he could get at least one 6, but he lost money when he bet that in 24 rolls of two dice, he could get a double 6.

Find the probability of each event and explain why he won the majority of the time on the first game but lost the majority of the time when playing the second game.

In many respects, investing in the stock market is just another form of gambling: you pay money for stocks, and when you sell them at some point, you can gain money, lose money, or break even. Use what you learned about expected value to answer the questions in Exercises 65 and 66 about buying and selling stock.

65. The Bui family members decide to invest their $4,000 tax refund in the stock market for 1 year. An analyst suggests that they choose between two stocks. A computer analysis of past performance predicts that if they invest in RZ Electronics, there's a 40% chance they'll make a profit of $1,600, a 40% chance they'll make $200, and a 20% chance they'll lose $2,000. For Jackson Builders, there's a 75% chance they'll make $800, and a 25% chance that they'll lose $300.
    (a) Without doing any calculations, which sounds like the better investment to you? Why?
    (b) Find the expected value of each investment.

66. You're given the option of investing $10,000 in one of three mutual funds. A prominent market analyst posts the following estimates of performance for the three funds. The Hetrick Fund: 40% chance of a 35% gain; 40% chance of a 30% loss; 20% chance of breaking even. The Abercrombie Fund: 80% chance of breaking even; 12% chance of an 18% gain; 8% chance of a 9%

loss. The Goldberg Fund: 25% chance of a 90% gain; 25% chance of a 5% gain; 40% chance of breaking even; 10% chance of losing everything. Answer parts (a) and (b) without doing any calculations.

(a) If your primary objective is to shoot for the largest possible return without regard to risk, which would you be likely to choose?

(b) If your primary objective is the least risk of losing big, which would you be likely to choose?

(c) Find the expected value for each fund. With these choices, who would be most likely to be successful: a timid investor or an aggressive one?

Section 11-7   The Addition Rules for Probability

Many interesting problems in probability involve finding the probability of more than one event. Usually, some careful thought is required. For example, when the U.S. House of Representatives is in session, suppose that a political commentator feels like a certain bill is most likely to be supported by women and Democrats. She would likely be interested in the probability that a member of the

House is either a woman or a Democrat. She could find the number of women representatives, and the number of Democratic representatives easily, but then what? Should she add those numbers and divide by the total number of representatives? What about those who are both women *and* Democrats? They would get counted twice.

The situation would be simpler if the commentator were interested in the probability of a representative being either a Republican or an Independent. The key difference is that any individual has to be one or the other. These two events are called *mutually exclusive*, which indicates that either one or the other must occur, but not both.

LEARNING OBJECTIVES

☐ 1. Decide if two events are mutually exclusive.

☐ 2. Use the addition rule for mutually exclusive events.

☐ 3. Use the addition rule for events that are not mutually exclusive.

> Two events are **mutually exclusive** if they cannot both occur at the same time. That is, the events have no outcomes in common.

EXAMPLE 1   Deciding if Two Events Are Mutually Exclusive

In drawing cards from a standard deck, determine whether the two events are mutually exclusive or not.

(a) Drawing a 4, drawing a 6.   (b) Drawing a 4, drawing a heart.

SOLUTION

(a) Every card has just one denomination, so a card can't be both a 4 and a 6. The events are mutually exclusive.

(b) You could draw the 4 of hearts, which is one outcome satisfying both events. The events are not mutually exclusive.

☑ 1. Decide if two events are mutually exclusive.

▼ Try This One 1

If student government picks students at random to win free books for a semester, determine whether the two events are mutually exclusive or not.

(a) The winner is a sophomore or a business major.
(b) The winner is a junior or a senior.

The probability of two or more events occurring can be determined by using the **addition rules**. The first addition rule is used when the events are mutually exclusive.

> ### Addition Rule 1
>
> When two events A and B are mutually exclusive, the probability that A or B will occur is
>
> $$P(A \text{ or } B) = P(A) + P(B)$$

We can use Venn diagrams to see why addition rule 1 makes perfect sense. In Figure 11-8, we see two events A and B that are mutually exclusive—the intersection is empty, so there are no outcomes in common. The number of outcomes that satisfies one event or the other is simply the sum of the number of outcomes in each event, and the probability of one or the other occurring is

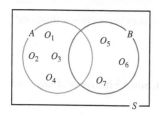

$$P(A \text{ or } B) = \frac{n(A) + n(B)}{n(S)}$$

Figure 11-8

This can be rewritten as

$$P(A \text{ or } B) = \frac{n(A)}{n(S)} + \frac{n(B)}{n(S)} = P(A) + P(B)$$

which is addition rule 1.

EXAMPLE 2   Using Addition Rule 1

A restaurant has three pieces of apple pie, five pieces of cherry pie, and four pieces of pumpkin pie in its dessert case. If a customer selects at random one kind of pie for dessert, find the probability that it will be either cherry or pumpkin.

SOLUTION

The events are mutually exclusive. Since there is a total of 12 pieces of pie, five of which are cherry and four of which are pumpkin,

$$P(\text{cherry or pumpkin}) = P(\text{cherry}) + P(\text{pumpkin})$$
$$= \frac{5}{12} + \frac{4}{12} = \frac{9}{12} = \frac{3}{4}$$

> ### Math Note
>
> Sometimes it's a bad idea to reduce fractions in the individual probabilities when using the addition rule: you'll need a common denominator to add them. Your final answer should always be reduced if possible, though.

> ### ▼ Try This One 2
>
> A liberal arts math class contains 7 freshmen, 11 sophomores, 5 juniors, and 2 seniors. If the professor randomly chooses one to present a homework problem at the board, find the probability that it's either a junior or senior.

EXAMPLE 3   Using Addition Rule 1

A card is drawn from a standard deck. Find the probability of getting an ace or a queen.

SOLUTION

The events are mutually exclusive. There are four aces and four queens, so

$$P(\text{ace or queen}) = P(\text{ace}) + P(\text{queen})$$
$$= \frac{4}{52} + \frac{4}{52} = \frac{8}{52} = \frac{2}{13}$$

▼ Try This One 3

At a political rally, there are 20 Republicans, 13 Democrats, and 6 Independents. If a person is selected at random, find the probability that he or she is either a Democrat or an Independent.

The addition rule for mutually exclusive events can be extended to three or more events as shown in Example 4.

EXAMPLE 4   Using the Addition Rule with Three Events

A card is drawn from a deck. Find the probability that it is either a club, a diamond, or a heart.

SOLUTION

In the deck of 52 cards there are 13 clubs, 13 diamonds, and 13 hearts, and any card can be only one of those suits. So

$$P(\text{club, diamond, or heart}) = P(\text{club}) + P(\text{diamond}) + P(\text{heart})$$
$$= \frac{13}{52} + \frac{13}{52} + \frac{13}{52} = \frac{39}{52} = \frac{3}{4}$$

▼ Try This One 4

In rolling two dice, find the probability that the sum is 2, 3, or 4.

☑ 2. Use the addition rule for mutually exclusive events.

In Example 4, we used an extended version of addition rule 1:

$$P(A \text{ or } B \text{ or } C) = P(A) + P(B) + P(C)$$

When two events are not mutually exclusive, any outcomes that are common to two events are counted twice. We account for this by subtracting the probability of both events occurring, which results in addition rule 2.

Math Note

Addition rule 2 can actually be used when events are mutually exclusive, too—in that case, $P(A$ and $B)$ will always be zero, and you'll get addition rule 1 back. But it's still important to distinguish between the two situations.

Addition Rule 2

When two events A and B are not mutually exclusive, the probability that A or B will occur is

$$P(A \text{ or } B) = P(A) + P(B) - P(A \text{ and } B)$$

We could justify addition rule 2 using Venn diagrams, but frankly we'd rather have you do it. See Problem 36.

EXAMPLE 5   Using Addition Rule 2

A single card is drawn from a standard deck of cards. Find the probability that it's a king or a club.

SOLUTION

There are 4 kings and 13 clubs in a deck, but the events aren't mutually exclusive because the king of clubs is both. So we'll use addition rule 2 and subtract the probability of the card being the king of clubs.

$$P(\text{king or club}) = P(\text{king}) + P(\text{club}) - P(\text{king and club})$$
$$= \frac{4}{52} + \frac{13}{52} - \frac{1}{52} = \frac{16}{52} = \frac{4}{13}$$

▼ Try This One 5

A card is drawn from an ordinary deck. Find the probability that it is a heart or a face card.

EXAMPLE 6   Using Addition Rule 2

Two dice are rolled. Find the probability of getting doubles or a sum of 6.

SOLUTION

Using the sample space shown in Section 11-2, there are six ways to get doubles: (1, 1), (2, 2), (3, 3), (4, 4), (5, 5), (6, 6). So $P(\text{doubles}) = \frac{6}{36}$. There are five ways to get a sum of 6: (1, 5), (2, 4), (3, 3), (4, 2), (5, 1). So $P(\text{sum of 6}) = \frac{5}{36}$. Notice that there is one way of getting doubles and a sum of 6, so $P(\text{doubles and a sum of 6}) = \frac{1}{36}$. Finally,

$$P(\text{doubles or a sum of 6}) = P(\text{doubles}) + P(\text{sum of 6}) - P(\text{doubles and sum of 6})$$

$$= \frac{6}{36} + \frac{5}{36} - \frac{1}{36} = \frac{10}{36} = \frac{5}{18}$$

▼ Try This One 6

When two dice are rolled, find the probability that both numbers are more than three, or that they differ by exactly two.

☑ 3. Use the addition rule for events that are not mutually exclusive.

In many cases, the information in probability problems can be arranged in table form in order to make it easier to compute the probabilities for various events. Example 7 uses this technique.

EXAMPLE 7   Using a Table and Addition Rule 2

In a hospital there are eight nurses and five physicians. Seven nurses and three physicians are females. If a staff person is selected, find the probability that the subject is a nurse or a male.

SOLUTION

The sample space can be written in table form.

Staff	Females	Males	Total
Nurses	7	1	8
Physicians	3	2	5
Total	10	3	13

Looking at the table, we can see that there are 8 nurses and 3 males, and there's one person who is both a male and a nurse. The probability is

$$P(\text{nurse or male}) = P(\text{nurse}) + P(\text{male}) - P(\text{male and a nurse})$$

$$= \frac{8}{13} + \frac{3}{13} - \frac{1}{13} = \frac{10}{13}$$

▼ Try This One 7

In one class, there are 15 freshmen and 10 sophomores. Six of the freshmen are education majors and four of the sophomores are education majors. If a student is selected at random, find the probability that the student is a sophomore or an education major.

Answers to Try This One

1 (a) Not mutually exclusive
    (b) Mutually exclusive

2 $\dfrac{7}{25}$

3 $\dfrac{19}{39}$

4 $\dfrac{1}{6}$

5 $\dfrac{11}{26}$

6 $\dfrac{5}{12}$

7 $\dfrac{16}{25}$

EXERCISE SET 11-7

Writing Exercises

1. Explain how to tell if two events are mutually exclusive or not.
2. Explain the difference between the two addition rules for probability.

For Exercises 3–10, decide if the events are mutually exclusive, and explain your answer.

3. Roll a die: get an even number, or get a number less than 3.
4. Roll a die: get a prime number (2, 3, 5), or get an odd number.

5. Roll a die: get a number greater than 3, or get a number less than 3.
6. Pick a student in your class: the student has blond hair, or the student has blue eyes.
7. Pick a student in your college: the student is a junior, or the student is a history major.
8. Pick any course: it is a calculus course, or it is an English course.
9. Pick a registered voter: the voter is a Republican, or the voter is a Democrat.
10. A chef decides to make either parmesan-crusted chicken or bacon-wrapped sirloin the daily special.

Applications in Our World

11. A young couple is arguing about what month they want to get married next year, so they decide to grab a calendar and choose a month at random. What's the probability that they get married in April or May?
12. At the animal shelter where Miguel volunteers on the weekends, there were two Siamese cats, four tabby cats, sixteen mixed-breed dogs, and four iguanas in their cages. If a customer picks any of these animals at random, find the probability that the animal is either a mixed-breed dog or a Siamese cat.
13. When Milo went to register for classes at the last minute, the only classes left to take were seven math courses, five computer science courses, three statistics courses, and four science courses. He shut his eyes and picked one at random. Find the probability that Milo selected either a science course or a math course. (The probability that Milo will ever graduate using this strategy is an interesting question, too.)
14. When Shana looked at the favorites list on her boyfriend's MP3 player, there were 10 songs she liked, 7 songs she'd heard but did not like, and 5 songs she hadn't heard. She let the MP3 player select a song at random. What is the probability that the selected song was one she liked or one she'd heard but did not like?

15. While conducting an experiment on perception, a psychologist randomly chooses a subject from nine adult males, six adult females, and seven children. Find the probability that the subject is

    (a) An adult male or a child.
    (b) An adult.

16. In my Tae Kwon Do class, there are two black belts, three red belts, five blue belts, three green belts, and six yellow belts. If the sensei selects a student at random to lead the warm-up, find the probability that the person is

    (a) Either a green belt or a yellow belt.
    (b) Either a black belt or a blue belt.
    (c) Either a black belt, a green belt, or a yellow belt.

17. On a small college campus, there are five English professors, four math professors, two science professors, three psychology professors, and three history professors. If a professor is chosen at random, find the probability that the professor is

    (a) An English or psychology professor.
    (b) A math or science professor.
    (c) A history, science, or math professor.
    (d) An English, math, or history professor.

674   **Chapter 11** Probability and Counting Techniques

18. A deck of cards is randomly dealt by the computer during a game of Spider Solitaire. Find the probability the first card dealt is
    (a) A 4 or a diamond.
    (b) A club or a diamond.
    (c) A jack or a black card.

19. In a statistics class there are 18 juniors and 10 seniors; 6 of the seniors are females, and 12 of the juniors are males. If a student is chosen at random, find the probability of selecting
    (a) A junior or a female.
    (b) A senior or a female.
    (c) A junior or a senior.

20. A cell phone company gets a really good deal on 400 Samsung phones. Of them, 250 have 5″ screens and the rest have 4″ screens. Of the phones with 5″ screens, 140 are silver and the rest are black. Of the phones with 4″ screens, 80 are silver and the rest are black. If one phone is picked at random for a customer, find the probability that it will
    (a) Be silver or have a 5″ screen.
    (b) Be black or have a 4″ screen.

21. BlueFly.com, an online designer clothing marketplace, purchases items from Kenneth Cole, Michael Kors, and Vera Wang. The most recent purchases are shown here:

Product	Kenneth Cole	Michael Kors	Vera Wang
Dresses	24	18	12
Jeans	13	36	15

If one item is chosen at random, find these probabilities:
    (a) It was purchased from Kenneth Cole or is a dress.
    (b) It was purchased from Michael Kors or Vera Wang.
    (c) It is a pair of jeans or it was purchased from Kenneth Cole.

22. In a recent campus survey, the following data were obtained in response to the question "Do you think there should be harsher penalties for underage drinking on campus?"

	Yes	No	No opinion
Males	72	81	5
Females	103	68	7

If a person is picked at random, find these probabilities:
    (a) The person has no opinion.
    (b) The person is a male or is against harsher penalties.
    (c) The person is a female or favors harsher penalties.

23. A grocery store employs cashiers, stock clerks, and deli personnel. The distribution of employees according to marital status is shown next.

Marital status	Cashiers	Stock clerks	Deli personnel
Married	8	12	3
Not married	5	15	2

If an employee is chosen at random, find these probabilities:
    (a) The employee is a stock clerk or married.
    (b) The employee is not married.
    (c) The employee is a cashier or is not married.

24. Students were surveyed on campus about their study habits. Some said they study in the morning, others study during the day between classes, and others study at night. Some students always study in a group and others always study alone. The distribution is shown below:

How students study	Morning	Between classes	Evening
Study in a group	2	3	1
Study alone	3	4	2

If a student who was surveyed is chosen at random, find these probabilities:
    (a) The student studies in the evening.
    (b) The student studies in the morning or in a group.
    (c) The student studies in the evening or studies alone.

25. Three cable channels (95, 97, and 103) air quiz shows, comedies, and dramas. The numbers of shows aired are shown here.

Type of show	Channel 95	Channel 97	Channel 103
Quiz show	5	2	1
Comedy	3	2	8
Drama	4	4	2

If a show is picked at random, find these probabilities:
    (a) The show is a quiz show or it is shown on Channel 97.
    (b) The show is a drama or a comedy.
    (c) The show is shown on Channel 103 or it is a drama.

26. A local postal carrier distributed first-class letters, advertisements, and magazines. For a certain day, she distributed the following number of each type of item.

Delivered to	First-class letters	Ads	Magazines
Home	325	406	203
Business	732	1,021	97

If an item of mail is chosen at random, find these probabilities:
    (a) The item went to a home.
    (b) The item was an ad or it went to a business.
    (c) The item was a first-class letter or it went to a home.

27. As part of her major in microbiology, Juanita spent 3 weeks studying the spread of a disease in the jungles of South America. When she returned, she found

that she had many e-mails sent to her home account and her school account, and that the e-mails were either spam, school announcements, or messages from friends as follows:

Delivered to	School announcements	Spam	Messages from friends
Home	412	910	342
School	791	1,206	68

If an e-mail is picked at random, find these probabilities:

(a) The e-mail was sent to her home.
(b) The e-mail was a school announcement or it was sent to her school account.
(c) The e-mail was spam or it was sent to her home account.

28. Before a Walk for the Cure 10-mile walk, participants could choose a T-shirt from a box with six red shirts, two green shirts, one blue shirt, and one white shirt. When the first participant randomly picks a shirt from the box, what is the probability she will get a red shirt or a white shirt?

29. You roll two dice as part of a casino game. Find the probability of getting

(a) A sum of 6, 7, or 8.
(b) Doubles or a sum of 4 or 6.
(c) A sum of greater than 9, less than 4, or equal to 7.

30. In another dice game, you begin by rolling three dice. Find the probability that

(a) All three dice show the same number.
(b) The three numbers sum to a number less than 6.
(c) The three numbers are all odd or divisible by 3.

31. In five-card poker, a flush is a hand where all cards have the same suit, and a pair is when two cards have the same denomination. You're dealt the 3, 7, 10, and jack of clubs and the 9 of diamonds and all of the other cards are still in the deck. If you discard the 9 of diamonds and draw one card to replace it, what's the probability of getting a flush or a pair?

32. A straight in five-card poker is five cards with consecutive denominations. If you're dealt 3, 4, 5, 6, and a queen, then discard the queen and draw one card to replace it, what's the probability of getting a straight or a pair? Assume that all other cards are still in the deck.

Critical Thinking

33. At Big Tony's Pizzas and Loans, 45% of customers order pizzas with either sausage or pepperoni. If 31% get only pepperoni and 26% only sausage, find the probability that the next person to call will order both sausage and pepperoni.

34. Use a Venn diagram to illustrate the probability calculation in Try This One 5 on page 672.

35. Use a Venn diagram to illustrate the probability calculation in Try This One 6 on page 672.

36. The Venn diagram shown can be used to show why addition rule 2 on page 671 works. Do it!

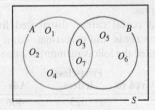

37. Use a Venn diagram to demonstrate the addition rule for probability when there are three mutually exclusive events.

38. Use Venn diagrams to see if you can develop an addition rule for probability when there are three events that are not mutually exclusive.

Exercises 39 through 42 require some careful thought (and maybe some research), and may be open to interpretation. Analyze the situation and decide if the two events are or are not mutually exclusive, then write an explanation of your answer.

39. Being acquitted of a crime and spending time in jail after the trial

40. Being born outside the boundaries of the United States and being elected president of the United States

41. Being a freshman, being a sophomore, and being a junior

42. Getting fewer votes than your opponent when running for the presidency and winning the election

Section 11-8 The Multiplication Rules and Conditional Probability

Even after learning about probability, a lot of people are tempted to play lottery games, looking for that one big score that will put them on easy street. Suppose that you play a daily game in which you try to match a randomly selected four-digit number. On Monday, the number is 2471. On Tuesday, the number is again 2471. Would you play 2471 on Wednesday? People are usually split on this question: some

LEARNING OBJECTIVES

☐ 1. Find the probability of two or more independent events all occurring.

☐ 2. Find the probability of two or more dependent events all occurring.

☐ 3. Find conditional probabilities.

Each day a professor picks a student at random to work out a homework problem on the board. If the student is selected regardless of who already went, the events are independent. If the student is selected from the pool of students who haven't gone yet, the events are dependent.

say "There's no way it's going to come up *three* days in a row!" while others say "That number's hot! Go with it!"

The logic in both of those arguments is faulty, however, assuming that the game isn't rigged and the numbers really are chosen at random. When Wednesday's numbers are being drawn, they have no idea what may have been drawn on Monday and Tuesday: that's all in the past and has no effect on Wednesday's draw.

Let's recast the question this way: What's the probability that 2471 will come up three times in a row? In this section, we'll study rules for finding the probability of consecutive events occurring. In every case, we'll have to decide if any event affects the outcome of the ones that follow.

> Two events A and B are **independent** if the fact that A occurs has no effect on the probability of B occurring.

Based on our description above, the lottery numbers that are drawn on Tuesday and Wednesday are independent events.

Here are other examples of independent events:

Rolling a die and getting a 6, and then rolling a second die and getting a 3.

Drawing a card from a deck and getting a queen, replacing it, and drawing a second card and getting a queen.

On the other hand, when the occurrence of the first event changes the probability of the occurrence of the second event, the two events are said to be *dependent*. For example, suppose a card is drawn from a deck and *not* replaced, and then a second card is drawn. The probability for the second card is changed since the sample space contains only 51 cards when the first card isn't replaced.

> Two events A and B are **dependent** if the outcome of A has some effect on the probability of B occurring.

Here are some examples of dependent events:

Drawing a card from a deck, not replacing it, and then drawing a second card.

Selecting a lottery ball from a tumbler, not replacing it, and then drawing a second ball.

Parking in a no-parking zone and getting a parking ticket.

When a coin is flipped twice, the outcomes of the first and second flips are independent, and in each case, the probability of getting tails is $\frac{1}{2}$. The sample space for the two flips is {HH, TT, HT, TH}, and the probability of getting tails twice is $\frac{1}{4}$. Notice that $\frac{1}{4} = \frac{1}{2} \cdot \frac{1}{2}$. This illustrates that the probability of two consecutive tails is the product of the probabilities of getting tails in each individual trial. This result is our first *multiplication rule*.

Multiplication Rule 1

When two events A and B are independent, the probability of both occurring is

$$P(A \text{ and } B) = P(A) \cdot P(B)$$

Section 11-8   The Multiplication Rules and Conditional Probability   677

| EXAMPLE 1 | **Using Multiplication Rule 1** |

A coin is flipped and a die is rolled. Find the probability of getting heads on the coin and a 4 on the die.

SOLUTION

The two events, the coin landing on heads and the die showing 4, are independent. We know from earlier examples that the probability of heads is $\frac{1}{2}$ and the probability of getting 4 with one die is $\frac{1}{6}$. Using the multiplication rule:

$$P(\text{heads and } 4) = P(\text{heads}) \cdot P(4) = \frac{1}{2} \cdot \frac{1}{6} = \frac{1}{12}$$

> *Math Note*
>
> The problem in Example 1 could be solved using standard sample space methods, but as outcomes get more complicated, it can be extremely difficult to list sample spaces. That's why the multiplication rules are so helpful.

▼ **Try This One 1**

If the probability of your alarm not going off is $\frac{1}{20}$, and the probability of getting a ticket on your way to work is $\frac{1}{200}$, find the probability that both will happen.

| EXAMPLE 2 | **Using Multiplication Rule 1** |

As part of a psychology experiment on perception and memory, colored balls are picked from an urn. The urn contains three red balls, two green balls, and five white balls. A ball is picked and its color is noted. Then it is replaced. A second ball is picked and its color is noted. Find the probability of each of these.

(a) Picking two green balls.
(b) Picking a green ball and then a white ball.
(c) Picking a red ball and then a green ball.

SOLUTION

Remember, selection is done with replacement, which makes the events independent, so multiplication rule 1 applies.

(a) The probability of picking a green ball on each trial is $\frac{2}{10}$, so

$$P(\text{green and green}) = P(\text{green}) \cdot P(\text{green}) = \frac{2}{10} \cdot \frac{2}{10} = \frac{4}{100} = \frac{1}{25}$$

(b) The probability of picking a green ball is $\frac{2}{10}$ and the probability of picking a white ball is $\frac{5}{10}$, so

$$P(\text{green and white}) = P(\text{green}) \cdot P(\text{white}) = \frac{2}{10} \cdot \frac{5}{10} = \frac{10}{100} = \frac{1}{10}$$

(c) The probability of picking a red ball is $\frac{3}{10}$ and the probability of picking a green ball is $\frac{2}{10}$, so

$$P(\text{red and green}) = P(\text{red}) \cdot P(\text{green}) = \frac{3}{10} \cdot \frac{2}{10} = \frac{6}{100} = \frac{3}{50}$$

▼ **Try This One 2**

As part of a card trick, a card is drawn from a deck and replaced; then a second card is drawn. Find the probability of getting a queen and then an ace.

EXAMPLE 3   **Finding Probabilities for Three Independent Events**

Three cards are drawn from a deck. After each card is drawn, its denomination and suit are noted and it's mixed back into the deck before the next card is drawn. Find the probability of getting

(a) Three kings.
(b) Three clubs.

SOLUTION

Since the card picked is shuffled back into the deck, each selection is independent of the others, and we can again use multiplication rule 1.

(a) Since there are four kings, the probability of getting a king on each draw is $\frac{4}{52}$ or $\frac{1}{13}$. The probability of getting three kings is

$$\frac{1}{13} \cdot \frac{1}{13} \cdot \frac{1}{13} = \frac{1}{2,197}$$

(b) Since there are 13 clubs, the probability of getting a club is $\frac{13}{52}$ or $\frac{1}{4}$. The probability of getting three clubs in a row is

$$\frac{1}{4} \cdot \frac{1}{4} \cdot \frac{1}{4} = \frac{1}{64}$$

> **Math Note**
>
> Multiplication rule 1 can be extended to three or more independent events using the formula
>
> $P(A_1 \text{ and } A_2 \text{ and } A_3 \cdots$
> $\text{and } A_n)$
> $= P(A_1) \cdot P(A_2) \cdot P(A_3) \cdots$
> $\cdot P(A_n)$

▼ **Try This One 3**

Given that the probability of rain on any given day in March in Daytona Beach is $\frac{1}{5}$, find the probability that

(a) It rains three straight days in March.
(b) It rains on March 10 and 12, but not March 11.

Assume that weather on any day is independent of the others.

As we've pointed out, when a card is picked from a deck and not replaced, this changes the probabilities for what will happen when a second card is drawn. That makes sense because if you draw a queen on the first card, now there are only three left, rather than the four there were originally. But what if the deck is actually 1,000 decks all mixed together? Now if you draw a queen, there are still 3,999 left in the deck, and the effect on the probability of drawing another queen isn't nearly as significant.

This illustrates a useful idea in computing probabilities in our world: if the sample space is really large, choosing a handful of objects without replacement technically makes the choices dependent, but the effect on probability is so small that we can pretend the choices are independent, making the calculations simpler. This is illustrated in Example 4.

EXAMPLE 4   **Using Multiplication Rule 1 with Large Samples**

According to a study done by the *Princeton Review* in 2012, 86 percent of college-bound students indicated that financial aid would be "very necessary" for them to attend college. If four college-bound students were chosen at random, find the probability that all four would rate financial aid as very necessary.

SOLUTION

For any individual student, the probability that financial aid is very necessary is 0.86 (because 86% of respondents gave that response). Treating the four choices as independent and using multiplication rule 1, the probability that all four described financial aid as very necessary is

$$0.86 \times 0.86 \times 0.86 \times 0.86 \approx 0.547$$

☑ 1. Find the probability of two or more independent events all occurring.

▼ Try This One 4

The *Princeton Review* also reported that just 29% of college-bound students reported that their stress level wasn't either high or very high. If three such students are picked at random, find the probability that all three rate their stress as high or very high.

CAUTION

Even though the three events in Example 4 are not independent because students were not replaced after being chosen, in an average year over 2 million students start college, so having one or two fewer in the sample has a negligible effect on the probabilities. Make sure to carefully consider the situation before using multiplication rule 1.

When we are interested in finding the probability of consecutive events that are dependent, we can still use the multiplication rule, but with a minor modification. For example, let's say we draw two cards at random from a standard deck. The probability of getting an ace on the first draw is $\frac{4}{52}$. But if the first card is not put back into the deck, that changes the probability of drawing another ace—it's now $\frac{3}{51}$. Using the multiplication rule, the probability of both events occurring is

$$\frac{4}{52} \cdot \frac{3}{51} = \frac{12}{2,652} = \frac{1}{221}$$

We can summarize this procedure as multiplication rule 2.

Multiplication Rule 2

When two events are dependent, the probability of both occurring is

$$P(A \text{ and } B) = P(A) \cdot P(B \text{ given that } A \text{ has already occurred})$$

EXAMPLE 5   Using Multiplication Rule 2

An appliance store gets a shipment of 25 plasma TVs, and 3 of them are defective. If two of the TVs are chosen at random, find the probability that both are defective. (The first TV is not replaced after it's tested.)

SOLUTION

Since there are 3 defective TVs out of a total of 25, the probability of the first being defective is $\frac{3}{25}$. After the first one is found to be defective and not replaced, there are 2 defective sets left out of 24, so the probability of the second being defective given that the first one is defective is $\frac{2}{24}$. Using multiplication rule 2, the probability that both are defective is

$$P(\text{1st defective and 2nd defective}) = P(\text{1st}) \cdot P(\text{2nd given 1st})$$
$$= \frac{3}{25} \cdot \frac{2}{24} = \frac{6}{600} = \frac{1}{100}$$

▼ Try This One 5

The 2012 NCAA men's basketball tournament field had (among 64 teams) 9 teams from the Big East conference, 6 from the Big Ten, 6 from the Big 12, and 4 from the Southeastern conference. If you were randomly assigned two teams in a dorm pool, find the probability that

(a) Both were from the Big East.
(b) The first was from the Southeastern conference and the second was from the Big 12.

Multiplication rule 2 can be extended to three or more events as shown in Example 6.

EXAMPLE 6   Using Multiplication Rule 2 with Three Events

Three cards are drawn from an ordinary deck and not replaced. Find the probability of

(a) Getting three jacks.
(b) Getting an ace, a king, and a queen in order.
(c) Getting a club, a spade, and a heart in order.
(d) Getting three clubs.

SOLUTION

(a) $P(\text{three jacks}) = \frac{4}{52} \cdot \frac{3}{51} \cdot \frac{2}{50} = \frac{24}{132,600} = \frac{1}{5,525}$

(b) $P(\text{ace and king and queen}) = \frac{4}{52} \cdot \frac{4}{51} \cdot \frac{4}{50} = \frac{64}{132,600} = \frac{8}{16,575}$

(c) $P(\text{club and spade and heart}) = \frac{13}{52} \cdot \frac{13}{51} \cdot \frac{13}{50} = \frac{2,197}{132,600} = \frac{169}{10,200}$

(d) $P(\text{three clubs}) = \frac{13}{52} \cdot \frac{12}{51} \cdot \frac{11}{50} = \frac{1,716}{132,600} = \frac{11}{850}$

▼ Try This One 6

When drawing four cards from a deck, what is the probability that

(a) All four are aces?   (b) All four are clubs?

☑ 2. Find the probability of two or more dependent events all occurring.

Math Note

We use the term conditional probability because the condition that A has already occurred affects the probability of B.

Conditional Probability

We know that to find the probability of two dependent events occurring, it's important to find the probability of the second event occurring given that the first has already occurred. We call this the **conditional probability** of event B occurring given that event A has occurred, and denote it $P(B|A)$.

Now that we have a symbol to represent the probability of event B given that A has occurred, we can rewrite multiplication rule 2, and solve the equation for $P(B|A)$:

$$P(A \text{ and } B) = P(A) \cdot P(B|A)$$
$$P(B|A) = \frac{P(A \text{ and } B)}{P(A)}$$

This gives us a formula for conditional probability.

Formula for Conditional Probability

The probability that a second event B occurs given that a first event A has occurred can be found by dividing the probability that both events occurred by the probability that the first event has occurred. The formula is

$$P(B|A) = \frac{P(A \text{ and } B)}{P(A)}$$

Example 7 illustrates the use of this rule.

EXAMPLE 7   **Finding a Conditional Probability**

Military strategies (and other types of strategies) use conditional probability. If *A* occurs, how likely is *B*? How likely is *B* if *A* doesn't occur?

Suppose that your professor goes stark raving mad and chooses your final grade from A, B, C, D, F, or Incomplete totally at random. Find the probability of getting an A given that you get a letter grade higher than D.

SOLUTION

We are asked to find $P(A|\text{letter grade higher than D})$.

Method 1 Knowing that you got a letter grade higher than D reduces the sample space to {A, B, C}, which has three outcomes. One of them is an A, so $P(A|\text{letter grade higher than D}) = \frac{1}{3}$.

Method 2 With the full sample space of {A, B, C, D, F, I}, $P(A) = \frac{1}{6}$, and $P(\text{letter grade higher than D}) = \frac{3}{6}$. Using the formula for conditional probability,

$$P(A|\text{letter grade higher than D}) = \frac{\frac{1}{6}}{\frac{3}{6}} = \frac{1}{6} \cdot \frac{6}{3} = \frac{1}{3}$$

▼ Try This One 7

A group of patients in a blind drug trial is assigned numbers from 1 through 8. The even numbers get an experimental drug, while the odd numbers get a placebo. If Eleanor is one of the patients, what's the probability that she's getting the experimental drug given that she wasn't assigned 1, 2, or 3?

EXAMPLE 8   **Finding a Conditional Probability**

Hate crimes are defined to be crimes in which the victim is targeted because of one or more personal characteristics, such as race, religion, or sexual orientation. The table below lists the motivation for certain hate crimes as reported by the FBI for 2010.

Motivation	Crimes against persons	Crimes against property	Crimes against society
Race	2,434	280	11
Religion	493	916	0
Sexual orientation	1,082	388	0
Total	4,009	2,584	11

(a) Find the probability that a hate crime was racially motivated given that it was a crime against persons.
(b) Find the probability that a hate crime was against property given that it was motivated by the victim's sexual orientation.

SOLUTION

(a) Since we're interested only in crimes against persons, we only need to look at that column. There were 4,009 such crimes total, and 2,434 were racially motivated, so the probability is

$$\frac{2,434}{4,009} \approx 0.607$$

(b) This time we're given that the crime was motivated by sexual orientation, so we only need to look at that row. There were 1,470 such crimes total, and 388 were against property, so the probability is

$$\frac{388}{1,470} \approx 0.264$$

▼ **Try This One 8**

✓ 3. Find conditional probabilities.

Based on the data in the above table, find the probability that

(a) A crime was motivated by either race or religion given that it was a crime against society.
(b) A crime was against persons given that it was motivated by religion or sexual orientation.

Answers to Try This One

1   $\dfrac{1}{4,000}$

2   $\dfrac{1}{169}$

3   (a) $\dfrac{1}{125}$ (b) $\dfrac{4}{125}$

4   Approximately 0.358

5   (a) $\dfrac{1}{56}$ (b) $\dfrac{1}{168}$

6   (a) $\dfrac{1}{270,725}$ (b) $\dfrac{11}{4,165}$

7   $\dfrac{3}{8}$

8   (a) 1   (b) $\dfrac{1,575}{2,879} \approx 0.547$

EXERCISE SET 11-8

Writing Exercises

1. What is the difference between independent and dependent events? Give an example of each.
2. What is meant by the term conditional probability?
3. Describe two methods for computing conditional probability.
4. Explain why the probability of two consecutive events occurring couldn't possibly be the sum of the two individual probabilities.
5. Describe how and when to use multiplication rule 1.
6. Describe how and when to use multiplication rule 2.

In Exercises 7–14, decide whether the events are independent or dependent, and explain your answer.

7. Flipping a coin and drawing a card from a deck.
8. Drawing a ball from a lottery machine, not replacing it, and then drawing a second ball.
9. Getting a raise in salary and purchasing a new car.
10. Driving on ice and having an accident.
11. Having a large shoe size and having a high IQ.
12. A father being left-handed and a daughter being left-handed.
13. Smoking excessively and having lung cancer.
14. Eating an excessive amount of ice cream and smoking an excessive amount of cigarettes.

Applications in Our World

15. On one large campus, 18% of students surveyed said that they spend less than an hour a night studying. If three students are picked at random, what's the probability that all three spend less than an hour a night studying? What's the probability that two of the three do?
16. A national study of patients who were overweight found that 56% also have elevated blood pressure. If two overweight patients are selected, find the probability that both have elevated blood pressure.
17. According to the National Highway Traffic Safety Administration, 84% of Americans used seat belts regularly in 2011. If four people are selected at random, find the probability that all four regularly use seat belts.

18. A computer salesperson at Best Buy claims that she has a 20% chance of selling a computer when helping out a customer. If this is true and she talks to four customers before lunch, find the probability that all four will buy computers.

19. If 25% of Michael's graduating class are not U.S. citizens, find the probability that two randomly selected graduating students are not U.S. citizens.

20. If two people are chosen at random, what is the probability that they were both born in December?

21. If two people are chosen at random, find the probability that they were born in the same month.

22. If three people are chosen, find the probability that all three were born in March.

23. If half of Americans believe that the federal government should take "primary responsibility" for eliminating poverty, find the probability that three randomly selected Americans will agree that it is the federal government's responsibility to eliminate poverty.

24. What is the probability that a husband, wife, and daughter have the same birthday?

25. A telecommunications company has six satellites, two of which are sending a weak signal. If two are picked at random without replacement find the probability that both are sending a weak signal.

26. In Exercise 25, find the probability that one satellite sends a strong signal and the other sends a weak signal.

The Federal Bureau of Investigation reported the statistics in the following table for homicides in 2009. Use the data to answer Questions 27–32.

Weapon	Number	Weapon	Number
Handgun	6,452	Cutting instrument	1,825
Rifle	348	Other weapons	1,864
Shotgun	418	Hands, feet, etc.	801
Unknown firearm	1,928	Total	13,636

27. If there were three unrelated murders in Chicago in June 2009, find the probability that all three were committed with a gun.

28. Find the probability that for two randomly selected murders, neither involved a gun.

29. Find the probability that a murder was committed with a handgun given that a gun was used.

30. Find the probability that a murder was committed with a shotgun given that some type of weapon was used (other than body parts).

31. Find the probability that if four unrelated murders are studied, two involved a gun and two involved a cutting instrument.

32. Find the probability that two unrelated murders were both committed with a handgun.

The U.S. Energy Information Administration reported the following statistics for electrical energy generation in 2010. Use the data to answer Questions 33–36.

Source	Billion kilowatt hours
Fossil fuels	2,880.7
Nuclear	807.0
Hydroelectric	257.1
Other renewables	168.1

33. If three homes are picked at random, find the probability that all three got their electricity from a source other than fossil fuels.

34. Find the probability that two of the three homes in Exercise 33 got their electricity from fossil fuels while the third got it from a nuclear plant.

35. Find the probability that a home got its power from a hydroelectric source given that it didn't come from fossil fuels.

36. Find the probability that a home got its power from fossil fuels given that it didn't come from a nuclear plant.

37. In a department store there are 120 customers, 90 of whom will buy at least one item. If five customers are selected at random, one by one, find the probability that all will buy at least one item.

38. During a game of online hearts, three cards are dealt, one at a time without replacement, from a shuffled, ordinary deck of cards. Find these probabilities:
    (a) All are jacks.
    (b) All are clubs.
    (c) All are red cards.

39. In a group of eight Olympic track stars, five are hurdlers. If three are selected at random without replacement, find the probability they are all hurdlers.

40. In a class consisting of 15 men and 12 women, two different homework papers were selected at random. Find the probability that both papers belonged to women.

41. I offer you the following bet: you flip a coin then roll a die, and I give you $10 if you get tails and a 5, but you give me $1 otherwise. What's the probability that you'll win given that the coin lands tails up?

42. Juan draws a black card from an ordinary deck as the first card for a game of Gin Rummy. What is the probability the card was a king? What's the probability that the next black card is also a king given that the first one was?

43. At a carnival gambling booth, two dice are rolled, and a sum of seven wins double your money. Find the probability that the sum is 7 given that one of the numbers was a 6.

44. After Frank and Sun order a pizza, they flip a coin to see who has to go pick it up (heads and Frank goes), then roll a die to see how many dollars Sun has to pay toward the cost. Find the probability that Frank has to pick up the pizza and pay more than $3.

45. A computer randomly deals an ordinary deck of cards for a game of FreeCell, and the first card dealt

is a face card. Find the probability that the card was also a diamond.

46. During a backgammon game, Kelly rolled the two dice on the board. Find the probability that the sum obtained was greater than 8 given that the number on one die was a 6.

Use this information for Exercises 47–50. Three red cards are numbered 1, 2, and 3. Three black cards are numbered 4, 5, and 6. The cards are placed in a box and one card is picked at random.

47. Find the probability that a red card was picked given that the number on the card was an odd number.

48. Find the probability that a number less than 5 was picked given that the card was a black card.

49. Find the probability that a number less than 5 was picked given that the card was red.

50. Find the probability that a black card was picked given that the number on the card was an even number.

Use the following information for Exercises 51–54. A survey of 200 college students shows the average number of minutes that people talk on their cell phones each month.

	Less than 600	600–799	800–999	1,000 or more
Men	56	18	10	16
Women	61	18	13	8

If a person is selected at random, find these probabilities:

51. The student talked less than 600 minutes given that it was a woman.

52. The student talked more than 999 minutes given that it was a man.

53. The student was a woman given that they used between 600 and 799 minutes.

54. The student was a man given that they used between 600 and 999 minutes.

The table below shows the number of active-duty personnel in each branch of the military in 2008, as well as the percentage that were women. Find each probability in Exercises 55–58.

Branch	Army	Navy	Marines	Air Force	Coast Guard
Total	539,170	331,785	193,040	328,771	42,424
% Women	13.6%	15.0%	6.1%	19.6%	12.2%

Source: *The World Almanac and Book of Facts, 2010*

55. An individual on active duty was a woman given that he or she was in either the air force, marines, or coast guard.

56. An individual was in the army given that it was a man.

57. An individual was a man given that he or she was not in the navy.

58. An individual was not a marine given that it was a woman.

Critical Thinking

59. (a) Use the multiplication rule for two independent events to show that the rule can be used for three events as well.
    (b) How can you use the result of (a) to conclude that the rule works for any number of independent events?

60. Suppose that I roll two dice and tell you that the result is definitely even, then offer you 3 to 1 odds that the total isn't 4. Draw a diagram to illustrate the outcomes, then use the diagram to compute the conditional probability. Finally, decide if the given odds are in your favor or not.

61. In many lotto games, the player chooses 6 numbers from a pool of 40 or more, and if he or she matches all 6 numbers drawn, he or she wins the jackpot. If there is more than one winner, the jackpot is split evenly among all winners.
    (a) First instinct, if you were playing a lotto game, would you choose the numbers 1, 2, 3, 4, 5, and 6? Why or why not?
    (b) After the first winning number is drawn, does it have any effect on what number is drawn next? Think carefully, then use your answer and the idea of independence of events and probability

to explain why there's nothing wrong with choosing 1, 2, 3, 4, 5, and 6.
    (c) In fact, something in the statement that begins this exercise indicates that 1, 2, 3, 4, 5, and 6 might be a desirable choice. What is it?

62. Classify each statement as sensible or silly, and briefly explain your answer.
    (a) I flipped a coin five times in a row and got heads, so I'm willing to bet $100 that it will be tails on the next flip.
    (b) There's a 30% chance of rain tomorrow and there's a 50–50 chance of my only class getting cancelled, so there's a 35% chance I'll be able to go golfing without missing class. (By the way, I'm not going to go golfing if it rains.)
    (c) According to duilawblog.com, the probability of being convicted when charged with DUI in California is 0.794. If 50% of those convicted get at least 48 hours in jail, the probability of spending at least 48 hours in jail if charged with DUI in California is 1.294.
    (d) If I buy one ticket to a multistate lottery, I have a better chance of being struck by lightning than I do of winning the grand prize.

Section 11-9   The Binomial Distribution

LEARNING OBJECTIVES

☐ 1. Identify binomial experiments.

☐ 2. Compute probabilities of outcomes in a binomial experiment.

☐ 3. Construct a probability distribution.

Many probability problems involve situations that have only two outcomes. When a baby is born, it will be either male or female. When a coin is flipped, it will land either heads or tails. When the New York Yankees play, they either win or they lose. That cute girl that sits behind you in class will either go out with you or she won't.

Other situations can be reduced to two outcomes. For example, medical procedures can be classified as either successful or unsuccessful. An answer to a multiple choice exam question can be classified as right or wrong even though there may be four answer choices.

Situations like these are called *binomial experiments*.

> A **binomial experiment** is a probability experiment that satisfies the following requirements:
>
> 1. Each trial can have only two outcomes, or outcomes that can be reduced to two outcomes. These outcomes can be considered as either a success or a failure.
> 2. The outcomes must be independent of each other.
> 3. There must be a fixed number of independent trials.
> 4. The probability of a success must remain the same for all trials of the experiment.

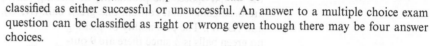

EXAMPLE 1   Deciding if an Experiment is Binomial

Decide whether or not each is a binomial experiment.

(a) Drawing a card from a deck and seeing what suit it is
(b) Answering a question on a true-false test
(c) Asking 100 people whether or not they smoke
(d) Drawing cards at random from a deck without replacement and deciding if they are red or black cards

SOLUTION

(a) No, since there are four outcomes: heart, diamond, spade, or club.
(b) Yes, there are only two outcomes: correct and incorrect.
(c) Yes, there are only two outcomes: yes or no.
(d) No; since the cards are not being replaced, the probability changes on each draw.

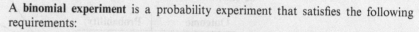

☑ 1. Identify binomial experiments.

▼ **Try This One 1**

Decide whether or not each experiment is a binomial experiment.

(a) Picking a colored ball with replacement from an urn containing three balls of different colors, and seeing if the chosen ball is orange
(b) Picking a number from a bingo machine
(c) Drawing a card at random from a deck with replacement and noting its color, red or black
(d) Rolling a die and getting a 3

Here's a more specific example of a binomial probability experiment. You're one of four finalists in a raffle, and each finalist is represented by a single colored ball thrown into a box. The colors are red, black, white, and green (you). A ball is picked from the box and its color is recorded, then it's mixed back into the box and a second ball is picked. If your green ball is picked twice, you win a 2-year lease on a Fiat convertible. If the first ball chosen isn't green, you don't care what color it is, so all you're interested in is whether the chosen ball is green or not. The tree diagram for this experiment is shown in Figure 11-9.

The probability of picking two green balls is $\frac{1}{16}$ since there is only one way to select two green balls, namely (G, G), and there are 16 total possible outcomes in the sample space. The probability of picking exactly one green is $\frac{6}{16}$ or $\frac{3}{8}$ since there are 6 outcomes that contain one green ball: (R, G), (B, G), (W, G), (G, R), (G, B), and (G, W). The probability of picking no green balls is $\frac{9}{16}$ since there are 9 outcomes that contain no green balls.

A table for the probabilities can be shown.

Outcome	Probability
0 green balls	$\frac{9}{16}$
1 green ball	$\frac{6}{16} = \frac{3}{8}$
2 green balls	$\frac{1}{16}$
Sum	$\frac{16}{16} = 1$

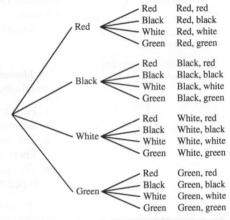

Figure 11-9

Math Note

There are actually four outcomes for any trial of the experiment described here, so from that standpoint this isn't a binomial experiment. But by focusing only on whether or not the drawn ball is green, we've reduced the number of outcomes to two (green or not green), making it a binomial experiment.

The experiment can be considered a binomial experiment since it meets the four conditions of a binomial experiment:

1. Each trial has only two outcomes: the ball chosen is either green or it isn't.
2. The outcomes are independent of each other: each ball is replaced before the second ball is selected.
3. There is a fixed number of trials. In this case, there are two draws.
4. The probability of a success remains the same in each case. In this case, since there is only one green ball and a total of four balls, $P(S) = \frac{1}{4}$ and $P(F) = 1 - \frac{1}{4} = \frac{3}{4}$. (Getting a green ball is considered a success. Getting any other colored ball is considered a failure.)

Now let's think about how we could get x successes in n trials of a binomial experiment. If p is the probability of success on any trial, the multiplication rule for independent events tells us that p^x is the probability of x successes. That leaves $n - x$ failures, and if q is the probability of failure, the probability of $n - x$ failures is q^{n-x}. We use the multiplication principle again to multiply those two probabilities. Finally, we have to choose *which* of the n trials result in success: there are $_nC_x$ ways to do this. Multiplying all the results, we get the binomial probability formula.

The Binomial Probability Formula

The probability of exactly x successes in n trials of a binomial probability experiment is

$$P(x) = {_nC_x} \cdot p^x \cdot q^{n-x}$$

where p = the probability of a success

q = the probability of a failure ($q = 1 - p$)

In our example of drawing balls from a box, let's find the probability of getting one green ball in two draws. In this case, $n = 2$, $x = 1$, and $n - x = 1$. The probability of success (p) is $\frac{1}{4}$, and the probability of failure (q) is $\frac{3}{4}$. Using the binomial probability formula,

$$P(1 \text{ green ball}) = {}_nC_x \cdot p^x \cdot q^{n-x}$$

$$= {}_2C_1 \cdot \left(\frac{1}{4}\right)^1 \cdot \left(\frac{3}{4}\right)^1$$

$$= \frac{2!}{(2-1)!1!} \cdot \frac{1}{4} \cdot \frac{3}{4}$$

$$= 2 \cdot \frac{3}{16} = \frac{3}{8}$$

This matches the probability found using a tree diagram.

EXAMPLE 2   **Using the Binomial Probability Formula**

Suppose that the morning after your birthday, you remember that you have a 20 question true or false quiz in your early class. Uh oh! Completely unprepared and a little woozy, you decide to guess on every question. What's the probability that you'll get 16 out of 20 right?

SOLUTION

> ### Math Note
>
> Notice that because there are 20 trials in Example 2, it would be cumbersome (to say the very least!) to use a tree diagram to find the probability.

Because the questions are true or false, and you're arbitrarily guessing, the probability of getting any given question right is $\frac{1}{2}$. The number of trials is $n = 20$, and the number of successes is $x = 16$. The probability of success is $p = \frac{1}{2}$, and the probability of failure is then $q = 1 - \frac{1}{2}$. Substituting these values into the binomial probability formula, we get

$$P(16 \text{ right}) = {}_nC_x \cdot p^x \cdot q^{n-x}$$

$$= {}_{20}C_{16} \cdot \left(\frac{1}{2}\right)^{16} \cdot \left(\frac{1}{2}\right)^{20-16}$$

$$= \frac{20!}{(20-16)!16!} \cdot \left(\frac{1}{2}\right)^{16} \cdot \left(\frac{1}{2}\right)^4$$

$$= 4{,}845 \cdot \frac{1}{1{,}048{,}576} \approx 0.0046$$

In short, your chances are not good.

▼ Try This One 2

If you take a 10-question multiple choice quiz, with four choices for each question, and completely guess on every one, what's the probability of getting exactly 6 questions right? (Only one of the choices is the right answer.)

EXAMPLE 3   **Using the Binomial Probability Formula**

Of five physical therapists that work at a rehab center, three have master's degrees and two have doctorates. Each therapist is equally likely to be assigned to a patient on any given visit. If Tom has five sessions scheduled in the next two weeks, find the probability that

(a) He gets a therapist with a doctorate twice.
(b) He gets a therapist with a doctorate less than two times.

SOLUTION

(a) This is a direct application of the binomial probability formula with $n = 5$, $x = 2$, $p = \frac{2}{5}$, and $q = \frac{3}{5}$.

$$P(2 \text{ doctorate}) = {}_5C_2 \cdot \left(\frac{2}{5}\right)^2 \left(\frac{3}{5}\right)^3$$

$$= \frac{5!}{(5-2)!2!} \cdot \frac{4}{25} \cdot \frac{27}{125} = 0.3456$$

(b) Fewer than two times means zero or one time, so we'll find the probability of each and then add the answers (because having one therapist with a doctorate and having zero therapists with a doctorate are mutually exclusive events).

$$P(1 \text{ doctorate}) = {}_5C_1 \cdot \left(\frac{2}{5}\right)^1 \left(\frac{3}{5}\right)^4$$

$$= \frac{5!}{(5-1)!1!} \cdot \frac{2}{5} \cdot \frac{81}{625} = 0.2592$$

$$P(0 \text{ doctorate}) = {}_5C_0 \cdot \left(\frac{2}{5}\right)^0 \left(\frac{3}{5}\right)^5$$

$$= \frac{5!}{(5-0)!0!} \cdot 1 \cdot \frac{243}{3,125} = 0.07776$$

$$P(1 \text{ or } 0 \text{ doctorate}) = 0.2592 + 0.07776 = 0.33696$$

▼ Try This One 3

If a different patient at the rehab center in Example 3 has seven appointments scheduled, find the probability that she gets a therapist with a master's degree

(a) Every time.
(b) At least five times.

Use of the binomial probability formula requires a series of trials that are independent. As we saw in Section 11-8, when subjects are chosen from a sample and not replaced, the choices aren't independent, but if the sample is really large, the lack of replacement has a negligible effect on probability. So we can treat the choices as independent even though they technically aren't, which comes in handy when using the binomial probability formula.

EXAMPLE 4   Using the Binomial Probability Formula

According to the U.S. General Accountability Office, 20% of college undergrads don't have health insurance. If 10 undergrads are surveyed at random, find the probability that half of them will be uninsured.

SOLUTION

The population here is all college undergraduates, a group of at least 15 million individuals. When 10 undergrads are chosen, we can assume there's no replacement, but the large sample size allows us to treat the choices as independent. There are two outcomes for each trial: the student either has health insurance or not. So this is a binomial probability problem with $n = 10$, $x = 5$, $p = 0.2$, and $q = 1 - 0.2 = 0.8$.

$$P(5 \text{ uninsured}) = {}_{10}C_5 \cdot (0.2)^5 \cdot (0.8)^5$$

$$= \frac{10!}{(10-5)!5!}(0.00032)(0.32768) \approx 0.0264$$

☑ 2. Compute probabilities of outcomes in a binomial experiment.

▼ Try This One 4

In a large community, it was determined that 44% of the residents use the public library at least once a year. If 10 people are picked randomly, find the probability that exactly 2 of them have used the library during the last year.

To describe all of the outcomes in a probability experiment, we can build a *probability distribution*.

A **probability distribution** consists of a list of all outcomes and the corresponding probabilities for a probability experiment.

EXAMPLE 5   Constructing a Probability Distribution

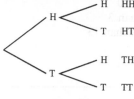

Figure 11-10

Construct a probability distribution for the possible number of tails when you flip two coins.

SOLUTION

When two coins are flipped, the outcomes can be shown using a tree diagram. See Figure 11-10.

The sample space is {HH, HT, TH, TT}. Each outcome has a probability of $\frac{1}{4}$. Notice that the outcome "No tails" is HH, and $P(\text{HH}) = \frac{1}{4}$. The outcome of one tail consists of HT and TH, and $P(\text{HT, TH}) = \frac{1}{4} + \frac{1}{4} = \frac{1}{2}$. The outcome of two tails is TT and $P(\text{TT}) = \frac{1}{4}$. Now a probability distribution can be constructed by considering the outcomes as the number of tails. The probability distribution is

Number of tails, x	0	1	2
Probability, $P(x)$	$\frac{1}{4}$	$\frac{1}{2}$	$\frac{1}{4}$

Math Note

In Example 5, the number of trials was small enough that a tree diagram was more efficient than using the binomial probability formula three times.

☑ 3. Construct a probability distribution.

▼ Try This One 5

Three cards are numbered 1, 2, 3 and placed into a bag. Another bag is set up the same way, then one card is drawn from each bag and the numbers are added. Find all possible totals, and construct a probability distribution for the experiment.

Answers to Try This One

1   (a) Yes   (b) No   (c) Yes   (d) Yes

2   About 0.016

3   (a) About 0.028   (b) About 0.420

4   About 0.084

5
Total	2	3	4	5	6
Probability	$\frac{1}{9}$	$\frac{2}{9}$	$\frac{1}{3}$	$\frac{2}{9}$	$\frac{1}{9}$

EXERCISE SET 11-9

Writing Exercises

1. What are the four requirements for a probability experiment to be a binomial experiment?
2. Give a brief description of how an experiment with several outcomes can be reduced to one with two outcomes.

3. What is a probability distribution?
4. In a binomial experiment, given the probability of any trial being a success, explain how to find the probability of a failure.

Computational Exercises

Find the probability of each using the binomial probability formula.

5. $n = 3$, $p = 0.40$, $x = 2$
6. $n = 5$, $p = 0.80$, $x = 3$
7. $n = 10$, $p = 0.66$, $x = 4$
8. $n = 5$, $p = 0.20$, $x = 8$
9. $n = 20$, $p = 0.93$, $x = 12$
10. $n = 13$, $p = 0.16$, $x = 7$

11. $n = 9$, $p = 0.33$, $x = 5$
12. $n = 6$, $p = 0.58$, $x = 2$
13. $n = 4$, $p = 0.72$, $x = 0$
14. $n = 7$, $p = 0.25$, $x = 1$
15. $n = 12$, $p = 0.33$, $x = 3$ or 4
16. $n = 15$, $p = 0.51$, $x = 7$ or 10
17. $n = 9$, $p = 0.42$, x is less than 3
18. $n = 16$, $p = 0.75$, x is more than 13

Applications in Our World

19. During a game of Yahtzee, a player needs three sixes. She rolls the same die three times. What is the probability she got three sixes?
20. A cooler held three energy drinks. One was a Monster, another was a Red Bull, and the third was Atomic X. Simon picks an energy drink at random, puts it back, picks another, puts it back and then picks a third drink. Find the probability that
    (a) No Red Bull drinks are picked.
    (b) Exactly one Atomic X drink is picked.
    (c) Exactly three Monster drinks are picked.
21. Of all identity thefts, 27% are solved in 1 day or less. If 10 cases are studied, find the probability that exactly 5 are solved in 1 day or less.
22. Of all people who do banking, 16% prefer to use ATMs. Of 20 people who are banking customers, find the probability that exactly 4 prefer to use the ATM.
23. According to the Bureau of Labor Statistics, among married-couple families where both the husband and wife have earnings, 26% of wives earned more than their husbands. If 18 wives are surveyed, find the probability that exactly 6 of them earn more than their husbands.
24. It is reported that 41% of people surveyed said that they eat meals while driving. If 12 drivers are picked at random, find the probability that exactly 6 will say that they eat meals while driving.
25. Approximately 45% of people who eat at fast food places choose McDonald's. If 10 randomly selected

people are surveyed, find the probability that 5 picked McDonald's.
26. About 30% of people who listen to commercial radio change the station in 1 to 2 minutes after the commercials begin. If six people are randomly selected, find the probability that two will change the station within 1 to 2 minutes after the commercials begin.
27. A survey shows that 65% of workers ages 42 to 60 would choose excellent retirement benefits over a high salary when seeking a job. If 15 people are randomly chosen, find the probability that 9 would choose excellent benefits over a high salary.
28. The Nielsen company reported that in 2011, 28% of smartphones in operation in the United States were iPhones. If this is still accurate, what's the probability that less than 3 of the next 10 smartphone users you see have iPhones?
29. The Gallup poll reported that in June 2012, 65.4% of U.S. adults in the workforce were working full time. If a pollster called 20 working adults at random, what's the probability that more than 17 are working full time?
30. A Telenav survey in August 2011 found that one in five people surveyed would rather go shoeless than cell phone-less for a week. Find the probability that if 25 people are surveyed, between 40% and 60% of them would be more willing to give up their shoes than their phones.
31. A survey found that 55% of people said that a diet was harder to stick to than a budget. (Source: Kelton

Research for Medifast.) If 22 people are randomly selected, find the probability that between 80% and 90% of them will say that a diet is harder to stick to than a budget.

32. A survey done by Harris found that 40% of the people surveyed said that their children will have between $5,001 and $20,000 in debt when they graduate from college. If 25 people are selected, find the probability that 14 or 15 will say that their children will have a debt between $5,001 and $20,000 when they graduate from college.

33. A survey done by Harris International QUICK-QUERY found that 10% of women had a fear of flying. If 50 women are randomly selected, find the probability that less than 3 will have a fear of flying.

34. In a Harris survey, 40% of the people surveyed said that they received error messages from doing online transactions. If 18 people are randomly selected, find the probability that 5 or 6 people would have received error messages while doing online transactions.

35. A survey found that 33% of people earning between $30,000 and $75,000 said that they were very happy. If 6 people who earn between $30,000 and $75,000 are selected at random, find the probability that at most 2 would consider themselves very happy.

36. In a recent survey, 2% of the people surveyed said that they would keep their current job if they won a multi-million-dollar lottery. If 20 people are chosen randomly, find the probability that 3, 4, or 5 of them would keep their job.

37. If you take a true-false quiz with 10 questions and totally guess on every one, find the probability that you pass (get at least 60% right).

38. Repeat Problem 37 for a 10-question multiple-choice quiz where there are four choices on each question (and only one is correct).

Critical Thinking

In Exercises 39–47, decide if the experiment or question described is or is not a binomial experiment, then explain your reasoning. You don't need to find probabilities.

39. Keeping track of the number of customers in a week that get pepperoni on their pizza.

40. Recording the numerical results of rolling two dice 20 different times.

41. Playing 10 different people in golf and recording whether or not you win.

42. Drawing 12 different cards from a standard deck with replacement and recording whether or not each is a spade.

43. Surveying 20 different homeowners in your state to find out if they have life insurance.

44. Playing 25 rounds of rock, paper, scissors against the same person and recording the result. (If you're not familiar with the game, you can find the rules online very easily.)

45. According to the U.S. Department of Health and Human Services, just 3.9% of men in America are

taller than 6'2". What is the probability that three out of five men chosen in your class are 6'3" or taller?

46. The Bureau of Labor Statistics reported that 13.7% of work-eligible residents in the Las Vegas metro area were unemployed in February 2011. If 30 people from that area were chosen at random, what was the probability that 5 were unemployed?

47. There are 27 people in my calc 2 class right now, and 22 of them are passing. If I pick 6 at random, what is the probability that all 6 are passing?

48. (a) Write an example of a binomial experiment in real life in which the conditions of a binomial experiment are all met and lack of replacement is not an issue.

    (b) Write an example of a binomial experiment in real life without replacement, in which case we would need a large sample to use the binomial probability formula.

CHAPTER 11 Summary

Section	Important Terms	Important Ideas
11-1	Fundamental counting principle Factorial notation Permutation Permutation rule	**In order** to determine the total number of outcomes for a sequence of events, the fundamental counting principle or the permutation rules can be used. When the order or arrangement of the objects in a sequence of events is important, then the result is called a permutation of the objects.
11-2	Combination Combination rule	**When the** order of the objects is not important, then the result is called a combination. In this case, the combination rules can be used to count the number of possible combinations.
11-3	Probability experiment Outcome Sample space Event Frequency distribution Complement Classical probability Empirical probability Observed frequency	**Flipping coins**, drawing cards from a deck, and rolling a die are examples of probability experiments. The set of all possible outcomes of a probability experiment is called the sample space. The two types of probability are classical and empirical. Classical probability uses sample spaces and is based on the assumption that all outcomes in the sample space are equally likely. Empirical probability uses frequency distributions and is based on observation. Probability is a number that represents how likely it is that something will occur. Probability can be zero, one, or any number in between. When the probability of an event is close to zero, the event is highly unlikely to occur. When the probability of an event is near one, the event is almost certain to occur.
11-4	Tree diagram	**When sample** spaces are difficult to identify, it's often helpful to use tree diagrams or tables to identify all possible outcomes for a probability experiment.
11-5		**Probabilities** of events can be found by using the fundamental counting principle, the permutation rule, or the combination rule, depending on the situation. In some cases, more than one of those rules may be needed to calculate a probability.
11-6	Odds in favor Odds against Expectation (expected value)	**In order** to determine payoffs, gambling establishments give odds. There are two ways to compute odds for a game of chance: "odds in favor of an event" and "odds against the event." When a probability experiment has numerical outcomes, we can find the expected value, which is a long-run average of the outcomes if the experiment is repeated over and over. We find the expected value by multiplying each outcome by its probability, then adding the results.
11-7	Mutually exclusive events Addition rules	**Two events** are said to be mutually exclusive if they cannot occur at the same time. If two events are mutually exclusive, the probability of one or the other occurring is the sum of the probabilities for each event. If the events are not mutually exclusive, the probability of one or the other occurring is the sum of the probabilities minus the probability that both occur.

11-8	Independent events Dependent events Multiplication rules Conditional probability	**Events can** be classified as independent or dependent. Events are said to be independent if the occurrence of the first event does not affect the probability of the occurrence of the next event. If the probability of the second event occurring is changed by the occurrence of the first event, then the events are dependent. If two events are independent, the probability of both occurring is the product of the probabilities for each event. If the probability of an event B occurring is affected by an event A occurring, then we say that a condition has been imposed on the event and the probability of event B occurring given that A has occurred is called a conditional probability. If two events are dependent, the probability of both occurring is the probability that the first occurs multiplied by the probability that the second occurs given the first.
11-9	Binomial experiment Probability distribution	**Many probability** experiments have two outcomes or can be reduced to two outcomes. If the trials are independent, fixed in number, and have the same probability of a success, then the experiment can be considered a binomial experiment. These problems can be solved using the binomial probability formula. For some probability experiments, a probability distribution can be constructed, listing all outcomes with the corresponding probabilities.

MATH IN ▶ Gambling REVISITED

1. Using the table for rolling two dice on page 651, the probability of rolling 2, 3, 11, or 12 is $\frac{1}{6}$, meaning the probability of losing is $\frac{5}{6}$. So the two outcomes are +\$4 with probability $\frac{1}{6}$, and −\$1 with probability $\frac{5}{6}$. The expected value of each trial is then

$$+4 \cdot \frac{1}{6} + (-1) \cdot \frac{5}{6} = -\frac{1}{6}$$

In 100 trials, you would expect to lose $100(\frac{1}{6})$, or \$16.67.

2. The probability of winning \$35 is $\frac{1}{38}$, and the probability of losing \$1 is $\frac{37}{38}$. The expected value of each spin is

$$+35 \cdot \frac{1}{38} + (-1) \cdot \frac{37}{38} = -\frac{2}{38} = -\frac{1}{19}$$

In 100 trials, you would expect to lose $100(\frac{1}{19})$, or \$5.26.

3. Using the same idea as scenarios 1 and 2, the expected value of each ticket is

$$+20,000,000 \cdot \frac{1}{175,711,536} + (-1) \cdot \frac{175,711,535}{175,711,536}$$
$$\approx -\$0.8862$$

Buying 100 tickets, you would expect to lose $100(-0.8862)$, or \$88.62.

4. You would win \$1 with probability $\frac{1}{2}$, and lose \$1 with probability $\frac{1}{2}$, so the expected value of each flip is

$$1 \cdot \frac{1}{2} + (-1) \cdot \frac{1}{2} = 0$$

In 100 flips you would expect to break even.

The best, by far is flipping a coin, followed by roulette, the church fair dice game, and, bringing up the rear by quite a bit, the multistate lottery. Notice that under the best of circumstances, you are likely to break even!

Review Exercises

Section 11-1

1. Compute $\frac{14!}{11!}$.
2. Compute $_{12}P_6$.
3. An automobile license plate consists of three letters followed by four digits. How many different plates can be made if repetitions are allowed? If repetitions are allowed in the letters but not in the digits?
4. How many different arrangements of the letters in the word *bread* are there?
5. How many different arrangements of the letters in the word *cheese* are there?
6. How many different three-digit odd numbers use only the digits 0, 1, 2, 3, 4?

Section 11-2

7. Compute $_9C_6$.
8. Find both the number of combinations and the number of permutations of 10 objects taken 4 at a time.
9. Describe the difference between combinations and permutations.
10. How many different three-digit combinations can be made by using the numbers 1, 3, 5, 7, and 9 without repetitions if the "right" combination can open a safe? Does a combination lock really use combinations?
11. How many two-card pairs (i.e., the same rank) are there in a standard deck?
12. How many ways can five different television programs be selected from 12 programs?
13. A quiz consists of six multiple-choice questions. Each question has three possible answer choices. How many different answer keys can be made?
14. How many different ways can a buyer pick four television models from a possible choice of six models?

Section 11-3

15. Which of the following numbers could represent a probability?
    (a) $\frac{3}{2}$
    (b) $\frac{2}{3}$
    (c) 0.1
    (d) $-\frac{1}{2}$
    (e) 80%
16. When a die is rolled, find the probability of getting
    (a) A 5   (b) A 6   (c) A number less than 5.
17. When a card is drawn from a deck, find the probability of getting
    (a) A heart.
    (b) A 7 and a club.
    (c) A 7 or a club.
    (d) A jack.
    (e) A black card.
18. In a survey conducted at the food court in a local mall, 20 people preferred Panda Express for lunch, 16 preferred Sbarro Pizza, and 9 preferred Subway. If a shopper is chosen at random, find the probability that he or she prefers Sbarro Pizza.

19. If a die is rolled one time, find these probabilities:
    (a) Getting a 7
    (b) Getting an odd number
    (c) Getting a number less than 3
20. In a recent survey in a college dorm that has 1,500 rooms, 850 have an Xbox 360. If a room in this dorm is randomly selected, find the probability that it has an Xbox 360.
21. During a Midnight Madness sale at Old Navy, 16 white cargo pants, 3 khaki cargo pants, 9 tan cargo pants, and 7 black cargo pants were sold. If a customer who made a purchase during the sale is surveyed at random, find the probability that he or she bought
    (a) A pair of tan cargo pants.
    (b) A pair of black cargo pants or a pair of white cargo pants.
    (c) A pair of khaki, tan, or black cargo pants.
    (d) A pair of cargo pants that was not white.
22. An urban art gallery runs an annual art competition. Among this year's finalists, there were 16 paintings, 4 metal sculptures, 3 kinetic sculptures, and 7 etchings. If the gallery decides to totally ignore ethics and chooses the winner randomly, find the probability that it's
    (a) A kinetic sculpture.
    (b) A metal sculpture or an etching.
    (c) Not a sculpture.
    (d) Not an etching.
23. When two dice are rolled, find the probability of getting
    (a) A sum of 5 or 6.
    (b) A sum greater than 9.
    (c) A sum less than 4 or greater than 9.
    (d) A sum that is divisible by 4.
    (e) A sum of 14.
    (f) A sum less than 13.
24. Two dice are rolled. Find the probability of getting a sum of 8 if the number on one die is a 5.

Section 11-4

25. A gambler rolls an eight-sided die and then flips a coin. Draw a tree diagram and find the sample space.
26. A student can schedule one of three courses at 8:00 A.M.: English, math, or chemistry. The student can schedule either psychology or sociology at 11:00 A.M. Finally, the student can schedule either world history or economics at 1:00 P.M. (a) Draw a tree diagram and find all the different ways the student can make a schedule. (b) Repeat part (a), but include the condition that the student will take classes only at 8 A.M. and 11 A.M. if his first class is chemistry.
27. As an experiment in probability, a two-question multiple choice quiz is given at the beginning of class, but the answers are all written in Hebrew, which none of the students can read. This forces everyone to guess. Each question has choices A, B, C, D, and E. Construct a table that displays the sample space, then use the table to find the probability that both questions in a randomly selected quiz were answered with D or E (either D-E, or E-D).

Section 11-5

28. A card is drawn from a deck. Find the probability that it is a diamond given that it is a red card.

29. An investor has six bond accounts, three stock accounts, and two mutual fund accounts. If three investments are chosen at random, find the probability that one of each type of account is selected.

30. A newspaper advertises five different movies, three plays, and two baseball games. If a couple picks three activities at random, find the probability they will attend two plays and one movie.

31. In putting together the music lineup for an outdoor spring festival, Fast Eddie can choose from 4 student bands and 12 nonstudent bands. There are five time slots for bands; the first at 3 P.M., the others on the hour until 7 P.M. If Eddie chooses the bands randomly, find the probability that no student bands will be picked.

Section 11-6

32. Find the odds in favor of an event E when $P(E) = \frac{1}{4}$.
33. Find the odds against an event E when $P(E) = \frac{5}{6}$.
34. Find the probability of an event when the odds in favor of the event are 6:4.
35. The table lists five outcomes for a probability experiment with the corresponding probabilities. Find the expected value.

Outcome	5	10	15	20	25
Probability	0.5	0.2	0.1	0.1	0.1

36. After being picked from the audience on *Let's Make a Deal*, Marlena gets to pick one of five envelopes. Each envelope has a single bill in it: $1, $10, $20, $100, or $500. Find the expected value of the game.

37. You bet $10 and get to pick one card. If it's red, you get back $5. If it's a black card with a number on it, you get back $15. A black face card gets you $20 and a black ace $30. Find the expected value of making this bet 25 times.

Section 11-7

In Exercises 38–40, decide if the two events are mutually exclusive.

38. You meet someone while out; she gives you her phone number or her email address.

39. You complete a course and either pass or fail.

40. You spend a weekend in Las Vegas; you either win money, lose money, or break even.

41. If one of the 50 states is selected at random to be the site of a new nuclear power plant,
    (a) Find the probability that the state either borders Canada or Mexico.
    (b) Find the probability that the state begins with either A or ends with S.

42. There are six patients waiting at a free clinic with pain issues, three with rashes, four with fevers, and two with irregular heartbeats. If the next patient is randomly called, find the probability that he or she has a fever or a rash.

Section 11-8

In Exercises 43–46, decide if the two events are independent.

43. Missing 3 straight days of class and failing the next test.

44. Missing 3 straight days of class and getting overloaded with spam e-mails.

45. Drawing an ace from a standard deck, then drawing a second ace.

46. Drawing an ace from a standard deck, then replacing that card, shuffling, and drawing another ace.

47. In a family of three children, find the probability that all the children will be girls if it is known that at least one of the children is a girl.

48. A Gallup Poll found that 78% of Americans worry about the quality and healthfulness of their diet. If five people are selected at random, find the probability that all five worry about the quality and healthfulness of their diet.

49. Twenty-five percent of the engineering graduates of a university received a starting salary of $50,000 or more. If three of the graduates are chosen at random, find the probability that all have a starting salary of $50,000 or more.

50. Three cards are drawn from an ordinary deck *without* replacement. Find the probability of getting
    (a) All black cards.
    (b) All spades.
    (c) All queens.

51. A coin is flipped and a card is drawn from a deck. Find the probability of getting
    (a) A head and a 6.
    (b) A tail and a red card.
    (c) A head and a club.

52. The results in the table were reported by the Center for Climate Change Communication at George Mason University in response to the fill-in question, "What do you think is the primary cause of global warming?"

	Democrat	Republican	Independent	Tea Party
Caused mostly by human activities	193	87	71	18
Caused mostly by natural changes	78	71	85	49
None of the above— global warming isn't happening	6	10	22	20

(a) Find the probability that a randomly selected person thinks global warming isn't happening given that she is a member of the Tea Party.
(b) Find the probability that a randomly selected person thinks global warming is caused mostly

by human activity given that he is neither a Republican nor a member of the Tea Party.

(c) Find the probability that a randomly selected person is a Democrat given that she thinks global warming is caused mostly by natural changes.

(d) Find the probability that a randomly selected person is not an independent given that he thinks global warming is caused mostly by human activities.

Section 11-9

53. Use the binomial probability formula to find the probability of five successes in six trials when the probability of success on each trial is 1/3.

54. A survey found that 24% of families eat at home as a family five times a week. If 10 families are surveyed, find the probability that exactly 3 will say that they eat at home as a family five times a week.

55. According to a survey, 45% of teenagers said that they have seen passengers in an automobile encouraging the driver to speed. If 16 teens are surveyed, find the probability that exactly 6 will say that they have seen passengers encouraging the driver to speed.

56. Construct a probability distribution for the possible number of heads when tossing a coin three times.

Chapter Test

In Exercises 1–3, compute the requested value.

1. $_7C_5$
2. $_{12}P_5$
3. The probability of 8 successes in 10 trials when the probability of success on each trial is $\frac{1}{4}$.
4. If someone saw the title of Chapter 11 in this book and asked you "What is probability?" what would you say?
5. Describe a situation where combinations would be used to count possibilities and one where permutations would be used.
6. One company's ID cards consist of five letters followed by two digits. How many cards can be made if repetitions are allowed? If repetitions are not allowed?
7. How many ways can five sopranos and four altos be chosen for a university chorus from seven sopranos and nine altos?
8. When a card is drawn from a deck, find the probability of getting
   (a) A diamond.
   (b) A 5 or a heart.
   (c) A 5 and a heart.
   (d) A king.
   (e) A red card.
9. A trooper has written 12 citations for speeding this week, along with 8 for driving under the influence, 4 for reckless driving, and 7 for failure to wear a seat belt. Find the probability that he writes a citation for
   (a) Reckless driving.
   (b) DUI or speeding.
   (c) Failure to wear a seat belt given that the citation isn't for speeding or reckless driving.
10. When two dice are rolled, find the probability of getting
    (a) A sum of 6 or 7.
    (b) A sum greater than 3 or greater than 8.
    (c) A sum less than 3 or greater than 8.
    (d) A sum that is divisible by 3.
    (e) A sum of 16.
    (f) A sum less than 11.

11. There are six cards numbered 1, 2, 3, 4, 5, and 6. A contestant flips a coin. If it lands heads up, he will draw a card with an odd number. If it lands tails up, he will draw a card with an even number. Draw a tree diagram and find the sample space.
12. Of the physics graduates of a university, 30% received a starting salary of $60,000 or more. If five of the graduates are chosen at random, find the probability that all had a starting salary of $60,000 or more.
13. Five cards are drawn from an ordinary deck *without* replacement. Find the probability of getting
    (a) All red cards.
    (b) All diamonds.
    (c) All aces.
14. Four coins are tossed. Find the probability of getting four heads given that two of the four coins landed heads up.
15. A coin is tossed and a die is rolled. Find the probability of getting a head on the coin if it is known that the number on the die is even.
16. Nurses at one hospital can be classified according to gender (male, female), income (low, medium, high), and rank (staff nurse, charge nurse, head nurse). Draw a tree diagram and show all possible outcomes.
17. Find the odds in favor of and odds against an event E when $P(E) = \frac{3}{8}$.
18. Find the probability of an event when the odds against the event are 3:7.
19. There are six cards placed face down in a box. Each card has a number written on it. One is a 4, one is a 5, one is a 2, one is a 10, one is a 3, and one is a 7. You pick a card. Find the expected value of the draw.
20. A gambler draws a card from an ordinary deck of cards. If it is a black card, she wins $2. If it is a red card between or including 3 and 7, she wins $10. If it is a red face card, she wins $25, and if it is a black jack, she wins an additional $100. If it is any other card, she wins nothing. Find the expectation of the game. (Careful! This is tricky.)
21. In a soda machine in the student union, there are five Diet Cokes, four Mountain Dews, and two Dr. Peppers. If a student picks three sodas at random, find the

probability that she'll get one Diet Coke, one Mountain Dew, and one Dr. Pepper.

22. At Sally's freshman orientation, there were six computer science majors, four electrical engineering majors, and three architecture majors in her group. If four students are selected at random to receive a free tote bag with the school's logo, find the probability that the selection will include two computer science majors, one electrical engineering major, and one architecture major.

23. The results of a survey revealed that 30% of the people surveyed said that they would buy home electronic equipment at post-holiday sales. If 20 people are selected, find the probability that 8 or 9 will purchase home electronic equipment after the holidays.

Projects

1. Make a set of three cards—one with the word "heads" on both sides, one with the word "tails" on both sides, and one with "heads" on one side and "tails" on the other side. With a partner, play the game described in Exercise 61 of Section 11-6 (page 668) 100 times and record how many times your partner wins. (*Note:* do not change options during the 100 trials.)
   (a) Do you think the game is fair (i.e., does one person win approximately 50% of the time)?
   (b) If you think the game is unfair, explain what the probabilities might be and why.

2. Take a coin and tape a small weight (e.g., part of a paper clip) to one side. Flip the coin 100 times and record the results. Do you think you have changed the probabilities of the results of flipping the coin?

3. This game is called "Diet Fractions." Roll two dice and use the numbers to make a fraction less than or equal to one. Player A wins if the fraction cannot be reduced; otherwise, player B wins.
   (a) Play the game 100 times and record the results.
   (b) Decide if the game is fair or not. Explain why or why not.
   (c) Using the sample space for two dice, compute the probabilities of player A winning and player B winning. Do these agree with the results obtained in part a?

   Source: George W. Bright, John G. Harvey, and Margariete Montaque Wheeler, "Fair Games, Unfair Games." Chapter 8, *Teaching Statistics and Probability*. NCTM 1981 Yearbook. Reston, Virginia: The National Council of Teachers of Mathematics, Inc., 1981, p. 49. Used with permission.

4. Remember looking through cereal boxes for toys when you were a kid? It always seemed like you didn't get the exact one you wanted. Let's say that there was a certain toy you wanted, and five others that you could take or leave, all packed one per box at random. About how many boxes would you expect to have to buy to get the toy you wanted? Of course, you might have gotten it in the first box. Or you might have exhausted mom and dad's savings without ever getting it. These are the extremes.
   (a) You can simulate this experience using a single die, and rolling until a particular number of your choice comes up. Keep track of how many rolls it took, then repeat 99 more times, and find the average number of times it took.
   (b) If there were 10 different choices, you could simulate that by using the ace through 10 of a certain suit. Pick a certain card, shuffle the deck, and start dealing out the cards, keeping track of how many it takes to get the one you picked. Repeat 99 times and find the average.
   (c) Summarize your findings for both experiments.
   (d) Call getting the number or card you wanted a value of 2, and not getting it a value of 1. Then find the probability of each on any given roll or draw, and find the expected value for each experiment. How does it compare to the experimental results?

5. When devising the payouts for a gambling game, there are two things you have to balance: you want to make sure that players have enough chance to win that they want to keep playing, but you also want to make sure that they lose enough so that you make enough money for it to be worth your effort.

   In this project, we'll be using probability and expected value to decide how much to pay out for certain events. The players will roll three regular dice. First, decide on how much you will charge to play the game one time. Find the probability and odds against for each event listed, then decide how much you will pay out for each. (Of course, you have to pay nothing for some of the events or you'll never make any money.) After setting the payouts for each event, compute the expected value of playing your game. (Don't forget to include the amount paid to play the game in the first place!) In order for you to make money, the expected value should be negative for the players. In order for players to want to play, the expected value should be no more than 20% of the amount it costs to play the game. If that's not the case, adjust your payouts until the expected value falls within that range.

List of Events

Sum of the three die: 3, 4, 5, 6, 7, 8, 9, 10, 11, 12, 13, 14, 15, 16, 17, 18

Special rolls: triples (all three dice the same), singles (all three dice different), odds (all three odd), evens (all three even), straight (three consecutive numbers), dozen (product of all three is 12).

APPENDIX A

Area Under the Standard Normal Distribution

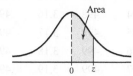

The area in the *A* column is the area under the normal distribution between $z = 0$ and the positive value of *z* found in the *z* column.

z	A	z	A	z	A	z	A	z	A	z	A	z	A
.00	.000	.25	.099	.50	.192	.75	.273	1.00	.341	1.25	.394	1.50	.433
.01	.004	.26	.103	.51	.195	.76	.276	1.01	.344	1.26	.396	1.51	.435
.02	.008	.27	.106	.52	.199	.77	.279	1.02	.346	1.27	.398	1.52	.436
.03	.012	.28	.110	.53	.202	.78	.282	1.03	.349	1.28	.400	1.53	.437
.04	.016	.29	.114	.54	.205	.79	.285	1.04	.351	1.29	.402	1.54	.438
.05	.020	.30	.118	.55	.209	.80	.288	1.05	.353	1.30	.403	1.55	.439
.06	.024	.31	.122	.56	.212	.81	.291	1.06	.355	1.31	.405	1.56	.441
.07	.028	.32	.126	.57	.216	.82	.294	1.07	.358	1.32	.407	1.57	.442
.08	.032	.33	.129	.58	.219	.83	.297	1.08	.360	1.33	.408	1.58	.443
.09	.036	.34	.133	.59	.222	.84	.300	1.09	.362	1.34	.410	1.59	.444
.10	.040	.35	.137	.60	.226	.85	.302	1.10	.364	1.35	.412	1.60	.445
.11	.044	.36	.141	.61	.229	.86	.305	1.11	.367	1.36	.413	1.61	.446
.12	.048	.37	.144	.62	.232	.87	.308	1.12	.369	1.37	.415	1.62	.447
.13	.052	.38	.148	.63	.236	.88	.311	1.13	.371	1.38	.416	1.63	.449
.14	.056	.39	.152	.64	.239	.89	.313	1.14	.373	1.39	.418	1.64	.450
.15	.060	.40	.155	.65	.242	.90	.316	1.15	.375	1.40	.419	1.65	.451
.16	.064	.41	.159	.66	.245	.91	.319	1.16	.377	1.41	.421	1.66	.452
.17	.068	.42	.163	.67	.249	.92	.321	1.17	.379	1.42	.422	1.67	.453
.18	.071	.43	.166	.68	.252	.93	.324	1.18	.381	1.43	.424	1.68	.454
.19	.075	.44	.170	.69	.255	.94	.326	1.19	.383	1.44	.425	1.69	.455
.20	.079	.45	.174	.70	.258	.95	.329	1.20	.385	1.45	.427	1.70	.455
.21	.083	.46	.177	.71	.261	.96	.332	1.21	.387	1.46	.428	1.71	.456
.22	.087	.47	.181	.72	.264	.97	.334	1.22	.389	1.47	.429	1.72	.457
.23	.091	.48	.184	.73	.267	.98	.337	1.23	.391	1.48	.431	1.73	.458
.24	.095	.49	.188	.74	.270	.99	.339	1.24	.393	1.49	.432	1.74	.459

Continued

z	A	z	A	z	A	z	A	z	A	z	A	z	A
1.75	.460	1.97	.476	2.19	.486	2.41	.492	2.63	.496	2.85	.498	3.07	.499
1.76	.461	1.98	.476	2.20	.486	2.42	.492	2.64	.496	2.86	.498	3.08	.499
1.77	.462	1.99	.477	2.21	.487	2.43	.493	2.65	.496	2.87	.498	3.09	.499
1.78	.463	2.00	.477	2.22	.487	2.44	.493	2.66	.496	2.88	.498	3.10	.499
1.79	.463	2.01	.478	2.23	.487	2.45	.493	2.67	.496	2.89	.498	3.11	.499
1.80	.464	2.02	.478	2.24	.488	2.46	.493	2.68	.496	2.90	.498	3.12	.499
1.81	.465	2.03	.479	2.25	.488	2.47	.493	2.69	.496	2.91	.498	3.13	.499
1.82	.466	2.04	.479	2.26	.488	2.48	.493	2.70	.497	2.92	.498	3.14	.499
1.83	.466	2.05	.480	2.27	.488	2.49	.494	2.71	.497	2.93	.498	3.15	.499
1.84	.467	2.06	.480	2.28	.489	2.50	.494	2.72	.497	2.94	.498	3.16	.499
1.85	.468	2.07	.481	2.29	.489	2.51	.494	2.73	.497	2.95	.498	3.17	.499
1.86	.469	2.08	.481	2.30	.489	2.52	.494	2.74	.497	2.96	.499	3.18	.499
1.87	.469	2.09	.482	2.31	.490	2.53	.494	2.75	.497	2.97	.499	3.19	.499
1.88	.470	2.10	.482	2.32	.490	2.54	.495	2.76	.497	2.98	.499	3.20	.499
1.89	.471	2.11	.483	2.33	.490	2.55	.495	2.77	.497	2.99	.499	3.21	.499
1.90	.471	2.12	.483	2.34	.490	2.56	.495	2.78	.497	3.00	.499	3.22	.499
1.91	.472	2.13	.483	2.35	.491	2.57	.495	2.79	.497	3.01	.499	3.23	.499
1.92	.473	2.14	.484	2.36	.491	2.58	.495	2.80	.497	3.02	.499	3.24	.499
1.93	.473	2.15	.484	2.37	.491	2.59	.495	2.81	.498	3.03	.499	3.25	.499
1.94	.474	2.16	.485	2.38	.491	2.60	.495	2.82	.498	3.04	.499		*
1.95	.474	2.17	.485	2.39	.492	2.61	.496	2.83	.498	3.05	.499		
1.96	.475	2.18	.485	2.40	.492	2.62	.496	2.84	.498	3.06	.499		

*For z values beyond 3.25 use $A = 0.500$.

APPENDIX B

Using the TI-84 Plus Graphing Calculator

This appendix is intended to give you brief instructions and tips for some useful features that can help you explore some of the concepts in this book.

Animator

We can use the Animator feature to draw and compare the right side and the left side of an equation.

To graph the equation $2(4x - 5) = 8x - 10$, press ⬜ and enter $2(4x - 5)$ in Y_1. Press either ⬤ or ⬜ to move to Y_2 and enter $8x - 10$. To access the Animated Line feature, use the left arrow key to move to the left of Y_2 and press ⬜ four times.

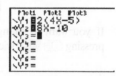

Using the Zoom features, we can quickly access a viewing window that shows the graph of the left and right sides (with animated line) of the equation.

Press ⬜ ⬜.

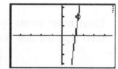

To show the animator, press the ⬜ key to pause the graphing process. The graphing process is restarted by pressing ⬜ a second time.

Contrast

We can contrast different graphs by choosing different types of lines for our graphs.

To contrast the left and right sides of $3x + 2 = -3x + 2$, press ⬜ and enter $3x + 2$ in Y_1 and $-3x + 2$ in Y_2. Use the left arrow key to move to the left of Y_2 and press ⬜ to access the bold line feature. This will help us differentiate the two lines in our graph.

Using the Zoom features we can quickly access a viewing window that shows the graph of the left and right sides (with bold line) of the equation.

Press [ZOOM] [4].

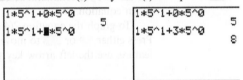

Edit

You can use previously entered expressions to create and edit new expressions.

If you had entered 1 * 5^1 + 0 * 5^0 and want to edit it to 1 * 5^1 + 3 * 5^0, begin by pressing [2nd] [ENTER] to recall the previously entered expression.

There are two types of editing modes: type-over mode and insert mode. Type-over mode is the default mode. To replace a number, move the cursor over the number to be replaced; then type the new number(s) or symbol(s) and press [ENTER].

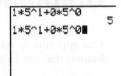

If you want to change 1 * 5^1 + 0 * 5^0 to 2 * 5^2 + 4 * 5^1 + 2 * 5^0, begin by pressing [2nd] [ENTER] twice. This recalls the second last entry.

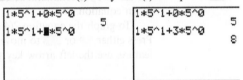

Enter insert mode by moving the cursor to the insertion point and pressing [2nd] [DEL]; then type the new number(s) or symbol(s).

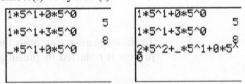

To get out of insert mode, move the cursor to the left or the right.

Finish editing the expression and press [ENTER].

You can easily tell which editing mode you are in by the type of cursor on the screen. Type-over mode's cursor is a flashing block, while insert mode has a flashing underline.

Horizontal and Vertical Lines

To graph a horizontal line, press ⬤ and enter a numerical value.

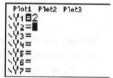

We can quickly access a viewing window that shows the graph of the horizontal line by pressing ⬤ ⬤.

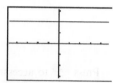

To graph a vertical line, first clear or turn off equations in the ⬤ screen. While this is not necessary it makes it clear where the vertical line is when graphed. From the home screen (accessed by pressing ⬤ ⬤), press ⬤ ⬤ to access the DRAW menu.

Press ⬤ to access the draw Vertical command. The command Vertical −2 will draw the vertical line $x = -2$.

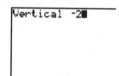

Press ⬤ to execute the command.

To clear this drawing from the graph screen, press ⬤ ⬤ ⬤ from the home screen or the graph screen.

Intersect

Using the Intersect feature will allow you to find solutions to an equation graphically.

The first step is to enter the expression from each side of an equation ($5x + 9 = 29$ in this example) in the ⬤ screen. Enter $5x + 9$ in Y_1 and 29 in Y_2.

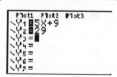

Using the Zoom features we can quickly access a viewing window that shows the intersection of the left and right sides of the equation.

Press 🔲 🔘 to access a window that fits the equation, showing the intersection.

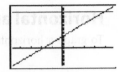

We can use the Calculate menu to calculate the intersection of the left and right sides of the equation, which is the solution.

Press 🔲 🔲 to access the calculate menu.

Press 🔲 to access the intersect command.

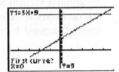

Press 🔲 ▶ to move the cursor to (or close to) the intersection. It may be necessary to press 🔲 ▶ more than once. In this example, we need to press it eight times.

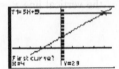

Press 🔲 to continue the calculation of the intersection.

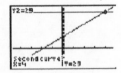

Press 🔲 to continue the calculation of the intersection.

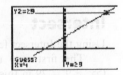

Press 🔲 to complete the calculation of the intersection.

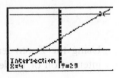

Parentheses

On most calculators, parentheses replace brackets and braces used in expressions. The resulting expression uses nested parentheses.

Example:

$$84 \div 4 - \{3 \times [10 + (15 - 2)]\}$$

becomes

$$84/4 - (3 * (10 + (15 - 2)))$$

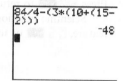

Probability

Graphing calculators offer probability functions. The probability functions include combination notation, factorial notation, and permutation notation.

Combination notation example:

How many combinations of four objects are there taken two at a time?

To determine the answer to this exercise use the calculator function nCr, where n is the number of objects and r is the number taken at a time.

To enter the information for this example using the combination function, press 4, MATH ▷ ▷ ▷ 3 (to access nCr), 2.

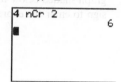

Factorial notation example:

How many different ways can five cities be ranked?

To determine the answer to this exercise use the factorial function.

To enter the information for this example using the factorial function, enter 5, MATH ▷ ▷ ▷ 4 (to access !).

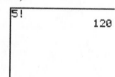

Permutation notation example:

How many different ways can a chairperson and an assistant chairperson be selected for a research project if there are seven scientists available?

To determine the answer to this exercise use the permutation function nPr, where n is the number of objects and r is the number of objects taken at a time.

To enter the information for this example using the combination function, enter 4 MATH ▷ ▷ ▷ 2 (to access nPr), 2.

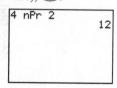

Scientific Notation

The calculator can be set to scientific notation mode by pressing  ⬤ ⬤.

Press ⬤ ⬤ to return to the home screen.

Scientific notation expressions can be entered into the calculator using the EE feature, ⬤ ⬤ or using powers of 10, as shown in the next screen.

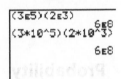

Shade

The Shade feature in the ⬤ screen can be used to show the graphic solution set when graphing inequalities.

To graph $x - y \geq 6$, first solve for y. The inequality becomes $y \leq x - 6$.

Press ⬤ ⬤ ⬤ to move to the left side of Y_1. Press ⬤ three times to have the graph shaded below the line (for < or ≤). Move the cursor to the right side of the equal sign to enter the expression $x - 6$.

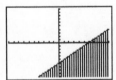

Using the Zoom features we can quickly access a viewing window that shows the shaded graph of the equation.

Press ⬤ ⬤.

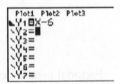

Statistics

Most graphing calculators offer statistics functions. The statistics functions included in this appendix are editing/entering data, clearing lists, copy list to list, sort (ascending or descending), and graphing vertical bar graphs (histograms), frequency polygons, and scatter plots.

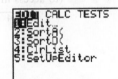 

Entering Data

To enter data, press [STAT],

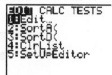

then [1] (for Edit).

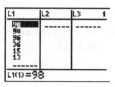

Previously entered data may exist in the list(s). If the list column (L1, L2, etc.) you plan to use to enter the data contains data, press ▲ to move to the column title (L1 in this case).

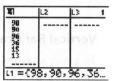

Press [CLEAR], then [ENTER] to clear the column of data. (Do not press [DEL]!)

Next, enter data one item at a time in the column, pressing [ENTER] after each number. Sample data:

53, 75, 27, 32, 15, 18

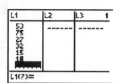

Up to 99 data entries are possible.

For some of the functions discussed next, it is necessary to access your saved lists. This is easily done by pressing [2nd] [LIST] and selecting the needed list.

Copy List

To copy a list, begin in the title edit line of the list where you want the data to appear.

Then, type in the number of the list to be copied and press [ENTER]. In this case, we begin in the title line of L2 and type L1 to copy the list. You can also press [2nd] [LIST] and select L1.

 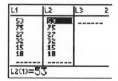

Sorting

To sort a list into ascending order, press [STAT] [2] then the list title (in this case, L2) and [ENTER].

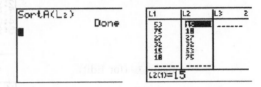

To sort a list into descending order, press [STAT] [3] then the list title (in this case, L2) and [ENTER].

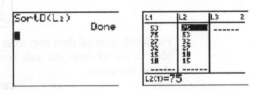

Vertical Bar Graph

To graph a vertical bar graph, begin by entering data in lists.
Sample:

Type	Frequency				
1	5				
2	7				
3	9				
4	4				

Press [Y=] and clear any entries. Press [2nd] [Y=] [1] to access a statistical plot.

Turn on the plot and select the vertical bar graph. Make sure the Xlist is L1, and the Freq is L2.

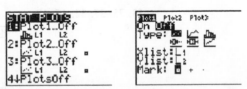

Press [ZOOM] [9].

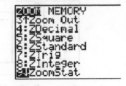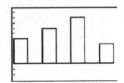

Histogram

To graph a histogram, use the same procedure as for the vertical bar graph. Then press ⓩⓄⓄⓜ and edit the options. The minimum and maximum of the data are Xmin and Xmax, respectively. The range of each class is the Xscl. The highest frequency in any class is the Ymax. The next window shows the settings using our sample data.

Next, press ⒼⓇⒶⓅⒽ.

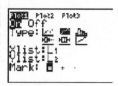

Frequency Polygon

To graph a frequency polygon, use the same procedure as for the vertical bar graph, except the Type should be frequency polygon (line graph).

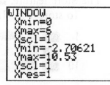

Press ⓦⒾⓃⒹⓄⓦ and edit the settings as was done for the histogram.

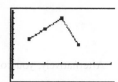

Next, press ⒼⓇⒶⓅⒽ.

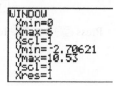

Scatter Plot

To graph a scatter plot, you will need to enter your data into lists, set up a plot, use the Zoom Stat feature, and adjust the window as needed.

Suppose we have these sample data:

L1 = {376, 650, 844, 1162, 1513, 1650, 2236, 3002, 4028, 4010}

L2 = {5, 20, 20, 28, 26, 34, 35, 56, 68, 55}

Press and enter the data.

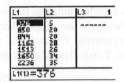

Press  to set up the scatter plot.

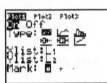

Press .

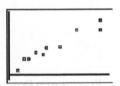

Press 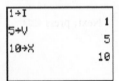 and edit the options for better viewing. A sample is shown.

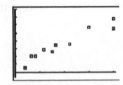

Store

The Store feature, , can be used to store values as letters or words.
To store 1 for I, 5 for V, and 10 for X press:

1 STO▸ ALPHA X² ENTER;
5 STO▸ ALPHA 6 ENTER; and
10 STO▸ X,T,θ,n ENTER.

```
1→I        1
5→V        5
10→X      10
```

Alternatively, you could store the numbers as follows:

1 STO▸ ALPHA X² 2nd · 5 STO▸ ALPHA 6 2nd · 10 STO▸ X,T,θ,n ENTER

```
1→I:5→V:10→X
            10
```

Table Setup

Using tables will assist you in viewing numerical values of an algebraic expression.

The first step in finding numerical values is to enter the expression in the 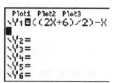 screen. Press ⬚ and enter ((2X + 6)/2) − X.

Next, we set up the table to view a set of integers in place of the *x* variable, and the value of the expression at each of the integer variables.

Press ⬚ ⬚ to access the TABLE SETUP menu. Start the table at an appropriate value and select an appropriate increment for the *x* values. In our example, we will start the table with −3 and choose 1 for our increment. This will evaluate the expression for *x* = −3, −2, −1, 0, etc. The starting value and increment can vary depending on the expression we plan to evaluate.

To view the TABLE press ⬚ ⬚.

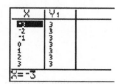

In this case, we see that no matter what number we use for *x*, the value of the expression is 3.

Another expression may show different values for *y*.

In ⬚, enter $2x + 3$.

To view the TABLE press ⬚ ⬚. Note that our table settings haven't changed from the previous example. We are still starting with −3 and our *x* increments are still 1.

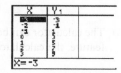

We see that for each value of *x* the value of *y* changes.

If we want to see the value of *y* when *x* = 100, we could use the down arrow to scroll to 100. We could also use the Ask feature from the Table Setup menu.

Press ⬜ ⬜ to access TBLSET. Press ⬜ twice, then ▶ ⬜ to turn on the Ask feature for the independent variable (X in this case).

To view the TABLE press ⬜ ⬜.

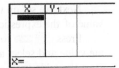

Begin with 100 ⬜.

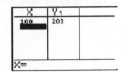

We see that when $x = 100$, $y = 203$. Next try 1000 ⬜; then 10000 ⬜. Next try 2345 ⬜; then 67890 ⬜.

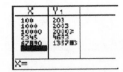

Any value of x can be entered to determine the corresponding value of y.

Test

The TEST feature includes symbols for both equalities and inequalities:

keystrokes	Symbol
⬜ MATH 1	$=$
⬜ MATH 2	$\neq$
⬜ MATH 3	$>$
⬜ MATH 4	$\geq$
⬜ MATH 5	$<$
⬜ MATH 6	$\leq$

The calculator can be used to verify that an inequality is true. When using the TEST feature, the calculator displays a result of 1 for true or 0 for false.

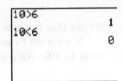

Zoom

The first step in viewing the graphical representation of the equation $5x + 9 = 29$ is to enter the expression from each side of the equation in the ⬜ screen. Press ⬜ and enter $5x + 9$ for Y_1 and 29 for Y_2.

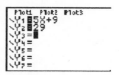

Using the Zoom features we can quickly access a viewing window that shows the graph of the left and right sides of the equation.

Press ⬜ ⬜ to begin with a centered window.

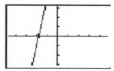

Then press ⬜ ⬜ to access a window that fits the equation.

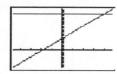

When Zoom Fit does not show the intersection, Zoom Out can assist you.

Enter each side of the equation $6x - 10 = 4x + 10$ in the ⬜ screen. Enter $6x - 10$ for Y_1 and $4x + 10$ for Y_2.

Using ⬜ ⬜ or ⬜ ⬜ for this equation does not show the intersection in the viewing window.

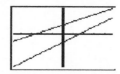

Press ⬜ ⬜ ⬜ to Zoom Out.

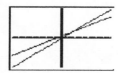

We can now see the intersection of the two lines.

SELECTED ANSWERS

CHAPTER 1: PROBLEM SOLVING

Exercise Set 1-1

7. 37   **9.** 10   **11.** 72   **13.**   **15.**

17. $5 + 13 + 17 = 35$, which is odd.   **19.** $5^2 \div 2 = 12.5$
21. Conjecture: the final answer is -10.
23. Conjecture: the final answer is 18.
25. $12,345,679 \times 72 = 12,345,679 \times 9(8) = 888,888,888$
27. $999,999 \times 9 = 8,999,991$ **29.** $99,999 \times 99,999 = 9,999,800,001$
31. $11,111 \times 11,111 = 123,454,321$
33. When multiplied by the numbers 1–6 the digits in the answer are a permutation of the original number. But the hypothesis fails when the number is multiplied by 7 and 8.
35. The next three sums are $\frac{9}{5}$, $\frac{11}{6}$, and $\frac{13}{7}$.
37. g e h   **39.** M J J   **41.** Inductive   **43.** Deductive
45. Inductive   **47.** Deductive   **49.** Deductive   **51.** Deductive
53. Deductive   **55.** Deductive   **57.** Deductive
59. (a) You'd be more likely to text while driving using inductive reasoning.
   (b) You'd be less likely to text while driving using deductive reasoning.
61. (a) Answers can vary, but the simplest answer is 16 and 32.
   (b) Each number is twice the one before it; 2^n.
   (c) Add 2 to the first term, then 4 to the second, 6 to the third, and 8 to the fourth. See part (d) for formula.
   (d)

n	1	2	3	4	5
$n^2 - n + 2$	2	4	8	14	22

; the formula is $n^2 - n + 2$.
   There may be more than one pattern that fits a string of numbers, especially if you only have the first three.
63. Answers vary.
65. (a) The average speed always works out to be 30 miles per hour.
67. 1 6 15 20 15 6 1   **69.** Weak   **71.** Strong   **73.** Strong
75. (a) 21, 28, 36   (b) 36, 49, 64   (c) 35, 51, 70   (d) 1, 6, 15, 28

Exercise Set 1-2

9. 2,900   **11.** 3,260,000   **13.** 63   **15.** 200,000   **17.** 3.67
19. 327.1   **21.** 5,460,000   **23.** 300,000   **25.** 264.9735   **27.** 482.60
29. Estimate: -44; exact value: -45.8469; 4% error
31. Estimate: -1.5; exact value: -1.8243 (to 4 decimal places); 17.8% error
33. $136   **35.** 6 hours   **37.** $72   **39.** $6.00   **41.** About $200
43. $25 per hour   **45.** $54   **47.** About $50   **49.** 3,200 acres
51. 4,400 acres   **53.** 471 people   **55.** 249   **57.** 40%   **59.** 3,333
61. 350 billion   **63.** 1940   **65.** About 7.8 billion per year.
67. 23%   **69.** 64%   **71.** $6 billion   **73.** $2 billion per year
75. Answers vary.
77. About $27 (Answers vary depending on how you rounded.)
79. The difference between the cost of milk in 1988 and the cost in 2006 is exaggerated by the fact that the picture changed in all three dimensions, rather than just vertically.
81. 1st hour: 45 mph; 1st 2 hours: 62.5 mph; 1st 3 hours: 58.3 mph; 1st 4 hours: 53.8 mph. The average speed was in the forties for the first hour, so a lot of it probably wasn't freeway. The second hour was the fastest; the third slowed them down some, and the fourth slowed them down even more.

83. 16–17 hours: -50 mph; 17–18 hours: zero. The negative indicates that the distance away was getting smaller, so they were headed back home. They weren't moving between 17 and 18 hours. Lunch break?
85. The steepness (slope) of the graph.

Exercise Set 1-3

5. 8 and 14   **7.** 12   **9.** 43   **11.** 7 years
13. Children $40,000, grandchildren $20,000
15. 132 and 312   **17.** Barney: $1.80, Betty $3.25
19. 35 girls   **21.** May earned $54.38 for working 5 hours.
23. 8 posts   **25.** 48 inches wide   **27.** 50 feet   **29.** 21 boxes, 252 lights
31. $\frac{1}{4}$ of the original   **33.** $1,093
35. There's no way to divide them evenly because 71 is a prime number.
37. $206.35
39. Mary: $1,187.50, Jean: $593.75, Claire: $296.88, Margie: $296.87
41. $465.50   **43.** 3-2-6-9-8-5-1-4-7-11-10-12
45. He cuts the bar at the 1-inch and the 3-inch marks, giving him bars of length 1, 2, and 3 inches. He pays the knight for the first day, then takes the one-inch piece back and gives him the two-inch on the second day (and continues in this fashion for six days).
47. Three, since the car in front is in front of two cars and the car at the end is behind two cars.
49. Start out with four full Jeeps and go $\frac{1}{4}$ of the way. Each will be half full. Use two of them to refill two others, then go another $\frac{1}{4}$ of the way. Each will be half full: use one to refill the other for the rest of the trip.
51. It's not possible.
53. The possibilities are: Maurice has 2 and Hani 3, Maurice has 3 and Hani 4, Maurice has 9 and Hani 8, or Maurice has 8 and Hani 7.

Review Exercises

1. 18, 19, 21   **3.** q, 1,024, n   **5.**

7. $5(7)(11) = 385$, which is odd
9. Conjecture: the final answer is 13 more than $\frac{1}{2}$ of the original even number.
11. $337 \times 12 = 4,044$
   $337 \times 15 = 5,055$
13. 9   **15.** Inductive   **17.** Deductive   **19.** 132,000   **21.** 14.6316
23. 3,730   **25.** $340   **27.** $340
29. There are many possible combinations. If you want to spend as close to $130 as possible:

T-shirts	6	5	4	3	2	1	0
Sweatpants	0	1	2	4	5	6	7

31. 80   **33.** Some people gave more than one response.   **35.** 1995
37. The graph looks steeper from 2000 to 2010. Actual rates are about $10/year for 1985–1995, and about $18/year for 2000–2010.
39. 9   **41.** 110 pounds   **43.** 67   **45.** $40
47. 20 years old   **49.** $2 \times 9 + 6 - 7 = 17$

51.

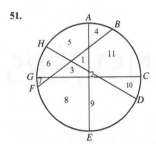

The cuts are *AE*, *BF*, *CG*, and *DH*.

53. 300 miles

55. 4 pounds of the nature mix and 6 pounds of the soy medley

Chapter 1 Practice Test

*When using estimation, other correct answers are possible.

1. 14   10   17   **3.** 88,888,888

5. The final answer is equal to the original number plus 13.

7. (a) Ninth   (b) $0.10   (c) $409.50

9. Move the last coin on the right on top of another coin or move the coin at top left below the coin at bottom left.

11. 84   **13.** 12

15. First person earns $36; second person earns $24.

17. (a) 90   (b) Not possible. She'd need 120%.

19. Mark is 17 years old and his mother is 49.   **21.** 1.38

23. (a) Number of hours per week in 1980 was about 35.5 hours.
Number of hours per week in 2005 was about 33.8 hours.
(b) About 1984   (c) −0.06 hours per year

25. Detroit

27.

Number of Homicides per 100,000 Residents in 2010

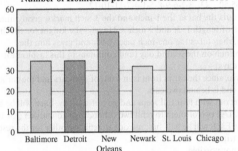

75. {10, 20, 30, 40}
⇕ ⇕ ⇕ ⇕
{40, 10, 20, 30}

77. {1, 2, 3, 4, 5, ...}
⇕ ⇕ ⇕ ⇕ ⇕
{4, 8, 12, 16, 20, ...}

79. 4   **81.** $n(C) = 7$ **83.** $n(E) = 1$ **85.** $n(G) = 0$

87. True   **89.** False   **91.** True

93. (a) {California, New York, Florida}
(b) {Illinois, Massachusetts, Virginia, Maryland, Georgia}
(c) {California, New York, Florida, Texas, New Jersey}
(d) {Illinois, New Jersey, Texas}

95. (a) {Drunk driving, Injury, Assault}
(b) {Injury, Unsafe sex, Health problems}
(c) {Injury, Assault, Drunk driving}
(d) {97,000, 1,825, 150,000}
(e) No. We don't know how many students were in more than one group, so adding the numbers together probably won't be correct.

97. (a) {Loan fraud, Bank fraud}
(b) {20–29, 30–39, 40–49}
(c) {Other, Government documents/benefits}
(d) {19, 15, 13}
(e) {Employment fraud, Utilities/phone fraud, Credit card fraud, Government documents/benefits}

99. (a) {2005, 2006, 2007}
(b) {2004, 2008, 2009, 2010}
(c) {2004, 2005, 2006, 2010}
(d) {2007, 2008, 2009}

101. No

103. (a) A appears to have more elements.
(b) { 1, 2, 3, 4, 5, 6, ...}
⇕ ⇕ ⇕ ⇕ ⇕ ⇕
{ 2, 4, 6, 8, 10, 12, ...}
This one-to-one correspondence shows that the two sets have the same number of elements.

105. (a) {2, 4, 6}, {2, 4}, {2, 6}, {4, 6}, {2}, {4}, {6}, ∅
(b) It's common to forget the empty set.

Exercise Set 2-2

11. $A' = \{2, 3, 17, 19\}$ **13.** $C' = \{2, 3, 5, 7, 11\}$

15. $A' = \{1, 2, 3, 5, 7, 9, 11, \ldots\}$

Note: for 17–24, the list of proper subsets is the same as the list of subsets with the original set excluded.

17. ∅, {r}, {s}, {t}, {r, s}, {r, t}, {s, t}, {r, s, t}

19. ∅, {1}, {5}, {1, 5}   **21.** ∅

23. ∅, {w}, {x}, {y}, {z}, {w, x}, {w, y}, {w, z}, {x, y}, {x, z}, {y, z}, {w, x, y}, {w, x, z}, {w, y, z}, {x, y, z}, {w, x, y, z}

25. True   **27.** False   **29.** False   **31.** False   **33.** True

35. 8 subsets, 7 proper subsets

37. 1 subset, no proper subsets

39. 4 subsets, 3 proper subsets

41. $U = \{1, 3, 5, 7, 9, 11, 13, 15, 17, 19\}$ **43.** $B = \{5, 11, 13, 15\}$

45. $A \cup B = \{1, 5, 9, 11, 13, 15, 17\}$ **47.** $B' = \{1, 3, 7, 9, 17, 19\}$

49. $(A \cap B)' = \{1, 3, 7, 9, 13, 15, 17, 19\}$

51. $A \cup C = \{12, 14, 15, 16, 17, 19, 20\}$

53. $A' = \{11, 12, 13, 18, 19, 20\}$

55. $A' \cap (B \cup C) = \{11, 12, 13, 19, 20\}$

57. $(A \cap B)' \cap C = \{12, 20\}$

59. $(B \cup C) \cap A' = \{11, 12, 13, 19, 20\}$ **61.** $W \cap Y = \varnothing$

63. $W \cup X = \{2, 4, 6, 7, 8, 9, 10, 11, 12, 13, 14\}$

65. $W \cap X = \{6, 8\}$ **67.** $(X \cup Y) \cap Z = \varnothing$

69. $W' \cap X' = \{1, 3, 5, 15, 16, 17, 18, 19, 20, 21, 22, 23, 24\}$

71. $A \cap B = B$

73. $A \cap (B \cup C') = \{x \mid x$ is an odd multiple of 3 or an even multiple of 9$\}$
$= \{3, 9, 15, 18, 21, 27, 33, 36, 39, \ldots\}$

75. $C - B = \{p\}$ **77.** $B - C = \{s, u\}$

79. $B \cap C' = \{s, u\}$ **81.** $D - M = \{11, 13, 15, 17, \ldots\}$

83. $(D - M) - T = \varnothing$

85. $A \times B = \{(9, 1), (9, 2), (9, 3), (12, 1), (12, 2), (12, 3), (18, 1), (18, 2), (18, 3)\}$

CHAPTER 2: SETS

Exercise Set 2-1

9. $T = \{t, h, i, n, k, g\}$

11. $P = \{51, 52, 53, 54, 55, 56, 57, 58, 59\}$

13. $C = \{1, 2, 3, 4, 5, 6, 7, 8\}$

15. $G = \{11, 12, 13, \ldots\}$

17. $Y = \{2,001, 2,002, 2,003, \ldots, 2,999\}$

19. $C = \{$white, red, blue, green, gray, brown, black, yellow$\}$

21. $L = \{$medial collateral, lateral collateral, anterior cruciate, posterior cruciate$\}$

23. True   **25.** True   **27.** True   **29.** The set of multiples of 5

31. The set of multiples of 13 from 13 to 52

33. The set of letters in the name Steven

35. The set of natural numbers from 100 to 199

37. $\{x \mid x$ is a multiple of 10$\}$

39. $X = \{x \mid x$ is odd and less than 16$\}$

41. $\{x \mid x$ is a color in the American flag$\}$ is one possibility.

43. There are no natural numbers less than zero so $H = \varnothing$.

45. {Spring, Summer, Fall, Winter}

47. {102, 104, 106, 108, 110, 112, 114, 116, 118}

49. Well-defined   **51.** Not well-defined   **53.** Not well-defined

55. False   **57.** True   **59.** True   **61.** Infinite

63. Finite   **65.** Infinite   **67.** Finite   **69.** Equal

71. Neither   **73.** Equivalent

87. $A \times A = \{(9, 9), (9, 12), (9, 18), (12, 9), (12, 12), (12, 18), (18, 9), (18, 12), (18, 18)\}$

89. B' **91.** $(A \cup B) - (A \cap B)$

93. {cell phone, laptop, iPod}, {cell phone, laptop}, {cell phone, iPod}, {laptop, iPod}, {cell phone}, {laptop}, {iPod}, ∅

95. $2^7 = 128$ **97.** $2^4 = 16$

99. The set of people with strong management skills, the set of people good at working as part of a team, and the set of people with 5 years' experience with a similar project

101. (a) The set of people who have been convicted of a felony
    (b) The set of people who have been convicted of a felony and have been released, or charged with a felony and found not guilty
    (c) The set of people who were charged with a felony and either found not guilty or had charges dropped before standing trial

103. (a) The set of people who have been convicted of a felony and have been released from prison
    (b) The set of people who have previously been convicted of a felony, and are currently awaiting trial on another felony charge
    (c) There's nobody in this set

105. $A \times B = \{$(chocolate, fudge icing), (chocolate, cream cheese icing), (yellow, fudge icing), (yellow, cream cheese icing), (angel food, fudge icing), (angel food, cream cheese icing)$\}$. This describes different possible cakes given three types of cake and two types of icing.

107. Answers vary.

109. Answers vary.

111. Given n elements, each has two choices: in the subset or not. So if we try to build a subset, there are $2 \cdot 2 \cdot 2 \cdot \cdots \cdot 2$ ways to choose, where there are n factors of 2. That's a long way to say 2^n.

Exercise Set 2-3

7.
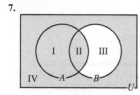

9.
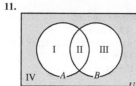

11.
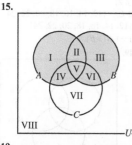

13.
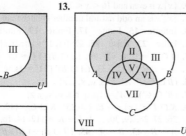

15.
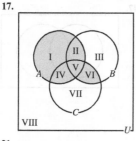

17.
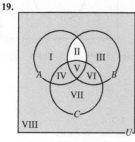

19.
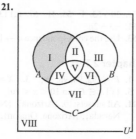

21.

23.
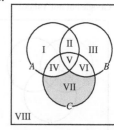

25.
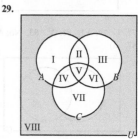

27.
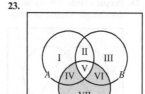

29.
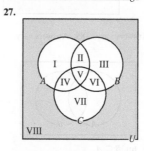

31. equal **33.** equal **35.** not equal **37.** not equal **39.** $n(A) = 10$

41. $n(A \cap B) = 4$ **43.** $n(A') = 13$ **45.** $n(A' \cap B') = 6$

47. $n(A - B) = 6$ **49.** $n(A \cap (B - A)) = 0$

51. $n(A) = 8$ **53.** $n(A \cap B) = 3$ **55.** $n(A \cap B') = 5$

57. $n(A') = 11$ **59.** $n(A - B) = 5$

61. People who drive an SUV or a hybrid vehicle
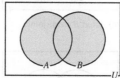

63. People who do not drive an SUV
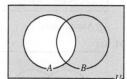

65. Students in online courses and blended or traditional courses
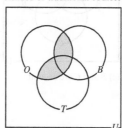

67. Students who are in blended, online, and traditional courses
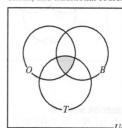

69. Students not voting democrat or voting republican
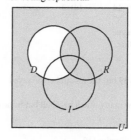

71. Students voting democrat or republican but not independent
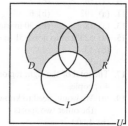

73. People who regularly use Google but not Yahoo!

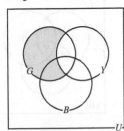

75. People who do not regularly use Google, Yahoo!, or Bing

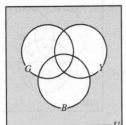

For 21 through 30 we will show each set is infinite by putting it into a one-to-one correspondence with a proper subset of itself.

21. $\{3, 6, 9, 12, 15, \ldots, 3n, \ldots\}$
$\updownarrow \ \updownarrow \ \updownarrow \ \updownarrow \ \updownarrow \ \ \ \ \updownarrow$
$\{6, 12, 18, 24, 30, \ldots, 6n, \ldots\}$

23. $\{9, 18, 27, 36, 45, \ldots, 9n, \ldots\}$
$\updownarrow \ \updownarrow \ \updownarrow \ \updownarrow \ \updownarrow \ \ \ \ \updownarrow$
$\{18, 36, 54, 72, 90, \ldots, 18n, \ldots\}$

25. $\{2, 5, 8, 11, \ldots, 3n - 1, \ldots\}$
$\updownarrow \ \updownarrow \ \updownarrow \ \updownarrow \ \ \ \ \ \updownarrow$
$\{5, 11, 17, 23, \ldots, 6n - 1, \ldots\}$

27. $\{10, \ \ 100, \ldots, \ 10^n, \ldots\}$
$\updownarrow \ \ \ \ \ \updownarrow \ \ \ \ \ \ \ \ \updownarrow$
$\{100, 10,000, \ldots, 10^{2n}, \ldots\}$

29. $\left\{\dfrac{5}{1}, \dfrac{5}{2}, \dfrac{5}{3}, \ldots, \ \dfrac{5}{n}, \ldots\right\}$
$\updownarrow \ \updownarrow \ \updownarrow \ \ \ \ \ \updownarrow$
$\left\{\dfrac{5}{2}, \dfrac{5}{3}, \dfrac{5}{4}, \ldots, \dfrac{5}{n+1}, \ldots\right\}$

31. Use the correspondence $n \to 5n$.

33. Use the correspondence $n \to (n-1)^2$. (The correspondence $n \to n^2$ shows that the natural numbers are countable, but the whole numbers include zero as well.)

35. The rational numbers can be put into a one-to-one correspondence with the natural numbers.

37. That the set in Example 2 is countable.

39. (a) Correspond every number to the number that is one less.
(b) $\aleph_0 + 1 = \aleph_0$

41. $\aleph_0$ **43.** 15   **45.** $\aleph_0$

77. I   **79.** VI   **81.** V   **83.** No; Answers vary.   **85.** Answers vary.

87. (a)

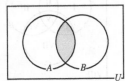 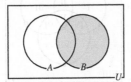

(b) Answers vary.   (c) $B \subseteq A$

89. (a)

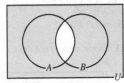 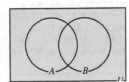

(b) Answers vary.   (c) A and B are disjoint

91. (a)

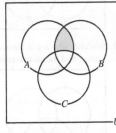 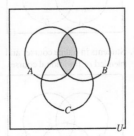

(b) Answers vary.   (c) B and C are disjoint

Exercise Set 2-4

1. (a) 10   (b) 51   (c) 3
3. (a) 22   (b) 36
5. (a) 50%   (b) 90%
7. (a) 2   (b) 9   (c) 35
9. (a) 16   (b) 7   (c) 14   (d) 3
11. (a) 192   (b) 6   (c) 87
13. (a) 18   (b) 30 in each league
15. (a) 52 listen to none, 51 to satellite.
(b) 13
(c) 30
17. The total of the eight regions is 39 but the researcher surveyed 40 people.
19. (a) We would need to know how many watch baseball but none of the other two sports.
(b) 1,000
(c) Football only: 205; basketball only: 110

Exercise Set 2-5

5. $7n$ **7.** 4^n **9.** $-3n$ **11.** $\dfrac{n}{4}$ **13.** $4n - 2$ **15.** $\dfrac{n+1}{n+2}$
17. $100n$ **19.** $-3n - 1$

Review Exercises

1. $D = \{52, 54, 56, 58\}$ **3.** $L = \{l, e, t, r\}$
5. $B = \{501, 502, 503, \ldots\}$
7. {Buzz Aldrin, Neil Armstrong, Alan Bean, Gene Cernan, Pete Conrad, Charles Duke, James Irwin, Edgar Mitchell, Harrison Schmitt, David Scott, Alan B. Shepard, John Young}
9. $\{x \mid x$ is even and $16 < x < 26\}$
11. $\{x \mid x$ is an odd natural number greater than $100\}$
13. Infinite   **15.** Finite   **17.** Finite   **19.** Finite
21. False   **23.** False   **25.** $\varnothing$; {r}; {s}; {t}; {r, s}; {r, t}; {s, t}; {r, s, t}
27. $A \cap B = \{t, u, v\}$ **29.** $(A \cap B) \cap C = \varnothing$
31. $A - B = \{p, r\}$ **33.** $(A \cup B)' \cap C = \{s, w, z\}$
35. $(B \cup C) \cap A' = \{s, w, x, y, z\}$
37. $(B' \cap C') \cup A' = \{p, q, r, s, w, x, y, z\}$
39. $K \cap L = \{x \mid x \in E, x > 25\}$; $K \cup L = \{12, 14, 16, 18, 20, 22, 24, 26, 27, 28, 29, 30, \ldots\}$; $L - K = \{12, 14, 16, 18, 20, 22, 24\}$
41. $A - B$ **43.** $B - A$ **45.** $(A \cup B) - (A \cap B)$
47. **49.**

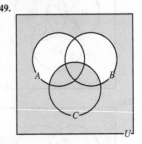

51. 20   **53.** I   **55.** II   **57.** (a) 132   (b) 28   **59.** (a) 3   (b) 5   (c) 6
61. $-3 - 2n$
63. Use the correspondence $n \to 12n$.

Chapter 2 Test

1. $P = \{92, 94, 96, 98\}$ **3.** $X = \{1, 2, 3, 4, \ldots, 79\}$
5. $\{x \mid x \in E$ and $10 < x < 20\}$ **7.** Infinite   **9.** Finite
11. All subsets: $\varnothing$, {Arizona}, {Nevada}, {Oregon}, {Arizona, Nevada}, {Arizona, Oregon}, {Nevada, Oregon}, {Arizona,

Nevada, Oregon}; proper subsets: all but the last one. There are 3 states that border California, so there are $2^3 = 8$ subsets.

13. $(A \cup B)' = \{c, h\}$ **15.** $(A - B) - C = \{b, d, f\}$

17. {(Arizona, e), (Nevada, e), (Oregon, e), (Arizona, h), (Nevada, h), (Oregon, h), (Arizona, j), (Nevada, j), (Oregon, j)} and {(e, Arizona), (h, Arizona), (j, Arizona), (e, Nevada), (h, Nevada), (j, Nevada), (e, Oregon), (h, Oregon), (j, Oregon)}

19.

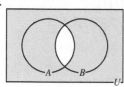

21. $n(A \cup B) = 2,300$ **23.** $15n$ **25.** True **27.** True **29.** False

CHAPTER 3: LOGIC

Exercise Set 3-1

7. Not a statement **9.** Statement **11.** Not a statement

13. Not a statement **15.** Not a statement

17. Compound statement **19.** Compound statement

21. Simple statement **23.** Compound statement

25. Compound statement **27.** Conjunction **29.** Biconditional

31. Disjunction **33.** Biconditional

35. The shirt I'm wearing to my interview is not white.

37. The hospital is full.

39. You're going to flunk this class. **41.** Universal **43.** Existential

45. Universal **47.** Existential **49.** Universal **51.** Existential

53. Not all fish swim in water; Some fish do not swim in water.

55. No people who live in glass houses throw stones.

57. Not every happy dog wags its tail; Some happy dog does not wag its tail.

59. There is no four-leaf clover.

61. Someone with green eyes wears glasses.

63. None of my friends have an iPhone.

65. $p \wedge q$ **67.** $\sim q \to p$ **69.** $\sim q$ **71.** $q \vee \sim p$ **73.** $q \leftrightarrow p$

75. $\sim q$ **77.** $\sim q \to p$ **79.** $p \vee \sim q$ **81.** $p \leftrightarrow q$ **83.** $\sim p \to q$

85. The plane is on time and the sky is clear.

87. If the sky is clear, then the plane is on time.

89. The plane is not on time and the sky is not clear.

91. The plane is on time or the sky is not clear.

93. If the sky is clear, then the plane is or is not on time.

95. Trudy does not live off campus.

97. Mark lives on campus or Trudy does not live off campus.

99. If Mark does not live on campus, then Trudy does not live off campus.

101. Mark lives on campus or Trudy lives off campus.

103. Trudy lives off campus or Mark lives on campus.

105. It cannot be classified as true or false.

107. (a) a is less than 20.

(b) a is not less than 20.

(c) $a \geq 20$ (This is if we assume that a is a real number. Otherwise, the statement would be $a \geq 20$ or a is not a real number.)

109. There will not be any fans at any of the games.

111. There is at least one person that likes my history professor.

Exercise Set 3-2

5. FFFT **7.** FFTF **9.** FTTF **11.** TTFF **13.** TFTT **15.** TTFF

17. TTFF **19.** TTFFTFFF **21.** TTTTTTTT **23.** TFFFTFTF

25. TTTFFFTF **27.** FTFTFTTT **29.** FFFTTTTN

31. FFFFTFFF **33.** TFTFFFFF **35.** True **37.** True **39.** True

41. False **43.** True **45.** True

47. Let p be "if you take their daily product," q be "you cut your calorie intake by 10%," and r be "you lose at least 10 pounds in the next 4 months."

49. TFTTTTTT **51.** True

53. Let p be "the attendance for the following season is over 2 million," q be "he will add 20 million dollars to the payroll," and r be "the team will make the playoffs the following year."

55. TFFFTTTT **57.** True

59. The truth table for $(p \wedge q) \vee r$ is different than the one for $p \wedge (q \vee r)$.

61. The statements are equivalent.

63. Answers vary.

Exercise Set 3-3

7. Tautology **9.** Self-contradiction **11.** Tautology **13.** Tautology

15. Neither **17.** Equivalent **19.** Neither **21.** Neither

23. Negations **25.** Neither **27.** $q \to p$; $\sim p \to \sim q$; $\sim q \to \sim p$

29. $\sim(q \wedge p) \to \sim p$; $p \to (q \wedge p)$; $(q \wedge p) \to p$

31. $(q \vee r) \to p$; $\sim p \to \sim(q \vee r)$; $\sim(q \vee r) \to \sim p$

33. The patient isn't septic and she's not in shock.

35. It is cold or I am not soaked.

37. I will not go to the beach or I will get sunburned.

39. The suspect is not a white male and the witness is correct.

41. It is not right and it is not wrong.

43. My grade isn't an A and it's not a B.

45. The prosecuting attorney for this case isn't experienced or prepared.

47. My friends are serious about school and prepared to work hard.

49. $p \to q$ **51.** $p \to q$ **53.** $p \to q$ **55.** $\sim p \to \sim q$

Note: for 57–62, explanations will vary.

57. *Converse*: if he did get a good job, then he graduated with a Bachelor's degree in Management Information Systems.
Inverse: if he did not graduate with a Bachelor's degree in Management Information Systems, then he will not get a good job.
Contrapositive: if he did not get a good job, he did not graduate with a Bachelor's degree in Management Information Systems.

59. *Converse*: if I host a party in my dorm room, then the *American Idol* finale is today.
Inverse: if the *American Idol* finale is not today, then I will not host a party in my dorm room.
Contrapositive: if I do not host a party in my dorm room, then the *American Idol* finale is not today.

61. *Converse*: if I go to Nassau for spring break then I will lose 10 pounds by March 1.
Inverse: if I do not lose 10 pounds by March 1 then I will not go to Nassau for spring break.
Contrapositive: if I do not go to Nassau for spring break then I did not lose 10 pounds by March 1.

63. He graduated with a Bachelor's degree in Management Information Systems and didn't get a good job.

65. The *American Idol* finale is today and I won't host a party in my dorm room.

67. I will lose 10 pounds by March 1 and won't go to Nassau for spring break.

69. True **71.** False **73.** False

75. $\sim(p \to q) \equiv p \wedge \sim q$ **77.** Answers vary.

Exercise Set 3-4

9. Valid **11.** Invalid **13.** Invalid **15.** Valid **17.** Invalid

Note: symbolic forms for 19–24 can be found on pages 133–135.

19. Valid **21.** Valid **23.** Invalid **25.** Valid **27.** Invalid **29.** Valid

31. Valid **33.** Invalid **35.** Invalid **37.** Invalid **39.** Valid

41. Invalid **43.** Valid **45.** Invalid **47.** Valid **49.** Valid

51. Invalid **53.** Invalid **55.** Valid **57.** Valid

59. Answers vary. **61.** Answers vary.

63. The argument is valid even though the conclusion is false.

Exercise Set 3-5

5.

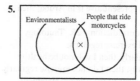

7.

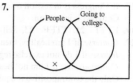

9.

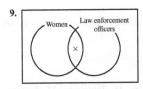

11.

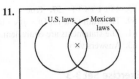

13.

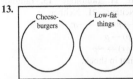

15. Invalid **17.** Valid **19.** Invalid **21.** Valid **23.** Invalid
25. Invalid **27.** Invalid **29.** Valid **31.** Invalid **33.** Invalid
35. Valid **37.** Invalid **39.** Invalid **41.** Invalid **43.** All *A* is *C*.
45. No calculators can make breakfast.
47. Example 1: *p* = person is a politician, *q* = person stretches the
truth, *r* = person takes bribes.
$(p \rightarrow q) \wedge (p \wedge r) \Rightarrow (q \wedge r)$
Example 3: *p* = person is a criminal, *q* = person is admirable,
r = person is an athlete.
$(p \rightarrow \sim q) \wedge (r \wedge \sim p) \Rightarrow (q \wedge r)$

Review Exercises
1. Not a statement **3.** Not a statement **5.** Not a Statement
7. Simple **9.** Compound; biconditional **11.** Compound; disjunction
13. The cell phone is not out of juice.
15. No failing students can learn new study methods.
17. Some SUVs are not gas guzzlers.
19. $p \wedge q$ **21.** $q \leftrightarrow p$ **23.** $\sim p \rightarrow \sim q$ **25.** $\sim(p \rightarrow q)$ **27.** $\sim(\sim q)$
29. It is cool or it is not cloudy.
31. It is cool if and only if it is cloudy.
33. It is not true that it is not cool or it is cloudy.
35. False **37.** TTFT **39.** TTTT **41.** TFTTTTTT
43. TTFTTTTT **45.** True **47.** True
49. Tautology **51.** Neither **53.** Neither **55.** Not equivalent
57. Social work is not lucrative and it's not fulfilling.
59. The signature is authentic or the check is valid.
61. Let *p* be the statement "I will be happy" and *q* be the statement
"I get rich." The compound statement is $p \rightarrow q$.
63. *Converse*: if I start riding my bike to work, gas prices will go higher.
Inverse: if gas prices do not go any higher, I will not start riding my
bike to work.
Contrapositive: if I do not start riding my bike to work, then gas
prices will not go any higher.
65. *Converse*: if the patient gets an MRI, then the X-rays are
inconclusive.
Inverse: if the X-rays aren't inconclusive then the patient won't get
an MRI.
Contrapositive: if the patient doesn't get an MRI, then the X-rays
aren't inconclusive.
67. Invalid **69.** Invalid **71.** Invalid **73.** Invalid **75.** Valid
77. Invalid **79.** Invalid

Chapter 3 Test
1. False **3.** Answers vary.
5. The image is not uploading to my online bio.
7. No students ride a bike to school.
9. $p \wedge q$ **11.** $p \leftrightarrow q$ **13.** $\sim(\sim p \wedge q)$
15. Congress is in session and my representative isn't in Aruba.
17. If Congress is in session or my representative is in Aruba, then
Congress is in session.
19. FTTT **21.** TTFF **23.** Self-contradiction **25.** Tautology
27. *Converse*: if I am healthy, then I exercise regularly.
Inverse: if I do not exercise regularly, then I will not be healthy.
Contrapositive: if I am not healthy, then I do not exercise regularly.
Only the contrapositive is equivalent to the original statement.
29. Valid **31.** Invalid **33.** Invalid

CHAPTER 4: NUMERATION SYSTEMS
Exercise Set 4-1
7. 123 **9.** 20,225 **11.** 30,163 **13.** 502,111
15. ∩∩∩|||||||
17. ꝯꝯꝯꝯꝯꝯꝯꝯꝯ|
19. ƒꝯꝯꝯ||||||
21.
23.
25.
27.
29.
31. 189 **33.** 52 **35.** 713
37.
八
十
九
39.
一
百
八
十
四
41.
一
千
三
百
五
十
六
43. (a) hundreds (b) thousands (c) ten thousands
45. (a) $1 \times 1{,}000 + 8 \times 100 + 5$
(b) $3 \times 10{,}000 + 2 \times 1{,}000 + 7 \times 100 + 1 \times 10 + 4$
47. (a) $1 \times 100{,}000 + 6 \times 10{,}000 + 2 \times 1{,}000 + 8 \times 100 + 7 \times 10 + 3$
(b) $2 \times 100{,}000{,}000 + 3 \times 100{,}000 + 2 \times 10{,}000 + 1 \times 1{,}000 +$
$4 \times 100 + 1 \times 10 + 6$
49. (a) 7,309 (b) 40,850 **51.** (a) 646,090 (b) 80,604,020
53. 51 **55.** 40,871 **57.** 79,893 **59.** 4,313
61.
63.
65.
67.
69. (a) 18 (b) 99 **71.** (a) 216 (b) 1,110
73. (a) 418 (b) 2,967
75. (a) 93,500 (b) 3,200,000 **77.** (a) LVIII (b) CXLVII
79. (a) DLXVII (b) MCCLVIII
81. (a) MCDLXII (b) MMMCMIX
83. (a) $\overline{\text{LXX}}$CCCXI (b) $\overline{\text{MML}}$X
85. (a) 98 (b) 46 (c) 5,324
87. (a) $\eta\varphi\ \varepsilon\alpha$ (b) $\chi\varphi\ \iota\alpha$ (c) $\delta\omega\ \alpha\rho\ \gamma\alpha$
89. $\varphi\varphi$ **91.** $\iota\varphi\ \theta\alpha$ **93.** (a) 277 (b) 6,852
95. (a) 3,387 (b) 113,053
97. (a) (b) **99.** (a) (b)

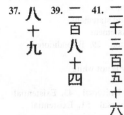

101. 1939 **103.** 1978 **105.** 2005 **107.** 423–9315 **109.** 605–12908
111. 8403–4096 **113.** Answers vary.
115. Because the Babylonian system is an ancient number system which
is not in use today. **117.** Answers will vary
119. Tally: 4; Egyptian: 4,000,000; Roman: 3,000,000; Multiplicative
grouping and Chinese: 1,100,000; Hindu-Arabic: 9,999; Babylonian:
2,196,610; Mayan: 37,905
121. IIV is the same as III; XXC is the same as LXXX. Subtraction is
used only when necessary to avoid writing the same symbol four
times consecutively.

Exercise Set 4-2

3. 252 5. 391 7. 3,740 9. 448 11. 216 13. 253 15. 368
17. 374 19. 392 21. 270 23. 10,488 25. 166,786 27. 791,028
29. 58,625 31. 203,912 33. 4,707 35. 1,035 37. 5,781
39. 36,344 41. 31 43. 73 45. 39 47. Answers vary.
49. Answers vary.
51. (a) $12\frac{7}{9}$
    (b) After finding the appropriate combination in the right column, the sum of the associated numbers in the left column is the whole number part of the quotient; the difference between the sum in the right column and the divisor is the remainder, which you then write over the dividend to form the fractional part of the quotient.

Exercise Set 4-3

7. 11 9. 33 11. 108 13. 106 15. 311 17. 69 19. 359
21. 184 23. 37,406 25. 40,530 27. 11111_{two} 29. 1333_{six}
31. 22_{seven} 33. 1017_{nine} 35. 10110_{two} 37. 33_{five} 39. $939_{sixteen}$
41. 1042212_{five} 43. $B019_{thirteen}$ 45. 100000000_{two} 47. 111010_{two}
49. 81_{twelve} 51. 310_{four} 53. $1B6_{twelve}$ 55. 15222
57. (a) 637_{eight} 61. (a) 3775_{eight} 63. (a) 4307_{eight}
    (b) $19F_{sixteen}$ (b) $7FD_{sixteen}$ (b) $8C7_{sixteen}$
59. (a) 2731_{eight}
    (b) $5D9_{sixteen}$

65. 1101111000_{two} 67. 110101000100_{two} 69. 110010000_{two}
71. 111010001110101_{two} 73. 110101000101011_{two}
75. 1101100010_{two} 77. 101001011101_{two} 79. 110010101001011_{two}
81. 5 lb 7 oz 83. 34 yd 2 ft 8 in. 85. STOP 87. CLASSISOVER
89. ITISRAINING 91. 13256 93. 67138 95. 44501
97. 99.
101.
103. 67.8%, 84.7%, 90.2% 105. 28.2%, 38.8%, 62.7%
107. 100%, 0%, 100% 109. 3; manufacturer's 111. 1; product
113. 7; manufacturer's 115. one symbol; same as tally system

Note that all binary numbers in problems 117 and 118 are written without the two subscript.

117. (a)

Base 10	1	2	3	4	5	6	7	8	9
Binary	1	10	11	100	101	110	111	1000	1001

Base 10	10	11	12	13	14	15	16	17	18
Binary	1010	1011	1100	1101	1110	1111	10000	10001	10010

    (b) Two digits: 2 and 3; Three digits: 4 through 7; Four digits: 8–15
    (c) Conjecture: 16–31. The binary form of 32 is 100000, making it the first one with six digits.

119. *Note that base three numbers in this problem are written without the three subscript.*
    (a)

Base 10	1	2	3	4	5	6	7	8	9
Base 3	1	2	10	11	12	20	21	22	100

Base 10	10	11	12	13	14	15	16	17	18
Base 3	101	102	110	111	112	120	121	122	200

Base 10	19	20	21	22	23	24	25	26	27
Base 3	201	202	210	211	212	220	221	222	1000

    (b) One digit: 2; Two digits: 6; Three digits: 18
    (c) Conjecture: 27–80; formula: $2 \cdot 3^{n-1}$

Exercise Set 4-4

5.

+	0	1	2
0	0	1	2
1	1	2	10
2	2	10	11

7.

×	0	1	2	3
0	0	0	0	0
1	0	1	2	3
2	0	2	10	12
3	0	3	12	21

9. 121_{four} 11. $B843_{fourteen}$ 13. 2020_{six} 15. 121122_{nine} 17. 1014_{five}
19. 43_{seven} 21. 40040_{nine} 23. 571_{twelve} 25. 3352_{six} 27. 56067_{nine}
29. $3976A_{twelve}$ 31. 1501220_{six} 33. 482_{nine} remainder 2_{nine}
35. 230_{five} remainder 3_{five} 37. 131_{five} 39. $1BD_{fourteen}$ 41. 10000_{two}
43. $403_{sixteen}$ 45. 1001_{two} 47. $4DCA_{sixteen}$ 49. 110010_{two}
51. $2894_{sixteen}$ 53. 11_{two} remainder 10_{two} 55. $B23_{sixteen}$ remainder $2_{sixteen}$
57. WORKHARD 59. MICHAELISASPY 61. L
63. G 65. 01000100 01001111 01010010 01001101
67. 01010101 01001110 01001001 01001111 01001110 69. base 8
71. Yes, but only if you're adding more than two numbers. You would only carry more than 1 if the sum is at least twice the base: that can't happen if you're adding two numerals from the base number system, each of which is always less than the base.
73. ♠ = 0, ♦ = 1, ♥ = 2
75. ♣ = 0, ♥ = 1, ♠ = 2, ♦ = 3

Review Exercises

1. 1,000,221 3. 681 5. 419 7. 2,604 9. 118
11. 13.
15. DIII 17. 19.
21.
23. 1990 25. XXXIV 27. 276 29. 756 31. 330 33. 156
35. 1,955 37. 365,687 39. 2,542 41. 13,965 43. 119
45. 17,327 47. 59 49. 19,481 51. 1024_{six} 53. 2663_{nine}
55. 1313_{four} 57. 12514_{seven}
59. (a) 733_{eight} 61. (a) 1547_{eight}
    (b) $1DB_{sixteen}$ (b) $367_{sixteen}$
63. 111011010100_{two} 65. 1010010110110011_{two}
67. 16.9%, 37.6%, 87.1% 69. 251_{nine} 71. $15AB6_{twelve}$ 73. 331_{four}
75. 21331_{nine} 77. $4C698_{sixteen}$ 79. 342_{eight} remainder 6_{eight}

Chapter 4 Test

1. 2,000,312 3. 1966 5. 5,408 7.
9. 八百七十三 11. 221 13. 267,904 15. 17,375 17. 103 19. 28,474
21. 6362_{nine} 23. 110000_{two} 25. 621_{twelve} 27. 331006_{eight}
29. 111011010100_{two}; $10100110110110010010_{two}$
31. $14B25_{twelve}$ 33. 10010111_{two} 35. 14223_{five} 37. 121_{three}

CHAPTER 5: THE REAL NUMBER SYSTEM

Exercise Set 5-1

7. 1, 2, 4, 8, 16 9. 1, 2, 3, 6, 7, 9, 14, 18, 21, 42, 63, 126
11. 1, 2, 4, 8, 16, 32 13. 1, 2, 5, 7, 10, 14, 35, 70
15. 1, 2, 3, 4, 6, 8, 12, 16, 24, 32, 48, 96 17. 1, 17
19. 1, 2, 4, 8, 16, 32, 64 21. 1, 3, 5, 7, 15, 21, 35, 105
23. 1, 2, 7, 14, 49, 98 25. 1, 71 27. 3, 6, 9, 12, 15
29. 10, 20, 30, 40, 50 31. 15, 30, 45, 60, 75 33. 17, 34, 51, 68, 85
35. 1, 2, 3, 4, 5 37. $2^2 \times 5$ 39. $2^4 \times 3$ 41. 67 is prime
43. $2^3 \times 5^2$ 45. $2 \times 3^3 \times 7$ 47. $3 \times 5^2 \times 11$ 49. $2^6 \times 5$
51. $3 \times 5^2 \times 29$ 53. $2^3 \times 5 \times 11$ 55. 5×103 57. 3 59. 1
61. 6 63. 21 65. 220 67. 12 69. 6 71. 12 73. 42
75. 10 77. 35 79. 126 81. 150 83. 630 85. 308 87. 120
89. 72 91. 1,040 93. 4 students 95. 72 minutes

97. 6 members per team; 5 female teams, 6 male teams   **99.** noon
101. 4 groups of Republicans, 5 groups of Democrats, 7 groups of Independents
103. 221 years   **105.** 120 fps   **107.** 150 fps
109. The only even prime number is 2.
111.
3 + 1 = 4   7 + 7 = 14
3 + 3 = 6   3 + 13 = 16
3 + 5 = 8   5 + 13 = 18
5 + 5 = 10   3 + 17 = 20
5 + 7 = 12
113. Answers vary, 13.
115. (a) 3, 7, 11   (b) 2, 3, 5, 6, 9, 10   (c) None   (d) 3, 5, 9

Exercise Set 5-2
9. 8   **11.** 10   **13.** 8   **15.** -10 **17.** 0   **19.** $<$ **21.** $>$ **23.** $>$
25. $<$ **27.** $<$ **29.** -1 **31.** 9   **33.** -11 **35.** -123 **37.** -33
39. 78   **41.** -65 **43.** 28   **45.** -68 **47.** -378 **49.** -24 **51.** -36
53. 42   **55.** 340   **57.** 0   **59.** 8   **61.** -5 **63.** -4 **65.** 7   **67.** 1
69. 0   **71.** Undefined   **73.** 0   **75.** 111   **77.** 51   **79.** 36   **81.** 6
83. -758 **85.** -56 **87.** 59   **89.** -492 **91.** \$1,180   **93.** 1,399 rats
95. 8 inches
97. DC: 16,273; Texas: 529,120; Utah: 53,337; Michigan: $-7,448$; Rhode Island: $-1,265$; Puerto Rico: $-19,099$
99. 7,000 pounds   **101.** 1.3%   **103.** 3.96%
105. No general statements can be made.
107. Answers vary.   **109.** Answers vary.

Exercise Set 5-3
9. $\frac{1}{6}$ **11.** $\frac{7}{10}$ **13.** $\frac{5}{8}$ **15.** $\frac{7}{8}$ **17.** $\frac{5}{9}$ **19.** 7/5   **21.** $\frac{15}{8}$ **23.** $\frac{38}{48}$ **25.** 189
27. 54   **29.** 3,195   **31.** $-\frac{1}{6}$ **33.** $-\frac{37}{24}$ or $-1\frac{13}{24}$ **35.** $\frac{7}{24}$ **37.** $\frac{7}{6}$ or $1\frac{1}{6}$
39. $\frac{7}{10}$ **41.** $-\frac{1}{16}$ **43.** $\frac{11}{12}$ **45.** $\frac{3}{4}$ **47.** $\frac{7}{36}$ **49.** $\frac{43}{64}$ **51.** $\frac{121}{1,728}$
53. 0.2   **55.** $0.66\ldots$ or $0.\overline{6}$ **57.** 2.25   **59.** $0.3055\ldots$ or $0.30\overline{5}$
61. 0.75   **63.** 0.9411764705882352   **65.** $\frac{3}{25}$ **67.** $\frac{3}{8}$ **69.** $\frac{863}{200}$
71. $\frac{7}{9}$ **73.** $\frac{6}{11}$ **75.** $\frac{210}{99}$ **77.** $\frac{34}{75}$ **79.** $-\frac{14}{39}$ **81.** $-\frac{4}{251}$
83. 171 miles   **85.** $\frac{1}{7}$ **87.** 75   **89.** 4,580   **91.** 12 feet   **93.** $\frac{3}{8}$
95. $1\frac{1}{4}$ cups of flour and $\frac{1}{3}$ cup of sugar   **97.** $\frac{9}{200}$ **99.** $\frac{3}{20}$ **101.** $\frac{47}{100}$
103. Any common denominator will do.
105. This question is a paradox, an answer of yes or no leads to a contradiction.
107. Add the fractions and divide by two.
109. All three pairs of numbers are equal, even thought most people fill in "less than" for each in part (a).
111. Answers vary.   **113.** Answers vary.

Exercise Set 5-4
9. rational   **11.** irrational   **13.** irrational   **15.** 3 and 4
17. 9 and 11   **19.** 14 and 15   **21.** 5.477   **23.** 37.829   **25.** -6.481
27. $2\sqrt{6}$ **29.** $4\sqrt{5}$ **31.** $\sqrt{30}$ **33.** $20\sqrt{5}$ **35.** $30\sqrt{7}$ **37.** $15\sqrt{2}$
39. $-10\sqrt{7}$ **41.** $2\sqrt{5}$ **43.** $3\sqrt{30}$ **45.** $24\sqrt{3}$ **47.** $\sqrt{30}$ **49.** $2\sqrt{2}$
51. $12\sqrt{7}$ **53.** $-7\sqrt{3}$ **55.** $-2\sqrt{3}$ **57.** $4\sqrt{5}$ **59.** $-6\sqrt{5}$
61. $18\sqrt{2}$ **63.** $\sqrt{2}+8\sqrt{3}$ **65.** $10\sqrt{10}-4\sqrt{2}$ **67.** $7\sqrt{15}$
69. $-108\sqrt{6}$ **71.** $588\sqrt{2}$ **73.** $\frac{\sqrt{5}}{5}$ **75.** $\frac{\sqrt{6}}{2}$ **77.** $\sqrt{\frac{21}{14}}$
79. $\frac{21\sqrt{118}}{59}$ **81.** $\frac{\sqrt{6}}{6}$ **83.** $\sqrt{9}+\sqrt{16}=3+4\neq5=\sqrt{25}$
85. $\sqrt{40}+\sqrt{40}\approx6.32+6.32\neq8.94\approx\sqrt{80}$
87. 3 seconds   **89.** 9.2 seconds
91. 3.5 seconds, 2.5 seconds, the difference is 1 second.
93. 20 volts   **95.** 141.4 volts   **97.** 4π seconds   **99.** 0.8 foot
101. The irrational numbers are not closed under multiplication. The rational numbers are closed under multiplication.
103. You cannot compute the square root of a negative number because there is no number that, when squared, is negative.
105. Answers vary.   **107.** (a) -2 (b) -4 (c) Undefined (d) -2
109. If you cube a negative number, you're multiplying it by itself three times, and when you multiply three negatives, the result is negative. So it is possible for the cube of a number to be negative. But the square of a number can't be negative, so there is no square root for any negative number.
111. (a) 1.774 (b) 1.647 (c) 1.67 (d) 1.781
(e) 1.75; explanations vary

Exercise Set 5-5
9. Integer, rational, real   **11.** Rational, real   **13.** Rational, real
15. Irrational, real   **17.** Irrational, real   **19.** Rational, real
21. Natural, whole, integer, rational, real
23. Natural, whole, integer, rational, real
25. Closure property of addition   **27.** Commutative property of addition
29. Commutative property of multiplication
31. Distributive property   **33.** Inverse property of multiplication
35. Commutative property of addition
37. Identity property of addition
39. Commutative property of multiplication
41. Distributive; commutative property of addition; distributive property
43. Addition, multiplication   **45.** Addition, subtraction, multiplication
47. None   **49.** 27.46, overweight   **51.** 23.73, normal   **53.** 19.02, normal
55. 38.10, obese   **57.** not commutative   **59.** commutative
61. associative   **63.** associative
65. The results are not the same, subtraction is not associative.
67. The results are not the same, addition does not distribute over multiplication.
69. You can write the difference as a sum: $b+(-c)$. Then a times $-c$ is the same as $-ac$.
71. (a) $(3+7)^2=10^2=100$; $3^2+7^2=9+49=58$. You cannot "distribute" an exponent.
(b) $\frac{25-10}{5}=\frac{15}{5}=3$; $\frac{25}{5}-\frac{10}{5}=\frac{15}{5}=3$ "Distributing" the denominator worked. This makes sense because we can write $\frac{25-10}{5}$ as $\frac{1}{5}(25-10)$, in which case it's a multiplication and the distributive property applies.
73. You can write subtraction as addition of the opposite and the opposite of a real number is also a real number.
75. It makes it look like there are real numbers that are neither rational nor irrational: the outside rectangle shouldn't be there.

Exercise Set 5-6
7. 243   **9.** 1   **11.** 1   **13.** $\frac{1}{243}$ **15.** $\frac{1}{64}$ **17.** $3^6=729$
19. $4^7=16,384$ **21.** $3^2=9$ **23.** $12^1=12$
25. $5^6=15,625$ **27.** $\frac{1}{3^2}=\frac{1}{9}$ **29.** $\frac{1}{3^5}=\frac{1}{52,521,875}$ **31.** $\frac{1}{2^2}=\frac{1}{4}$
33. $\frac{1}{100^3}=\frac{1}{1,000,000}$ **35.** $\frac{1}{3^2}=\frac{1}{9}$ **37.** a^{20} **39.** $\frac{1}{m^3}$
41. a^{14} **43.** x^7 **45.** 6.25×10^8 **47.** 7.3×10^{-3} **49.** 5.28×10^{11}
51. 6.18×10^{-6} **53.** 4.32×10^4 **55.** 59,000   **57.** 0.0000375
59. 2,400   **61.** 0.000003   **63.** -0.0000000146
65. $6\times10^{10}=60,000,000,000$ **67.** $2.67\times10^{-7}=0.000000267$
69. $8.8\times10^{-3}=0.0088$ **71.** $1.5\times10^{-9}=0.0000000015$
73. $2\times10^2=200$ **75.** $6\times10^0=6$ **77.** $6\times10^{-2}=0.06$
79. 2.58×10^{15} **81.** 2.4×10^1 **83.** 1×10^{-12}
85. $\frac{80}{d^2}$; it goes from 80% to 20%, 8.9% and then 5%.
87. 1.116×10^8 miles   **89.** 56%   **91.** 2.4696×10^{13} miles
93. 7.96×10^{-4} light years   **95.** 10 billion   **97.** 421 million miles
99. \$112,493,150.70 per day   **101.** 5,261,905
103. Each entry is half the previous entry so the last three entries are 1, $\frac{1}{2}$, and $\frac{1}{4}$.
105. Answers vary.
107. 66,621 miles per hour (using a 365.25 day year); it would take about 2 minutes and 13 seconds.

Exercise Set 5-7
9. (a) 1, 7, 13, 19, 25   (b) 6   (c) 67   (d) 408
11. (a) $-9, -12, -15, -18, -21$ (b) -3 (c) -42 (d) -306
13. (a) $\frac{1}{4}, \frac{5}{8}, 1, \frac{11}{8}, \frac{7}{4}$ (b) $\frac{3}{8}$ (c) $\frac{35}{8}$ (d) $\frac{111}{4}$
15. (a) $4, \frac{11}{3}, \frac{10}{3}, 3, \frac{8}{3}$ (b) $-\frac{1}{3}$ (c) $\frac{1}{3}$ (d) 26
17. (a) 5, 13, 21, 29, 37   (b) 8   (c) 93   (d) 588
19. (a) 50, 48, 46, 44, 42   (b) -2 (c) 28   (d) 468
21. (a) $\frac{1}{8}, \frac{19}{24}, \frac{35}{24}, \frac{17}{8}, \frac{67}{24}$ (b) $\frac{2}{3}$ (c) $\frac{179}{24}$ (d) $\frac{91}{2}$
23. (a) 0.6, 1.6, 2.6, 3.6, 4.6   (b) 1   (c) 11.6   (d) 73.2
25. (a) 12, 24, 48, 96, 192   (b) 2   (c) 24, 576   (d) 49,140
27. (a) $-5, -\frac{5}{4}, -\frac{5}{16}, -\frac{5}{64}, -\frac{5}{256}$ (b) $\frac{1}{4}$ (c) $-\frac{5}{4,194,304}$ (d) ≈-6.7
29. (a) $\frac{1}{6}, -1, 6, -36, 216$ (b) -6 (c) 60,466,176   (d) $-\frac{310,968,905}{6}$
31. (a) $100, -25, \frac{25}{4}, -\frac{25}{16}, \frac{25}{64}$ (b) $-\frac{1}{4}$ (c) $-\frac{25}{1,048,576}$ (d) ≈80

33. (a) 4, 12, 36, 108, 324 (b) 3 (c) 708,588 (d) 1,062,880
35. (a) $\frac{1}{2}, \frac{1}{4}, \frac{1}{8}, \frac{1}{16}, \frac{1}{32}$ (b) $\frac{1}{2}$ (c) ≈ 0.000244 (d) ≈ 0.9998
37. (a) $-3, 15, -75, 375, -1,875$ (b) -5 (c) 146,484,375
(d) 122,070,312
39. (a) 1, 3, 9, 27, 81 (b) 3 (c) 177,147 (d) 265,720
41. geometric **43.** neither **45.** arithmetic **47.** arithmetic
49. $3 \cdot 4^{n-1}$ **51.** $8n + 3$ **53.** $50 - 10n$ **55.** $\frac{0.5}{5^{n-1}}$ **57.** $\frac{5 \cdot 3^{n-1}}{4^{n-1}}$
59. $4(0.6)^{n-1}$ **61.** 1,020.75 **63.** 795 **65.** (a) $500 (b) $13,000
67. no **69.** $18,000 **71.** 160 ft **73.** $3,766.11 **75.** 8 questions
77. First job pays $5,300.65 more in ten years.
79. Yes, $2,438.81 higher.
81. $a_1 = \frac{3}{10}$ and $r = \frac{1}{10}$. The sum is $\frac{1}{3}$. **83.** Answers vary.

Review Exercises

1. 1, 2, 3, 4, 5, 6, 10, 12, 15, 20, 30, 60
3. 1, 2, 4, 5, 10, 19, 20, 38, 76, 95, 190, 380 **5.** 4, 8, 12, 16, 20
7. 9, 18, 27, 36, 45 **9.** $2^5 \times 3$ **11.** 2×5^3 **13.** 2; 30
15. 20; 1,200 **17.** 198 months, or 16.5 years **19.** -14 **21.** -4
23. 44 **25.** 89 **27.** -157 **29.** $\frac{15}{19}$ **31.** $\frac{53}{6}$ **33.** $\frac{3}{20}$ **35.** $-\frac{25}{14}$
37. $\frac{51}{80}$ **39.** $\frac{21}{16}$ or $1\frac{5}{16}$ **41.** 1 **43.** $-\frac{19}{48}$ **45.** $0.85\overline{7142}$ **47.** $\frac{11}{16}$ **49.** $\frac{23}{90}$
51. NFL: 12; MLB: 8; NBA and NHL: 16 **53.** $4\sqrt{7}$
55. $\frac{\sqrt{15}}{6}$ **57.** $22\sqrt{2}$ **59.** 2 **61.** 8
63. Rational, real **65.** Irrational, real
67. Natural, whole, integer, rational, real
69. Commutative property of addition
71. Distributive property
73. 1 **75.** 117,649 **77.** 6,561 **79.** $\frac{1}{7,776}$ **81.** 2.59×10^{10}
83. 4.8×10^{-4} **85.** 2,330,000,000 **87.** 0.0000088
89. 6×10^{-8} **91.** 1.41×10^4 seconds or about 3.9 hours
93. $-\frac{1}{5}, \frac{3}{10}, \frac{4}{5}, \frac{13}{10}, \frac{9}{5}, \frac{23}{10}; a_9 = \frac{19}{5}, S_9 = \frac{81}{5}$
95. $-\frac{2}{5}, \frac{1}{5}, -\frac{1}{10}, \frac{1}{20}, -\frac{1}{40}, \frac{1}{80}; a_9 = -\frac{1}{640}, S_9 = -\frac{171}{640}$
97. The profit for the sixth year is $25,525.63, and the total earnings for the six years are $136,038.26

Chapter 5 Test

1. Integer, rational, real **3.** Rational, real **5.** Irrational, real
7. 14; 168 **9.** $\frac{3}{7}$ **11.** $\frac{16}{25}$ **13.** $9\sqrt{3}$ **15.** -5 **17.** $-\frac{31}{126}$
19. -8 **21.** $2\sqrt{2}$ **23.** $\frac{7}{8}$
25. Commutative property of addition
27. Identity property of addition
29. Associative property of multiplication
31. 4,096 **33.** 1 **35.** $\frac{1}{32}$ **37.** 2.36×10^{-3} **39.** -0.00006 **41.** 3×10^3
43. $\frac{3}{4}, -\frac{1}{8}, \frac{1}{48}, -\frac{1}{288}, \frac{1}{1,728}, -\frac{1}{10,368}, \frac{1}{62,208}$
$a_{15} \approx 9.57 \times 10^{-12}, S_{15} \approx 0.643$
45. $320; $620

CHAPTER 6: TOPICS IN ALGEBRA

Exercises Set 6-1

9. $11x$ **11.** $-18y$ **13.** $9p - q - 17$ **15.** $11x^2 - x + 5$
17. $30x - 35$ **19.** $-48x + 40$ **21.** $-26x - 50$
23. $-15x^2 - 21x + 51$ **25.** $25x - 44y - 5$ **27.** $-2x^2 - 10x - 2$
29. $-4x^2y + 18xy^2 - 9$ **31.** $13m - 9$ **33.** $\frac{7}{2}yz - \frac{3}{4}$
35. $31m - \frac{15}{2}$ **37.** $-\frac{81}{20}xz + \frac{21}{4}$ **39.** $-59.4tz + 94.8$
41. $0.25tz$ **43.** 83 **45.** 79 **47.** 466 **49.** 136 **51.** 997
53. 205 **55.** $\frac{2}{5}$ **57.** $127\frac{7}{12}$ **59.** $\frac{47}{2}$ **61.** $-\frac{1}{8}$ **63.** 40.6
65. -27.5 **67.** 376.8 sq in. **69.** $6,050 **71.** 267.95 mm^3
73. $31,876.96 **75.** 604.45 **77.** $100
79. The 10-hour worker will make three more defective chips.
81. 1.47 **83.** 312,375 **85.** 1.8×10^{11} joules
87. 3,540 feet; 3,680 feet; 620 feet; It hits the ground in less than 40 seconds.
89. $3,528, $3,886.80, $3,377.40 **91.** $0.07x + 2,000$; $596.75 less
93. $1.05x$; $1,258.95
95. (a) $0.65x$; $0.690625x$
(b) $58.18; $61.81
97. 95.5 mg **99.** $P = 0.03x^2 + 27.3x - 633$
101. $P = -0.2x^2 + 6.14x + 223$

Exercise Set 6-2

9. not linear **11.** linear **13.** not linear **15.** linear **17.** yes
19. no **21.** yes **23.** No **25.** $\{26\}$ **27.** $\{45\}$ **29.** $\{3\}$
31. $\{-12\}$ **33.** $\{6\}$ **35.** $\{16\}$ **37.** $\{20\}$ **39.** $\{4\}$ **41.** $\{\frac{20}{3}\}$
43. $\{3\}$ **45.** $\{54\}$ **47.** $\{-\frac{7}{31}\}$ **49.** $\{-\frac{8}{5}\}$ **51.** $\{36\}$ **53.** $\{\frac{76}{3}\}$
55. $\{\frac{180}{7}\}$ **57.** $\{\frac{1}{7}\}$ **59.** $\{\frac{30}{11}\}$ **61.** $\{\frac{4}{9}\}$ **63.** $\{\frac{252}{17}\}$ **65.** $\{\frac{9}{4}\}$
67. $\{3\}$ **69.** $\{-\frac{63}{4}\}$ **71.** $y = \frac{3x+4}{2}$ **73.** $x = \frac{7y+16}{5}$
75. $y = \frac{9-7x}{2}$ **77.** identity; $\{x \mid x$ is a real number$\}$
79. contradiction; $\varnothing$ **81.** contradiction; $\varnothing$
83. identity; $\{x \mid x$ is a real number$\}$
85. $L = \frac{Rd^2}{k}$ **87.** $h = \frac{V}{\pi r^2}$ **89.** $h = \frac{V}{lw}$ **91.** $a = \frac{2d}{t^2}$
93. $H = \frac{4P - S - 2D - 3T}{4}$ **95.** $b = 2a - c$
97. $55.50 **99.** about 1,571 minutes **101.** 81.7
103. 65 **105.** 62.5 watts **107.** 9 ohms
109. (a)

	'91 – '92	'96 – '97	'01 – '02	'06 – '07
Equation	2.85	2.90	2.95	3.00
Actual	2.85	2.90	2.97	3.01

(b) 2036; 2056 (c) Answers vary.

111. (a) 820,755; 17.6 years (b) 2037 (c) Answers vary.
113. Dividing is the same as multiplying by the reciprocal and subtracting is the same as adding the opposite.
115. This could introduce solutions that weren't solutions before, or eliminate solutions that were solutions before.
117. Answers vary.

Exercise Set 6-3

5. $x - 3$ **7.** $x + 9$ **9.** $11 - x$ **11.** $x - 6$ **13.** $\frac{1}{2}x + x$ or $\frac{3}{2}x$
15. $\frac{3x}{6}$ or $(3x) \div 6$ **17.** $\frac{x}{14}$ or $x \div 14$ **19.** $3(x + \pi)$ **21.** $\frac{2x}{x+8} - 3x$
23. $(5x + 3y)^2$ **25.** 8 **27.** 16 **29.** 17 and 11 **31.** 12 **33.** 28
35. There are 27 students in one section and 30 students in the other section.
37. $18,295 **39.** $20.30 **41.** 18 games **43.** $270
45. $1.25 billion on costumes and $1.93 billion on candy
47. 12 **49.** $36,000 **51.** $40 **53.** No **55.** $563.20
57. Paul 10.2%, Santorum 38.5%, Romney 51.3%
59. $1,700 + 900x$; 3.67 fugitives per month
61. wind chill = temperature $-$ 1.5(wind speed); 3° **63.** 60.3 mph
65. (a) $P = 8.775x + 11.856y$, where x is hours worked at the first job, and y is hours worked at the second.
(b) 11.5 hours

Exercise Set 6-4

7. $\frac{18}{28} = \frac{9}{14}$ **9.** $\frac{14}{32} = \frac{7}{16}$ **11.** $\frac{12}{15} = \frac{4}{5}$ **13.** $\frac{3}{8}$ **15.** $\frac{60}{30} = \frac{2}{1}$ **17.** $x = \frac{135}{14}$
19. $x = 35$ **21.** $x = 10$ **23.** $x = \frac{31}{3}$ **25.** $x = \frac{21}{4}$ **27.** 15 cones
29. $\frac{14}{3}$ inches **31.** 4 gallons **33.** 103 or 104 **35.** 37 or 38
37. 30 feet **39.** 20 professors **41.** 153,925,000 **43.** 96,734
45. $1,200 **47.** 298 lb **49.** 117 lb **51.** 24 lb **53.** 3 lb
55. 9 more students
57. To solve a proportion, you can cross multiply.
59. 25 pounds for $7.49 is a better buy.
61. 7 ounces for $1.99 is a better buy.
63. 34.5 ounces for $7.49 is a better buy.
65. (a) a varies inversely with the square of d.
(b) 250/9 or $27\frac{7}{9}$
(c) No; you can't find the individual constant of proportionality relating a and b.
67. (a) Inversely; too much time on Facebook means less time studying.
(b) Directly; bigger apartments are likely to cost more.
69. (a) Directly; as the age of a car goes up, it tends to have more mechanical problems.
(b) Directly; it is a documented fact that areas with a depressed economy have more crime.

Exercise Set 6-5

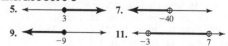

13.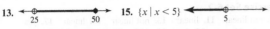

13. (number line from 25 to 50) **15.** $\{x \mid x < 5\}$

17. $\{y \mid y \geq 6\}$

19. $\{x \mid x < -35\}$

21. $\{x \mid x < 27\}$

23. $\{t \mid t > -3\}$

25. $\{z \mid z \geq 12\}$

27. $\{x \mid x \geq -8\}$

29. $\{x \mid x \leq 21\}$

31. $\{y \mid y \leq 8\frac{2}{5}\}$

33. $\{y \mid y \leq \frac{16}{7}\}$

35. $\{x \mid x < 14\}$

37. $\{n \mid n \leq -10\frac{3}{5}\}$

39. $\{x \mid x \geq -46\frac{1}{2}\}$

41. $\{y \mid y \leq -\frac{12}{11}\}$

43. $\{x \mid x \leq -\frac{13}{45}\}$

45. $\{t \mid t \geq -\frac{46}{65}\}$

47. $\{x \mid -7 \leq x < 8\}$

49. $\{y \mid -3 < y < 3\}$

51. $\{z \mid -5 \leq z < \frac{5}{4}\}$

53. $\{x \mid -1 < x < \frac{3}{2}\}$

55. $\{y \mid \frac{8}{11} < y \leq \frac{42}{11}\}$

57. $\{x \mid \frac{15}{2} \leq x \leq \frac{75}{2}\}$

59. Texas, Florida, Kansas, Colorado   **61.** Missouri, West Virginia
63. Maryland, California, Pennsylvania, Missouri, West Virginia
65. $x \geq 6$; x is the number of hours spent working out.
67. $x < 6,500$; x is tuition for next year.
69. $46 \leq x \leq 98$; x is the test score.   **71.** \$435.51 or more
73. at least 93   **75.** Up to \$156.25   **77.** at least 312.5 miles
79. Between zero and 944 minutes   **81.** at most \$76,923.08
83. Any height less than 6.6 feet will work.   **85.** 88% to 100%
87. between 20 and 30 hours
89. You can always move the variables to the side of the inequality that will leave the coefficient positive.
91. Answers vary.   **93.** Answers vary.   **95.** Answers vary.

Exercise Set 6-6
7. $3x^2 + 2x - 5 = 0$; $a = 3, b = 2, c = -5$
9. $30x^2 - 10 = 0$; $a = 30, b = 0, c = -10$
11. $2x^2 + 5x = 0$; $a = 2, b = 5, c = 0$
13. $x^2 + 16x + 63$ **15.** $y^2 - 17y + 70$ **17.** $x^2 - 7x - 120$
19. $14x^2 - 67x + 63$ **21.** $15z^2 - 19z - 56$ **23.** $\{-4, 3\}$
25. $\{-3, 17\}$ **27.** $\{-27, 3\}$ **29.** $\{3, 5\}$ **31.** $\{-3, \frac{7}{2}\}$ **33.** $\{-\frac{4}{3}, \frac{3}{2}\}$
35. $\{-\frac{4}{3}, \frac{3}{2}\}$ **37.** $\{-\frac{3}{5}, 6\}$ **39.** $\{-3, 2\}$ **41.** $\{-\frac{1}{2}, -4\}$

43. $\left\{\frac{-1 + \sqrt{13}}{6}, \frac{-1 - \sqrt{13}}{6}\right\}$ **45.** $\{-\frac{3}{2}, 4\}$ **47.** $\left\{\frac{-7 - \sqrt{111}}{6}, \frac{-7 + \sqrt{111}}{6}\right\}$
49. $\{-\frac{13}{3}, \frac{4}{7}\}$ **51.** $\left\{\frac{-5 + \sqrt{37}}{2}, \frac{-5 - \sqrt{37}}{2}\right\}$ **53.** $\left\{\frac{21 + \sqrt{321}}{2}, \frac{21 - \sqrt{321}}{2}\right\}$
55. $\left\{\frac{7 + \sqrt{199}}{5}, \frac{7 - \sqrt{199}}{5}\right\}$ **57.** $\left\{\frac{-13 + \sqrt{73}}{4}, \frac{-13 - \sqrt{73}}{4}\right\}$
59. $\left\{\frac{-8 + 7\sqrt{6}}{10}, \frac{-8 - 7\sqrt{6}}{10}\right\}$ **61.** $\{9.06, 0.51\}$
63. 16 and 18 or -18 and -16 **65.** 9 seconds
67. 16 and 10 inches   **69.** 9 square feet   **71.** 40 gift baskets
73. 5 feet by 21 feet   **75.** 6 feet   **77.** 19.7 mph
79. About 1.17 hours
81. horizontal distance 407 feet and vertical distance 419 feet
83. Since $x = 1$, $x - 1 = 0$. Division by 0 is undefined.
85. Answers vary.
87. (a) $x = \frac{5}{2}$
   (b) When the discriminant is zero, there is one real solution.
89. (a) The first one cannot be solved using factoring; the other two can. When the discriminant is a perfect square, a quadratic expression factors.

(b)
If the discriminant is ...	Description of solutions
Negative	No real solutions
Zero	One real solution
Positive	Two real solutions
A perfect square	Two rational solutions

(c) Because it helps to discriminate between types of solutions to quadratic equations.

Review Exercises
1. $-2x + 5y - 7$ **3.** $7x - 36$ **5.** $3x + 31$ **7.** $\frac{79}{4} - \frac{1}{2}$ **11.** 120
13. $\{-10\}$ **15.** $\{-13\}$ **17.** $\{67\}$ **19.** $\{12\}$ **21.** $\{\frac{8}{3}\}$
23. $c = P - a - b$ **25.** $y = \frac{xz}{z + x}$ **27.** $h = \frac{2A}{b}$ **29.** $4n + 3$ **31.** $\frac{18}{5x} - \frac{3}{4}$
33. 6 pounds of mixed soy nuts and 8 pounds of Asian trail mix
35. About 1,429 mg   **37.** 18   **39.** $\frac{82 \text{ miles}}{15 \text{ gallons}}$ **41.** $\frac{4 \text{ months}}{24 \text{ months}} = \frac{1}{6}$ **43.** $x = 9$
45. $\{10\}$ **47.** 34 people   **49.** 25.5   **51.** 9 pints   **53.** \$450   **55.** $y > 7$
57. $x \geq -\frac{27}{10}$ **59.** $\{x \mid -\frac{11}{3} \leq x < 6\}$ **61.** Between 13 and 28 months
63. $\{-13, 2\}$ **65.** $\{\frac{1}{2}, -3\}$ **67.** $\{\frac{3}{2}, 3\}$ **69.** $\left\{\frac{7 + \sqrt{129}}{10}, \frac{7 - \sqrt{129}}{10}\right\}$
71. $\left\{\frac{2 + \sqrt{11}}{3}, \frac{2 - \sqrt{11}}{3}\right\}$ **73.** $\left\{\frac{-3 - 3\sqrt{551}}{55}, \frac{-3 + 3\sqrt{551}}{55}\right\}$ **75.** 8 seconds

Chapter 6 Test
1. $5x - 10y + 5$ **3.** 91   **5.** $\{\frac{9}{7}\}$ **7.** $\{\frac{14}{61}\}$ **9.** $y = \frac{10 - 3x}{2}$
11. $\{x \mid x \geq \frac{26}{37}\}$ **13.** $x = 4$ **15.** $2x^2 - 13x - 24$ **17.** $\{-3, 17\}$
19. $\{-\frac{3}{2}, \frac{4}{3}\}$ **21.** $\{-1, \frac{3}{3}\}$ **23.** \$2,466.67
25. 200 vibrations per second   **27.** -26 and -24 or 24 and 26

CHAPTER 7: ADDITIONAL TOPICS IN ALGEBRA
Exercise Set 7-1
9. 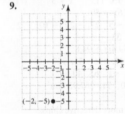   **11.**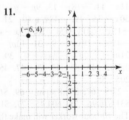

13. 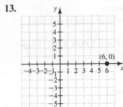   **15.**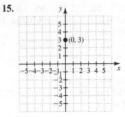

17.

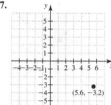

19.

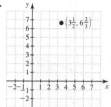

21.

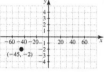

23. $(-4, 2)$ **25.** $(3, 4)$

Note: answers for 27–30 are approximate.

27. $(-3, -3)$ **29.** $\left(3\frac{1}{2}, 0\right)$

31.

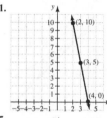

33.

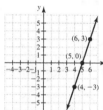

35.

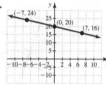

37.

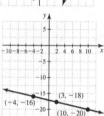

39.

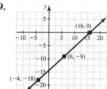

41. 1 **43.** $-\frac{7}{4}$ **45.** $-\frac{34}{19}$ **47.** $-\frac{43}{16}$

49. x intercept $= (8, 0)$; y intercept $= (0, 6)$

51. x intercept $= (-6, 0)$; y intercept $= (0, -5)$

53. x intercept $= (72, 0)$; y intercept $= (0, -27)$

55. x intercept $= (-40, 0)$; y intercept $= (0, -56)$

57. $m = -\frac{7}{5}$, y int $= (0, 7)$ **59.** $m = \frac{1}{4}$, y int $= (0, -4)$

$y = -\frac{7}{5}x + 7$ $y = \frac{1}{4}x - 4$

61. $y = \frac{3}{8}x - \frac{25}{2}$, $m = \frac{3}{8}$,
y int $= \left(0, -\frac{25}{2}\right)$

63. $y = -\frac{2}{3}x + \frac{4}{3}$, $m = -\frac{2}{3}$,
y int $= \left(0, \frac{4}{3}\right)$

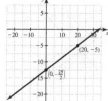
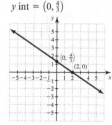

65.

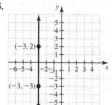

67.

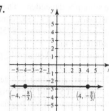

69. $y = 6.5x + 50$; (a) $69.50, (b) $82.50, (c) $115

71. $y = 0.2x + 26$; (a) $32, (b) $37, (c) $70

73. $y = 167 + 13x$ where x is years after 2009; 310; 2027

75. $y = 17{,}524 - 797x$; 10,351; 2017   **77.** $y = 36.3 + 1.1x$; 2062

79. (a) $181.153 billion; $286.101 billion; $391.049 billion

(b) 2032

(c) Projected amount is $469.76 billion.

81. (a) $y = 12{,}000 + 1.73x$; $13,730

(b) No; lose $740

83. $w = 160 - 3x$; 10 months   **85.** $y = 350 - 5x$; 70 years

87. (a)

(b) The percentage either declined or stayed about the same for 20 years, from 1968 until 1988. There was a 1-year spike in 1992 but then it started to increase steadily after 1996.

89. (a)

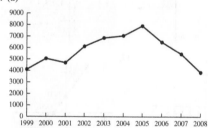

(b) Other than one down year in 2001, the number of adoptions increased steadily from 1999 to 2005 then suddenly decreased very rapidly for the next 3 years.

91. The denominator of the fraction for the slope will always be zero.

93. $D = \sqrt{(y_2 - y_1)^2 + (x_2 - x_1)^2}$

95. $y = -\frac{a}{b}x + \frac{c}{b}$; slope $= -\frac{a}{b}$; y int $= \left(0, \frac{c}{b}\right)$

97. 1980–1990: -0.25; 1990–2000: -0.05; 2000–2005: -0.48; 2005–2010: -0.14. No; rate of change varies dramatically.

Exercise Set 7-2

7. $(3, 4)$ is a solution; $(5, 10)$ is not a solution

9. $(11, -6)$ is not a solution; $\left(\frac{1}{2}, 3\right)$ is a solution.

11. $\left(24, \frac{7}{3}\right)$ is a solution; $\left(-16, \frac{10}{3}\right)$ is not a solution.

13. $(7, 0)$ **15.** $(-2, 0)$ **17.** $(2, -2)$

19. The system is inconsistent. The solution set is $\varnothing$.

21. $(-3, 3)$ **23.** $(4, -1)$ **25.** $(5, 3)$ **27.** $\left(\frac{54}{11}, \frac{16}{11}\right)$

29. The system is dependent. The solution set is $\{(x, y) \mid 3x = 5y + 16\}$.

31. The system is inconsistent. The solution set is $\varnothing$.

33. $\left(\frac{76}{21}, \frac{3}{7}\right)$ **35.** $(2, -1)$

37. The system is dependent. The solution set is $\{(x, y) \mid 5x - 2y = 11\}$.

39. The system is dependent. The solution set is $\{(x, y) \mid 4x + 8y = 32\}$.

41. $\left(-\frac{23}{11}, -\frac{8}{11}\right)$ **43.** $\left(\frac{51}{4}, 19\right)$

45. consistent; $(1, -2)$ **47.** consistent; $(7, -2)$

49. consistent; $\left(-\frac{15}{2}, -\frac{11}{2}\right)$

51. The system is dependent. The solution set is $\{(x, y) \mid 4x - y = 3\}$.

53. consistent: $\left(\frac{43}{7}, -\frac{26}{35}\right)$ **55.** consistent: $\left(\frac{6}{11}, -\frac{26}{11}\right)$

57. Starbucks: $220; campus: $350; $259 goes into checking

59. 71 adults, 21 kids

61. 10 pounds of chicken and 12 pounds of filet mignon

63. sandwich $2.19 fries $1.15

65. 322 students attending, 178 general admission

67. The tops cost $4 and the pants cost $6. **69.** $22

71. 200 carnations and 600 bagels

73. paperbacks $7.22; hard cover books $15.15

75. Answers vary. **77.** Answers vary.

79. When using graphing, sometimes only an approximate answer can be obtained. **81.** Answers vary.

83. (a) $-2x + 6z = 32$; like the first equation, the result has only x and z as variables.

    (b) $x = 2, z = 6$

    (c) $y = -3$

85. 280 microwaves, 160 stoves, and 880 dishwashers

Exercise Set 7-3

7.

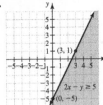

9.

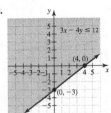

11.

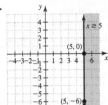

13.

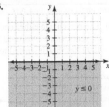

15.

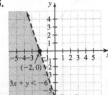

17.

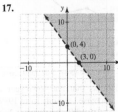

19.

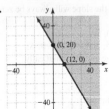

21.

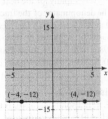

23.

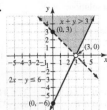

25.

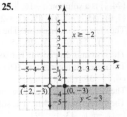

27.

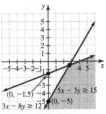

29.

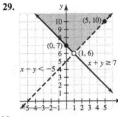

31.

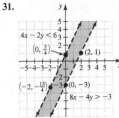

33.

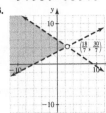

35.

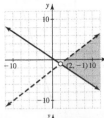

37.

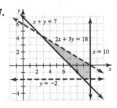

39.

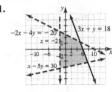

41.

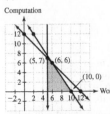

43. (a)

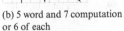
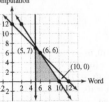

    (b) 5 word and 7 computation or 6 of each

45. w = number of wraps, p = number of pita chips.

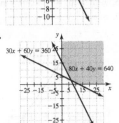

47. g = number of graduate classes, u = number of undergraduate classes.

49.

51. C = number of civil suits, M = number of malpractice suits.

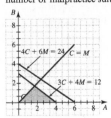

53. Answers vary. **55.** Answers vary.

Exercise Set 7-4

5. $x \le 50$; x = number of calculators

7. $x = 2y$; x = number of pens and y = number of pencils

9. $P = 85d + 130l$; d = number of desktop computers sold and l = number of laptop computers sold

11. $P = 4t + 3h$; t = number of turkeys sold and h = number of hams sold

13. $2v + 3c \le 6$; v = number of Blu-ray players assembled and c = number of handheld gaming systems assembled

15. $40x + 20y \le 240$; x = number of pendants, y = number of earrings

17. (5, 6) gives a maximum profit of $390.

19. (7, 0) gives a maximum profit of $105.

21. (0, 62) gives a maximum profit of $21,080.

23. (8, 0) gives a maximum profit of $438.

25. Maximum: 525 at (15, 15); minimum: 175 at (5, 5)

27. Maximum: 360 at (3, 4); minimum: $-4,800$ at (0, 16)

29. 20 television sets and 10 Blu-ray players

31. 50 hats and 0 scarves

33. 18 square feet of tomatoes and 12 square feet of squash

35. 4 cats and 26 dogs **37.** 100 laptops and 200 desktops

39. Answers vary. **41.** 14 item 1 and 16 item 2

Exercise Set 7-5

9. Function **11.** Function **13.** Function **15.** Function

17. Function **19.** Not a function **21.** Not a function

23. $f(3) = 17$; $f(-2) = 2$ **25.** $f(10) = 32$; $f(-10) = -48$

27. $f(0) = 0$; $f(6) = 306$ **29.** $f(-3.6) = 5.56$; $f(4.5) = 45.25$

31. $f(\frac{1}{2}) = \sqrt{5}$; $f(-2\frac{1}{4})$ is undefined **33.** $f(-\frac{1}{2}) = 7$; $f(9\frac{1}{2}) = 25$

35. Domain $\{x \mid -\infty < x < \infty\}$; Range $\{y \mid y \ge 0\}$

37. Domain $\{x \mid x \ne 2\}$; Range $\{y \mid y \ne 1\}$

39. Domain $\{x \mid x \ge 0\}$; Range $\{y \mid y \ge 3\}$

41. Domain $\{x \mid -\infty < x < \infty\}$; Range $\{y \mid -\infty < y < \infty\}$

43. Domain $\{x \mid x \ge -1\}$; Range $\{y \mid y \le -1\}$

45. Domain $\{x \mid x \le 5\}$; Range $\{y \mid y \ge 7\}$

47.  **49.**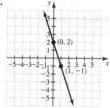

51. 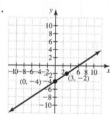 **53.**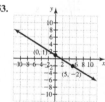

55.

57. 40% **59.** 1985 **61.** -5% **63.** 1995–2015 **65.** $P(x) = -\frac{1}{2}x + 40$

67. $88.08 for a 4-hour shift and $98.16 for an 8-hour shift

69. No, they lose $128; $2,422 **71.** $C(d) = 27 + 22d$; $181

73. $D(G) = 3G - 10$; 65 mg **75.** $d(t) = 80 + 65t$; 3 hours

77. $n(r) = 3r$; 135 minutes, or 2 hours and 15 minutes

79. $s(p) = 0.8p$; $95.82 **81.** $n(x) = \frac{2}{3}x + 4$; 24

83. $d(x) = 48 + 7.5x$; $20

85. (a) $c(p) = -20p + 1,000$

(b) No; 2nd quadrant means negative price, 4th means negative number of customers.

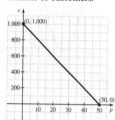

(c) 100 (d) $35 (e) (50, 0): at $50, no customers will pay.

(f) (0, 1,000); 1,000 customers will take the tour for free.

87. (a) $d(t) = 70t$

(b)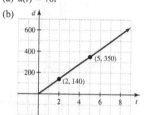

(c) 560 miles (d) 3 hours

89. $f(3) = 19$; $f(-3) = 1$;

$f(x + 3) = x^2 + 9x + 19$;

$f(x - 3) = x^2 - 3x + 1$

91. (a) [0, 120]; we're not given any information about what happened before the oven was turned on, so we'll start at time zero. I'm guessing that it will take at most an hour after the oven was turned off for it to return to room temperature.

(b) [72, 450]; the oven was at room temperature before it was turned on, which I'm guessing is 72 degrees. The oven heats to 450 degrees and doesn't go over that, and every temperature in between will be reached at some time.

(c)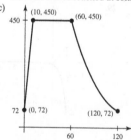

93. (a) [1, 100]; You're not going anywhere on foot until you're at least 1; after the age of 100, it's time to rest—let someone carry you.

(b) $[\frac{1}{4}, 5]$; I don't think a one-year-old could go much more than a quarter mile, and the average man in his twenties could probably make about five miles.

(c)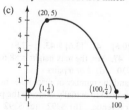

95. Function **97.** Not a function

99. If any vertical line hits the graph in more than one point the relation graphed isn't a function.

Exercise Set 7-6

11.

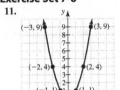

13.

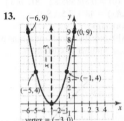
vertex = (−3, 0)

15.

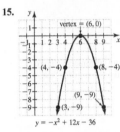
vertex = (6, 0)
$y = -x^2 + 12x - 36$

17.

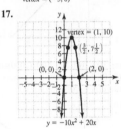
vertex = (1, 10)
$y = -10x^2 + 20x$

19.

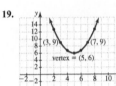
vertex = (5, 6)

21.

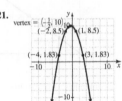
vertex = $(-\frac{1}{2}, 10)$

23.

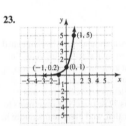

25.

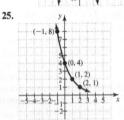

27.

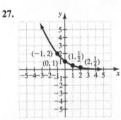

29.

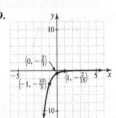

31.

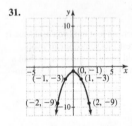

33. 3.3   **35.** 6.1   **37.** {5}   **39.** {0.6}   **41.** {3.6}   **43.** {−2.8}
45. 62 feet, 3 inches; 3.85 seconds   **47.** Yes, the max height is 88.6 feet.
49. (a) 4 pairs   (b) $146   (c) $930   (d) 2 or 6 pairs
51. (a) The most revenue is $411 and the number of price hikes needed
is −3. This means that they need to actually decrease the price
by $1.50 to maximize their revenue.   (b) $392   (c) $392
53. (a) $A = \frac{5}{8}W^2$ (b) $A = 250$ square inches and $l = 25$ inches
(c) width 4 inches; length 10 inches   (d) $A = 5w^2$
55. 4,969,507   **57.** $699.21
59. (a) $9,434.32   (b) $11,125.80

61.

Compounded	Value
Quarterly	$24,403.80
Monthly	$24,419.93
Weekly	$24,426.18
Daily	$24,427.79

More interest is paid as the number of compounding periods goes up.

63. 678 years ago, in the year 1320   **65.** 45,117 years old   **67.** 9
69. 8.7   **71.** 27.2 decibels   **73.** 65.1 decibels
75. There is no difference.   **77.** It's completely above the x axis.
79. 75.1 ft/sec
81. (a) $f(1) = 2(1) = 2, f(2) = 2(2) = 4$;
$g(1) = 2(1)^2 - 4(1) + 4 = 2; g(2) = 2(2)^2 - 4(2) + 4 = 4$;
$h(1) = 2^1 = 2; h(2) = 2^2 = 4$

x	3	4	5	6	7
$2x$	6	8	10	12	14
$2x^2 - 4x + 4$	10	20	34	52	74
2^x	8	16	32	64	128

(b)

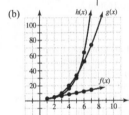

(c) Linear growth is at a steady rate. The others grow faster, with
exponential growing the quickest in the long run.
83. (a) Answers vary, but most choose 1.
(b) Choice 1: $1,050; Choice 2: $1,015; Choice 3: $1,638.30
(c) Choice 1: linear; Choice 2: quadratic; Choice 3: exponential

Review Exercises
1. Answers vary.
3.

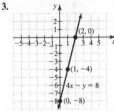
$4x - y = 8$

5.

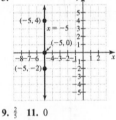
$x = -5$

7.

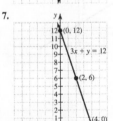
$3x + y = 12$

9. $\frac{2}{5}$ **11.** 0

13. $y = -3x + 12; m = -3$

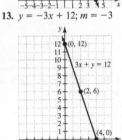
$3x + y = 12$

15. $y = \frac{4}{7}x - 4; m = \frac{4}{7}$

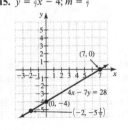
$4x - 7y = 28$

17. (a) $y = -16,333x + 81,000$ (b) $53,778

(c) Decreasing by $16,333 per year

(d) $-16,998$; obviously a house can't have a negative value.

19. Answers vary. **21.** $(10, 2)$ **23.** $\{(x, y) \mid 4x - y = 10\}$ **25.** $(6, 3)$

27. $\{(x, y) \mid 3x - 6y = 15\}$ **29.** $\left(\frac{3}{2}, -\frac{5}{2}\right)$

31. coffee $2.50 per pound; tea $1.75 per pound **33.** Answers vary.

35. 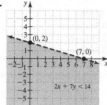 **37.**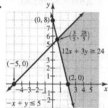

39.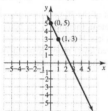

41. (a)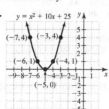

(b) 4 social work and 6 sociology, 6 social work and 4 sociology, or 5 of each.

43. 24 of model I and 12 of model II **45.** Answers vary.

47. Not a function

49. Domain = $\{x \mid x \leq 3\}$; range = $\{y \mid y \geq 0\}$; function

51. Domain = $\{x \mid x > 0\}$; Range = $\{x \mid -\infty < x < \infty\}$; not a function

53. $f(-10) = 40$, $f\left(\frac{3}{4}\right) = \frac{253}{16}$

55.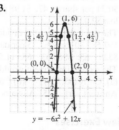

57. (a) 43 million (b) 2005

(c) $y = -3.6x + 518$, where x is years after 2000; 536 million

(d) Because the slope changed after 2009.

59. Answers vary.

61. **63.**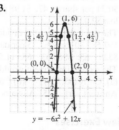

65. 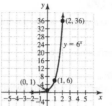 **67.**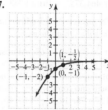

69. $\{12.04\}$ **71.** (a) 6.25 pounds (b) About 4.6 days

Chapter 7 Test

1. 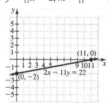 **3.**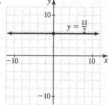

5. $\frac{17}{7}$; upward

7. $y = \frac{2}{11}x - 2$; $m = \frac{2}{11}$

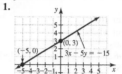

9. $\left(\frac{23}{5}, -\frac{17}{5}\right)$ **11.** The system is inconsistent. The solution set is $\varnothing$.

13.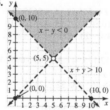

15. Function **17.** $f(3) = 31$; $f\left(\frac{5}{2}\right) = \frac{45}{2}$

19. 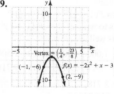 **21.**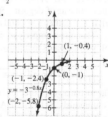

23. 62 *Daily News* and 34 *Tribune* **25.** 24 snowmen and 0 wreaths

27. $2,064.86

CHAPTER 8: CONSUMER MATHEMATICS

Exercise Set 8-1

7. 63% **9.** 2.5% **11.** 156% **13.** 20% **15.** 66.$\overline{6}$% **17.** 125%

19. 0.18 **21.** 0.06 **23.** 0.625 **25.** 3.2 **27.** 0.$\overline{6}$ **29.** $\frac{6}{25}$ **31.** $2\frac{9}{25}$

33. $\frac{1}{200}$ **35.** $\frac{1}{6}$ **37.** $15; $314.99 **39.** $15.00; $264.99 **41.** 60%

43. 24% **45.** $76.79 **47.** $126 **49.** $1,256 **51.** 51.9% **53.** $800

55. 2000–2005: 98.4 million, 89.9%; 2005–2010: 92.6 million, 44.5%. Even though the actual changes were similar, the percent change was far less with a larger beginning number.

57. 52.8%; 19.5%; 7.5% per year; 9.8% per year

59. 25% off saves $12.25.

61. (a) 464,375 (b) 14,043 (c) 2.9%

Note: The answers for 63–66 can vary some depending on how you read the values from the graph.

63. (a) 26.8%; 20% **65.** Almost 8 years; almost 4 years
67. No; the total discount is 44%.
69. Total discount will be 75%, not 100%.
71. There's no comparison: 20% more what? 20% more than what?
73. $4.57 **75.** 14.3%; $4.67; 16.75%

Exercise Set 8-2
7. $1,440 **9.** $220,340.63 **11.** 4.4% **13.** $985 **15.** $8,000
17. $1,333.80 **19.** $497.70 **21.** 3 years **23.** $960 **25.** $1,102.27
27. $7.88 **29.** $5.03
31. (a) $720 (b) $2,280 (c) 10.5%
33. (a) $2,025 (b) $3,975 (c) 11.3%
35. 8.43% **37.** $141,509.43 **39.** 3 years
41. 4.25 years or 51 months **43.** $2,096.25 **45.** $7,316 **47.** $92.97
49. (a) Answers vary. (b) 10-year: $84; 5-year: $157.50
(c) 5-year has $630 less interest
51. 13.1% **53.** 16.4% **55.** $6 **57.** $4.40
59. (a) $5,400 (b) $12,600 (c) 7.1%
61. The personal loan **63.** The repair loan
65. (a) $3,000

(b)
End of year	1	2	3	4	5
Future value ($)	10,600	11,236	11,910	12,625	13,383

(c) $383

(d)
End of year	$2\frac{1}{2}$	5
Future value ($)	11,500	13,225

You'd pay $225 more.
67. The interest will be WAY too high.
69. They are the same regardless of principal.

Exercise Set 8-3
7. $I = $396.20 and $A = $1,221.20 **9.** $I = $75.72, $A = $635.72
11. $I = $38.10 and $A = $358.10 **13.** $10,805.48 **15.** $66,649.19
17. $574.85 **19.** $1,021.18 **21.** 6.14% **23.** 6.66%
25. 4.5% compounded semiannually
27. 3.1% compounded quarterly **29.** $12,175.94 **31.** $335,095.61
33. $9,507.11 **35.** $4,011.25 **37.** 4.45 years
39. 10.54 years; 10.19 years **41.** $20,548.25 **43.** $27,223.76
45. (a) $24,664.64 (b) $5,153.40
47. (a) $59,556.16 (b) $19,556.16 (c) $29,398.60
49. $2,095.18 **51.** $114,717.32 **53.** $148.20; $1,163.29 **55.** $199.71
57. The certificate of deposit **59.** 11.6 years
61. (a) If $u = \frac{n}{r}$, then $\frac{r}{n} = \frac{1}{u}$ and $n = ur$, so $P\left(1 + \frac{r}{n}\right)^{nt} = P\left(1 + \frac{1}{u}\right)^{urt}$.
Then use a property of exponents to write as $A = P\left[\left(1 + \frac{1}{u}\right)^u\right]^{rt}$.
(b) When n tends to infinity, $\frac{n}{r}$ does as well.

(c)
u	50	100	500	1,000	1,500	2,000	2,500
$\left(1 + \frac{1}{u}\right)^u$	2.692	2.705	2.716	2.717	2.717	2.718	2.718

The formula gets closer and closer to 2.718.
63. Continuously: $11,127.70; Annually: $10,955.62
65. $8,347.30 **67.** $1,235.34 **69.** 6.47%
71. (a) $40,488.76 (b) $38,902.85; $1,585.91 too low

Exercise Set 8-4
9. $480 **11.** Down payment: $56.25; installment Price: $383.25
13. $43.17

	Amount financed	Total installment price	Finance charge
15.	$11,695.41	$16,011.20	$1,715.79
17.	$17,642.50	$26,915	$5,772.50
19.	$20,666	$35,018.56	$1,952.56

21. 8.5% **23.** 12% **25.** 9.5%
27. u = $709.50; payoff amount: $10,956.50
29. u = $14.54; payoff amount: $482.81
31. u = $14.66; payoff amount: $615.34
33. $180.13 **35.** $8.22 **37.** $5.18

39. (a) $10,552 (b) $6,390.48 (c) Answers vary.
41. Lender; $45.42 **43.** (a) $7,769.23 (b) $2,000 more
45. $16.65; $1,124.15 **47.** $39.49; $3,368.60 **49.** $13.32; $411.35
51. (a) $602.14 (b) $7.23 (c) $669.15
53. (a) $370.55 (b) $5.19 (c) $350.76
55. (a) $370.92 (b) $4.08 (c) $533.30
57. $892.76
59. (a) #51: $669.45; #39: $347.78; #41: $529.94
(b) #37: unpaid balance method is $0.30 higher.
#53: unpaid balance method is $2.98 lower.
#55: unpaid balance method is $3.36 lower.
(c) When purchases total a lot more than payments, unpaid balance is the better method, especially if payments are made late in the month.
61. $641.67 **63.** $3,636.36
65. The calculation ends up being $(0.99)^6 \times 2,300 = $2,165.40.
67. About 12.65 years

Exercise Set 8-5
9. $40.20; $2,050.20 **11.** $109.50; $5,584.50 **13.** $106.45
15. $303.42 **17.** $7,306.20 **19.** $3,053.70 **21.** $384.44
23. (a) $73.20 (b) $150.76 (c) $1,840.80
25. Subsidized loan at 6.8% is $3,368.40 less than the federal unsubsidized loan and $7,257.60 less than the private.
27. $326.84
29. (a) $21,750 (b) $123,250 (c) $871.38 (d) $138,164
31. (a) 80,000 (b) $120,000 (c) $720.00 (d) $139,200
33. (a) $32,500 (b) $295,700 (c) $1,945.71 (d) $638,240.80
35. (a) $360,000 (b) $840,000 (c) $5,779.20 (d) $547,008
37. $1,108.02; $61,970.40 **39.** $261,165.60 **41.** $1,499.44
43. $1,148.90 **45.** $4,215.22 **47.** $3,746.38

49.
Payment number	Interest	Payment on Principal	Balance of Loan
1	$718.96	$152.42	$123,097.58
2	$718.07	$153.31	$122,944.27
3	$717.17	$154.21	$122,790.06

51.
Payment number	Interest	Payment on Principal	Balance of Loan
1	$3,850	$1,929.20	$838,070.80
2	$3,841.16	$1,938.04	$836,132.76
3	$3,832.28	$1,946.92	$834,185.84

53. $255,947 **55.** $162,444
57. If you can afford the higher payment of the 20-year mortgage at 9% after making the 25% down payment, then that is the better option since the total interest paid is less. However, if you can only manage a 10% down payment, or need lower monthly payments, the 25-year mortgage at 7% would be the better choice.
59. $9,822.40; 75.0%; $138,164; 112.1%

Exercise Set 8-6
11. $97.25 per share **13.** $1.23 per share **15.** 4,626,000 shares
17. 8.87 per share **19.** $766.29 **21.** $40.08 per share **23.** $0.04
25. 345,000 shares **27.** $1.49 per share **29.** $156.20
31. $50.87 per share **33.** $0.67 **35.** 9,662,000 shares
37. $2.53 per share **39.** $820.75 **41.** 24.91 **43.** 15.02
45. $0.34 per share **47.** $1.98 per share **49.** lost $432.48
51. lost $2,022.63
53. The stock that pays the dividend results in $1,550 more profit.
55. $97,582.30, or $267.35 per day **57.** $1,245 **59.** $3,660.63
61. $320 **63.** $860.63 **65.** 11.5% **67.** 5.9%
69. The second investment would be the better choice.
71. (a) Curly ($3,550) (b) Curly (31.1%) (c) Moe (8.3%/yr)
73. Answers vary. **75.** Answers vary.

Review Exercises
1. 0.875; 87.5% **3.** $\frac{37}{20}$; 1.85 **5.** 5.75; 575% **7.** 69.12 **9.** 1,100
11. $60 **13.** 73.5%
15. (a) The 10% is taken off the discount price, not the original.
(b) $45.05

17. $2,322 **19.** 2.5 years **21.** 7% **23.** $1,375
25. $I = \$1,800$ and $A = \$7,800$ **27.** 1.4% **29.** $25.56
31. Discount: $1,080; David received $4,920
33. $I = \$603.67$ and $A = \$2,378.67$ **35.** $5.03; $50.03
37. 12.55% **39.** $8,937.54 **41.** 8.42 years; 0.17 years, or about 62 days
43. $719.56 **45.** $15,518.75; $25,524; $1,905.25
47. 8% **49.** $1,473.96 **51.** $u = \$757.80$; payoff amount = $7,017.20
53. $9.86; $786.36 **55.** $748.82 **57.** $62.41 **59.** $275.04
61. $1,827.94
63. The 52-week high was $38.28 per share and the 52-week low was $27.09 per share.
65. 5,528,000 shares **67.** $1.09 per share **69.** Answers vary.
71. The buyer makes $16.55 more.

Chapter 8 Test
1. 31.25% **3.** $\frac{7}{25}$ **5.** 80% **7.** 347 **9.** $2,568 **11.** $486
13. $I = \$8.16$, $A = \$443.16$. The monthly payment is $73.86.
15. Simple interest, by $461.69
17. Discount: $5,692.50; Latoya received $6,957.50
19. $I = \$7,885.08$ and $A = \$17,635.08$ **21.** 8.16%
23. Total installment price: $967.73; Monthly payment: $114.54
25. The unearned interest is $438.36 and the payoff amount is $7,186.64.
27. The finance charge is $20.
The new balance is $1,030.
29. (a) $62.70 (b) $14,585.80 (c) $167.85
31. (a) $9,000 (b) $171,000 (c) $1,026

(d) Payment number	Interest	Payment on Principal	Balance of Loan
1	$855	$171	$170,829
2	$854.15	$171.85	$170,657.15

33. The 52-week high is $36.98 and the 52-week low is $23.17.
35. $26.65
37. Original owner: $250; buyer: $190; original owner made a better investment: more profit over a shorter time period.

CHAPTER 9: MEASUREMENT
Exercise Set 9-1
7. 4 yd **9.** $5\frac{2}{3}$ yd **11.** $39\frac{3}{4}$ ft **13.** $1\frac{3}{4}$ ft **15.** $\frac{1}{2}$ yd **17.** $24\frac{1}{3}$ yd
19. 800 cm **21.** 120 m **23.** 6 hm **25.** 900 dm **27.** 3.756 m
29. 0.4053 km **31.** 2,370 cm **33.** 560 mm **35.** 127,500 dm
37. 0.8 km **39.** ≈196.85 in. **41.** 406.4 mm **43.** ≈7.16 dam
45. ≈4,429.13 ft **47.** 499.53 mm **49.** ≈19.69 ft **51.** 172.21 dm
53. ≈1.46 mi **55.** ≈4.59 yd **57.** ≈8.46 m **59.** $76\frac{1}{2}$ ft; 23.32 m
61. 60 yd; 54.86 m **63.** 0.85 mi; 1.37 km **65.** $3\frac{1}{2}$ yd **67.** 2,300 mg
69. 14 km; 8.7 mi **71.** ≈104.60 km per hour **73.** ≈19.16 m
75. 38.1 mm by 76.2 mm **77.** 7.92×10^{9} ft **79.** 573 boards
81. 20 g **83.** 488 Canadian dollars **85.** 37.85 francs

Note: for Exercises 87–103, answers can vary: these are one guy's interpretation. The important thing is to think about the relative sizes of the different units in both systems.

87. Meters **89.** Millimeters **91.** Centimeters **93.** Millimeters
95. Yards, meters **97.** Inches, centimeters **99.** Inches, millimeters
101. Yards, hectometers **103.** Inches, centimeters
105. the first runner **107.** millimeters

Exercise Set 9-2
Note: answers can vary, depending on rounding and on the conversion factors used.

7. 24 ft^2 **9.** 2.6 mi^2 **11.** $166\frac{1}{2}$ ft^2 **13.** ≈0.07 acre **15.** ≈505 yd^2
17. ≈4.84 m^2 **19.** 43.0 km^2 **21.** 124.5 cm^2 **23.** 473.7 dm^2
25. 38,763.3 acres **27.** ≈0.021 ft^2 **29.** ≈29.26 m^2 **31.** 142.7 ft^2
33. ≈2,872.32 fluid oz **35.** ≈18.44 yd^3 **37.** ≈6.94 ft^3
39. 1,570.1 in.^{3} **41.** 0.000097 m^3 **43.** 382.51 dL **45.** 87.25 L
47. 0.00437 m^3 **49.** 0.5 L **51.** 920 dL **53.** 42,000 mL
55. ≈45.28 L **57.** 357,169.8 mL **59.** ≈22.31 qt **61.** 46,428 gal

63. ≈0.34 kL **65.** 45,843.75 pounds **67.** 3.3 ft^3 **69.** 2 gallons
71. 7.4 cubic yards **73.** 1.56 mi^2 **75.** ≈0.67 ft^3 **77.** 634 tiles
79. 520 lb **81.** 5 bikers **83.** ≈$15\frac{1}{2}$ km^2 **85.** Acres
87. Square miles **89.** Square miles **91.** Liters **93.** Milliliters
95. 9 trips **97.** Answers vary.
99. Answers vary depending on your school.
101. Answers vary depending on your classroom.
103. (a) About 9,434
(b) About 110.7 lb
(c) About 52 years, 117 days

Exercise Set 9-3
7. 2.0625 lb **9.** 36.8 oz **11.** 8,400 lb **13.** 1.75 T **15.** ≈1.08 T
17. 90 cg **19.** 440 hg **21.** 5.15 dg **23.** 72.6 dg **25.** 32.17 g
27. 0.00543 g **29.** 22,555.6 g **31.** ≈4.29 oz **33.** ≈0.106 lb
35. ≈27,272.73 hg **37.** ≈162.36 t **39.** ≈5.23 t **41.** ≈59,640 dg
43. ≈291.07 oz **45.** ≈0.03 lb **47.** 57.2°F **49.** 92°F **51.** 0.4°F
53. −15°C **55.** 35.7°C **57.** ≈ −23.33°C **59.** −53.85°C
61. −7.9°F **63.** −279.1°F **65.** 6.25 lb
67. The elevator is more than able to hold their weight.
69. She will not pack a coat. **71.** The cars are too heavy.
73. 68°F **75.** 2,240 grams **77.** She lost 57.6 oz of fat.
79. They should not let him on!
81. $12\frac{2}{5}$°F **83.** Yuan did not buy the right cement.
85. The sugar should be melted. **87.** 67.5 kg
89. (a)

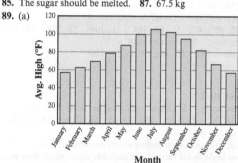

Month
The Celsius graph appears to show a greater variation in temperatures.

(b)

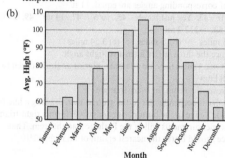

Month
Now the temperature variation looks much greater.

91. San Antonio **93.** Football player **95.** Kilogram **97.** Gram

Review Exercises
1. $13\frac{1}{2}$ ft **3.** 1.75 ft **5.** ≈130.13 mi **7.** 3.6 dm **9.** 34.5 m
11. 290.35 in. **13.** ≈33.46 in. **15.** 1,051.56 dm **17.** 91.44 m
19. ≈330 km/h; ≈300.67 ft/sec **21.** The Eiffel Tower
23. ≈39.57 ft^2 **25.** 68,302,080 ft^2 **27.** ≈8.82 mi^2
29. 131.13 dm^2 **31.** ≈0.03 ft^2 **33.** ≈6,702 oz **35.** ≈1,212 gal
37. ≈1,299.47 in.^{3} **39.** 67,300 L **41.** 2.31 L **43.** 85 drops
45. The second is cheaper. **47.** Acres **49.** 4.0625 lb
51. 17.25 T **53.** ≈18 T **55.** 457 mg **57.** 343.45 hg **59.** 1,274 g
61. ≈0.05 lb **63.** 55.4°F **65.** 33.5°C **67.** −31.45°C
69. ≈7.04 lb **71.** 66.4°F
73. It appears the deal on the Canadian side is better, but only if they're both using the same currency!

Chapter 9 Test
1. ≈3.67 yd **3.** 12.3 cm **5.** ≈13.39 in. **7.** ≈24.13 ft² **9.** 3.31 in.²
11. ≈6.10 in.³ **13.** 846.38 gal **15.** 22.8125 lb **17.** 59.1 cg
19. ≈0.06 lb **21.** 29.56°C **23.** 6 hr, 31 min
25. The first at $1.39 per square foot is cheaper.
27. ≈3.37 hours **29.** 19.44 hr **31.** The agent is wasting her time.
33. 15.12°F

CHAPTER 10: GEOMETRY
Exercise Set 10-1
7. Ray; $\overrightarrow{AB}$ **9.** Line; l **11.** Segment; $\overline{TU}$
13. $\angle RST$; $\angle TSR$; $\angle S$; $\angle 3$ **15.** straight **17.** obtuse
19. vertical angles **21.** corresponding angles
23. corresponding angles **25.** alternate exterior angles **27.** 82°
29. 57.6° **31.** $71\frac{3}{4}°$ **33.** $(80 - x)°$ **35.** 24° **37.** 117.5° **39.** $68\frac{1}{6}°$
41. $(195 - y)°$ **43.** $\frac{100}{3}$ **45.** $\frac{43}{2}$ **47.** $\frac{135}{2}$ **49.** 33
51. $m\angle 1 = 37°$; $m\angle 2 = 143°$; $m\angle 3 = 37°$
53. $m\angle 1 = 90°$; $m\angle 2 = 90°$; $m\angle 3 = 90°$
55. $m\angle 1 = m\angle 3 = m\angle 5 = m\angle 7 = 15°$
$m\angle 2 = m\angle 4 = m\angle 6 = 165°$
57. $m\angle 1 = 55°$; $m\angle 2 = 55°$; $m\angle 3 = 55°$; $m\angle 4 = 125°$; $m\angle 5 = 125°$;
$m\angle 6 = 55°$; $m\angle 7 = 70°$
59. $3x = 114°$, $2x - 10 = 66°$
61. $4t - 31 = 85°$, $2t + 27 = 85°$, $x = 95°$, $y = 95°$
63. 90° **65.** 60° **67.** 15° **69.** 104° **71.** 104° **73.** 104° **75.** 104°
77. Answers vary. **79.** Answers vary.
83. π radians = 180° **85.** $m\angle 1 + m\angle 2 = 180°$
87. $m\angle 1 - m\angle 3 = 0°$

Exercise Set 10-2
11. Isosceles; acute **13.** Obtuse **15.** Scalene; acute **17.** 70°
19. $48\frac{2}{3}°$ **21.** 40° **23.** 34 ft **25.** 13.8 yd **27.** 19 mi **29.** 36.1 ft
31. 12 ft **33.** 24 in.
35. All three pairs of corresponding angles are equal. $21\frac{9}{11}$ in.
37. The two angle Bs are vertical and therefore equal, so all three pairs of corresponding angles are equal. 17 m
39. Each triangle has a right angle and they share angle A, so all three pairs of corresponding angles are equal. 11 ft
41. ≈84.9 ft **43.** Yes, just barely **45.** 16'6″ **47.** 14 mi **49.** 270 ft
51. 10 ft **53.** ≈212.2 mi
55. (a) 2.5 miles (b) 5 miles (c) 3.54 miles
57. 180° since the three angles form a straight angle
59. $m\angle 1 = m\angle 4$ since they are alternate interior angles between two parallel lines
61. This proves the result for every triangle.
65. If the edge is perpendicular to the ground then drawing a line from the top left edge to the bottom right edge will form a right triangle, and the measurements will fit the Pythagorean theorem. That distance should be (to the nearest eighth of an inch) $12'10\frac{3}{8}″$.

Exercise Set 10-3
7. Octagon, 1,080° **9.** Triangle, 180° **11.** Hexagon, 720°
13. Rectangle **15.** Trapezoid **17.** 76 yd **19.** 28 ft **21.** 44 in.
23. 42 ft **25.** 42 mi **27.** 39 in. **29.** 25 ft **31.** 224 cm **33.** 10 ft
35. 360 ft **37.** 241 ft **39.** 66 in. **41.** 5.08 times **43.** $392
45. ≈1.74 mph **47.** 118.4 yd and 191.6 yd
49. Only the longest side, at 1,325 ft
55. (a) About 1.4 miles (b) 400 feet less (c) About 5.4%

Exercise Set 10-4
7. 289 in.² **9.** 450 yd² **11.** 400 m² **13.** 120 mi² **15.** 467.5 in.²
17. 101.5 ft² **19.** 60.7 yd² **21.** 72 in.² **23.** $123\frac{1}{2}$ in.² **25.** 26.2 in.²
27. $C ≈ 50.27$ in.; $A ≈ 201.06$ in.² **29.** $C ≈ 50.27$ m; $A ≈ 201.06$ m²
31. $C ≈ 131.95$ km; $A ≈ 1,385.44$ km² **33.** 24.0 in.² **35.** 136.3 ft²
37. 20.0 m² **39.** 3.2 ft **41.** $8\frac{1}{3}$ mi **43.** 11.11 yd² **45.** 40 images
47. $1,620 **49.** (a) 90.2 ft² (b) One gallon; 0.48 gallon left over
51. $188.50 **53.** $458.04 **55.** 16.28 ft²

57. (a) That the two longest sides are parallel and the angles at the top are right angles.
(b) 16,790.6 ft²; 0.39 acre
59. 10.6 ft **61.** When the radius is 2. **63.** Answers vary. **65.** 30 in.²
67. (a) 175 sq ft
(b) 10: 300 sq ft; 15: 375 sq ft; 20: 400 sq ft
(c) Largest is 400 sq ft; there is no smallest area because you can make one of the sides as small as you like.
69. (a) 58.65 yards longer (b) 2 minutes

Exercise Set 10-5
7. 125 in.³ **9.** 210 m³ **11.** 48 m³ **13.** 19,704.07 cm³
15. 1,005.31 ft³ **17.** 33,510.32 in.³ **19.** 461.81 cm³ **21.** 150 in.²
23. 214 m² **25.** 96 m² **27.** 4,046.4 cm² **29.** 628.3 ft² **31.** 5,026.5 in.²
33. 648 ft³ **35.** 190,228,656 ft³ **37.** 13,684.78 in.³ **39.** 141.11 in.³
41. 55,417,694.41 mi² **43.** 2,304 in.³ **45.** 1,080 in.² **47.** 3.4 in.
49. two 5-gallon cans *or* one 5-gallon can and four 1-gallon cans
51. 1 1-gallon can **53.** (a) 2,000 ft³ (b) 2.53 times
55. 154 in.³ **57.** Area of the base is 36 m²; area of each face is 15 m²
61. (a) 2,016 (b) 347.4 cu ft (c) 51.9% (d) 52.4% **63.** $33\frac{1}{3}$%

Exercise Set 10-6
7. $\cos A = \frac{3}{5}$; $\sin A = \frac{4}{5}$; $\tan A = \frac{4}{3}$
9. $\cos A = \frac{35}{72}$; $\sin A = \frac{\sqrt{15{,}836}}{144}$; $\tan A = \frac{\sqrt{15{,}836}}{70}$
11. $\cos A = \frac{15}{17}$; $\sin A = \frac{8}{17}$; $\tan A = \frac{8}{15}$
13. $\cos A = \frac{\sqrt{51}}{10}$; $\sin A = \frac{7}{10}$; $\tan A = \frac{7}{\sqrt{51}}$ **15.** 92.71 cm
17. 76.88 in. **19.** 1.39 mm **21.** 53.82 in. **23.** 1,857.41 ft
25. 77.47 mi **27.** ≈48° **29.** 60° **31.** ≈29° **33.** ≈41°
35. $c = 25.8″$, $A = 54.5°$, $B = 35.5°$ **37.** $b = 8.9$ m, $c = 21.9$ m, $B = 24°$
39. 23,644.67 ft **41.** 4,980.76 m **43.** 1,218.93 ft **45.** 0° to 6.4°
47. 359.50 ft **49.** 3,932.92 ft **51.** 1.2° **53.** 6.9°
55. The angle works out to be negative.
57. Each is the ratio of one leg of a triangle to the hypotenuse. The ratios have to be greater than zero because both lengths are positive. They have to be less than one because the hypotenuse is the longest side, so the denominator of each ratio is larger than the numerator.
59. height of plane = 737.6 ft and distance of car = 673.8 ft
61. Use the cosine then use the Pythagorean theorem.
63. When you know two sides, you can quickly find the third using the Pythagorean theorem. The angles in a triangle have measures that add to 180°, and you always know the 90° angle, so when you know one of the others, you can subtract from 90° to get the remaining angle.

Exercise Set 10-7
19. Answers vary.
21. Yes; the result of the first four iterations is shown here. **23.** Yes yet again.

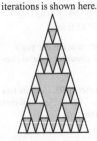
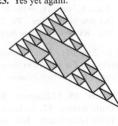

25.
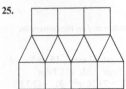

27. It can, and the pattern looks basically the same as the one in Figure 10-39(a).
29. Answers vary.
33. Only regular triangles, squares, and hexagons tessellate with themselves.

35. Answers vary.

37. The measure of each angle is $\frac{(n-2)360}{n}$, and the sum of the angles around a vertex has to be 360°, while there's already a 90° angle at each vertex from the square. So I set up and solved the equation $90 + 2\frac{(n-2)360}{n} = 360$ to find n.

Review Exercises

1. line **3.** line segment **5.** trapezoid **7.** triangle **9.** hexagon
11. obtuse **13.** vertical angles **15.** alternate exterior angles
17. (a) 63° (b) 2° **19.** $m\angle 2 = 163°$; $m\angle 3 = m\angle 1 = 17°$
21. 43° **23.** 72 ft **25.** obtuse and scalene
27. acute and equilateral **29.** 6 units **31.** $a = 15$ and $b = 18$
33. 15.8 ft **35.** 166.4 ft **37.** decagon; 1,440° **39.** 16 ft
41. 28 m **43.** 1,376 cm² **45.** 9,160.88 km²
47. $C = 51.84$ yd; $A = 213.82$ yd² **49.** $49.94 **51.** 24,429.02 cm³
53. 84.82 yd³ **55.** 5,736 in.² **57.** 775.71 revolutions **59.** 38.79 cm³
61. $\sin B = \frac{3}{\sqrt{34}}$; $\cos B = \frac{5}{\sqrt{34}}$; $\tan B = \frac{3}{5}$ **63.** ≈2.33 yd
65. ≈51.8° **67.** 33.04 ft² **69.** 9 minutes
71.

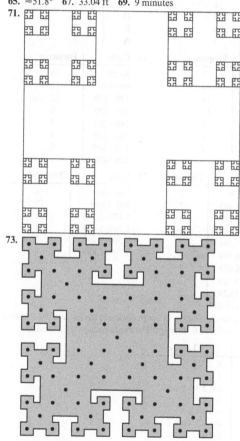

73.

Chapter 10 Test
1. Complement: 17°; supplement: 107°
3. $m\angle 1 = m\angle 4 = m\angle 5 = 32°$;
$m\angle 2 = m\angle 3 = m\angle 6 = m\angle 7 = 148°$
5. $\frac{5}{2}$ ft **7.** 1,080° **9.** 75 ft² **11.** 429.3 yd² **13.** 282.7 cm³; 245.04 cm²
15. 923.63 yd³; 190 ft² **17.** 33,510.32 m³; 5,026.55 m²
19. A brick wall is a tessellation.
21. 6,280 ft² **23.** $41.08 **25.** 3,463.32 pounds

CHAPTER 11: PROBABILITY AND COUNTING TECHNIQUES

Exercise Set 11-1
7. 3,628,800 **9.** 1 **11.** 336 **13.** 990 **15.** 1,814,400 **17.** 420
19. 22,350 **21.** 56 **23.** 479,001,600 **25.** 720 **27.** 990
29. ≈0.0055 **31.** 840; 2,401 **33.** 151,200; 1,000,000

35. 5,527,200 **37.** 300 **39.** 210 **41.** 7,776 **43.** 57,120
45. 12,600 **47.** 60 **49.** 27,720 **51.** 248,832 **53.** ≈7.414 × 10¹¹
55. 332,640 **57.** 1,800 **59.** 300 **61.** 30 choices

Exercise Set 11-2
9. 10 **11.** 35 **13.** 15 **15.** 1 **17.** 66 **19.** 600 **21.** 9
23. $_8C_5 = 56$ **25.** $_6C_2 = 15$
    $_8P_5 = 6,720$ $_6P_2 = 30$
27. $_9C_9 = 1$ **29.** $_{12}C_4 = 495$
    $_9P_9 = 362,880$ $_{12}P_4 = 11,880$
31. Combination **33.** Permutation **35.** Permutation
37. Combination **39.** Combination **41.** 2,598,960 **43.** 126; 35
45. 120 **47.** 462 **49.** 166,320 **51.** 14,400 **53.** 67,200
55. 1,302 **57.** 246 **59.** 870 minutes, or 14.5 hours
61. (a) 714,420 (b) 982,080 **63.** Answers vary.

Exercise Set 11-3
11. Yes **13.** No **15.** No **17.** Yes **19.** Empirical **21.** Classical
23. (a) $\frac{1}{6}$ (b) $\frac{1}{2}$ (c) $\frac{1}{3}$ (d) 1 (e) 1 (f) $\frac{5}{6}$ (g) $\frac{1}{6}$
25. (a) $\frac{1}{7}$ (b) $\frac{2}{7}$ (c) $\frac{2}{7}$ (d) 1 (e) 0
27. $\frac{4}{9}$ **29.** $\frac{9}{16}$ **31.** (a) ≈0.05 (b) ≈0.71 (c) ≈0.82
33. 0.84 **35.** $\frac{3}{13}$ **37.** $\frac{5}{11}$ **39.** 0.32
41. (a) 0.69 (b) 0.15 (c) 0.54
43. 0 **45.** (a) ≈0.26 (b) ≈0.96
47. (a) 0.42 (b) 0.90
49. (a) $\frac{6}{25}$ (b) $\frac{2}{5}$ (c) $\frac{9}{25}$ (d) $\frac{12}{25}$ (e) $\frac{1}{5}$
51. Answers vary.
53. (a) $\frac{1}{3}$ (b) Answers vary. **55.** Answers vary.

Exercise Set 11-4
3. (a) $\frac{1}{8}$ (b) $\frac{3}{8}$ (c) $\frac{1}{2}$
5. (a) $\frac{5}{12}$ (b) $\frac{1}{4}$ (c) $\frac{1}{6}$
7. (a) $\frac{1}{3}$ (b) $\frac{1}{3}$ (c) $\frac{1}{9}$ (d) $\frac{4}{9}$ (e) $\frac{1}{3}$
9. (a) $\frac{1}{4}$ (b) $\frac{3}{4}$ (c) $\frac{1}{4}$ (d) $\frac{1}{8}$
11. (a) $\frac{2}{5}$ (b) $\frac{1}{5}$ (c) $\frac{4}{5}$
13. (a) $\frac{1}{2}$ (b) $\frac{1}{6}$ (c) $\frac{1}{4}$
15. (a) $\frac{1}{13}$ (b) $\frac{1}{4}$ (c) $\frac{1}{52}$ (d) $\frac{2}{13}$ (e) $\frac{4}{13}$ (f) $\frac{1}{13}$ (g) $\frac{1}{2}$ (h) $\frac{1}{26}$ (i) $\frac{7}{13}$ (j) $\frac{1}{26}$
17. (a) $\frac{1}{9}$ (b) $\frac{2}{9}$ (c) $\frac{1}{6}$ (d) $\frac{5}{18}$ (e) $\frac{11}{36}$ (f) $\frac{1}{2}$ (g) $\frac{3}{4}$ (h) 1
19. The outcomes are not equally likely because there is a $\frac{1}{4}$ probability of getting WW; each of the other six outcomes has a probability of $\frac{1}{8}$.
21. 216 **23.** $\frac{5}{108}$
25. (a) $\frac{1}{4}$ (b) $\frac{1}{12}$
    (c) Multiply the individual probabilities.
27. Bob: $\frac{1}{2}$; Fran: $\frac{3}{8}$; Julio: $\frac{1}{8}$

Exercise Set 11-5
3. (a) 0.0004 (b) 0.15 (c) 0.383 (d) 0.45
5. (a) 0.033 (b) 0.0083 (c) 0.3 (d) 0.075 (e) 0.15
7. (a) 0.255 (b) 0.745 (c) 0.0182 (d) 0
9. (a) 0.07 (b) 0.42 (c) 0.015 (d) 0.16 (e) 0.336
11. 0.01 **13.** 0.42 **15.** 0.115 **17.** $\frac{1}{658,008}$ **19.** 0.018 **21.** 0.0093
23. 0.00144 **25.** 0.0211 **27.** 0.0000015 **29.** 0.0049
31. Answers vary.
33. (a) The probability of the letters appearing in any order is six times as great as the probability of them appearing in order.
    (b) The probability of any order should be 24 times as great. The difference between the number of possibilities is the number of permutations of the letters chosen. When it was 3 letters, any order was 3! = 6 times more likely. For 4 letters, it should be 4! = 24 times more likely.

Exercise Set 11-6
7. In favor: 7:1; against: 1:7 **9.** In favor: 5:6; against: 6:5
11. In favor: 9:4; against: 4:9 **13.** $\frac{5}{13}$ **15.** $\frac{5}{11}$
17. $\frac{3}{10}$ **19.** 3.6 **21.** $2.29
23. (a) 1:11 (b) 1:35 (c) 5:1 (d) 17:1 (e) 1:5
25. (a) 1:12 (b) 3:10 (c) 3:1 (d) 1:12 (e) 1:1
27. (a) $\frac{7}{11}$ (b) $\frac{5}{7}$ (c) $\frac{3}{4}$ (d) $\frac{4}{5}$

29. $\frac{5}{14}$ **31.** 1:37; −$0.053 **33.** 6:13; −$0.053
35. 2:17; −$0.053 **37.** 29:121 **39.** 49:101 **41.** 8:67
43. L.A.: 0.38; Miami and Chicago: 0.25; Boston: 0.15
45. 13:2 **47.** 4:1 **49.** 6′5″ **51.** −$3.00 **53.** $0.83
55. −$1.00 **57.** −$0.50; −$0.52 **59.** −$70.25
61. No; the two-headed coin is now twice as likely.
65. (a) Answers vary. (b) RZ Electronics: +$320; Jackson Builders: +$525

Exercise Set 11-7
3. No **5.** Yes **7.** No **9.** Yes **11.** $\frac{1}{6}$ **13.** $\frac{11}{19}$
15. (a) $\frac{8}{11}$ (b) $\frac{15}{22}$
17. (a) $\frac{8}{17}$ (b) $\frac{6}{17}$ (c) $\frac{9}{17}$ (d) $\frac{12}{17}$
19. (a) $\frac{6}{7}$ (b) $\frac{4}{7}$ (c) 1
21. (a) $\frac{67}{118}$ (b) $\frac{81}{118}$ (c) $\frac{44}{59}$
23. (a) $\frac{38}{45}$ (b) $\frac{22}{45}$ (c) $\frac{2}{3}$
25. (a) $\frac{14}{31}$ (b) $\frac{23}{31}$ (c) $\frac{19}{31}$
27. (a) $\frac{1,664}{3,729}$ (b) $\frac{2,477}{3,729}$ (c) $\frac{2,870}{3,729}$
29. (a) $\frac{4}{9}$ (b) $\frac{1}{3}$ (c) $\frac{5}{12}$ **31.** $\frac{21}{47}$ **33.** 0.12
35.

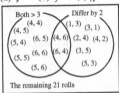

The remaining 21 rolls

39. Not mutually exclusive. You could be acquitted of a crime and convicted of a different one at the same time, leading to jail time after being acquitted. Or you could have been in the middle of a sentence for a different crime when tried.
41. Not mutually exclusive. There are different ways of being categorized: you could be a chronological junior (in your third year) but only have enough credits to be considered a sophomore academically.

Exercise Set 11-8
7. Independent **9.** Dependent **11.** Independent **13.** Dependent
15. 0.0058; 0.027 **17.** 0.498 **19.** 0.0625 **21.** $\frac{1}{12}$ **23.** $\frac{1}{8}$ **25.** $\frac{1}{15}$
27. 0.302 **29.** 0.705 **31.** 0.008 **33.** 0.027 **35.** 0.209 **37.** 0.2306
39. 0.1786 **41.** $\frac{1}{6}$ **43.** $\frac{2}{11}$ **45.** $\frac{1}{4}$ **47.** $\frac{2}{3}$ **49.** 1 **51.** 0.61 **53.** $\frac{1}{2}$
55. 0.14 **57.** 0.86
61. (a) Answers vary.
  (b) Every number drawn is independent of the previous numbers chosen, so the probability of 1, 2, 3, 4, 5, 6 is no different than the probability of any other 6 numbers.
  (c) That combination might be desirable because it's likely nobody else will choose it and you won't have to split the prize if it wins.

Exercise Set 11-9
5. 0.288 **7.** 0.0616 **9.** 0.0000304 **11.** 0.0994 **13.** 0.00615
15. 0.4535 **17.** 0.1960 **19.** 0.00463 **21.** 0.0750 **23.** 0.1546
25. 0.2340 **27.** 0.1906 **29.** 0.0133 **31.** 0.0080 **33.** 0.1117
35. 0.6870 **37.** 0.3769 **39.** Yes **41.** Yes **43.** Yes **45.** Yes **47.** No

Review Exercises
1. 2,184 **3.** 175,760,000; 88,583,040 **5.** 120 **7.** 84
9. In a permutation order matters, in a combination order does not matter.
11. 78 **13.** 729 **15.** b, c, and e
17. (a) $\frac{1}{4}$ (b) $\frac{1}{52}$ (c) $\frac{4}{13}$ (d) $\frac{1}{13}$ (e) $\frac{1}{2}$
19. (a) 0 (b) $\frac{1}{2}$ (c) $\frac{1}{3}$
21. (a) $\frac{9}{35}$ (b) $\frac{23}{35}$ (c) $\frac{19}{35}$ (d) $\frac{19}{35}$
23. (a) $\frac{1}{4}$ (b) $\frac{1}{6}$ (c) $\frac{1}{4}$ (d) $\frac{1}{4}$ (e) 0 (f) 1
25. $S = $ {1H, 1T, 2H, 2T, 3H, 3T, 4H, 4T, 5H, 5T, 6H, 6T, 7H, 7T, 8H, 8T}
27. $\frac{2}{25}$ **29.** $\frac{12}{25}$ **31.** $\frac{33}{182}$ **33.** 1:5 **35.** 10.5 **37.** $28.85
39. Mutually exclusive **41.** (a) $\frac{17}{50}$ (b) $\frac{4}{25}$ **43.** Dependent
45. Dependent **47.** $\frac{1}{7}$ **49.** 0.016
51. (a) $\frac{1}{26}$ (b) $\frac{1}{4}$ (c) $\frac{1}{8}$ **53.** 0.0165 **55.** 0.1684

Chapter 11 Test
1. 21 **3.** 0.00039 **5.** Answers vary. **7.** 2,646
9. (a) $\frac{4}{31}$ (b) $\frac{20}{31}$ (c) $\frac{7}{15}$
11. $S = $ {H1, H3, H5, T2, T4, T6}
13. (a) 0.025 (b) 0.000495 (c) 0
15. $\frac{1}{2}$ **17.** In favor: 3:5; against: 5:3 **19.** $5\frac{1}{6}$ **21.** $\frac{8}{33}$ **23.** 0.18

CHAPTER 12: STATISTICS
Exercise Set 12-1
11. Cluster **13.** Random **15.** Stratified
17. No; students that are well-off might be underrepresented.
19. Yes; the target group is everyone that has a phone, and everyone surveyed obviously has a phone.
21. No; the first five products on a shelf are likely to be older so that the store can get rid of older food first.

23.

Rank	Frequency
Fr	18
So	12
Jr	6
Sc	4

25.

Show	Frequency
S	6
D	5
B	7
A	7

27.

Class	Frequency
27−33	7
34−40	14
41−47	14
48−54	12
55−61	3
62−68	3
69−75	2

29.

Cents	Frequency
0−59	10
60−119	12
120−179	12
180−239	6
240−299	5
300−359	4
360−419	0
420−479	1

31.

Class	Frequency
150−1,276	2
1,277−2,403	2
2,404−3,530	5
3,531−4,657	8
4,658−5,784	7
5,785−6,911	3
6,912−8,038	7
8,039−9,165	3
9,166−10,292	3
10,293−11,419	2

33.

Value	Frequency
700–899	8
900–1,099	17
1,100–1,299	3
1,300–1,499	2
1,500–1,699	1
1,700–1,899	1

35. Most registered vehicles per car stolen are in the range of 80–89, while the least are in the 0–49 range. The most common are 84 and 89.

Stems	Leaves
3	8
4	1
5	0 0 2 3 3 6 8 9
6	6 8 9 9
7	0 0 3 4 5 8
8	0 1 3 3 4 4 4 5 7 9 9 9
9	0 2 4

37.

Stems	Leaves
0	3
1	5 9
2	2
3	1 1
4	1 4 6 6
5	2 6 6 6 9
6	0 0 6 6
7	7
8	7 8
9	6 8

39. Inferential **41.** Inferential **43.** Inferential
45. Answers vary. **47.** Answers vary. **49.** Answers vary.
51. The majority of states has taxes below $1.80, and just a handful are over $3.00. Explanations vary.

Exercise Set 12-2

5. By far the most common type of transplant is kidney, while pancreas is easily the least common.

7.

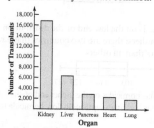

9.

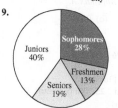

11.

13.

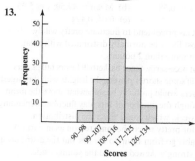

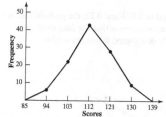

15.

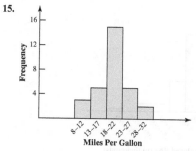

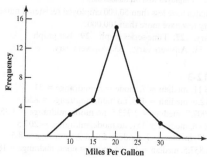

17.

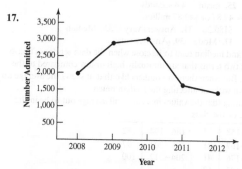

19. Downloads increased very steadily from 2004 to 2010, then decreased from 2010 to 2012.

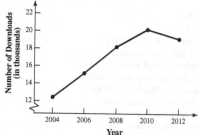

21. (a)

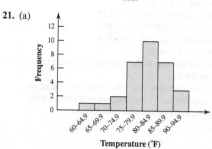

(b) The most likely high temperature in May is between 80 and 85 degrees; highs less than 75 are very unusual, and the 90s occur occasionally.

23. (a)

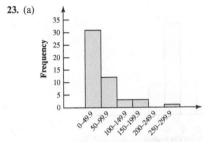

Employed RNs (in thousands)

(b) Most states have less than 50,000 employed registered nurses, and very few have more than 100,000.

25. Answers vary. **27.** Time series graph **29.** Bar graph
31. Pie chart **33.** Answers vary. **35.** Answers vary.

Exercise Set 12-3

11. mean $\approx$ 15.11, median = 7, mode = 3, midrange = 31
13. mean = 612.6, median = 475, no mode, midrange = 820
15. mean = 2,907.7, median = 2,723.5, no mode, midrange = 3,353.5
17. mean = 189.6, median = 151, no mode, midrange = 207.5
19. mean $\approx$ 7.47, median = 7, mode = 5 and 9, midrange = 8.5
21. mean $\approx$ 16,857.5, median = 16,485, mode = none, midrange = 18,179
23. 23.05 **25.** mean $\approx$ 4.4 seconds
27. mean $\approx$ 42.87 or $42.87 million
29. mean = $180.28 **31.** Answers vary. **33.** Median
35. Mode **37.** Mode **39.** Answers vary.
41. Mean and median tend to be close when the data set doesn't have one or two terms that are unusually high or low compared to the others. But when there are outliers like that, it skews the average up or down without affecting the median much.
43. Estimating that the values in a class will average out to be in the middle of the class.
45.

150−158	5	186−194	82
159−167	21	195−203	97
168−176	41	204−212	100
177−185	62		

47. 9th: 42.9%; 10th: 47.6%; 180 and 181; median $\approx$ 180.5

Exercise Set 12-4

7. $s_1 < s_2$ **9.** $s_1 > s_2$
11. R = 60, variance = 406.75, $s \approx$ 20.17
The number of junk emails varies pretty widely.
13. R = 1,799, variance = 438,113.6, $s \approx$ 661.90
The odometer readings vary pretty widely.
15. R = 99, variance $\approx$ 1,288.19, $s \approx$ 35.89
The weights don't vary all that much.
17. R = 10, variance = 9, s = 3
The heights are pretty uniform.
19. R = 8.68, variance $\approx$ 9.87, $s \approx$ 3.14
21. R = $39.50, variance $\approx$ 242.59, $s \approx$ 15.58
23. R = 738, variance $\approx$ 57,844.95, $s \approx$ 240.5
25. R = 1,289, variance $\approx$ 245,818, $s \approx$ 495.8
27. The variation is not the same.
29. (a) Average would be close to the hole for Pat, close to the center of the green for Ron.
(b) Pat has a large variation, Ron has a very small variation.
(c) Answers vary, but this example shows that variation can sometimes be more meaningful than average.
31. Answers vary.

Exercise Set 12-5

7. (a) 20th percentile (b) 75th percentile (c) 35th percentile
(d) 5th percentile (e) 90th percentile **9.** 75th percentile
11. 79th percentile **13.** 10 **15.** 19 **17.** Maurice is ranked higher.
19. Football: 60th percentile, basketball 52nd
21. (a) 60th percentile (b) 8 (c) 23 years

23. Q_1 = 22.5, Q_2 = 34, Q_3 = 53.5 **25.** Q_1 = 78, Q_2 = 88.5, Q_3 = 93
27. Q_1 = 103, Q_2 = 114.5, Q_3 = 123
29.

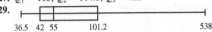

(a) The majority of values is on the low end of the distribution.
(b) 538.0 and 245.2 are outliers; there are two countries that have far more Internet users than all others.
31.

66   103 114.5 123 127

(a) The majority of years has homicides on the higher end of the range.
(b) 66 is an outlier; one year had an exceptionally low homicide total.
33. yes; yes **35.** Answers vary.
37. Find the quartiles in the current order, then switch Q_1 and Q_3.

Exercise Set 12-6

11. 34 **13.** 499 **15.** 54 **17.** 0.474 **19.** 0.192 **21.** 0.159
23. 0.345 **25.** 0.077 **27.** 0.223 **29.** 0.463 **31.** 0.885 **33.** 0.971
35. 0.274 **37.** 0.003 **39.** (a) About 97.5% (b) 340 **41.** 8.28 ounces
43. z = +0.45 **45.** (a) z = ±2.05 (b) z = ±1.75 (c) z = ±2.40

Exercise Set 12-7

Probabilities were found using the table in Appendix A.

5. (a) 0.301 (b) 0.456 **7.** (a) 0.312 (b) 0.268
9. (a) 0.005 (b) 0.162 (c) 0.749
11. (a) 0.153 (b) 0.774 (c) 0.187
13. (a) 0.841 (b) 0.067 **15.** (a) 0.776 (b) 0.405
17. (a) 0.755 (b) 0.811 (c) 0.284
19. (a) 638 (b) 184 (c) 1,074 (d) 136
21. (a) 14 (b) 495 (c) 46 **23.** 72nd **25.** 0th percentile
27. (a)   **29.** (a)

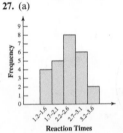   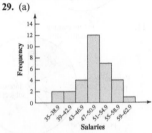

(b) Mean $\approx$ 2.34; $s \approx$ 0.58   (b) Mean $\approx$ 49.59; $s \approx$ 5.95
(c) 0.073; 0.72   (c) 0.04; 0.474
31. (a) Very unlikely. Gas prices tend to fluctuate pretty wildly.
(b) This would most likely be normally distributed with mean something a bit more than 2 pounds.
(c) Possibly but not necessarily. Since basketball favors tall players but there are still some shorter players, the heights with the largest number of players would probably be somewhat above the mean.
(d) Probably, although the number of hits may fluctuate depending on day of the week, which could affect the distribution.
(e) Probably not, for pretty much the same reason as in part (c). The ages probably go from 18 up to the 60s, but the distribution would be very strongly skewed toward the younger side.
33. No **35.** 90, 110
37. 0.04 and 0.72, compared to 0.073 and 0.72; the probabilities are reasonably close, so our assumption that the data were approximately normally distributed seems reasonable.

Exercise Set 12-8

11. (a)

(b) $r \approx 0.977$
(c) r is significant at the 5% and the 1% level
(d) $y = 4.1 + 2.7x$
(e) There is a positive linear relationship.

13. (a)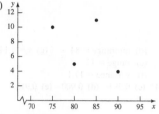

(b) $r \approx -0.441$
(c) r is not significant at 5% nor at 1% level.
(d) no regression line
(e) No relationship exists.

15. (a)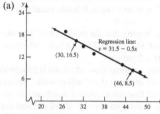

(b) $r \approx -0.983$
(c) r is significant at the 5% and 1% level.
(d) $y = 31.5 - 0.5x$
(e) There is a negative linear relationship.

17. (a)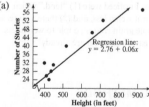

(b) $r \approx 0.909$
(c) r is significant at the 5% level
(d) $y = 3.1x + 10.2$
(e) There is a positive linear relationship.

19. (a)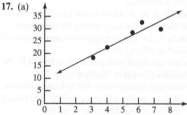

(b) $r \approx 0.942$
(c) r is significant at the 5% and 1% level.
(d) $y = 2.76 + 0.06x$
(e) There is a positive linear relationship.
(f) 33 Stories

21. (a)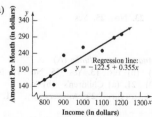

(b) $r \approx 0.896$
(c) r is significant at the 5% and 1% level.
(d) $y = -122.5 + 0.355x$
(e) There is a positive linear relationship.
(f) $205.88

23. (a)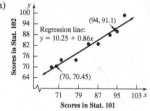

(b) $r \approx 0.963$
(c) r is significant at the 5% and 1% level.
(d) $y = 10.25 + 0.86x$
(e) There is a positive linear relationship. (f) 88

25. (a)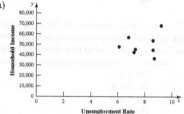

(b) $r \approx 0.212$
(c) r is not significant at the 5% nor the 1% level
(d) no regression line
(e) There appears to be no relationship at all.
(f) We can't make a prediction based on these data.
27. $r = 1$ in both cases; the points lie on a line.
29. (a)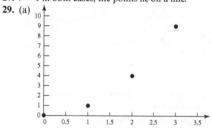

Now there appears to be a positive linear relationship
(b) Answers vary.
(c) $r \approx 0.958$; Removing the change of direction made it possible to find a linear relationship between the remaining points.
31. Answers vary.

Some of the answers in 33–39 are open to interpretation.

33. Positive
35. None (but you could make a case that small town students might get a better education than those in large urban districts, in which case it would be negative.)
37. Positive 39. Negative

Review Exercises

1.
Item	Frequency
B	4
F	5
G	5
S	5
T	6

3.
Rank	Frequency
102–116	4
117–131	3
132–146	1
147–161	4
162–176	11
177–191	7

5.

7.

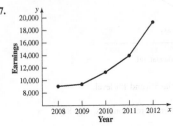

9. mean = 7.25

11. Mean = 399.75, range = 266, variance ≈ 10,799.64, s ≈ 103.92. The range of 266 tells us that the numbers vary from lowest to highest by a good amount compared to their sizes. The standard deviation tells us that overall the numbers are fairly spread out.

13. (a) 82nd; 41st   (b) 171,000
15. (a) 0.474   (f) 0.828
   (b) 0.155   (g) 0.023
   (c) 0.061   (h) 0.912
   (d) 0.833   (i) 0.018
   (e) 0.229   (j) 0.955
17. (a) 28   (b) 5
19. (a) 0.004   (b) 0.023   (c) 0.5   (d) 0.324
21. 22
23.

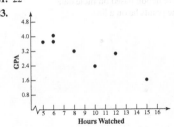

$r ≈ -0.914$, r is significant at the 5% level.
$y = 4.95 - 0.21x$
$y = 3.06$ when $x = 9$

Chapter 12 Test

1.

Source	Frequency
W	6
L	7
K	7
E	5

3.

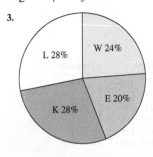

5.

Stems	Leaves
20	0 4 9
21	0 1 2 7 8 8
22	2 7 7 7 8
23	0 1 3 7 8
24	1 2 2 3 7
25	1 1 3 4 6
26	0

7. (a) mean ≈ 84.1   (d) midrange = 84   (g) $s ≈ 4.14$
   (b) median = 85   (e) range = 12
   (c) no mode   (f) variance ≈ 17.1
9. (a) 0.433   (b) 0.034   (c) 0.291   (d) 0.900   (e) 0.913
11. 20

Chapter 12 Supplement

1. First, 20 people is a very small sample. Second, we have no idea how those 20 were chosen. Are they representative of the general population or did they all come from a group like college students?
3. "The road less traveled" is at best vague. It could mean wildly different things to different people.
5. The writer was probably hoping that the reader would mistake 11% of patients with 11 out of 18 patients. That's a huge difference, since 11% of 18 patients is 2 patients.
7. More than what? Without a comparison, the claim is meaningless.
9. First "can provide" is a lot different than "will provide." Second, what level of acid control? Enough to cause a significant decrease in symptoms, or enough to register on a sophisticated medical exam?
11. There's no scale at all on the vertical axis, so we can't judge at all how significant the difference in energy released is.
13. The second graph is improperly drawn: the scale on the vertical axis doesn't begin at zero, so it makes the changes in height seem much greater than they actually are.
15. The question is worded to draw attention to the fact that the cost will increase, when in fact the question is asking for opinions on the importance of safety locks. The wording is designed to make it more likely that responders will say no.
17. Each of those behaviors are illegal, and people are a lot less likely to admit to doing something illegal or clearly wrong.
19. As the negative effects of lead became more widely known, it's a lot more likely that certain illnesses would be recognized as lead-related.
21. It would take some further analysis. In a country of over 300 million people, it's entirely possible that one murder every 20 minutes is a relatively low rate compared to other countries.
23. The second graph is misleading because the scale on the vertical axis starts at 4,600 rather than zero. It makes the increase appear to be much greater than it really was.
25. Answers vary, but the two I noticed were (1) "tend," which means they may or may not weigh less, and (2) there's no reason to believe that eating whole grain *causes* people to weigh less. More likely, people that eat whole grain are already health-conscious.

CHAPTER 13: VOTING METHODS
Exercise Set 13-1
5. (a) 22   (b) 4   (c) 8   (d) X
7. (a) 18   (b) 9   (c) 4   (d) Philadelphia
9. (a) 208   (b) Swimming pool   **11.** (a) 20   (b) Children's
13. No   **15.** No
17. (a) 1960, 1968, 1992, 1996, 2000
   (b) 2000
19. Answers vary.   **21.** 9   **23.** No   **25.** Yes

Exercise Set 13-2
7. role-playing (R)   **9.** *Anatomy of a Murder* (A)
11. (a) swimming pool (S)   (b) Yes   **13.** Yes   **15.** No   **17.** No
19. Professor Donovan (D)   **21.** (a) Children's   (b) Yes
23. Yes   **25.** No   **27.** Answers vary.   **29.** Answers vary.   **31.** Yes

33. If there are six candidates, there are 720 different ballots, making it very cumbersome to list all of the possibilities and build a preference table.

35. (a) Answers vary.

    (b) It would be possible for a candidate listed last on the majority of ballots to win if he or she were listed first on enough, due to the exaggerated number of points for being listed first.

Exercise Set 13-3

9. 6   **11.** 45   **13.** Steel Center (S)

15. (a) There is a three-way tie.   (b) The results are different.

17. (a) Rosa's Restaurant (R)   (b) Yes

19. No   **21.** No   **23.** Dr. Zhang   **25.** green

27. inmate Z   **29.** Answers vary.

31. Using pairwise comparison puts the candidates head-to-head against each other.

33. Ignore all but the top-ranked candidate on each ballot: it's the plurality method.

35. (a) Rather than the candidate with the most approval votes winning, the candidates with the three highest approval totals are all named to council.

    (b) Answers vary.

37. Answers vary.

Exercise Set 13-4

9. 29.2   **11.** 18.9   **13.** 1: 1.40; 2: 0.65; 3: 2.95

15. A: 5.77; B: 4.97; C: 2.80; D: 6.46

17. 4   **19.** 8.49   **21.** 19.60

23. (a) 32

    (b) South: 1.9375

        Central: 4.625

        North: 3.4375

    (c)

Campus	South	Central	North
Lower	1	4	3
Upper	2	5	4

    (d)

Campus	South	Central	North
Promotions	2	5	3

25. (a) 64,444

    (b) District 1: 3.755

        District 2: 2.374

        District 3: 2.871

    (c)

District	1	2	3
Lower	3	2	2
Upper	4	3	3

    (d)

District	1	2	3
Representatives	4	2	3

27. (a) 14.6

    (b) Terminal A: 3.493

        Terminal B: 2.534

        Terminal C: 4.542

        Terminal D: 1.507

    (c)

Terminal	A	B	C	D
Lower	3	2	4	1
Upper	4	3	5	2

    (d) Jefferson's Method:

Terminal	A	B	C	D
Trucks	4	2	5	1

    Adams' Method:

Terminal	A	B	C	D
Trucks	3	3	4	2

    (e) 12.7; 17.1

29. (a) 54

    (b) Store 1: 2.204

        Store 2: 1.833

        Store 3: 3.444

        Store 4: 2.519

    (c)

Store	1	2	3	4
Lower	2	1	3	2
Upper	3	2	4	3

    (d)

Store	1	2	3	4
Computers	2	2	3	3

    (e) Use the standard divisor

31. (a) 1,217.875

    (b) Precinct 1: 2.925

        Precinct 2: 6.956

        Precinct 3: 1.762

        Precinct 4: 4.358

    (c)

Precinct	1	2	3	4
Lower	2	6	1	4
Upper	3	7	2	5

    (d)

Precinct	1	2	3	4
Officers	3	7	2	4

    (e) Use the standard divisor

33. (a) 1,098

    (b) Office 1: 2.032

        Office 2: 0.907

        Office 3: 1.424

        Office 4: 1.638

    (c)

Office	1	2	3	4
Lower	2	0	1	1
Upper	3	1	2	2

    (d)

Office	1	2	3	4
Therapists	2	1	1	2

    (e) 1,106

35. Answers vary.   **37.** Answers vary.

39. (a) Up; more

    (b)

Population	20	40	60	80	; large district
Divisor 2.5	8	16	24	32	
Divisor 2.3	8.7	17.4	26.1	34.8	
Divisor 2.7	7.4	14.8	22.2	29.6	

41. Down; more

Exercise Set 13-5

7. Alabama paradox occurred   **9.** Alabama paradox occurred

11. population paradox did not occur

13. (a)

Campus	North	South
Podiums	9	52

    (b)

Campus	North	South	Campus 3
Podiums	8	53	7

    (c) new states paradox occurred

15. (a)

State	A	B	C
Seats	11	46	40

    (b)

State	A	B	C	D
Seats	10	47	40	13

    (c) the new states paradox occurred

17. Answers vary.

Review Exercises

1.

Number of votes	5	5	5
First choice	Q	P	R
Second choice	R	Q	P
Third choice	P	R	Q

3. 5

5.

Number of votes	6	4	10
First choice	C	P	H
Second choice	P	C	P
Third choice	H	H	C

7. 6   **9.** 58   **11.** Style A   **13.** Style A   **15.** No   **17.** No

19. 47   **21.** Midwest Health Care   **23.** Midwest Health Care

25. Yes   **27.** No   **29.** The Screen

31.

Location	A	B	C	D
Asst. Pastors	5	1	1	3

33.

Location	A	B	C	D
Asst. Pastors	5	2	1	2

35.

Location	A	B	C	D
Asst. Pastors	5	1	1	3

37.

Location	A	B	C	D
Asst. Pastors	5	2	1	2

39. Alabama paradox occurred
41. population paradox did not occur
43. new states paradox did not occur (Note that rounding the standard divisor differently can change the answer.)

Chapter 13 Test

1.

Number of votes	1	7	4
First choice	A	B	C
Second choice	B	A	B
Third choice	C	C	A

3. 7 **5.** Pittsburgh (P) **7.** Pittsburgh (P) **9.** No **11.** No
13. *Big Brother Nursing Home*
15.

Flight	A	B	C
Flight Attendants	4	6	2

17.

Flight	A	B	C
Flight Attendants	4	6	2

19. Alabama paradox occurred
21. new states paradox occurred

CHAPTER 14: GRAPH THEORY

Exercise Set 14-1

13. *A, B, C, D, E, F, G* **15.** *B, G, F* **17.** *B* and *E*
19. Answers vary; one such path is *A, B, E, F.*
21. *G* **23.** There is no edge connecting *E* and *D.*

Note: for 25–30, there are other possible colorings.

25. 3;

27. 4;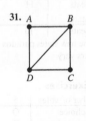

29. 3;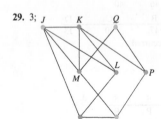

31.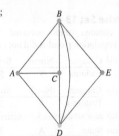

33.   **35.**

37.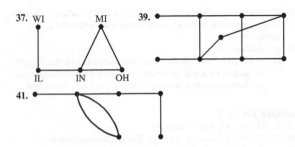

39.

41.

43. 2 **45.** 3 **47.** 3 **49.** 4 **51.** 2 **53.** 2 **55.** Answers vary.
57. No; a vertex is adjacent to itself if there's a loop, so it will be adjacent to a vertex with the same color.
59. Answers vary. **61.** Answers vary.
63. (a) The house is split into distinct parts that are not connected.
   (b) There's a door that connects one part of a room to another.
   (c) There's a door that, if removed, would make it impossible to get from one part of the house to another.

Exercise Set 14-2

7. Euler circuit **9.** Neither
11. (a) Euler path (b) *A, B, C, A, I, C, D, G, I, H, G, F, E, D, F*
13. (a) Euler circuit (b) *A, B, D, H, I, G, D, C, G, F, E, C, A*
15. (a) Neither **17.** (a) Euler circuit (b) *A, B, A, C, B, C, A*
19. (a) Neither
21. 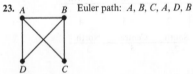 Euler circuit: *A, B, C, D, C, A*

23. Euler path: *A, B, C, A, D, B*

25. Euler path: *A, B, E, D, A, C, D*

27. 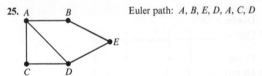 Neither

29. 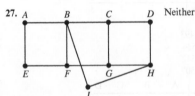 Euler path: *A, B, E, D, C, F, A, G, E*

31.

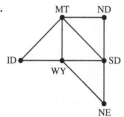

Euler circuit: WY, ID, MT, ND, SD, MT, WY, NE, SD, WY

33.

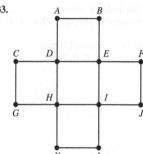

Euler circuit: A, B, E, F, J, I, L, K, H, I, E, D, H, G, C, D, A

35. Neither can be done. Since all four vertices are odd, either removing one bridge or adding one more will make two of the vertices even and the other two odd, in which case there is still no Euler circuit.

37. Path: you can pass through every door in the house exactly once. Circuit: you can do so and end up in the room you started in.

39. Graphs will vary, but such a graph cannot have an Euler circuit because any graph with a bridge will always have at least two odd vertices.

41. Draw an edge connecting any two unconnected odd vertices.

43. There would be no way to traverse every edge if the graph was not connected.

45. Answers vary.

Exercise Set 14-3

11. Answers vary, two possibilities are: A, B, C, D, E, F and A, C, D, E, F, B.

13. Answers vary, two possibilities are: A, B, E, F, J, I, L, K, H, G, C, D and A, B, E, D, C, G, H, K, L, I, J, F.

15. Answers vary, two possibilities are: A, B, E, C, D and A, B, E, D, C.

17. Answers vary, two possibilities are: A, B, D, E, C, F, G, H and A, B, D, E, C, F, H, G.

19. Answers vary, two possibilities are: A, B, C, E, D, A and C, B, A, D, E, C.

21. Answers vary, two possibilities are: A, B, D, G, F, E, H, I, C, A and D, B, A, C, I, H, E, F, G, D.

23. Answers vary, two possibilities are: A, B, C, D, E, A and A, D, B, E, C, A.

25. 2; easy to use brute force method

27. 40,320; ridiculous to use brute force method

29. P, Q, R, S, P and P, S, R, Q, P; 200

31. A, C, B, E, D, A; 42   **33.** A, B, C, D, E, A; 651

35. A, C, B, E, D, A; 42, the same result as the nearest neighbor method

37. A, D, C, B, E, A; 600, a better result than the nearest neighbor method

39. Let T = Pitt, L = Phil, B = Balt and W = Wash.

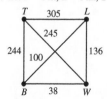

41. T, B, W, L, T; 723 miles. This route is longer than the optimal solution.

43. Let N = New York, D = Cleveland, O = Chicago, and B = Baltimore.

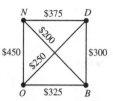

45. O, D, B, N, O; $1,200. This route is $50 more expensive than the optimal solution.

47.

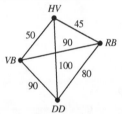

49. H, 3, 1, 4, 5, 2, H; 12:00

In Exercises 51–54, times and distances could vary depending on how you did the search.

51. Times are in minutes.

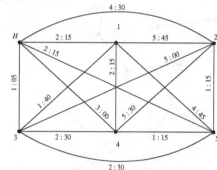

53. The results are the same: Rose Bowl – Downtown Disney – Venice Beach – Hollywood and Vine – Rose Bowl (or the reverse).

55. Answers vary.   **57.** Answers vary.   **59.** Answers vary.

61. Answers vary.

63. No; in a complete graph, every vertex is connected to every other, and there's only one way to do that.   **65.** Answers vary.

Exercise Set 14-4

7. The graph is not a tree because it contains a circuit.

9. The graph is a tree.

11. The graph is not a tree because it is disconnected.

13. The graph is a tree.

15. The graph is not a tree because it contains a circuit.

17.

19.   **21.**

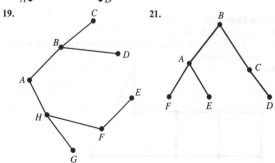

23. 260;

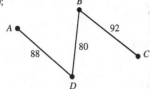

25. 360;

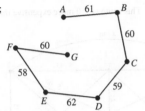

27. 633;

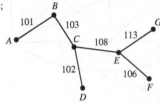

29. 89; *A*

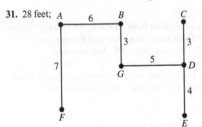

31. 28 feet;

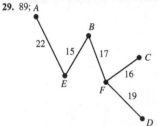

33. 162 feet;

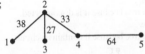

35. Every room can be reached from any other room using some path, but you can't start in one room and return to that room without retracing part of your route.

37. Answers vary. **39.** Answers vary. **41.** Answers vary.

Review Exercises

1. *A, B, C, D, E, F* **3.** odd **5.** *C, E* **7.** Yes

9. Yes. Each has three vertices with degree 3, one with degree 4, and one with degree 1.

11.

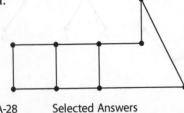

13. 4;

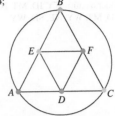

15. Euler circuit **17.** Euler path but no Euler circuit

19. The graph from Exercise 17; one possible answer: *E, D, C, A, B, C, E, B, G, E, F, G.*

21. Euler path: *C, E, W, F, V, C, W, V* is one possible path.

23. Answers vary; one Hamilton path is *A, E, B, D, C, H.*

25. 39,916,800

27.

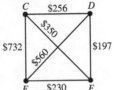

29. *C, D, F, E, C* or *C, E, F, D, C;* $1,415; the cheapest link approximate solution is $19 more than the optimal solution.

31.

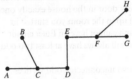

33. A minimum spanning tree connects all vertices with exactly one path that has the lowest possible overall weight. In a traveling salesperson problem, we find a circuit that visits each vertex once and has minimum weight.

Chapter 14 Test

1. (a) 4 (b) *E* (c) Answers vary; one possible path is *A, B, C, E, D, F.* (d) *FD* (e) *A, B, D, E* (f) *C* and *E* are even; *A, B, D,* and *F* are odd.

3. (a)

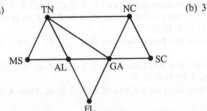

(b) 3

5. (a) Answers vary: one Euler path is *B, A, F, B, C, D, E, C, F.*
(b) Answers vary: one Hamilton path is *A, B, F, C, E, D.* The Hamilton path will typically vary from the Euler path.

7.

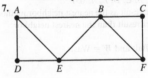

A, D, E, A, B, E, F, B, C, F

9. 64 miles

11.

SELECTED ANSWERS

CHAPTER 15: OTHER MATHEMATICAL SYSTEMS (Online Only)

Exercise Set 15-1

7. C **9.** E **11.** E **13.** D **15.** D **17.** Yes **19.** Yes **21.** D
23. E **25.** $\bigcirc$ **27.** $\triangle$ **29.** $\triangle$ **31.** $\triangle$ **33.** $\triangle$ **35.** No **37.** Yes: $\triangle$
39. $\square$ is the inverse of $\bigcirc$ **41.** closure, associative
43. closure, commutative, identity **45.** closure
47. closure, commutative, identity, inverse
49. closure, commutative, identity, inverse, associative; Abelian group
51. Abelian group **53.** not a group **55.** not a group
57. not a group **59.** not a group
61.

*	0	1	2	3
0	0	1	2	3
1	1	2	3	0
2	2	3	0	1
3	3	0	1	2

63. yes

65. yes, 0 is its own inverse, 2 is its own inverse, and 1 and 3 are inverses.
67.

M	R	B	Y
R	R	P	O
B	P	B	G
Y	O	G	Y

69. no **71.** no
75.

→	T	F	Closure
T	T	F	
F	T	T	

77.

	1	2	3	4
1	−1	−1	−1	−1
2	−1	0	1	2
3	−1	1	3	5
4	−1	2	5	8

79. It should not. If we use @ to represent the operation in this system:

$$(a @ b) @ c = (ab - (a + b)) @ c$$
$$= (ab - (a + b))c - ((ab - (a + b)) + c)$$
$$= abc - ac - bc - ab + a + b - c$$
$$a @ (b @ c) = a @ (bc - (b + c))$$
$$= a(bc - (b + c)) - (a + (bc - (b + c)))$$
$$= abc - ab - ac - a - bc + b + c$$

These two expressions are not equal.

81. The result of combining two identical elements results in a tie; there is no element that represents the winner. (In fact, we would have to define "tie" as the outcome in that case for the system to be well-defined.)

83.

	Rock	Paper	Scissors
Rock	Tie	Paper	Rock
Paper	Paper	Tie	Scissors
Scissors	Rock	Scissors	Tie

85. $A*A*A$ can be interpreted as either $(A*A)*A$ or $A*(A*A)$. The system would have to be associative.

Exercise Set 15-2

9. (a) 3 (b) 3 (c) 3 **11.** (a) 11 (b) 5 (c) 3

13. (a) 6 (b) 0 (c) 2 **15.** (a) 4 (b) 4 (c) 0
17. (a) 7 (b) 1 (c) 3 **19.** (a) 9 (b) 3 (c) 5
21. 2 **23.** 10 **25.** 3 **27.** 11 **29.** 10 **31.** 2 **33.** 10 **35.** 6 **37.** 3
39. 11 **41.** 6 **43.** 12 **45.** 10 **47.** 6 **49.** 12 **51.** 2 **53.** 0 **55.** 5
57. 3 **59.** 2 **61.** 0 **63.** 12 **65.** 7 **67.** 10 **69.** 5 **71.** None
73. None **75.** 1 **77.** Answers vary. **79.** Answers vary. **81.** $y = 10$
83. $y = 1$ **85.** $y = 11, 2, 5,$ and 8 **87.** $y = 6$ **89.** $y = 6$
91. 5:00 P.M. **93.** 9:48 A.M. **95.** 5:00 A.M. **97.** 7:38 P.M.
99. 8:00 P.M. **101.** 0352 **103.** 2006 **105.** 2136 **107.** 10:09 A.M.
109. 2:36 P.M. **111.** The property holds.
113. All are 4; 7, 11, and 15 are three values for b.
115. (a) −3 (b) −4 **117.** (a) −4 (b) −3
119.

Hours	4	5	6	7	8	9	10	11	12
Mult. Inverse	3	2	None	5	3	None	7	4	None

121. In general, n has a multiplicative inverse on an m-hour clock if m and n have no factors in common other than 1.

Exercise Set 15-3

5. 2 **7.** 2 **9.** 7 **11.** 2 **13.** 3 **15.** 2 **17.** 2 **19.** 2 **21.** 4
23. 1 **25.** 4 **27.** 3 **29.** 3 **31.** 2 **33.** 0 **35.** 6 **37.** 6 **39.** 6
41. 4 **43.** 3 **45.** 11 **47.** $\{4, 10, 16, 22, 28, \ldots\}$
49. $\{3, 11, 19, 27, 35, \ldots\}$ **51.** $\{2, 10, 18, 26, 34, \ldots\}$
53. $\{6, 14, 22, 30, 38, \ldots\}$ **55.** $x = 2, 4\frac{1}{2}, 7, 9\frac{1}{2}, 12, \ldots$
57. $y = -3, -4\frac{1}{3}, -5\frac{2}{3}, -7, -8\frac{1}{3}, -9\frac{2}{3}, -11, \ldots$
59. Tuesday **61.** Friday **63.** Tuesday **65.** Valid
67. Invalid **69.** 6 cans **71.** Friday
73. April 22nd, 10 P.M.; 24 (you could also use 12) **75.** south
77. 17 tables; one empty space **79.** 10 oz
81. (a) $212 \equiv x \bmod 12$; 8″ (b) $586 \equiv x \bmod 60$; 46 minutes
83. Answers vary.
85. (a) We would need to find group sizes g for which $124 \equiv 0 \bmod g$.
 (b) There are only 4: 2, 4, 31, and 62 (and the last two are pretty ridiculous group sizes).
87. There are 366 days in the next year (2012 is a leap year), plus 3 more, so we need to find 369 mod 7; this will tell us how many days of the week after Thursday that day is. The answer is Tuesday.
89. Answers vary. **91.** You did not take your second dose.

Review Exercises

1. C **3.** B **5.** C **7.** yes **9.** yes **13.** Abelian group
15. not a group **17.** 3 **19.** 12 **21.** 6 **23.** 2 **25.** 6 **27.** 17
29. Friday at 3 P.M. **31.** 2 **33.** 4 **35.** 7 **37.** 2 **39.** 5 **41.** 9
43. 3 **45.** 1 **47.** 4 **49.** 2 **51.** 2 **53.** 6 **55.** $\{4, 12, 20, 28, 36, \ldots\}$
57. $\{5, 13, 21, 29, 37, \ldots\}$ **59.** $\{2, 10, 18, 26, 34, \ldots\}$
61. $y = 1$ **63.** 4 cookies **65.** no

Chapter 15 Test

1. z **3.** s **5.** z **7.** Yes **9.** x, y **11.** $a = x$ or y
13. (a) 4 (b) 4 (c) 3 (d) 2 (e) 3 **15.** 2 **17.** 0
19. 5 **21.** 0 **23.** $\{0, 4, 8 \ 12, 16, \ldots\}$ **25.** 30 people

SELECTED ANSWERS

CHAPTER 7: SUPPLEMENTAL SECTION

Exercise Set 7-7

5. row echelon form   **7.** not in row echelon form

9. row echelon form   **11.** not in row echelon form

13. (2, 1)   **15.** (3, 7)   **17.** (2, −1, 1)   **19.** (−1, 5, 3)

21. $\left(\frac{3t+1}{13}, \frac{11t+21}{13}, t\right)$ where t is any real number   **23.** (1, 1, −1)

25. 10 adult tickets, 22 child tickets, 7 senior citizen tickets

27. lawn tickets cost $40, general admission costs $80 and ground floor seating costs $150

29. $500 in Fund A, $1,200 in Fund B, and $300 in Fund C

31. won 9 games, lost 5 games, tied 2 games

33. 100 watched beam, 300 watched floor, 250 watched uneven bars

35. Answers vary.

CREDITS

Design Elements

(Pizza for Learning Objectives): MBPHOTO/iStockphoto; (Silver pan under pizza): Laurent Renault/iStockphoto; (Calculator): iStockphoto.

Chapter 1

Opener: © Sonja Flemming/CBS via Getty Images; p. 4: © Royalty-Free/Corbis; p. 5: © Photodisc/Getty Images RF; p. 8: © Ingram Publishing/SuperStock RF; p. 17: © Photodisc/Alamy RF; p. 19: © Jupiterimages RF; p. 29: © Alinari Archives/Corbis; p. 31: © Thinkstock Images/Jupiterimages RF; p. 32: © De Agostini/Getty Images; p. 37: © Sonja Flemming/CBS via Getty Images.

Chapter 2

Opener: © Marc Serota/Getty Images; p. 44: © S. Meltzer/PhotoLink/Getty Images RF; p. 51: © Royalty-Free/Corbis; p. 57: © McGraw-Hill Education. Barry Barker, photographer; p. 62: © Momentum Creative Group/Alamy RF; p. 74: © Getty Images/Digital Vision RF; p. 77: © Digital Vision/SuperStock RF; p. 79(top): © Digital Vision RF; p. 79(bottom): © BananaStock Ltd. RF; p. 87: © Royalty-Free/Corbis; p. 88: © IMS Communications Ltd./Capstone Design/FlatEarth Images RF; p. 93: © Marc Serota/Getty Images.

Chapter 3

Opener: © Colin Anderson/Blend Images LLC RF; p. 98: © McGraw-Hill Education. Jill Braaten, photographer; p. 101: National Library of Medicine, #81192; p. 104(top): © John Dakers/Life File/Getty Images RF; p. 104(bottom): © Cat Sobecki; p. 108: © McGraw-Hill Education. Mark Dierker, photographer; p. 111: © Comstock Images/Alamy RF; p. 112: © Photodisc/Getty Images RF; p. 113: © Creatas/PictureQuest RF; p. 114: © Getty Images RF; p. 119: © McGraw-Hill Education.Jill Braaten. Jill Braaten, photographer; pp. 121–124: © Cat Sobecki; p. 126: © Doug Menuez/Getty Images RF; p. 130: © Christina Lane; p. 132: © TRBfoto/Getty Images RF; p. 134(top): © StockTrek/Getty Images RF; p. 134(bottom): © Comstock Images RF; p. 139: Library of Congress, Prints and Photographs Division [LC-USZ62-13016]; p. 140: © Royalty-Free/Corbis; p. 148: © Colin Anderson/Blend Images LLC RF.

Chapter 4

Opener: © MBI/Alamy RF; p. 154: © The Studio Dog/Getty Images RF; p. 158: © ThinkStock/Jupiterimages RF; p. 162: © Getty Images/Digital Vision RF; p. 164: © Scala/Art Resource, NY; p. 170: © Digital Vision/Getty Images RF; p. 175: © SSPL/The Image Works; p. 176: © Hulton Archive/Getty Images; p. 179: National Radio Astronomy Observatory; p. 182: © Photodisc/Getty Images RF; p. 184: © Kevin Winter/Getty Images; p. 186: © Nick Koudis/Getty Images RF; p. 188: Screen capture by Cat Sobecki, artwork by Mircea Gabriel Eftemie, © Benedictum; p. 199: Courtesy, Naval Historical Center; p. 202: © MBI/Alamy RF.

Chapter 5

Opener: © Photodisc/Punchstock RF; p. 208: © Purestock/SuperStock RF; p. 217: © The Granger Collection, New York; p. 220: © Steve Bronstein/Getty Images; p. 221: © Christina Lane; p. 226: © Creatas/PunchStock RF; p. 229: © C Squared Studios/Getty Images RF; p. 232(top): © Ed Reinke/AP Photo; p. 232(bottom): © McGraw-Hill Companies; p. 239(top): © Cat Sobecki; p. 239(bottom): © Royalty-Free/Corbis; p. 250: © DAJ/Getty Images RF; p. 257: © Stockdisc/Getty Images RF; p. 260: © Duncan Smith/Getty Images RF; p. 265: © Stephen Dunn/Getty Images; p. 271(top): © Getty Images/Digital Vision RF; p. 271(bottom): © Lawrence Lawry/Getty Images RF; p. 274: © Ariel Skelley/Getty Images RF; p. 277: © Thinkstock Images/Jupiterimages RF; p. 278: © Kaz Chiba/Getty Images RF; p. 286: © Photodisc/Punchstock.

Chapter 6

Opener: © PhotoLink/Getty Images RF; p. 292: © Grant V Faint/Getty Images RF; p. 297: © The Trustees of the British Museum. All rights reserved; p. 298: © Blend Images/Getty Images RF; p. 312: © McGraw-Hill Education. Ken Cavanagh, photographer; p. 320: © Royalty-Free/Corbis; p. 321(top): © Ryan McVay/Getty Images RF; p. 321(bottom): © Tom Grill/Corbis RF; p. 328: © 1999 Copyright IMS Communications Ltd./Capstone Design. All Rights Reserved RF; p. 329: © Jack Star/PhotoLink/Getty Images RF; p. 330(top): USDA; p. 330(bottom): Photo of touchscreen by Dave Sobecki. Background photo of Jacobs Field © Michael Frain, Jr.; p. 331: © Emma Lee/Life File/Getty Images RF; p. 332: © Photodisc/PunchStock RF; p. 337: © Stockbyte/Getty Images RF; p. 342: © Kim Steele/Getty Images RF; p. 343: © McGraw-Hill Education. Christopher Kerrigan, photographer; p. 344: © Ryan McVay/Getty Images RF; p. 347: © Brand X Pictures/Jupiterimages RF; p. 361: © PhotoLink/Getty Images RF.

Chapter 7

Page 370(top): © Aaron Roeth Photography RF; p. 370(bottom): © C Squared Studios/Getty Images RF; p. 373: © Arthur S. Aubry/Getty Images RF; p. 376: © Steve Mason/Getty Images RF; p. 385: © Tomi/PhotoLink/Getty Images RF; p. 391: © Skip Nall/Getty Images RF; p. 403: © Royalty-Free/Corbis; p. 405: © Susan Van Etten/PhotoEdit; p. 407: © Jack Star/PhotoLink/Getty Images RF; p. 410: © Royalty-Free/Corbis; p. 422(top): © Comstock RF; p. 422(bottom): © McGraw-Hill Education/Ron Carboni; p. 423: © Comstock Images/Alamy RF; p. 426: © David Buffington/Getty Images RF; p. 427: © Colin Paterson/Getty Images RF; p. 429: © James L. Amos/Photo Researchers, Inc.

Chapter 7 (Online Section)

Supplemental Section-1: © Stock Trek/Getty Images RF; ss-7: © Digital Vision/Getty Images RF.

Chapter 8

Opener: © Digital Vision/SuperStock RF; p. 442: © PhotoLink/Getty Images RF; p. 445: © Jupiterimages/Imagesource RF; p. 446: © Royalty-Free/Corbis; p. 447: © Ryan McVay/Getty

INDEX

absolute unfairness, 819
absolute value, 221, 285
   of improper fraction, 233
   of proper fraction, 233
absolute zero (temperature), 542
acre(s)
   and square miles, conversion
      between, 530–531
   and square yards, conversion
      between, 531
actuarial method, 477–478, 511
acute angle, 554
acute triangle, 562
Adams, John Quincy, 789, 816
Adams' method, 816–817, 829
addition
   associative property of, 260, 262
   in base five system, 191–193
   in base sixteen (hexadecimal)
      system, 194
   in base two (binary) system, 193
   closure property of, 259, 262
   commutative property of, 259, 262
   in Egyptian system, 157
   of fractions, 237–239
   identity property of, 260, 262
   of integers, 222–224
   inverse property of, 260, 262
   of like radicals, 251
   phrases that represent, 318
   in Roman system, 158
   of square roots, 251–252
addition method, solving a system of
      equations by, 387–390
addition property of equality, 306–307
addition property of inequality, 339
addition rule 1, 670–671
addition rule 2, 671–672
additive inverse, 220, 260–261
adjacent angles, 554
adjacent vertices, 840, 874
adjustable-rate mortgage, 492, 495
Ahmes, 297
Aiken, Howard, 199
Alabama paradox, 822–823, 829
algebra, 291, 361
   applications of, 298–300
   definition of, 292
   historical perspective on, 297
algebraic expression(s), 361. *See also*
      binomial(s)
   definition of, 292
   and equations, differences
      between, 304
   evaluating, 296–297
   simplifying, 294–296
   terms of, 293
algorithm
   definition of, 170
   Egyptian, 170–171, 202
Al-khwarizmi, 297
alternate exterior angles, 558, 612
alternate interior angles, 557–558, 612
alternating sequence(s), 282
amortization schedule, 496–497, 512
amount financed

calculation of, 475–476
   for fixed installment loan, 474
analytic geometry, 369
angle(s), 612
   acute, 554
   adjacent, 554
   alternate exterior, 558, 612
   alternate interior, 557–558, 612
   complementary, 554–556, 612
   corresponding, 558, 566, 612
   definition of, 553
   exterior, 557–558
   finding using trigonometric ratios,
      599–600
   formed by transversal, 557–559
   interior, 557–558
   measurement of, 554, 556–557
   naming of, 553
   obtuse, 554
   pairs of, 554
   radian measure for, 561
   rays of, 553
   right, 554, 565
   sides of, 553
   straight, 554
   sum of, in triangle, 563
   supplementary, 554–556, 612
   symbol for, 553
   of triangle, finding, 563–564
   trigonometric ratios and, 599–600
   vertex of, 553
   vertical, 557, 612
angle of depression, 601–602
angle of elevation, 601–602
annual percentage rate, 476–477, 511
annual yield, 465–466, 511
annuity(ies), 511
   definition of, 467
   future value of, 467–469
   monthly payment for, calculating,
      469–470
antecedent, in conditional statement,
      109, 125–126, 147
application problems, 29
apportionment, 785, 810–819, 829
   Adams' method, 816–817, 829
   definition of, 811
   Hamilton's method, 813–815,
      822–826, 829
   Huntington-Hill method,
      818–819, 829
   Jefferson's method, 815–817, 829
   Webster's method, 817–818, 826, 829
apportionment flaws, 822–826
approval voting, 806–807, 828
APR, 476–477, 511
Arabic numeration system, 154,
      161–162, 202
arbitrary, 10
Archimedes, 32
area, 546, 613. *See also* surface area
   calculus and, 582
   of circle, 583
   English and metric equivalents
      for, 530
   English-metric conversions, 530–532

of parallelogram, 579–580
   of polygons, 578–582
   of rectangle, 578–579
   of square, 578–579
   of trapezoid, 581
   of triangle, 580–581
   units of, 529–530
argument(s)
   common valid forms of, 133–136
   conclusion of, 129, 147
   Euler circles for deciding validity
      of, 141–144
   fallacies, 129, 134–135, 148
   invalid, 129, 135–136, 147–148
   logical, 129–137, 147
   premises of, 129, 147
   valid, 129–133, 135–137, 147–148
Aristotle, 101
arithmetic, fundamental theorem of,
      211, 285
arithmetic average, 719
arithmetic sequence(s), 275–278, 286, 289
   application of, 281
   common difference in, 275
   definition of, 275
   finding a particular term of,
      276–277
   finding terms of, 275–276
   nth term of, 275–277
   sum of, finding, 277–278
Arrow, Kenneth, 805–806, 828
Arrow's impossibility theorem,
      805–806, 828
associative property, 260
astronomical units, 280
asymptote, 424
average(s), 718–719
   ambiguous, 778
   arithmetic, 719
   definition of, 719
   measures of, 719, 724–725, 771
average daily balance method,
      480–483, 511
axis, definition of, 368
axis of symmetry, 420–421, 435

Babylonian numeration system, 163–165
Balinski, Michael L., 826
Banker's rule, 457–458
banking, historical perspective on, 446
bar graph(s), 20–21, 710–711, 771
base eight (octal) system, 182–183
   and computers, 185–186
   digits, binary equivalents for, 187
base five system, 178–183, 202
   addition in, 191–193
   division in, 197–198
   multiplication in, 195–197
   subtraction in, 194–195
base number systems, 178–188, 202
   operations in, 191–198
base of exponent, 202, 265
   definition of, 161
base of logarithm, 427–428
base sixteen (hexadecimal) system,
      182–183

addition in, 194
   and computers, 185–186
   digits, binary equivalents for, 187
base sixty system, 164
base ten system, 154, 162–163, 178, 183
   converting numbers to, 183–184
   numbers in, converting to other
      base numbers, 184–185
base three system, 183
base two (binary) system, 153, 182–183
   addition in, 193
   and computers, 185–186
   and computer storage, 188
   and hexadecimal system, conversion
      between, 187–188
   multiplication in, 197
   and octal system, conversion
      between, 187
bell curve, 743
biconditional, 100, 103, 147
biconditional statement, truth values
      for, 111–112
binary system. *See* base two (binary)
      system
binomial(s)
   definition of, 348
   multiplying, 348–349
binomial experiment(s), 685–686, 693
binomial probability formula, 686–689
bit(s), 185, 188
Bok, Derek, 441
Bolyai, János, 606
bond(s), 506–507, 512
   coupon, 506
   definition of, 501
   face value of, 501, 506
   maturity date of, 506
bond trade(s), 506–507
Boole, George, 101
Borda, Jean-Charles de, 793, 795
Borda count method, 785, 793–796,
      828–829
box plot, 771
   definition of, 739
   drawing and interpreting, 739–740
bridge, in graph theory, 840–841, 874
Briggs, Henry, 176
Bruno, Giordano, 89
brute force method, 857–858, 874
Bush, George W., 789, 802–803
byte(s), 185, 188

calculation, problem solving by, 31
calculator(s)
   graphing, 426
   regression, on-line, 426
calculus, and area, 582
"canceling," of fractions, 235
Cantor, Georg, 87–89
Cantor diagonal, 95
Cantor set, 95
capacity, 532–536, 546, 588
capitalized interest, on student loans,
      491, 512
cardinality of set, 48–49, 73–74, 90
cardinality of union of sets, 73–74

cardinal number (cardinality) of set, 48–49, 73–74, 90
Cartesian plane, 368–369, 434
    slope of a line on, 373–374
Cartesian product, 63, 369
categorical frequency distribution, 703–704, 710–712, 771
causation, correlation versus, 767
Celsius temperature, 300, 312, 546
    and Fahrenheit, conversion between, 542–543
center
    of circle, 582, 613
    of sphere, 591
centigrade, 542
centimeter, cubic, 534–535
certificate of deposit, 463
change of base formula, for logarithms, 428
cheapest link algorithm, 860–861, 874
chest radiography, 37
Chevalier de Mere, 668
Chinese numeration system, 159–161
chromatic number, 842–843, 874
Churchill, Winston, 139
circle(s), 582, 613
    area of, 583
    center of, 582, 613
    circumference of, 582, 613
    diameter of, 582, 613
    radius of, 582, 613
circle graph, 21, 711
circuit, 848, 874
    Euler, 848–851, 874
    in graph theory, 840
    Hamilton, 855–857, 874
circular reasoning, 135
circumference
    of circle, 582
    definition of, 561
    formula for, 561, 582
classical probability, 637–640, 642–643, 692
    computing, 638–639
classification, Venn diagrams in, 77–83
closed-ended credit, 479
closed geometric figure(s), 562
closed under multiplication, 256
closing costs, 494
closure property, 259
cluster sample, 701
coefficient
    definition of, 251
    in terms, 293
coloring, for graph, 842, 874
combination(s), 630–634, 692
    applications of, 632–633
    definition of, 630
    identifying, 631
    and permutations, comparison of, 630–631
combination rule(s), 631–632, 634, 692
    with fundamental counting principle, 632–633
commas, in set notation, 44
commission, stock brokerage's, 501, 505–506
common difference, in arithmetic sequence, 275
common ratio, of geometric sequence, 278
common sense, 97, 129
commutative property, 259
complement
    probability of, 640
    of set, 56–57, 62, 70–71, 92
complementary angles, 554–556, 612
complete graph, 856, 874
    and Hamilton circuits, 856
complete weighted graph, 857, 874
    drawing, 861
component(s), of ordered pair, 63

composite numbers, 210, 285
compound interest, 462–470, 511
    computing, 463–464
    definition of, 452, 462
    and simple interest, comparison of, 462–463
compound statement, negation of, 124
compound statement(s)
    parentheses in, 115–116
    truth tables for, 112–116
computer design, logical gates and, 109
conclusion, of argument, 129, 147
conditional, 100, 103, 147
conditional probability, 680–682, 693
conditional statement
    converse of, 124–126, 147
    inverse of, 124–126, 147
    negation of, 123–124
    truth values for, 109–112
    variations of, 124–126
cone(s), 613
    right circular, 591
    surface area of, 592–593
    volume of, 591
conjecture, 4–5
conjunction, 100, 103, 107–108, 147
    negation of, 122
    truth values for, 107–108, 112
connected graph, 840–841, 874
connective(s), 100, 147
    hierarchy of, 116
    symbols for, 103
consequent, in conditional statement, 109, 125–126, 147
consistent system of linear equations, 383, 434
constant of proportionality, 331–332
constraints, 404, 435
contradiction, 313–314
contrapositive, 124–126, 147
convenience sample, 777–778
converse, 124–126, 147
    fallacy of, 134–135, 148
coordinate(s), of points
    definition of, 369
    finding, 370
coordinate system, rectangular, 368–370, 434
correlation, 703, 759
    versus causation, 767
correlation coefficient (r), 761–763, 772
    and regression line, relationship between, 766
    significant values for, 763–764
corresponding angles, 558, 566, 612
corresponding sides, of similar triangles, 566
cosine, 597–599, 613
    inverse of, 600
countable set, 88–89, 92
counterexample, 6–7
coupon, definition of, 506
coupon bonds, definition of, 506
credit
    closed-ended, 479
    open-ended, 479
credit cards, 511
    historical perspective on, 446
criminal investigation, 3
criminology, 699
criterion, definition of, 789
cross multiplying, 327–328
cross product, 63
cube(s) (polyhedra), 588, 613
    surface area of, 592
    volume of, 588
cube roots, 256
cubic centimeter, 534–535
cubic feet (foot), 533
    and gallons, conversion between, 533–534
cubic inch(es), 588

cubic meter, 534–535
cubic units, 546, 588, 613
cubic yard, 533
cubit, 522
cyclical trend(s), 714
cylinder, 613
    definition of, 589
    surface area of, 592–593
    volume of, 589–590
data, 699, 771
    definition of, 700
    gathering, 700
    normally distributed, identifying, 754–755
    picturing, 710–714
    raw, 703
data sets, possible relationships between/among, 767–768
da Vinci, Leonardo, 29
debate, formal, 130
decagon, 572
decimal(s), 285
    fractions written as, 240
    and numbers in scientific notation, conversion between, 268–269
    and percents, conversion between, 21, 442–444
    place values for, 239
    repeating, 241, 285
    terminating, 240, 285
decimal part, of numbers in scientific notation, 270
deductive reasoning, 8–12, 37
degree(s)
    of angles, 554
    and radians, conversion between, 561
    of vertex, in graph theory, 840, 874
demographics, 43, 93
De Morgan, Augustus, 70, 101, 844
De Morgan's laws
    for logic, 122–123, 147
    for sets, 70–71, 92
denominator
    definition of, 232
    rationalizing, 252–253
dependent event(s), 676, 693
dependent system of linear equations, 383–384, 390–391, 434
dependent variable, 411–412, 759
depression, angle of, 601–602
Descartes, René, 297, 369
descriptive method, 46–47, 94
descriptive statistics, 702
detached statistics, 778
detachment, law of, 133, 135–136
diagram. See also tree diagram; Venn diagram(s)
    problem solving by, 28–29
diameter
    of circle, 582, 613
    of sphere, 591
difference, of sets, 62–63, 92
digit(s), 202
digit (length unit), 522
dimensional analysis, 520–522, 546
    conversions in metric system using, 525–526
Diophantus, 40, 297
direct variation, 331–332
disconnected graph, 840–841, 874
discount, definition of, 458
discounted loan(s), 458–459
discriminant, 360
disjoint sets, 60, 140
disjunction, 100, 103, 147
    negation of, 122
    truth values for, 108–109, 112
distributive property, 261–262, 293–294
divide by primes method, for finding greatest common factor, 214

dividend(s)
    definition of, 501
    on stocks, 501–502
divisibility, 6
    definition of, 209
    tests for, 209, 219
division
    in base five system, 197–198
    Egyptian algorithm in, 171
    of fractions, 236–237
    of integers, 226
    of numbers in scientific notation, 270–271
    phrases that represent, 318
    of square roots, 249–250
division method, of prime factorization, 212
division property of equality, 307–308
division property of inequality, 339
divisor(s), definition of, 209
dodecagon, 572
domain, of function, 413, 435
double sampling, 710
down payment, 474, 511

e (Euler's number), 852
edge(s), in graph theory, 836, 874
effective interest rate, 465–466, 511
    of two investments, comparison of, 466
Egyptian algorithm, 170–171, 202
Egyptian numeration system(s), 155–157
election poll(s), 789
element, of set, 44, 58, 92
elevation, angle of, 601–602
elimination, solving a system of equations by, 387–390
ellipse, 583
ellipsis, in set notation, 45, 47
elliptic geometry, 605–606, 613
empirical probability, 640–643, 692
empirical rule, 743–744
empty set, 47–48, 92
encryption, 200
endpoints, definition of, 552
English system of measurement, 520–522
    area measurements, conversions between, 530–531
    area units, and metric system, conversion between, 530–532
    capacity conversion factors, 533
    capacity measurements, and metric system, conversion between, 535–536
    capacity units, 533
    length units, and metric system, conversion between, 526–527
    metric equivalents for length, 526
    and metric system, conversion between, 526–527, 530–532, 535–536, 539, 541, 546
    volume units, 533
    weight conversions in, 539–540
    weight measurements, and metric system, conversion between, 539, 541
    weight units, 539–540
equal set(s), 49–50, 71–73, 92
equals sign (=), 222
equation(s), 361, 367. See also linear equation(s); quadratic equation(s)
    contradiction, 313–314
    definition of, 304
    equivalent, 306
    and expressions, differences between, 304
    graph of, 434

identity, 313–314
    solution of, 304–305, 361
    solving, 304, 361
    solving word problems using, 318
equilateral triangle, 562, 574
equivalent equations, 306
equivalent fractions, 234
equivalent graphs, 839
equivalent sets, 49–51, 92
Eratosthenes, sieve of, 210
Escher, M. C., 610
estimation, 16–20
Euclid, 101, 211, 247, 556
Euclidean geometry, 101, 556, 605
Euler, Leonhard, 71, 101, 139, 835,
    848, 852
Euler circle(s), 101, 139–144, 147
    statements illustrated by, 140
    and testing validity of arguments,
        141–144
Euler path, 848–851, 874
Euler's number, 852
Euler's theorem, 848–852, 874
event(s), 637
    dependent, 676, 693
    independent, 676, 678, 680, 693
    mutually exclusive, 669, 692
even vertex, 840
exclusive *or*, 108–109
expanded notation, 162–163
expected value, 663–666, 692
    definition of, 663
    in gambling games, 666
exponent(s), 161
    definition of, 265
    expressions with, evaluating, 265–266
    negative, 265, 268
    positive, in scientific notation, 268
    power rule for, 266–267
    product rule for, 266–267
    quotient rule for, 266–267
    rules for, 266–267
    zero as, 265
exponential expression, 161, 265–266
exponential function(s), 424–429, 435
    applications of, 426–429
    definition of, 424
    graphing, 424–426
expression(s). *See also* algebraic
        expression(s)
    exponential, 161, 265–266
    factorial, evaluating, 624
exterior angle(s), 557–558
extraterrestrial life, 179

face value, of bond, 501
factor(s), 285
    definition of, 208
    finding, 208–209
    greatest common, 212–215
    of prime numbers, 209–212
factorial expression(s), evaluating, 624
factorial notation, 624
factoring, 361
    definition of, 350
    solving quadratic equations using,
        353–354
    of trinomials, 350–353
Fahrenheit temperature, 300, 312, 546
    and Celsius, conversion between,
        542–543
fairness criterion, 790
fallacies, 129, 134–135, 148
fallacy of converse, 134–135, 148
fallacy of inclusive *or*, 135–136
fallacy of inverse, 134, 136, 148
feasible region, 406
federal student loan, 488, 512
feet (length unit)
    cubic, 533–534
    historical perspective on, 522
    and miles, conversion between, 521
    and yards, conversion between, 521

Fermat, Pierre de, 217
Fermat numbers, 217
Fibonacci, 278, 297
Fibonacci sequence, 278, 288–289
finance charge, 511
    average daily balance method,
        480–483
    calculation of, 475–476
    for fixed installment loan, 474
    unpaid balance method, 480
finite set, number of subsets of, 59
fixed installment loan(s), 474–476, 511
    amount financed, 474
    finance charge for, 474
    payoff amount, calculation of,
        477–479
    total installment price for, 474
fixed-rate mortgage, 492
Fleury's algorithm, 850–851, 874
FOIL method, 348–349
foreclosure, 495
forensics, 130
formula(s), 361
    definition of, 299
    for distance, 299–300
    solving, for a specific variable,
        312–313
four color theorem, 844
fractal(s), 613
    definition of, 607
    iteration of, 607
    self-similarity of, 607, 613
fractal dimension, 607, 613
fractal geometry, 607–608
fraction(s), 232, 285. *See also* rational
        numbers
    addition of, 237–239
    "canceling," 235
    with common denominator, adding
        and subtracting, 237–239
    and decimals, 240
    denominator of, 232
    with different denominators, adding
        and subtracting, 238–239
    division of, 236–237
    equivalent, 234
    improper, 232–233
    least common denominator of,
        238–239
    linear equations containing,
        solving, 310–311
    multiplication of, 235–236
    multiplicative inverse of, 236
    music and, 239
    numerator of, 232
    odds expressed as, 661
    and percents, conversion between,
        443–444
    proper, 232–233
    ratios expressed as, 325–326
    reciprocal of, 236, 261
    reducing to lowest terms, 234–235
    repeating decimal written as,
        241–243
    rewriting, with larger
        denominator, 235
    sign of, 234
    square root of, simplifying, 253
    subtraction of, 237–239
    terminating decimal written as, 241
    unit, 520, 546
    unreducing (building up), 235
    written in decimal form, 240
frequency distribution, 642, 692,
        703–705, 771
    categorical, 703–704, 710–712, 771
    grouped, 704–705, 712–713, 771
frequency polygon, 713, 771
function(s), 367, 403–404, 410–415, 435
    definition of, 411
    dependent variable of, 411–412
    domain of, 413
    evaluating, 412–413

exponential, 424–429, 435
    graph of, 414–415
    identifying, 411
    independent variable of, 411–412
    input of, 412
    linear, 413–414
    for modeling real quantities, 426
    objective, 403–405, 435
    output of, 412
    quadratic, 420–424, 435
    range of, 413
function notation, 411–412, 435
fundamental counting principle,
        622–623, 627, 632–634, 692
    with repetition, 623
fundamental theorem of arithmetic,
        211, 285
future value, 511
    of annuity, 467–469
    definition of, 453
    finding, 453–454

Galileo, 422
gallon(s)
    and cubic feet, conversion between,
        533–534
    and liters, conversion between,
        535–536
Gauss, Carl Friedrich, 743
Gaussian distribution, 743
general term, for an infinite set, 88
geometric figure(s), 612. *See also*
        line(s); plane(s); point(s)
    closed, 562
geometric mean, 818–819, 829
geometric sequence(s), 278–282, 286, 289
    application of, 281–282
    common ratio of, 278
    definition of, 278
    finding a particular term of, 279–280
    finding terms of, 279
    *n*th term of, 279
    sum of, finding, 280–281
geometry, 551
    analytic, 369
    elliptic, 605–606
    Euclidean, 101, 556, 605
    fractal, 607–608
    hyperbolic, 606
    non-Euclidean, 101, 556, 605–610
gigabyte, 188
Goldbach, Christian, 219
golden ratio, 250, 256, 278, 288–289,
        360, 577
googol, 19
Gore, Al, 789, 802
graduated payments, on mortgage, 492
gram(s), 523, 539, 546
graph(s), 367–368, 435, 771, 874
    of an equation, 371, 434
    bar, 20–21, 710–711, 771
    complete, 856, 874
    complete weighted, 857, 861, 874
    connected, 840–841, 874
    definition of, 836
    disconnected, 840–841, 874
    equivalent, 839
    of exponential function, 424–426
    features of, 840–841
    of a function, 414–415
    of horizontal lines, 375
    of inequalities, 337–338
    of linear equation in two variables,
        371–372
    misleading, 26, 779–780
    of quadratic function, 421–422
    representing border relationships,
        837–838
    representing city streets, 838
    representing floor plan, 837
    representing islands, 836–837
    representing public
        transportation, 839

slope-intercept form for, 375
    of solution sets for simple
        inequalities, 338
    of vertical lines, 375
graph coloring, 842–843, 874
    and maps, 843–844
    in scheduling, 842–843
graphing calculator, 426
graph theory, 835–836
great circle(s), of sphere, 605–606
greater than or equal to sign (≥), 222
greater than sign (>), 222
greatest common factor, 212–214, 285
    application of, 215
    finding, divide by primes
        method, 214
    of three numbers, 213–214
    of two numbers, 213
grouped frequency distribution,
        704–705, 712–713, 771
grouping system(s)
    multiplicative, 159–161, 202
    simple, 155–159, 202
Guthrie, Francis, 844

half line(s), 612
    definition of, 552
    figure for, 552–553
    symbol for, 552–553
half plane, 396–398, 434
Halley, Edmond, 583
Halley's Comet, 583
Hamilton, Alexander, 813
Hamilton, William Rowan, 859
Hamilton circuit(s), 855–857, 874
Hamilton path(s), 855–856, 874
Hamilton's method, 813–815,
        822–826, 829
Hamilton's puzzle, 859
head-to-head comparison criterion,
        789–790, 805, 828
height, measurement of, using similar
        triangles, 567–568,
        570–571
heptagon, 572
    sum of angle measures of, 573
Herchel, William, 280
Heron's formula, 587
hexadecimal system. *See* base sixteen
        (hexadecimal) system
hexagon, 572
    sum of angle measures of, 574
hierarchy of connectives, 116
Hill, Joseph, 818
Hindu-Arabic numeration system, 154,
        161–162, 202
histogram(s), 712–713, 754, 771–772
home buying, 491–497
Hopper, Grace Murray, 199
horizontal asymptote, 424
horizontal line(s)
    graph of, 375
    slope of, 373–374, 434
Huntington, Edward V., 818
Huntington-Hill method, 818–819, 829
hyperbolic geometry, 606, 613
hypoteneuse, 597
    definition of, 564
hypothesis testing, 702

icosagon, 572
    sum of angle measures of, 573
identity
    for addition, 260, 262
    equation, 313–314
    for multiplication, 260
imaginary numbers, 259
implication. *See* conditional statement
improper fraction
    absolute value of, 233
    definition of, 232
    and mixed numbers, conversion
        between, 233

inch(es)
   cubic, 588
   square, 529–530, 613
inclusive *or,* 108–109
   fallacy of, 135–136
inconsistent system of linear equations, 383–384, 390, 434
independent event(s), 676, 678, 680, 693
independent system of linear equations, 383
independent variable, 411–412, 759
induction. *See* inductive reasoning
inductive argument, weak vs. strong, 15–16
inductive reasoning, 4–9, 11–12, 37, 59
inequality(ies). *See also* linear inequality(ies)
   addition property of, 339
   division property of, 339
   graph of, 337–338
   multiplication property of, 339
   subtraction property of, 339
   three-part, 338, 341–342
inequality signs, 222
inferential statistics, 702–703
infinite set(s)
   definition of, 86–87
   a general term for, 88
   illustration of, 87–88
infinity, 86, 88
   Cantor's study of, 89
installment buying, 474–484
   definition of, 474
instant runoff voting, 796
integer(s), 259, 285
   addition of, 222–224
   closed under multiplication, 256
   as countable set, 89
   definition of, 220
   division of, 226
   multiplication of, 224–226
   negative, 220–221
   positive, 220–221
   subtraction of, 223–224
intercept(s), 372
interest, 511. *See also* unearned interest, calculation of
   Banker's rule for, 457–458
   capitalized, on student loans, 491, 512
   compound, 452, 462–470, 511
   compounded annually, 463, 469
   compounded continuously, 469, 473
   compounded daily, 463, 469
   compounded monthly, 463
   compounded quarterly, 463, 469
   compounded semiannually, 463, 469
   credit card, 511
   definition of, 452
   on discounted loans, 458–459
   simple, 452–459, 462–463, 511
   on student loans, 489, 491, 512
   unpaid balance method, 480
interest rate *(r)*, 452–453. *See also* effective interest rate
   computing, 456
   nominal, 466
interior angles, 557–558
interquartile range, 739
intersection, of sets, 60–61, 92
invalid argument, 129, 135–136, 147–148
inverse, 124–126, 147, 260
   fallacy of, 134, 136, 148
inverse trigonometric functions, 599
inverse variation, 332–333
IRA, 469
irrational numbers, 246–254, 259, 285
   approximating, with calculator, 254
   definition of, 246
irrelevant alternatives criterion, 804–805, 828
Ishango bone, 155

isosceles triangle, 562
iteration, of fractals, 607, 613

Jackson, Andrew, 789
Jefferson, Thomas, 815
Jefferson's method, 815–817, 829

Kelvin scale, 542, 546
Kennedy, John F., 789
kilobyte(s), 188
kilogram(s), 539
Koch snowflake, 607–608
Königsberg bridge problem, 835, 850
Kronecker, Leopold, 89
Kruskal's algorithm, 867–868, 875

Laplace, Pierre-Simon, 852
lattice method, 173–174, 202
law of contraposition, 133–135, 139
law of detachment, 133, 135–136, 139
law of disjunctive syllogism, 134, 136
law of syllogism, 134–135
law of transitivity, 134, 136
least common denominator, 310–311
   of fractions, 238–239
least common multiple, 285
   application of, 216
   definition of, 215
   of two or more numbers, 216
Lebombo bone, 155
leg(s), of right triangle, 564
length
   English and metric equivalents for, 526
   English-metric conversions, 526–527
   in English system of measurement, 520–522
   measurement of, 520–527
   measurements, conversion using two unit fractions, 521–522
   in metric system, 523–527
   units of, 520
less than or equal to sign (≤), 222
less than sign (<), 222
like radicals, 251
   addition of, 251
   subtraction of, 251
like term(s)
   combining, 294–296
   definition of, 294
Lincoln, Abraham, 139
line(s), 612. *See also* half line(s)
   on Cartesian plane, slope of, 373–374, 434
   definition of, 552
   in elliptic geometry, 605–606
   figure for, 552–553
   horizontal, 373–375, 434
   in hyperbolic geometry, 606
   parallel, 557–558
   symbol for, 552–553
   vertical, 373–374, 434
linear equation(s), 382
   applications of, 317–322
   containing fractions, solving, 310–311
   definition of, 305
   general procedure for solving, 308–310
   identifying, 305–306
   modeling with, rate of change in, 376
   solving using addition and subtraction properties, 306–307, 361
   solving using multiplication and division properties, 307–308, 361
   systems of, 382–392, 434
linear equation in one variable, 305
linear equation in two variables, 370–372, 434

applications of, 375–377
   satisfying, 371
   solution to, 371
linear functions
   definition of, 414
   graphing, 414
linear inequality(ies), 361, 396–400
   addition and subtraction properties, 339
   applications of, 342–344
   graphing, 337–338
   multiplication and division properties, 339
   solution set for, 337–338
   solving, 337
   systems of, 396, 398–400
   three-part, 338, 341–342
linear inequality in one variable, 337
   solving, 339–341
linear inequality in two variables, 396–400
   graphing, 396–398, 434
linear programming, 403–408, 435
   using, procedure for, 406–407
linear relationship
   negative, 760–761
   positive, 760–761
linear units, 529
line graph, 22–23
line of best fit, 765
line segment, 612
   definition of, 552
   figure for, 552–553
   symbol for, 552–553
liquid capacity, 532–536, 546, 588
liter(s), 523, 534–535
   and gallons, conversion between, 535–536
loan(s)
   discounted, 458–459
   down payment on, 474, 511
   fixed installment, 474–479, 511
   student, 488–491, 512
   term of, 456–457
Lobachevsky, Nikolay, 606
logarithm(s), 176, 427–428, 435
   change of base formula for, 428
logarithm function with base *b,* 427–428
logic, 97, 101
   De Morgan's laws for, 122–123
   and forensics, 130
logical argument, 129–137, 147
logical gates, and computer design, 109
logically equivalent statement(s), 121–122, 147
logistics, 403
loop, in graph theory, 836, 874
lower quota, 813, 816, 829

majority criterion, 795–796, 805, 828
Mandelbrot, Benoit, 607
map coloring problem, 843–844
market research, 79
mass, and weight, relationship of, 523
matryoshka, 257
maturity date of bond(s), 506
maximum value of objective function, 404–405, 435
Mayan calendar, 166
McGrevey, John D., 641
mean, 771, 778
   of data set, 719, 725
   definition of, 719
   geometric, 818–819, 829
   for grouped data, 719–720
measurement, 519. *See also* English system of measurement; metric system
   of angle, 554, 556–557
   units of, 519
measures of central tendency, 719

median, 771, 778
   of data set, 721–722, 725
   definition of, 721
mediation and duplation, method of, 172
megabyte(s), 188
member, of set, 44
meter(s), 523
   cubic, 534–535
metric system, 519, 523–527
   area measurements, and English system, conversion between, 530–532
   area units, 530
   capacity conversion factors, 535
   capacity measurements, and English system, conversion between, 535–536
   capacity units, 534–535
   conversions in, 524–525, 535, 540, 546
   English equivalents for length, 526
   and English system, conversion between, 526–527, 530–532, 535–536, 539, 541, 546
   length measurements, and English system, conversion between, 526–527
   length units, 523
   prefixes used in, 523
   volume measurements, conversions between, 535
   volume units, 534–535
   weight conversions in, 540
   weight measurements, and English system, conversion between, 539, 541
   weight units, 539–540
metric ton, 539
midrange, 771, 778
   of data set, 725
   definition of, 724
   finding, 724
mile(s)
   and feet, conversion between, 521
   historical perspective on, 522
mind control, 97, 148
minimum spanning tree, 867–868, 875
minimum value of objective function, 404–405, 435
mixed number
   definition of, 232
   and improper fraction, conversion between, 233
Mobius, Augustus Ferdinand, 608
Mobius strip, 608
mode, 771, 778
   for categorical data, 723
   of data set, 722–723, 725
   definition of, 722
modified divisor, 815–816, 829
modus ponens, 139
modus tollens, 139
money, historical perspective on, 446
monotonicity criterion, 797–799, 805
monthly payments, computing, 454–455
mortgage(s)
   adjustable-rate, 492, 495
   definition of, 492, 512
   with different terms, comparison of, 494–495
   fixed-rate, 492
   graduated payments on, 492
   monthly payment for, calculation of, 492–493, 495–496
   term of, 492
   total interest on, calculation of, 493–494
mortgage crisis, 495
multiple(s), definition of, 215
multiple sampling, 710
multiplication
   associative property of, 260, 262
   in base five system, 195–197

in base two (binary) system, 197
of binomials, 348–349
closure property of, 259, 262
commutative property of,
    258–259, 262
distributive property of, 261–262,
    293–294
Egyptian algorithm in, 170–171
of fractions, 235–236
identity property of, 260, 262
of integers, 224–226
integers closed under, 256
inverse property of, 261–262
lattice method, 173–174
Napier's bones in, 175–177
of natural numbers, 208
of numbers in scientific notation,
    269–270
phrases that represent, 318
Russian peasant method, 171–173
of square roots, 249
multiplication property of equality,
    307–308
multiplication property of inequality, 339
multiplication rule 1, 676–679
multiplication rule 2, 679–680
multiplicative grouping system(s),
    159–161, 202
multiplicative inverse, 261
    of fraction, 236
music, 239
mutual fund(s), 501, 507–508, 512
    definition of, 507
    ratings for, 507–508
mutually exclusive events, 669, 692
Myspace use, and illiteracy, 767

Napier, John, 175–176
Napier's bones, 175–177, 202
natural number(s), 285
    as infinite set, 87–88, 90
nearest neighbor method, 858–860, 874
negation, 147
    of compound statement, 124
    of conditional statement, 123–124
    of conjunction, 122
    of disjunction, 122
    notation for, 103
    of statements, 101–102
    truth values for, 107, 112
    writing, using De Morgan's
        laws, 123
negative numbers, 220–221
new states paradox, 824–825, 829
n factorial, 624
Nixon, Richard, 789
nominal interest rate, 466
nonagon, 572
non-Euclidean geometry, 101, 556,
    605–610
nonlinear relationship, 760–761
normal distribution, 742–749, 772
    applications of, 751–756
    of data, identifying, 754–755
    definition of, 742–743
    in finding percentages, 751–752
    and percentile rank, 753–754
    and probability, 752–753
    properties of, 743
not equal to sign (≠), 222
number(s), 179, 202
    additive inverse of, 220
    arbitrary, 10
    cardinal of set, 48–49, 73–74, 90
    cardinal of union of sets, 73–74
    classifying, 258
    composite, 210, 285
    counting, 208
    definition of, 154
    divisible, 209
    Fermat, 217
    Fibonacci, 278
    imaginary, 259

irrational, 246–254, 285
    mixed, 232–233
    natural, 45, 87–88, 208, 285
    negative, 220–221
    opposite of, 220–221, 260, 285
    pentagonal, 16
    perfect, 212
    prime, 208–212, 285
    rational, 232–243, 285
    real, 95, 257–262, 285
    really large, 19
    rounding, 17–18
    square, 16
    triangular, 16
    whole, 220, 285
number line, 220, 222
    graphing inequalities on,
        337–338
numeracy, 207
numeral(s), 179, 202
    definition of, 154
numeration system(s), 153, 202
    ancient, 155
    Babylonian, 163–165
    Chinese, 159–161
    definition of, 154
    Egyptian, 155–157
    Hindu-Arabic, 154, 161–162, 202
    Mayan, 165–166
    multiplicative grouping,
        159–161, 202
    positional, 161–165, 202
    Roman, 157–159, 162
    simple grouping, 155–159, 202
    tally, 154–155, 202
numerator, definition of, 232
numerical coefficient, 293

objective function, 435
    definition of, 403
    maximum value of, 404–405, 435
    minimum value of, 404–405, 435
obtuse angle, 554
obtuse triangle, 562
octagon, 572
octal system. *See* base eight (octal)
    system
odds
    computing, 661–662
    expression of, 661
    finding, from probability, 662
    finding probability from, 662
    formulas for, in terms of
        probability, 661
odds against, 660, 692
odds in favor, 660, 692
odd vertex, 840
one, as identity for multiplication, 260
one-to-one correspondence of sets,
    50–51, 92
open-ended credit, 479
opinion polls, faulty questions in,
    780–781
opposite, of number, 220–221, 260, 285
optimal solution, on weighted graph,
    857, 874
ordered pair, 63
order of operations, 226–229, 285
origin
    of number line, 220
    of rectangular coordinate
        system, 368
ounce(s), 539, 546
outcome(s)
    and odds, 660
    of probability experiments,
        636–637, 660, 664, 692
outliers, 739, 771

Pacioli, Luca, 297
pairwise comparison method,
    802–805, 828
palm (length unit), 522

parabola, 435
    axis of symmetry of, 420–421, 435
    definition of, 420
    graphing, 421–422
    opening downward, 420
    opening upward, 420
    symmetric, 420
    vertex of, 420, 435
paradox(es), 99, 822, 829
parallel lines, 557–558
parallelogram, 573, 612
    area of, 579–580
parallel postulate, 605, 613
parentheses, in compound statement,
    115–116
Parthenon, 250
Pascal's triangle, 15
path, 848, 874
    Euler, 848–851, 874
    Hamilton, 855–856, 874
patterns, finding, 4–5
payoff amount, for fixed installment
    loan, calculation of, 477–479
PEMDAS, 227
pentagon, 572, 612
Pentagon (government building), 575
P/E ratio, of stock, 503–504, 512
percent(s), 442–449, 511
    applications of, 447–449
    and decimals, conversion between,
        21, 442–444
    definition of, 442
    finding whole amount based on,
        446–447
    finding with normal distribution,
        751–752
    and fractions, conversion between,
        443–444
    misuse of, in advertising, 448–449
    problems involving, 444–447
    of whole, calculation of, 445
percent decrease, 448
percentile, 771
    in comparison of data from
        different sets, 737–738
    definition of, 736
    finding, 736–737
    finding data value corresponding
        to, 737
percentile rank, 736–737, 771
    normal distribution and, 753–754
percent increase, 448
perfect numbers, 212
perfect squares, 247
perimeter, 29, 34, 612
    definition of, 574
    of polygon, 574–575
    of rectangle, 574
permutation(s), 692
    and combinations, comparison of,
        630–631
    definition of, 625
    identifying, 631
    of n objects, 625
    of n objects taken r at a time, 626
    number of, calculating, 625–627
permutation rule(s), 625, 634, 692
    for duplicate objects, 634
    when objects are alike, 627
phi (φ), 250
pi (π), 247–248, 582–583
pie chart, 21, 711–712, 771
Pisano, Leonardo, 278, 297
place value, 17, 161–162, 182, 202
    for decimals, 239
plane(s), 612
    definition of, 552
    half, 396–398, 434
plurality, versus majority, 788
plurality method, 788–789, 828
plurality-with-elimination method,
    796–799, 828
Poincaré, Henri, 89

point(s), 612
    definition of, 552
Polya, George, 27–28, 37, 41, 317
polygon(s), 572–574, 612
    area of, 578–582
    in making tessellations, 608–610
    perimeter of, 574–575
    regular, 574, 612
    sum of angle measures of,
        572–574, 612
polygonal region, 404, 435
polyhedron
    definition of, 588
    surface area of, 592
population(s)
    definition of, 700
    in statistical studies, 700–701, 771
population paradox, 823–824, 829
portfolio, investor's, 501
positional numeration system,
    161–165, 202
postulate(s), definition of, 605
pound(s), 539, 546
power rule, for exponents, 266–267
preference tables, 786–787, 828
premise(s), of argument, 129, 147
prime factorization, 211, 285
    division method, 212
    tree method, 211
prime number(s), 285
    definition of, 209
    finding, 210
    twin, 211
principal
    computing, 455
    definition of, 452
private student loan, 488, 512
probability
    addition rules and, 670–672, 692
    and area under normal
        distribution, 752–753
    basic concepts of, 636–643
    classical, 637–640, 642–643, 692
    of a complement, 640
    computing, 648–652
    computing using counting
        techniques, 655–658
    computing using permutations,
        656–657
    conditional, 680–682, 693
    definition of, 636
    empirical, 640–643, 692
    and expected value (expectation),
        663–666
    expression of, 639
    finding from odds, 662
    finding odds from, 662
    formula for, in terms of odds, 662
    multiplication rules and,
        676–680, 693
    and sets, 640
    theoretical, 638
    of three independent events,
        finding, 678, 680
probability distribution, 693
    constructing, 689
    definition of, 689
probability experiment(s), 636–637,
    692
problem(s)
    involving money, solving, 30–31
    with no solution, 32
    understanding, strategies for, 33
problem solving, 3, 27–28, 37, 317
    by calculation, 31
    by diagram, 28–29
    by trial and error, 30
    Venn diagrams in, 77–83
proceeds, from selling stock, 505–506
product, definition of, 225
product rule
    for exponents, 266–267
    for square roots, 247–249

proper fraction
absolute value of, 233
definition of, 232
proper subset, 58, 92
property(ies)
definition of, 258
of real numbers, 258–262
proportion, 361
applications of, 329–330
definition of, 327
solving, 327–328
true versus false, 327
protractor, 554, 612
pseudosphere, 606, 613
Pujols, Albert, 265
pyramid, 565, 613
definition of, 590
square base, surface area of, 592, 594
volume of, 590–591
Pythagoras, 239, 564–565
Pythagoreans, 212
Pythagorean theorem, 251, 564–566, 612
Pythagorean triple, 565, 619

quadrant(s)
definition of, 368
of rectangular coordinate system, 368, 370, 434
quadratic equation(s), 347–357, 361
applications of, 357
definition of, 347
solving using factoring, 353–354
solving using quadratic formula, 355–356
standard form for, 347–348
quadratic formula, 361
definition of, 355
using, 355–356
quadratic functions, 420–424, 435
applications of, 422–424
definition of, 420
graph of, 420
quadrilateral(s), 572–574, 612
quantified statement(s), negations of, 102
quantifier(s)
existential, 100–101
universal, 100–101
quantum computing, 109
quartile(s), 771
for data set, finding, 738–739
definition of, 738
quota
lower, 813, 816, 826
standard, 812–813, 829
upper, 813, 829
quota rule, 826, 829
quotient, definition of, 226
quotient rule
for exponents, 266–267
for square roots, 249–250

radian(s), 561
radical(s)
definition of, 247
like, 251
simplifying, 247–248
radical sign, 247
radicand, definition of, 247
radius
of circle, 582, 613
of sphere, 591
random sample, 701
random variable, 751, 772
range
of data set, 729–730, 771
of function, 413, 435
rate (r), interest. *See* interest rate (r)
rate of change
in modeling with linear equation, 376
slope and, 376

ratio, 361. *See also* trigonometric ratios
common, of geometric sequence, 278
definition of, 232, 325
golden, 250, 256, 278, 288–289, 360, 577
odds expressed as, 661
P/E, of stock, 503–504, 512
with units, 326
writing, 325–326
rationalizing the denominator, 252–253
rational numbers, 232–243, 246, 259, 285
application to fitness training, 243
definition of, 232
ray(s), 612
of angle, 553
definition of, 552
figure for, 552–553
symbol for, 552–553
reach, of Internet sites, 25
real number(s), 257–262, 285
definition of, 257
properties of, 258–262, 285
as uncountable set, 88–90, 95
real number system, structure of, 257–258
reasoning, 4, 37
circular, 135
deductive, 8–12, 37, 702–703
inductive, 4–9, 11–12, 37, 59, 702–703
mathematical, 4–12
reciprocal
of fraction, 236, 261
of number, 261
rectangle
area of, 578–579
definition of, 573
golden, 250, 256
perimeter of, 574
rectangular coordinate system, 368–370, 434
coordinates of points in, 369–370
plotting points in, 369
rectangular solid, 588, 613
surface area of, 592, 594
volume of, 588–589
regression, 426, 703
regression analysis, 760
regression line, 764–765, 772
and correlation coefficient (r), relationship between, 766
equation of, 765
finding, 765
in making predictions, 766–767
regular polygon(s), 612
definition of, 608
in making tessellations, 608–610
relation(s), 410–411, 435
definition of, 410
relative unfairness, 819
repeating decimal
definition of, 241
written as fraction, 241–243
Rhind papyrus, 171, 297
rhombus, 573, 612
Rickey, Branch, 43
Riemann, Bernhard, 605
right angle, 554, 565
right triangle, 562, 564, 597, 612
legs of, 564
and trigonometry, 597
Robinson, Jackie, 43
Romanesco broccoli, 607
Roman numerals, 158–159
roster method, 44–45, 47
rounding numbers, 17–18
rule of 72, 469
rule of 78, 478–479, 511
Russian peasant method, 171–173, 202

sample (statistical), 771
cluster, 701, 771
convenience, 777–778

definition of, 701
random, 701, 771
representative, 701
selection of, 701–702, 710, 777
size of, 777
stratified, 701, 771
suspect, and misuse of statistics, 777–778
systematic, 701, 771
sample space, 637, 647–648, 692
determining with tables, 650–652
sampling methods, 701–702, 771
scalene triangle, 562
scatter plot, 772
analyzing, 760–761
definition of, 759
drawing, 760
scientific notation, 267–271, 286
in applied problems, 271
dividing numbers in, 270–271
multiplying numbers in, 269–270
numbers in, and decimals, conversion between, 268–269
operations with numbers in, 269–271
writing numbers in, 267–268
seasonal trend(s), 714
secular trends, 713–714
self-contradiction, 120–121, 147
self-similarity, of fractals, 607, 611, 613
sequence(s), 286
alternating, 282
arithmetic, 275–278, 286, 289
definition of, 275
Fibonacci, 278, 288–289
finite, 276
geometric, 278–282, 286, 289
infinite, 276
sequence sampling, 710
set(s), 43, 92
cardinal number (cardinality) of, 48–49, 73–74, 90
Cartesian product (cross product) of, 63, 92
complement of, 56–57, 62, 70–71, 92
corresponding to a Venn diagram, finding, 69–70
countable, 88–89, 92
definition of, 44
descriptive method for, 46–47, 92
difference of (subtraction of), 62–63, 92
disjoint, 60, 140
element of, 44, 58, 92
empty, 47–48, 92
equal, 49–50, 71–73, 92
equivalent, 49–51, 92
finite, 49, 59, 87, 92
infinite, 49, 86–88, 92
intersection of, 60–61, 92
member of, 44, 92
notation for, 44–46
null, 47–48, 92
one-to-one correspondence of, 50–51, 92
probability and, 640
roster method for, 44–45, 47, 92
set-builder notation for, 46–47, 92
subsets of, 57–59, 92
symbol ∈ for, 45
uncountable, 88–90, 92
union of, 60–61, 70–71, 73–74, 92
universal, 56, 62, 92
well-defined, 44
set operation(s)
definition of, 60
performing, 61–63
using Venn diagrams for, 67–74
set theory, founders of, 89
shareholder, definition of, 501
side(s)
of angle, 553

corresponding, of similar triangles, 566
of triangle, 598–599, 612
Sierpinski triangle, 607–608, 611
Sieve of Eratosthenes, 210, 219
significance levels, 763–764
similar triangle(s), 566–568, 570–571, 612
simple grouping system(s), 155–159, 202
simple interest, 452–459, 511
and compound interest, comparison of, 462–463
computing, 453
definition of, 452
on student loans, 489, 512
for term in months, computing, 454
simplification
of algebraic expression, 294–296
of radicals, 247–248
of square root of fraction, 253
simplified daily interest formula, 489
sine, 597–598, 613
inverse of, 600
slope
definition of, 373
of horizontal line, 373–374, 434
of line on Cartesian plane, 373–374, 434
and rate of change, 376
undefined, 373–374
of vertical line, 373–374, 434
slope-intercept form, 374–375
sociology, 699, 772
SOHCAHTOA mnemonic, 597
solution of an equation
definition of, 304
identifying, 304–305
solution set
definition of, 304
for linear equation, 304
for linear inequality, 337–338
spanning tree(s), 866–870, 875
in agriculture, 869
in civil engineering, 870
definition of, 866
finding, 867
minimum, 867–868, 875
speed, units for, conversion between, 522
sphere, 613
center of, 591
definition of, 591
diameter of, 591
great circles of, 605–606
radius of, 591
surface area of, 592
volume of, 592
square (quadrilateral), 573–574, 612
area of, 578–579
square inch(es), 529, 613
and square feet, conversion between, 530
square root(s), 285
addition of, 251–252
approximating, with calculator, 254
definition of, 247
division of, 249–250
of fraction, simplifying, 253
as irrational numbers, 247
multiplication of, 249
product rule for, 247–249
quotient rule for, 249–250
as rational numbers, 247
subtraction of, 251–252
square units, 529, 546, 613
standard deviation
of data set, 730–732, 771
interpreting, 732–733
standard divisor, 811–812, 816
standard form, for quadratic equations, 347–348
standard normal curve, area under, 746–749, A1–A2
standard normal distribution, 744–745, 772

standard quota, 812–813, 829
statement(s), 147
  biconditional, truth values for, 111–112
  compound, 100, 147
  conditional, 109–112, 123–126, 147
  definition of, 98
  illustrated by Euler circles, 140
  logically equivalent, 121–122, 147
  negation of, 101–102, 107
  notation for, 103
  particular affirmative, 140
  particular negative, 140
  quantified, 100–102
  recognizing, 99
  self-contradictory, 120–121, 147
  simple, 99–100, 147
  tautological, 120, 147
  translation from symbols to words, 104
  types of, 119–126
  universal affirmative, 140
  universal negative, 140
  writing symbolically, 103–104
statistics, 699, 771. *See also* sample (statistical)
  definition of, 700
  descriptive, 702
  detached, 778
  historical perspective on, 726
  inferential, 702–703
  misuse of, 777–781
  population in, 700–701, 771
  sampling methods in, 701–702, 771
stem and leaf plots, 705–706, 771
stock(s), 501–506, 512
  annual earnings per share, 504
  current yield for, 504–505
  definition of, 501
  P/E ratio of, 503–504, 512
  proceeds from sale of, 505–506
  total cost of buying, 505
stockbroker, 501
stock exchange, 501
stock listing, 501–503
stock table, 501–503, 512
story problems, 29
straight angle, 554
stratified sample, 701
stroke, in tally system, 154
student loan(s), 488–491, 512
  capitalized interest on, 491, 512
  federal, 488, 512
  interest on, 489, 512
  monthly payments on, 490
  private, 488, 512
  subsidized, 490, 512
  unsubsidized, 490, 512
subset(s), 57–59
  notation for, 58–59
  number of, 59
  proper, 58, 92
substitution, solving a system of equations by, 385–387
subtraction
  in base five system, 194–195
  in Egyptian system, 157
  of fractions, 237–239
  of integers, 223–224
  of like radicals, 251
  phrases that represent, 318
  in Roman system, 158
  of sets, 62–63, 92
  of square roots, 251–252
subtraction property of equality, 306–307
subtraction property of inequality, 339
sum, definition of, 222

supplementary angles, 554–556, 612
surface area, 592–594, 613
  definition of, 592
survey results
  biased questions and, 780–781
  Venn diagrams for, 78–83
suspect sample (statistical), 777–778
syllogism, definition of, 141
symbolic logic, 98, 101, 147
systematic sample, 701
system of equations
  definition of, 382
  solution to, 382
  solving, 382
  the solution to, 382
system of linear equations, 434
  applications of, 391–392
  consistent, 383, 434
  definition of, 382
  dependent, 383–384, 390–391, 434
  inconsistent, 383–384, 390, 434
  independent, 383
  solving by addition method (elimination), 387–390
  solving by substitution, 385–387
  solving graphically, 382–385
system of linear inequalities, 396, 398–400, 434
  applications of, 399–400
  solving, 398–399, 434

table(s)
  and addition rule 2, 672
  in computing probabilities, 650–652
  for determining sample space, 650–652
tally system, 154–155, 202
tangent, 597–599, 613
  inverse of, 600
tautology, 120, 147
temperature, 546
  Fahrenheit-Celsius conversions, 542–543
  Kelvin scale, 542
term
  for interest calculation, 453
  of loan, computing, 456–457
  of mortgage, 492
term(s)
  of algebraic expressions, 293–296. *See also* like term(s)
  of sequence, 275
terminating decimal
  definition of, 240
  written as fraction, 241
tessellations, 608–611, 613
test point, 396–398, 434
theorem, definition of, 564
theoretical probabilities, 638
three-part inequality, 338
  solving, 341–342
tie breaking, 807–808
tiling, 608
time *(t)*, for interest calculation, 453
time series graph, 22–23, 713–714, 771
Titius-Bode law, 280
ton(s), 539, 546
topology, 608
total installment price, 511
  calculation of, 475–476
  for fixed installment loan, 474
transversal, 557–559
trapezoid, 573, 612
  area of, 581
traveling salesperson problem, 857–858, 874
tree(s), 865–870, 875

  definition of, 865
  properties of, 865
  recognizing, 866
  spanning, 866–870
tree diagram, 622, 647–648, 692
  in computing probability, 648–649
tree method, of prime factorization, 211
trend(s)
  cyclical, 714
  seasonal, 714
  secular, 713–714
triangle(s), 561–568, 572, 612
  acute, 562
  area of, 580–581
  definition of, 562
  in elliptic geometry, 606
  equilateral, 562, 574
  finding an angle in, 563–564
  finding side using cosine, 599
  finding side using tangent, 598–599
  in hyperbolic geometry, 606
  isosceles, 562
  naming of, 562
  obtuse, 562
  right, 562, 564, 597, 612
  scalene, 562
  sides of, 612
  Sierpinski, 607–608
  similar, 566–568, 570–571, 612
  sum of angle measures in, 563
  symbol for, 562
  types of, 562–563, 612
trigonometric ratios, 597–598, 613
  finding angles using, 599–600
trigonometry, 597, 613
trinomial(s)
  definition of, 350
  factoring of, 350–353
truth tables, 107–115, 147
  application of, 117
  in classifying a statement, 120–121
  construction of, 112–116
  for determining validity of arguments, 130–133
  for three components, 114–115
twin primes, 211

uncountable set, 88–90, 92
unearned interest, calculation of, 477–479
  actuarial method, 477–478, 511
  rule of 78 for, 478–479
union of sets, 60–61, 70–71, 73–74, 92
unit fraction, 520, 546
universal affirmative statement, 140
universal negative statement, 140
universal quantifier, 100–101
universal set, 56, 62, 92
unlike term(s), 294
unpaid balance method, 511
  for finance charge calculation, 480
upper quota, 813, 829

valid argument, 129–133, 135–137, 147–148
variable(s), 361
  definition of, 46, 291–292
  dependent, 411–412, 759
  implied connections between, 778
  independent, 411–412, 759
  possible relationships between/among, 767–768
  random, 751, 772
variance, of data set, 730–732, 771
variation
  direct, 331–332
  inverse, 332–333
  measures of, 729, 771

Venn, John, 43, 56, 71, 92, 101
Venn diagram(s), 43, 56–57, 92, 101
  for addition rule 1, 670
  in classification, 77–83
  for equality of sets, 71–73
  finding a set corresponding to, 69–70
  illustrating a set statement with, 67–68
  for intersection of sets, 60
  in problem solving, 77–83
  for proper subset, 58
  in studying set operations, 67–74
  for study survey results, 78–79
  for survey results, 78–83
  with three sets, 68–69, 79–83
  with two sets, 78
  for union of sets, 60
verbal statements, translation into symbols, 319–320
vertex (pl., vertices)
  adjacent, 840, 874
  of angle, 553
  even, 840
  of graph, 836, 840, 874
  in linear programming, 404, 435
  odd, 840
  of parabola, 420, 435
  of triangle, 562
vertical angle, 557, 612
vertical line(s), slope of, 373–374, 434
vertical line test, 419
Vieta, François, 297
volume, 532–536, 546
  of three-dimensional geometric figure, 587–592, 613
voting, 785–786, 789, 829

Webster, Daniel, 817
Webster's method, 817–818, 826, 829
weight, 546
  English-metric conversions, 539, 541
  English units, 539–540
  of liquid, 534
  and mass, relationship of, 523
  metric units, 539–540
  units of, 539
  of water in bottles, 534
weight(s), in graph theory, 857
whole numbers, 285
  definition of, 220
Widman, Johann, 297
Wilde, Oscar, 139
Woods, Tiger, 43, 154, 724
word problems, 29
  inequality, common phrases used in, 342
  solving, using equations, 318–320

x axis, 368, 434
x intercept, 372

yard(s), 522
  cubic, 533
  and feet, conversion between, 521
y axis, 368, 434
y intercept, 372, 434
Young, H. Peyton, 826

zero, 220
  dividing by, 226
  as exponent, 265
  as identity for addition, 260
zero product property, 353
z score(s), 745–746, 772
  area to left of, finding, 748–749
  area to right of, finding, 748
  two, finding area between, 747

Our Digital Solutions.

|MATHEMATICS

Hosted by **ALEKS Corp.**

Connect® Features:

- Straightforward course and assignment set up
- Interactive learning content
- At-risk reporting
- Customizable content
- Simple integration with every learning management system (LMS)

Online exercises and solutions were developed by faculty to provide a seamless transition from textbook to technology.

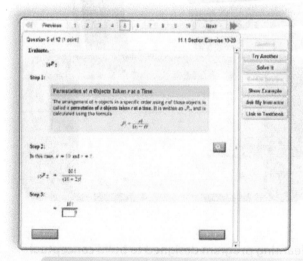

Guided solutions match the style and voice of the text as though the author is guiding the students through the problems.

McGraw-Hill LearnSmart®

LearnSmart is an adaptive learning program designed to build students' conceptual understanding of math. LearnSmart is the perfect study tool for math concepts.

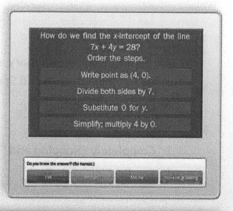

To learn more visit **www.SuccessInMath.com**

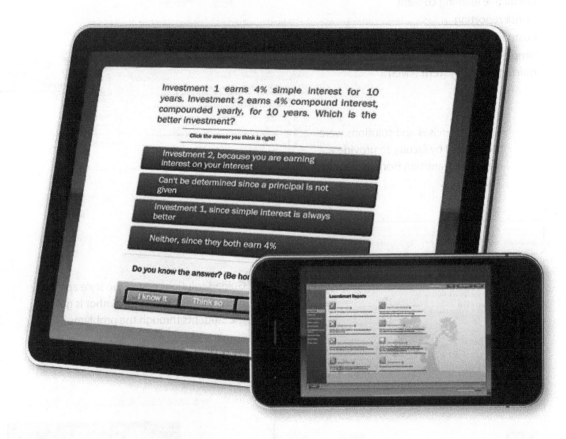

Brief Table of Contents

Chapter 1: **Problem Solving**

MATH IN Criminal Investigation — Page 2

Chapter 2: **Sets**

MATH IN Demographics — Page 43

Chapter 3: **Logic**

MATH IN Mind Control — Page 97

Chapter 4: **Numeration Systems**

MATH IN Retail Sales — Page 153

Chapter 5: **The Real Number System**

MATH IN Government Spending — Page 207

Chapter 6: **Topics in Algebra**

MATH IN Drug Administration — Page 291

Chapter 7: **Additional Topics in Algebra**

MATH IN The Stock Market — Page 367

Chapter 8: **Consumer Math**

MATH IN Student Loans — Page 441

Chapter 9: **Measurement**

MATH IN Travel — Page 519

Chapter 10: Geometry

MATH IN Home Improvement — Page 551

Chapter 11: Probability and Counting Techniques

MATH IN Gambling — Page 621

Chapter 12: Statistics

MATH IN Sociology — Page 699

Chapter 13: Voting Methods

MATH IN College Football — Page 785

Chapter 14: Graph Theory

MATH IN Road Trips — Page 835

Chapter 15: Other Mathematical Systems

MATH IN Encryption — Accessible online

Chapter 1: **Problem Solving**

MATHLAN **Criminal Investigation** Page 2

Chapter 2: **Sets**

MATHLAN **Demographics** Page 63

Chapter 3: **Logic**

MATHLAN **Mind Control** Page 107

Chapter 4: **Numeration Systems**

MATHLAN **Retail Sales** Page 153

Chapter 5: **The Real Number System**

MATHLAN **Government Spending** Page 205

Chapter 6: **Topics in Algebra**

MATHLAN **Drug Administration** Page 291

Chapter 7: **Additional Topics in Algebra**

MATHLAN **The Stock Market** Page 397

Chapter 8: **Consumer Math**

MATHLAN **Student Loans** Page 441

Chapter 9: **Measurement**

MATHLAN **Travel** Page 515

Chapter 10: **Geometry**

MATHLAN **Home Improvement** Page 551

Chapter 11: **Probability and Counting Techniques**

MATHLAN **Gambling** Page 621

Chapter 12: **Statistics**

MATHLAN **Sociology** Page 695

Chapter 13: **Voting Methods**

MATHLAN **College Football** Page 755

Chapter 14: **Graph Theory**

MATHLAN **Road Trips** Page 835

Chapter 15: **Other Mathematical Systems**

MATHLAN **Encryption** Accessible online